PERTURBATION METHODS IN THE QUANTUM MECHANICS OF *n*-ELECTRON SYSTEMS

PERTURBATION METHODS IN THE QUANTUM MECHANICS OF *n*-ELECTRON SYSTEMS

BY

E. M. CORSON, Ph.D.

Member, Institute for Advanced Study, 1946–1949; Consultant, Brookhaven National Laboratory; Research Physicist, Union Carbide and Carbon Research Laboratories

HAFNER PUBLISHING COMPANY

NEW YORK

Printed in Great Britain by Blackie & Son, Ltd., Glasgow

FOREWORD

It has been observed often that the enormous expansion of science is a danger to human society. Gone are the days when any single person was able to claim a fair knowledge of the whole of science, or even only a branch, like physics. To-day, only the specialist has a chance to prosper—and even he is unable to weld his tiny piece of knowledge on to the whole of human experience.

There is, however, another difficulty produced by the expanding universe of research, a difficulty of a more personal kind. It affects not so much those who are already in active research, and picking the fruit from their slice of cake, as the young and the old. I remember still the deep discouragement I felt when, almost half a century ago, as a young student, I made the first uncertain steps towards research and found myself faced with a heap of wisdom accumulated over centuries and increasing at a furious rate. How much worse must it be to-day for one who is not resigned, right from the beginning, to follow obediently the lead of a master. Now I am old, but a similar difficulty crops up. How can a man whose receptive powers are declining keep abreast even with the progress in that field which he regarded as his own? Business of all kinds—teaching, administration, committee work—absorb most of the time and leave little leisure for reading the literature. And how are we to pick out of the endless rows of periodicals the really important papers? It is a desperate situation, and every help is welcome.

The greatest help in the dilemma comes from books written by those who are in the prime of life and productivity, but willing to sacrifice time and effort to gather together the fruits of a field of research for the aid of their brothers in learning. The young as well as the old (to whom I belong) are indebted to the authors of such textbooks, and that is the reason why I have willingly agreed to write a few words of introduction to the present book. Not that I agree to everything in it—I have, for instance, no great love for certain notations where brackets of every description replace ordinary symbols. Yet the book seems to me a great help in assimilating the modern methods of quantum mechanics. The author, who spent almost a complete academic year in my department, is known to me as a scientific enthusiast of high purpose, great erudition and acute mind. I wish his book every success.

MAX BORN.

EDINBURGH,
August, 1950.

AUTHOR'S PREFACE

The overall scope of this book may be described succinctly as a general survey of the methods—exact and approximate—for studying the properties and behaviour of many-particle systems, in particular, as related to the restriction to symmetric and antisymmetric states.

At an early stage in the writing of this volume it became clear that limitations as to size would not permit inclusion of illustrative examples in all cases, and so, with some reluctance, it was decided to concentrate on elucidating the general principles and methodology, and, in certain instances, to refer the reader to more specific treatises and papers which this volume may supplement. As a notable feature of this volume we may mention the detailed treatment of the Dirac vector model and the second quantization, which includes both general theoretical derivations and varied applications; moreover, the interrelation of these two theories is shown as well as their common kinship with the methods of group theory, antisymmetrized wave-functions, and self-consistent fields, which are treated on a parallel basis. This, and the unified treatment in terms of the Dirac-Jordan representation theory, should be of special value to the graduate student of physics and to the research physicist.

Inasmuch as the purpose of this work is expository, a definite effort has been made to give derivations in considerable detail, and no particular apology need be made for including proofs which will be obvious to some readers. By the same token, a brief introduction to general representation theory was eventually deemed to be desirable, since this does not appear to be standard equipment as yet, and here, as elsewhere in the book, it may well be that certain aspects are emphasized more than others. This, of course, merely reflects the author's opinion and personal observation as to the questions which are more or less familiar—or have led to misunderstanding, interpretative and methodological. It is the author's belief that the subject-matter presented constitutes a representative cross-section of applied non-relativistic quantum mechanics in its intermediate, present-day stage of development, midway between the Bohr theory and the next radical advance of the future. There is no doubt that, whatever form the future development may ultimately take, the present theory will continue to have great value conceptually and in application, but it is all too infrequently noted that the present formulation is not so much a quantum theory as a correspondence principle extension or hybridization of classical theory.

A final brief chapter on the new Heisenberg S-matrix theory is included, not because this development has found its rightful independent place, but because the conceptual aspects leading up to its formulation perhaps most clearly crystallize some of the fundamental philosophical difficulties in present theory as well as indicate a hopeful line of approach for the future.

The author has had the good fortune to be able to work on the major part of this book at the Institute for Advanced Study, and owes much to Dr. Frank Aydelotte, director, and various members for generous counsel and assistance; particular thanks being due Professors V. Bargmann and S. T. Ma, with whom the author had many stimulating and helpful discussions. Inasmuch as this book is largely based on the definitive theory of Professor P. A. M. Dirac, the author is deeply in his debt for permission to use material from various of his published works and his Princeton lectures. By the same token, thanks are due Professor F. D. Murnaghan for permission to base the survey of relevant aspects of group theory on his authoritative text, *The Theory of Group Representations.* Other primary sources are articles by Fock, Heisenberg, Johnson, Jordan, Møller, Serber, Van-Vleck, and Wigner, as indicated in the text.

The author also takes pleasure in expressing his appreciation of the enthusiastic assistance and encouragement given by Mr. J. H. Critchett, vice-president retired, and Dr. A. B. Kinzel, now president of the Union Carbide and Carbon Research Laboratories. The entire work of preparation of the manuscript was done by my wife, Mary Wickham Corson, to whom this book is gratefully dedicated.

E. M. C.

PRINCETON,
NEW JERSEY,
March, 1948.

CONTENTS

CHAPTER I

Mathematical Introduction

§ 1. Introduction

There exist a number of essentially equivalent formulations of the basic quantal problem of the description and correlation of physical phenomena in the atomic domain. Two broad classifications of method are generally recognized: namely, the wave mechanics and the matrix mechanics. Here, and throughout this book, we depart from the traditional labelling of these two methods, since this does not give adequate recognition of the actual part played by different authors—as may be seen below.[1] Moreover, the conventional nomenclature is not especially descriptive, since the usual connotation is not strictly realized in all cases (cf. Chap. IV).

The wave formulation concerns itself primarily with the determination of eigenvalues of the Hamiltonian operator and the associated wave-functions (probability amplitudes of a special type), and has certain advantages in that it utilizes the more fully developed methods of analysis, in the mathematical sense. On the other hand, the matrix formulation is basically concerned with the representation of physical quantities, including the Hamiltonian, in matrix form subject to fundamental quantal restrictions; and the probability concepts are not introduced as naturally or simply. From the modern point of view the matrix method may have some claim to logical superiority and, conceptually, it is certainly more in keeping with the basic non-commutative aspect of modern abstract theory; but its independent use is rather limited by the comparative lack of development of the theory of infinite matrices *per se*. This latter defect results in an apparent lack of prescription as to how to formulate and solve general problems, since the matrix method is manageable only in special cases, and is practically useless in problems involving continuous eigenvalue spectra.

Our main interest in this book is not in the logical formulation of quantal concepts *per se*; but, in order to achieve the greatest clarity and understanding of the perturbation methods which will be our primary interest, it is essential that we have at our disposal the advantages of both the aforementioned techniques and, if possible, avoid their respective limitations. As a matter of fact, both methods are

[1] De Broglie, L.: *Nature*, **112**, 540 (1923). Born, M.: *Zeits. f. Phys.*, **26**, 379 (1924). Born, M., and Jordan, P.: *ibid.*, **33**, 479 (1925). Heisenberg, W.: *ibid.*, **33**, 879 (1925). Born, M., and Jordan, P.: *ibid.*, **34**, 858 (1925). Dirac, P. A. M.: *Proc. Roy. Soc.* A, **109**, 642 (1925). Born, M., Heisenberg, W., and Jordan, P.: *Zeits. f. Phys.*, **35**, 557 (1926). Born, M., and Wiener, N.: *ibid.*, **36**, 174 (1926). Dirac, P. A. M.: *Proc. Roy. Soc.* A, **110**, 561 (1926). Born, M.: *Zeits f. Phys.*, **37**, 863 (1926). Schroedinger, E.: *Ann. d. Phys.*, **79**, 361, 489, and 734 (1926). Dirac, P. A. M.: *Proc. Roy. Soc.* A, **111**, 281 (1926). Schroedinger, E.: *Ann. d. Phys.*, **80**, 437, and **81**, 109 (1926). Heisenberg, W.: *Zeits. f. Phys.*, **38**, 411 (1926). Jordan, P.: *ibid.*, **38**, 513 (1926). Born, M.: *ibid.*, **38**, 803 (1926). Dirac, P. A. M.: *Proc. Roy. Soc.* A, **112**, 674 (1926). Born, M: *Zeits. f. Phys.*, **40**, 167 (1926).

essentially different aspects of the more general discipline which is now called the *quantum mechanics*.[2] Again in this more general presentation we have some freedom in method, particularly in the mathematical formalism, and to some extent in fundamental viewpoint. Perhaps the most rigorous treatment is that of von Neumann,[3] but we shall follow rather closely the formulation of Dirac.[4]

We need hardly offer apology for this selection of approach, but a brief commentary seems desirable. It is quite true that the Dirac-Jordan presentation, in the treatment of continuous eigenvalues, requires the formal use of functions which in the strict function sense are entirely fictitious, if taken too literally, i.e. they satisfy none of the usual conditions of continuity, differentiability, etc., in the ordinary sense of these terms. Nonetheless, of all the presently available treatments, Dirac's appears to be the most unified in notation and method, and by the same token the most useful for general theoretical reasoning. The question of the formalism of the Dirac δ function will be considered more fully at the appropriate stage in this book, but we may here point out that in all quantal formulations at present there are far more serious issues, such as the assumption of a general expansion theorem.[5] This latter the critics have not attacked with such vehemence, possibly because, unlike the δ function, it can at present neither be avoided nor justified. The use of the δ formalism avoids a complex network of theorems and proofs and, if nothing else, allows more time for theoretical physics as distinct from mathematical physics. In particular, it is important to realize that all physical theories represent to some degree a necessary idealization of natural phenomena as we see, or perhaps more accurately, as we choose to see them. From this standpoint the δ formalism is not an accident, but a logical consequence of attempting to describe a particular phenomenon in hyper-idealized form.

In presenting a brief review of the general quantum theory on which our further investigations will depend, we are faced with a choice in the mode of approach. We may either develop the mathematical methods first, and then pass to the physical interpretation which will show *a posteriori* the reason for the particular mathematical structure developed, or we may proceed on physical reasoning, thereby showing the necessity of the particular relations adopted and the type of analysis which is developed. Neither entry into the theory follows the course of historical development, and the choice is one of convenience. For our purposes the possibly greater *Anschaulichkeit* of the latter method is offset by the resulting rather piecemeal development that necessitates the use of makeshift notations for various mathematical constructs which must then be discarded at a later stage. In many respects a uniform methodological approach is a tremendously valuable asset both for ultimate ease in physical interpretation and general economy of writing.

[2] It may be mentioned that, of the two, the spirit of the matrix method is more intimately related to the quantum mechanics.

[3] VON NEUMANN, J.: *Quantenmechanik*, Dover (1943).

[4] In this and the following chapter the essential results of representation theory are given as convenient reference for later use in the general theory and applications. For this reason some proofs are omitted, and for these as well as detailed discussion, the reader should refer to DIRAC, P. A. M.: *Quantum Mechanics* (Oxford).

[5] Cf. § 4, Theorem 3, *et seq.*

§ 2. Vectors and Operators

(*a*) *Vectors.*

From the purely mathematical viewpoint we shall be primarily interested in certain equations relating operators and vectors. Dealing with vectors first, we may note that the vectors in the Dirac theory are not essentially different from the usual vector concept; the main distinction being in the number of dimensions of the vector space which will be infinite [6] in most cases of physical interest. Furthermore, the components of a vector relative to a given basis [7] or representation will in general be complex, and we shall recognize two types of vectors closely analogous to the contravariant and covariant vectors of differential geometry. An arbitrary vector will be denoted by the symbol $|\,\rangle$, and is most conveniently visualized in terms of its components [8] relative to some chosen basis, as a column matrix, i.e. a matrix of n rows and 1 column,[9] where n may possibly be infinite. It is important to remember that the components of a vector are not properties of the vector, but merely give the relationship of the vector to a chosen basis. We may observe that a unit vector of a basis such as indicated in the preceding footnote would be represented by a column matrix, all of whose elements are zero except the element corresponding to the ordinal number of the vector in question, which will be unity (at least in the denumerable case). The second type of vector mentioned above will be denoted by the symbol $\langle\,|$, and is called the adjoint [10] or Hermitian conjugate of $|\,\rangle$, i.e. $\langle\,| = |\,\rangle^*$. Corresponding to the above matrix picture of $|\,\rangle$, the symbol $\langle\,|$ would be visualized as a $1 \times n$ row matrix whose components are conjugate to those of $|\,\rangle$. We note immediately that vectors of the type $|\,\rangle$ and $\langle\,|$ are essentially distinct, and there is no possibility for the addition of these two types of vectors, although vectors of each type may be added to vectors of the same type.[11] Inasmuch as we recognize only two types of vectors, denoted [12] by the symbols $|\,\rangle$ and $\langle\,|$, it will be necessary to insert further labels in these symbols to distinguish different sets of vectors, and establish a sequence within a given vector set. Thus, for example, in a given vector space we shall indicate two distinct vector sets [13] as $|\,\alpha'\,\rangle$, $|\,\alpha''\,\rangle$, $|\,\alpha'''\,\rangle, \ldots$ and $|\,\beta'\,\rangle$, $|\,\beta''\,\rangle$, $|\,\beta'''\,\rangle, \ldots$ rather than some more common notation

[6] The number of dimensions may be infinite denumerable or not, depending on the particular physical case.

[7] I.e. coordinate system; in most cases of interest, a prescribed set of independent orthonormal vectors, the number of elements of the set being equal to the number of dimensions of the space; i.e. a complete set.

[8] We shall frequently use the term *representatives* just as we use coordinate system, basis, and representation interchangeably at present.

[9] Cf. eq. (1:8*a*). We shall always use the order row–column; e.g. $|\,\rangle$ above is represented by an $n \times 1$ matrix.

[10] The operation of taking the adjoint is indicated by the asterisk (star superscript), and in matrix language consists in interchanging rows and columns, and taking the conjugate complex of each element. We shall often use this symbol even to denote ordinary conjugate since for a 1×1 matrix, i.e. scalar, $a^* = \bar{a}$ is just the usual conjugate.

[11] The two types of vectors are said to exist in dual spaces.

[12] Dirac: "A New Notation for Quantum Mechanics", *Proc. Camb. Phil. Soc.*, **35**, 416 (1939), calls these "ket" and "bra" vectors respectively, from their positions in the "bracket" expressions (cf. below).

[13] We frequently indicate the whole set by $\{\,|\,\alpha'\,\rangle\,\}$, i.e. curly brackets about a typical vector of the set.

such as u_1, u_2, u_3, . . . and v_1, v_2, v_3, . . . respectively. For the moment we need only consider that a symbol associated with an arbitrary $|\,\rangle$ vector, as in $|\,\alpha''\,\rangle$ say indicates that $|\,\alpha''\,\rangle$ belongs to a particular set of vectors distinguished by the letter α, and the superscript primes indicate ordinality.[14] Likewise, we define a generalized scalar product of any two vectors $|\,\alpha'\,\rangle$, $|\,\beta'\,\rangle$ in the order $\langle\,\alpha'\,|\,\beta'\,\rangle = \langle\,\alpha'\,|\cdot|\,\beta'\,\rangle$, and it is clear from the above matrix representative picture that this is the only possible product combination which can yield a scalar.

The vector spaces of the quantum theory are of the type generally termed unitary,[15] and are characterized by the following fundamental axioms:

$$(\langle\,\alpha'\,| + \langle\,\beta'\,|)\cdot|\,\gamma'\,\rangle = \langle\,\alpha'\,|\,\gamma'\,\rangle + \langle\,\beta'\,|\,\gamma'\,\rangle \quad . \quad . \quad . \quad (1{:}1)$$

(distributive axiom),

$$\langle\,\alpha'\,|\,\beta'\,\rangle = \langle\,\beta'\,|\,\alpha'\,\rangle^*, \quad . \quad . \quad . \quad . \quad . \quad . \quad . \quad (1{:}2)$$ [16]

$$\langle\,\alpha'\,|\,\alpha'\,\rangle \geqslant 0 \quad . \quad . \quad . \quad . \quad . \quad . \quad . \quad . \quad (1{:}3)$$

(squared length of $|\,\alpha'\,\rangle$, and in particular normality means $\langle\,\alpha'\,|\,\alpha'\,\rangle = 1$; $|\,\alpha'\,\rangle$ then being determined up to a possible factor of unit modulus),

$$\langle\,\alpha'\,|\,\alpha''\,\rangle = 0 \qquad (\alpha' \neq \alpha'') \quad . \quad . \quad . \quad . \quad . \quad . \quad (1{:}4)$$

(condition of orthogonality for vectors of a basis).

Further, there is no significance to the question of the reality of a vector of either type, nor to the resolution of components into real and imaginary parts. We shall in the future refer to the components of a vector relative to some given basis as the *representatives* of the vector in the given *representation*, and indeed the term representative is most appropriate since it carries the connotation that the components merely represent the vector relative to a basis. There is an additional and fundamental geometric property of the space of our vectors still to be considered, namely, the type of coordinate transformation which we shall admit; i.e. the relation between representatives of a vector in two or more different representations. This question, which gives rise to the so-called Transformation Theory, is at the base of all physical interpretation.

Let us consider two distinct sets of basic vectors $\{\,|\,\alpha'\,\rangle\,\}$, $\{\,|\,\beta'\,\rangle\,\}$, or briefly the α- and β-representations, which we assume to be complete-orthonormal. Otherwise stated, this hypothesis assumes that the number of independent basic vec- is equal to the dimensionality of the vector space, so that an arbitrary vecto this space can be expanded in terms of them. We write the expansion of a vector $|\,\rangle$ in the α-representation as

$$|\,\rangle = \sum_{\alpha'} |\,\alpha'\,\rangle\langle\,\alpha'\,|\,\rangle, \quad . \quad . \quad . \quad . \quad . \quad . \quad . \quad . \quad (1{:}5a)$$ [17]

from which the adjoint expansion is

$$\langle\,| = \sum_{\alpha'} \langle\,|\,\alpha'\,\rangle\langle\,\alpha'\,|. \quad . \quad . \quad . \quad . \quad . \quad . \quad . \quad . \quad (1{:}5b)$$

[14] This choice of notation may appear somewhat oblique at this point, but it fits very well the eigenvalue problem to be considered later.

[15] Also called linear metric space.

[16] The exterior asterisk here obviously applies to the whole expression; no other meaning is possible since $\langle\,\beta'\,|\,\langle\,\alpha'\,|$ and $|\,\beta'\,\rangle\,|\,\alpha'\,\rangle$ are as yet undefined, cf. § 6, equations (1:35–37).

[17] α' is, of course, an umbral index. — not if you put in the Σ sign.

These expressions differ from more familiar forms in that instead of denoting the expansion coefficients as $c(\alpha')$, $c^*(\alpha')$ say, we write $\langle \alpha' \mid \rangle$ and $\langle \mid \alpha' \rangle$ as prototype representatives of the vector $\mid \rangle$ and its adjoint, with the intervening vertical bar to permit insertion of a symbol to identify the vector being expanded. This is a rather expressive notation since it directly indicates that the representative $\langle \alpha'' \mid \rangle$, for example, is the projection of the vector $\mid \rangle$ on the axis whose unit vector is $\mid \alpha'' \rangle$, as follows directly from (1:5*a*) on pre-multiplying by $\langle \alpha'' \mid$. Moreover, it is especially well adapted for later physical interpretation.

Applying (1:5*a*, *b*) to basic vectors $\mid \beta'' \rangle$, $\mid \beta' \rangle$ of the other set, we have

$$\mid \beta'' \rangle = \sum_{\alpha''} \mid \alpha'' \rangle \langle \alpha'' \mid \beta'' \rangle, \qquad (1:6a)$$

$$\langle \beta' \mid = \sum_{\alpha'} \langle \beta' \mid \alpha' \rangle \langle \alpha' \mid ; \qquad (1:6b)$$

whence

$$\langle \beta' \mid \beta'' \rangle = \sum_{\alpha', \alpha''} \langle \beta' \mid \alpha' \rangle \langle \alpha' \mid \alpha'' \rangle \langle \alpha'' \mid \beta'' \rangle \qquad (1:7a)$$

$$= \sum_{\alpha'} \langle \beta' \mid \alpha' \rangle \langle \alpha' \mid \beta'' \rangle = \delta(\beta', \beta''),$$

and, reversing the roles of the two representations in the expansions (1:6*a*, *b*),

$$\langle \alpha' \mid \alpha'' \rangle = \sum_{\beta'} \langle \alpha' \mid \beta' \rangle \langle \beta' \mid \alpha'' \rangle = \delta(\alpha', \alpha''). \qquad (1:7b)$$

Since $\langle \alpha' \mid \beta' \rangle$ and $\langle \beta' \mid \alpha' \rangle$ are conjugate complex numbers, equations (1:7*a*, *b*) are just the conditions which characterize a unitary transformation; the $\langle \beta' \mid \alpha' \rangle$ denoting the elements of the unitary matrix (cf. equation 1:10*b*). If we write out equations (1:6*a*, *b*) for all basic vectors of the β-representation we obtain the explicit matrix forms

$$\| \mid \beta' \rangle, \mid \beta'' \rangle, \mid \beta''' \rangle, \ldots \| =$$

$$\| \mid \alpha' \rangle, \mid \alpha'' \rangle, \mid \alpha''' \rangle, \ldots \| \begin{Vmatrix} \langle \alpha' \mid \beta' \rangle & \langle \alpha' \mid \beta'' \rangle & \langle \alpha' \mid \beta''' \rangle \ldots \\ \langle \alpha'' \mid \beta' \rangle & \langle \alpha'' \mid \beta'' \rangle & \langle \alpha'' \mid \beta''' \rangle \ldots \\ \langle \alpha''' \mid \beta' \rangle & \langle \alpha''' \mid \beta'' \rangle & \langle \alpha''' \mid \beta''' \rangle \ldots \\ \cdot & \cdot & \cdot \\ \cdot & \cdot & \cdot \\ \cdot & \cdot & \cdot \end{Vmatrix}, \qquad (1:8a)$$

$$\begin{Vmatrix} \langle \beta' \mid \\ \langle \beta'' \mid \\ \langle \beta''' \mid \\ \cdot \\ \cdot \\ \cdot \end{Vmatrix} = \begin{Vmatrix} \langle \beta' \mid \alpha' \rangle & \langle \beta' \mid \alpha'' \rangle & \langle \beta' \mid \alpha''' \rangle \ldots \\ \langle \beta'' \mid \alpha' \rangle & \langle \beta'' \mid \alpha'' \rangle & \langle \beta'' \mid \alpha''' \rangle \ldots \\ \langle \beta''' \mid \alpha' \rangle & \langle \beta''' \mid \alpha'' \rangle & \langle \beta''' \mid \alpha''' \rangle \ldots \\ \cdot & \cdot & \cdot \\ \cdot & \cdot & \cdot \\ \cdot & \cdot & \cdot \end{Vmatrix} \begin{Vmatrix} \langle \alpha' \mid \\ \langle \alpha'' \mid \\ \langle \alpha''' \mid \\ \cdot \\ \cdot \\ \cdot \end{Vmatrix}. \qquad (1:8b)$$

It follows that the basic vectors $\{ \mid \alpha' \rangle \}$ transform contragrediently to the adjoint basic vectors $\{ \langle \alpha' \mid \}$, and hence to the set of representatives $\{ \langle \alpha' \mid \rangle \}$ of an arbitrary vector $\mid \rangle$, as follows by post-multiplying each element of the column matrices in (1:8*b*) by $\mid \rangle$. An equivalent statement of the condition on the geometry of our vector spaces is that the relation between representatives of a vector in two distinct representations be such as to leave the scalar product of vectors invariant, e.g. for any two vectors $| \lambda' \rangle$, $| \mu' \rangle$,

$$\langle \lambda' | \mu' \rangle = \sum_{\beta'} \langle \lambda' | \beta' \rangle \langle \beta' | \mu' \rangle = \sum_{\beta', \alpha', \alpha''} \langle \lambda' | \alpha' \rangle \langle \alpha' | \beta' \rangle \langle \beta' | \alpha'' \rangle \langle \alpha'' | \mu' \rangle$$

$$= \sum_{\alpha'} \langle \lambda' | \alpha' \rangle \langle \alpha' | \mu' \rangle. \qquad (1:9)$$

If now we introduce a third set of basic vectors $\{ | \gamma' \rangle \}$ constituting the γ-representation, and pre-multiply (1:6a) by $\langle \gamma' |$, we find

$$\langle \gamma' | \beta'' \rangle = \sum_{\alpha''} \langle \gamma' | \alpha'' \rangle \langle \alpha'' | \beta'' \rangle, \qquad (1:10a)$$

and considering this equation for every basic vector of the three representations we obtain the full matrix form

$$\begin{Vmatrix} \langle \gamma' | \beta' \rangle & \langle \gamma' | \beta'' \rangle & \langle \gamma' | \beta''' \rangle \ldots \\ \langle \gamma'' | \beta' \rangle & \langle \gamma'' | \beta'' \rangle & \langle \gamma'' | \beta''' \rangle \ldots \\ \langle \gamma''' | \beta' \rangle & \langle \gamma''' | \beta'' \rangle & \langle \gamma''' | \beta''' \rangle \ldots \\ \cdot & \cdot & \cdot \quad \cdot \\ \cdot & \cdot & \cdot \quad \cdot \\ \cdot & \cdot & \cdot \quad \cdot \end{Vmatrix} = \qquad (1:10b)$$

$$\begin{Vmatrix} \langle \gamma' | \alpha' \rangle & \langle \gamma' | \alpha'' \rangle & \langle \gamma' | \alpha''' \rangle \ldots \\ \langle \gamma'' | \alpha' \rangle & \langle \gamma'' | \alpha'' \rangle & \langle \gamma'' | \alpha''' \rangle \ldots \\ \langle \gamma''' | \alpha' \rangle & \langle \gamma''' | \alpha'' \rangle & \langle \gamma''' | \alpha''' \rangle \ldots \\ \cdot & \cdot & \cdot \quad \cdot \\ \cdot & \cdot & \cdot \quad \cdot \\ \cdot & \cdot & \cdot \quad \cdot \end{Vmatrix} \begin{Vmatrix} \langle \alpha' | \beta' \rangle & \langle \alpha' | \beta'' \rangle & \langle \alpha' | \beta''' \rangle \ldots \\ \langle \alpha'' | \beta' \rangle & \langle \alpha'' | \beta'' \rangle & \langle \alpha'' | \beta''' \rangle \ldots \\ \langle \alpha''' | \beta' \rangle & \langle \alpha''' | \beta'' \rangle & \langle \alpha''' | \beta''' \rangle \ldots \\ \cdot & \cdot & \cdot \quad \cdot \\ \cdot & \cdot & \cdot \quad \cdot \\ \cdot & \cdot & \cdot \quad \cdot \end{Vmatrix}.$$

We shall not have much specific use for the full matrix form, but presented as above we see in striking fashion the symmetry which exists between the several representations. Thus, for example, the columns of the left-hand matrix give the γ-representatives of the set $\{ | \beta' \rangle \}$, while the rows give the β-representatives of the set $\{ \langle \gamma' | \}$, and similarly for the other matrices. In particular we note that the quantity $\langle \gamma' | \alpha' \rangle$, which is a typical representative of $| \alpha' \rangle$ in the γ-representation, or equivalently a representative of $\langle \gamma' |$ in the α-representation, is at the same time an element of the transformation from the γ- to α-representation of an arbitrarily selected vector $| \beta' \rangle$.

(*b*) *Operators.*

We must now introduce certain symbolic quantities which are termed linear operators, and which, operating on vectors such as $| \, \rangle$ and $\langle \, |$ in a specified direction (i.e. as pre- or post-multiplier, respectively), generate other vectors. In a general theoretic sense it is often possible and desirable to deal with these operators and vectors in purely symbolic fashion,[18] but in any given practical calculation it is

[18] I.e. not introducing their representatives.

usually necessary to give the operators an explicit form as indicated for vectors, i.e. a matrix representative in a selected representation. In this sense an operator will be visualized as a square matrix which represents the operator in the chosen basis or representation. As for vectors, we note that the representative of an operator is not a property of the operator. Thus, given an operator $\boldsymbol{\alpha}$ (bold face type), and assuming for the moment that we know or can obtain its representative matrix,[19] we can consider the possibility of $\boldsymbol{\alpha}$ operating as pre-multiplier to a $|\,\rangle$, and post-multiplier to a $\langle\,|$ (i.e. operating to right and left, respectively), viz. $\overrightarrow{\boldsymbol{\alpha}\,|\,\rangle}$ and $\overleftarrow{\langle\,|\,\boldsymbol{\alpha}}$ where for emphasis the arrows here indicate the direction of application of the operator.

In the algebraic sense these equations relate the representative of $|\,\rangle$ to the representative of some other vector of the same column type which is generated by this operation, and similarly for the $\langle\,|$ type. Geometrically we may consider these equations as a linear mapping of our space into itself, or of vectors of our space into other vectors of our space. The linearity of the operators is described by the statement that a linear operator acting on a vector generates a new vector whose representative is a linear function of the representative of the original vector.[20] Alternately, one may characterize the linear property by the equation

$$\boldsymbol{\alpha}\,(\,|\,\beta'\,\rangle + |\,\gamma'\,\rangle\,) = \boldsymbol{\alpha}\,|\,\beta'\,\rangle + \boldsymbol{\alpha}\,|\,\gamma'\,\rangle. \quad . \quad . \quad . \quad . \quad (1{:}11)$$

Just as the representatives of a vector are not properties of the vector, but rather characterize its relation to a basis, so the representatives (elements of the matrix form) of an operator will depend on the particular representation used. Let us take some operator $\boldsymbol{\alpha}$, and inquire as to its matrix form relative to some proper basis $\{\,|\,\xi'\,\rangle\,\}$. In keeping with our previous notation we shall not denote a representative of $\boldsymbol{\alpha}$ as α_{ij} say, but as $\langle\,\xi'\,|\,\boldsymbol{\alpha}\,|\,\xi''\,\rangle$. This form again has a deeper physical significance of great utility, but for the moment we need merely observe that we can always order the basis vectors in some definite sequence,[21] so that the statement that $\langle\,\xi'\,|\,\boldsymbol{\alpha}\,|\,\xi''\,\rangle$ is the element of $\boldsymbol{\alpha}$ in the ξ' row and ξ'' column, relative to the ξ-representation, is as definite as the more common notation.

Now $\boldsymbol{\alpha}$ operating on a basic vector $|\,\xi''\,\rangle$ say, produces another vector which by definition can be expanded in terms of the complete-orthonormal set $\{\,|\,\xi'\,\rangle\,\}$, viz. [cf. eqn. (1:5a)]

$$\boldsymbol{\alpha}\,|\,\xi''\,\rangle = |\,\rangle = \sum_{\xi'''} |\,\xi'''\,\rangle\langle\,\xi'''\,|\,\rangle = \sum_{\xi'''} |\,\xi'''\,\rangle\langle\,\xi'''\,|\,\boldsymbol{\alpha}\,|\,\xi''\,\rangle, \quad . \quad (1{:}12)$$

which states that the projection of the vector $\boldsymbol{\alpha}\,|\,\xi''\,\rangle$ on the $|\,\xi'\,\rangle$ axis is $\langle\,\xi'\,|\,\boldsymbol{\alpha}\,|\,\xi''\,\rangle$, as follows by pre-multiplying with $\langle\,\xi'\,|$.

[19] I.e. one of the infinitely many possible representatives relative to different representations.

[20] I.e. the coordinates of the new vector are linear functions of coordinates of the original.

[21] Only for the denumerably infinite case, if we mean ordering in the strict sense, but we can generalize this term for the continuous case.

§ 3. The Eigenvalue-eigenvector Equation

We consider now the fundamental equation of our calculus, namely, the special case in which an operator acting on a vector merely multiplies it by a constant:

$$\boldsymbol{\alpha} \mid \rangle = \lambda \mid \rangle \qquad (\lambda \text{ a constant}). \qquad \text{(1:13)}$$

This is the basic eigenvalue-eigenvector equation, and our vector notation is already adapted to the present needs. Thus, the various eigenvalues of $\boldsymbol{\alpha}$ (i.e. the different possible values of λ) are designated by the same symbol as the operator, but in ordinary type with a superscript, e.g. α', α'', α''', . . . , etc., and the associated eigenvector, which may be said to belong to the particular eigenvalue, is denoted by $\mid \alpha' \rangle$, $\mid \alpha'' \rangle$, $\mid \alpha''' \rangle$, . . . , etc. Then we write (1:13) as

$$\boldsymbol{\alpha} \mid \alpha' \rangle = \alpha' \mid \alpha' \rangle, \qquad \text{(1:14)}$$

and here, as in most calculations of the general theoretical nature, we shall use any one of the primed symbols, e.g. α', to denote a general or prototype eigenvalue.

In order to fit the mathematical development to the requirements of further physical theory to be considered, it is necessary to confine our attention to operators having real eigenvalues. This condition is satisfied if our linear operators are Hermitian (self-adjoint), viz.

$$\boldsymbol{\alpha} = \boldsymbol{\alpha}^*, \qquad \text{(1:15}a\text{)}$$

i.e. for any representation $\{ \mid \xi' \rangle \}$ (such that $\langle \xi' \mid = \mid \xi' \rangle^*$) (see Footnote 21*a*)

$$\langle \xi' \mid \boldsymbol{\alpha} \mid \xi'' \rangle = \langle \xi' \mid \boldsymbol{\alpha}^* \mid \xi'' \rangle = \langle \xi'' \mid \boldsymbol{\alpha} \mid \xi' \rangle^*. \qquad \text{(1:15}b\text{)}$$

This expression for the condition of Hermiticity is a typical example of the twofold meaning contained in our equations in consequence of the close relation between symbolic quantities and representatives, implicit in the notation. Thus, the right-hand term considered as a symbolic product undergoes the adjoint operation giving the middle term, but as a numeric it is just the complex conjugate of the *transposed* matrix element $\langle \xi'' \mid \boldsymbol{\alpha} \mid \xi' \rangle$ which gives the familiar condition on a Hermitian matrix. That the eigenvalues of $\boldsymbol{\alpha}$ are real with this assumption of Hermiticity now follows immediately from (1:14) by pre-multiplying by $\langle \alpha' \mid$ and noting the fact that $\langle \alpha' \mid \alpha' \rangle$ is real.

Theorem 1.—*The eigenvalues of a Hermitian operator are real.*

However, the assumption of Hermiticity of our operators gives more than we originally demanded, namely, the additional and necessary property of orthogonality.

Theorem 2.—*Eigenvectors of a Hermitian operator belonging to different eigenvalues are orthogonal.*

This follows immediately on expressing the matrix element $\langle \alpha' \mid \boldsymbol{\alpha} \mid \alpha'' \rangle$ in its two equivalent forms $\alpha' \langle \alpha' \mid \alpha'' \rangle = \alpha'' \langle \alpha' \mid \alpha'' \rangle$, according to the direction of application of $\boldsymbol{\alpha}$.

[21a] This condition does not obtain for *complex* representation. Cf. § 96.

§ 4. Eigenvectors as Basic Vectors

The reader will observe that we have derived in symbolic form various properties of Hermitian operators, their eigenvectors and eigenvalues, assuming that these exist, which is not at all self-evident. Indeed, it is just at this point that we arrive at one of the weakest points of the mathematical structure of quantum theory.

As indicated in § 2*a*, the Transformation Theory is the keystone of physical interpretation in the general theory, and this in turn rests on the following theorem: [22]

Theorem 3.—*The eigenvectors of a Hermitian operator form a complete-orthonormal set.*

The importance of this hypothesis cannot be over-emphasized, but at the same time it is necessary to point out that it has not been possible to prove it rigorously except in the case of a finite number of dimensions. In the general case we are forced to rely on physical reasonableness and consistency of results to guide us in application of this theorem, and in principle we consider (as physically meaningful) only those Hermitian operators which satisfy the theorem.[23]

Accepting this theorem, we can now take over all the results of the preceding sections with the interpretation that a basis $\{ \mid \xi' \rangle \}$ is that basis afforded by the eigenvectors of a Hermitian operator $\boldsymbol{\xi}$; the alternate description as the ξ-representation meaning the ξ-diagonal representation, since

$$\langle \xi' \mid \boldsymbol{\xi} \mid \xi'' \rangle = \xi' \delta (\xi', \xi''), \qquad (1:16)$$

i.e. the operator $\boldsymbol{\xi}$ is represented by a diagonal matrix, or briefly, $\boldsymbol{\xi}$ *is diagonal* in its own representation, and the diagonal elements are the eigenvalues of $\boldsymbol{\xi}$. It is this result which makes the choice of a representation in which the basic vectors are eigen-$\mid \rangle$'s of a Hermitian operator so significant, and we have the important theorem that we can set up a representation in which any Hermitian operator is diagonal. With but few exceptions (cf. § 96), the basic vectors in physical applications are eigenvectors of some Hermitian operator.

§ 5. Projection Operators

The expansion theorem in the form (1:5*a*, *b*) suggests the introduction of the *operator* product of a basic vector $\mid \alpha' \rangle$ by its adjoint, viz.

$$\boldsymbol{\pi}_{\alpha'} = \mid \alpha' \rangle \langle \alpha' \mid = \boldsymbol{\pi}^*_{\alpha'}, \qquad (1:17)$$

which is evidently Hermitian, and is termed a projection operator since, from (1:5*a*, *b*), $\boldsymbol{\pi}_{\alpha'}$ operating suitably on a $\langle \mid$ or $\mid \rangle$ vector gives the corresponding projection in the α' direction:

$$\boldsymbol{\pi}_{\alpha'} \mid \rangle = \mid \alpha' \rangle \langle \alpha' \mid \rangle, \qquad (1:18a)$$

$$\langle \mid \boldsymbol{\pi}_{\alpha'} = \langle \mid \alpha' \rangle \langle \alpha' \mid. \qquad (1:18b)$$

[22] In the case of a finite number of dimensions this can be proved, and we might call it the special expansion theorem. See Dirac, *loc. cit.*, p. 34 *et seq.*

[23] This is to some extent a meaningless restriction since we can rarely test a particular operator to see whether or not it fits the bill, but in most cases of physical interest it seems to hold [cf. § 9, eqns. (2:1–3), *et seq*].

$\boldsymbol{\pi}_{\alpha'}$ is readily seen to annihilate any other distinct basic vector $|\,\alpha''\,\rangle$, or equivalently,

$$\boldsymbol{\pi}_{\alpha'}\boldsymbol{\pi}_{\alpha''} = \boldsymbol{\pi}_{\alpha'}\delta\,(\,\alpha', \alpha''\,), \qquad (1{:}19)$$

which states that $\boldsymbol{\pi}_{\alpha'}$ is *idempotent*,[24] i.e. its only eigenvalues are 0 and 1. The use of the expansion theorem is greatly facilitated by introducing the *total* projection operator

$$\sum_{\alpha'} |\,\alpha'\,\rangle\langle\,\alpha'\,| = \sum_{\alpha'} \boldsymbol{\pi}_{\alpha'} = \mathbf{I} \qquad \text{(unit or identity operator)}, \qquad (1{:}20)$$

which is defined over the complete-orthonormal set of eigenvectors, and follows directly from the expansion theorem (cf. eqns. 1:5*a*, *b*). In fact, this operator axiom and the axiom of linear independence,

$$\sum_{\alpha'} c\,(\,\alpha'\,)\,|\,\alpha'\,\rangle = 0 \qquad [\text{implies } c\,(\,\alpha'\,) = 0 \text{ for every } \alpha'], \qquad (1{:}21)$$

are necessary and sufficient conditions that a set of eigenvectors $\{\,|\,\alpha'\,\rangle\,\}$ form a proper basis, since it is readily seen that they imply, and are implied by, the equivalent necessary and sufficient conditions of orthonormality and completeness.

With the form (1:20) one can immediately write down, for example, that the representative of the product of two operators $\boldsymbol{\beta}$, $\boldsymbol{\gamma}$ is given by the usual law of matrix multiplication,

$$\langle\,\alpha'\,|\,\boldsymbol{\beta\gamma}\,|\,\alpha''\,\rangle = \sum_{\alpha'''} \langle\,\alpha'\,|\,\boldsymbol{\beta}\,|\,\alpha'''\,\rangle\langle\,\alpha'''\,|\,\boldsymbol{\gamma}\,|\,\alpha''\,\rangle, \qquad (1{:}22)$$

thus avoiding the laborious expansion term by term and the subsequent reduction by the condition of orthonormality. Similarly, the operation of taking the adjoint of any two operators takes the symbolic form

$$(\,\boldsymbol{\beta\gamma}\,)^* = \boldsymbol{\gamma}^*\boldsymbol{\beta}^*, \qquad (1{:}23a)$$

or, in representative form,

$$\begin{aligned}\langle\,\alpha'\,|\,(\,\boldsymbol{\beta\gamma}\,)^*\,|\,\alpha''\,\rangle &= \sum_{\alpha'''} \langle\,\alpha'\,|\,\boldsymbol{\gamma}^*\,|\,\alpha'''\,\rangle\langle\,\alpha'''\,|\,\boldsymbol{\beta}^*\,|\,\alpha''\,\rangle \\ &= \sum_{\alpha'''} \langle\,\alpha''\,|\,\boldsymbol{\beta}\,|\,\alpha'''\,\rangle^*\langle\,\alpha'''\,|\,\boldsymbol{\gamma}\,|\,\alpha'\,\rangle^*, \qquad (1{:}23b)\end{aligned}$$

which is the usual matrix rule.

§ 6. Commuting Operators and Simultaneous Eigenvectors

In case there is but one independent eigen-$|\,\rangle$ corresponding to a given eigenvalue, we say that the system or eigenvalue spectrum is non-degenerate. This, however, appears to be rather the exceptional case, and in application it is usually found that there are several independent eigen-$|\,\rangle$'s corresponding to a given eigenvalue (i.e. coincidence of eigenvalues); this situation is termed degenerate, the number of independent eigen-$|\,\rangle$'s giving the degree of degeneracy. However, in this case

[24] The projection operator furnishes a simple example of an (infinite) orthogonal set of idempotent Hermitian operators (cf. §§ 27, 99).

we can always select from all the eigen-$| \rangle$'s corresponding to a degenerate eigenvalue, a set which is orthonormal.[25]

Thus suppose that for some Hermitian operator $\boldsymbol{\eta}$, the eigenvalue η' is g-fold degenerate. Then we can select a set $| \eta' a' \rangle, | \eta' a'' \rangle, \ldots | \eta' a^g \rangle$, such that

$$\langle \eta' a' | \eta' a'' \rangle = \delta (a', a''), \quad \ldots \ldots \quad (1:24)$$

where a is merely an auxiliary letter to distinguish individual members of a degenerate set, and $\delta(a', a'')$ is the Kronecker delta with the values 1 or 0, according as a' is or is not equal to a''. We use a letter with superscript instead of additional numbers alone because, as we shall see, a significant physical characterization of members of a degenerate set can be obtained so that the symbol a, attached for convenience at this point, takes on physical meaning. It is clear that any linear combination of eigen-$| \rangle$'s belonging to a given eigenvalue (degenerate case) is also an eigen-$| \rangle$ belonging to the given eigenvalue. In addition, we can conclude from the orthogonality theorem that eigen-$| \rangle$'s belonging to different eigenvalues are all necessarily independent.

An orthonormal set of eigenvectors belonging to the g-fold degenerate eigenvalue η' are said to span the g-dimensional η' subspace, but we have as yet no significant characterization of axes in this subspace. To this end we introduce another linear operator $\boldsymbol{\nu}$, such that $\boldsymbol{\eta}$ and $\boldsymbol{\nu}$ satisfy the commutation relation (C.R.)

$$\boldsymbol{\eta\nu} - \boldsymbol{\nu\eta} = [\, \boldsymbol{\eta}, \boldsymbol{\nu} \,]_- = 0, \quad \ldots \ldots \quad (1:25)$$

i.e. $\boldsymbol{\eta}$ and $\boldsymbol{\nu}$ are said to commute. We note incidentally that this is the condition that the operator product $\boldsymbol{\eta\nu}$ be Hermitian when $\boldsymbol{\eta}$ and $\boldsymbol{\nu}$ are each Hermitian, since we can write $\boldsymbol{\eta\nu}$ as the sum of a real and an imaginary (Hermitian and anti-Hermitian) part, viz.

$$\boldsymbol{\eta\nu} = \tfrac{1}{2}\{\boldsymbol{\eta\nu} + (\boldsymbol{\eta\nu})^*\} + \tfrac{1}{2}\{\boldsymbol{\eta\nu} - (\boldsymbol{\eta\nu})^*\} = \tfrac{1}{2}[\boldsymbol{\eta}, \boldsymbol{\nu}]_+ + \tfrac{1}{2}[\boldsymbol{\eta}, \boldsymbol{\nu}]_-. \quad . \quad (1:26)$$

From (1:25) it follows that

$$\boldsymbol{\eta\nu} | \eta' a' \rangle = \eta' \boldsymbol{\nu} | \eta' a' \rangle, \quad \ldots \ldots \quad (1:27)$$

i.e. $\boldsymbol{\nu} | \eta' a' \rangle$ is also an eigen-$| \rangle$ of $\boldsymbol{\eta}$ belonging to η', and hence, in general, a linear combination of the g-fold set. Noting that

$$\langle \eta' a' | \boldsymbol{\eta} | \eta'' a'' \rangle = \eta' \delta (\eta', \eta'') \, \delta (a', a''), \quad \ldots \quad (1:28)$$

we see from the representative form of (1:25), viz.

$$(\eta' - \eta'') \langle \eta' a' | \boldsymbol{\nu} | \eta'' a'' \rangle = 0, \quad \ldots \ldots \quad (1:29)$$

that the matrix representing $\boldsymbol{\nu}$ in the η-representation need only have a block diagonal form, i.e. a matrix of square matrices along the diagonal, which is sometimes termed a super-matrix. The problem of bringing $\boldsymbol{\nu}$ to true diagonal form is essentially trivial since *within each subspace* $\boldsymbol{\eta}$ is represented by a scalar matrix, and we have just

[25] By Schmidt's orthogonalization process, see, for example, MURNAGHAN, *op cit.*, p. 24.

the previously considered problem of diagonalizing a Hermitian matrix by a unitary transformation. Thus,

$$\langle \eta'\nu' \mid \boldsymbol{\nu} \mid \eta''\nu'' \rangle = \nu' \, \delta(\eta', \eta'') \, \delta(\nu', \nu'')$$

$$= \sum_{a', a''}^{g} \langle \eta'\nu' \mid \eta'a' \rangle \langle \eta'a' \mid \boldsymbol{\nu} \mid \eta''a'' \rangle \langle \eta''a'' \mid \eta''\nu'' \rangle, \qquad (1:30)$$

where, as indicated, the *simultaneous* eigen-$|\,\rangle$'s of $\boldsymbol{\eta}$ and $\boldsymbol{\nu}$ are given by the unitary transformation

$$\mid \eta'\nu' \rangle = \sum_{a''}^{g} \mid \eta'a'' \rangle \langle \eta'a'' \mid \eta'\nu' \rangle. \quad . \quad . \quad . \quad . \quad . \quad (1:31)$$

The transformation coefficients, or representatives $\langle \eta'a'' \mid \eta'\nu' \rangle$, are given by the equations

$$\sum_{a''}^{g} \langle \eta'a' \mid \boldsymbol{\nu} \mid \eta'a'' \rangle \langle \eta'a'' \mid \eta'\nu' \rangle = \nu' \langle \eta'a' \mid \eta'\nu' \rangle, \quad . \quad . \quad (1:32)$$

as follows on pre-multiplying (1:31) by $\langle \eta'a' \mid \boldsymbol{\nu}$. In explicit form we may write these g equations as:

$$\begin{aligned} &[\langle \eta'a' \mid \boldsymbol{\nu} \mid \eta'a' \rangle - \nu'] \langle \eta'a' \mid \eta'\nu' \rangle + \langle \eta'a' \mid \boldsymbol{\nu} \mid \eta'a'' \rangle \langle \eta'a'' \mid \eta'\nu' \rangle + \ldots = 0. \\ &\langle \eta'a'' \mid \boldsymbol{\nu} \mid \eta'a' \rangle \langle \eta'a' \mid \eta'\nu' \rangle + [\langle \eta'a'' \mid \boldsymbol{\nu} \mid \eta'a'' \rangle - \nu'] \langle \eta'a'' \mid \eta'\nu' \rangle + \ldots = 0. \\ &\qquad \cdot \qquad\qquad\qquad\qquad\qquad\qquad \cdot \\ &\qquad \cdot \qquad\qquad\qquad\qquad\qquad\qquad \cdot \\ &\qquad \cdot \qquad\qquad\qquad\qquad\qquad\qquad \cdot \end{aligned} \qquad (1:33)$$

Solving these equations we obtain the required linear combinations of the $\mid \eta'a' \rangle$, all a', such that both $\boldsymbol{\eta}$ and $\boldsymbol{\nu}$ are simultaneously diagonal.[26]

The condition of solvability of the homogeneous equations (1:33) is the vanishing of the determinant:

$$\begin{Vmatrix} \langle \eta'a' \mid \boldsymbol{\nu} \mid \eta'a' \rangle - \nu' & \langle \eta'a' \mid \boldsymbol{\nu} \mid \eta'a'' \rangle \ldots \\ \langle \eta'a'' \mid \boldsymbol{\nu} \mid \eta'a' \rangle & \langle \eta'a'' \mid \boldsymbol{\nu} \mid \eta'a'' \rangle - \nu' \ldots \\ \cdot & \cdot \quad\quad \cdot \\ \cdot & \cdot \quad\quad \cdot \\ \cdot & \cdot \quad\quad \cdot \\ \langle \eta'a^g \mid \boldsymbol{\nu} \mid \eta'a' \rangle & \langle \eta'a^g \mid \boldsymbol{\nu} \mid \eta'a'' \rangle \ldots \end{Vmatrix}, \quad . \quad (1:34)$$ [27]

i.e. the so-called secular equation determining the g eigenvalues of $\boldsymbol{\nu}$ which now label the specially selected eigen-$|\,\rangle$'s of $\boldsymbol{\eta}$ of our g-dimensional subspace.

If the g eigenvalues of $\boldsymbol{\nu}$ are distinct, then we have a uniquely determined representation in which $\boldsymbol{\eta}$ and $\boldsymbol{\nu}$ are simultaneously diagonal, and we speak of the simul-

[26] This process is perhaps more familiarly known as the simultaneous diagonalization of commuting Hermitian matrices. We consider this process in some detail because of the rather important role it plays in perturbation theory.

[27] Note that in (1:33) we have g equations in $g + 1$ unknowns, so that we can only determine the ratio of the representatives, which corresponds to determining the direction of that part of $\mid \eta'\nu' \rangle$ which lies in the g-dimensional subspace belonging to η'. In actual solution we assign an arbitrary value to any one of the representatives in terms of which the others are obtained; normalization takes up the single degree of freedom for a complete determination.

taneous eigen-$|\,\rangle$'s of $\boldsymbol{\eta}$ and $\boldsymbol{\nu}$. However, it frequently happens that the eigenvalues of $\boldsymbol{\nu}$, which now characterize the g-dimensional subspace and basic eigen-$|\,\rangle$'s thereof, are not all distinct, and there is more than one independent simultaneous eigen-$|\,\rangle$ belonging to a particular pair of eigenvalues η', ν'. In this case we introduce a third linear operator, say $\boldsymbol{\xi}$, which commutes with both $\boldsymbol{\eta}$ and $\boldsymbol{\nu}$, and requires the basic $|\,\rangle$'s to be eigen-$|\,\rangle$'s of all three, so that $\boldsymbol{\eta}$, $\boldsymbol{\nu}$, and $\boldsymbol{\xi}$ are all simultaneously diagonal. We can continue this process until finally we obtain a representation such that the basic $|\,\rangle$'s are simultaneous eigen-$|\,\rangle$'s of a set of commuting operators, such that there is but one independent simultaneous eigen-$|\,\rangle$ of them all, belonging to a given set of eigenvalues. Such a set is called a complete set of commuting operators, and the corresponding representation may be called a complete representation.[28] We have then the theorem:

Theorem 4.—*There exists a representation in which a set of commuting operators is simultaneously diagonal, and if the set is complete, the representation is uniquely determined apart from arbitrary phase factors of unit modulus in the basic* $|\,\rangle$*'s.*

In this event we can infer from the simultaneously valid equations

$$\left.\begin{aligned} \boldsymbol{\eta}\,|\,\eta'\nu'\,\rangle &= \eta'\,|\,\eta'\nu'\,\rangle \\ \boldsymbol{\nu}\,|\,\eta'\nu'\,\rangle &= \nu'\,|\,\eta'\nu'\,\rangle \end{aligned}\right\} \qquad (1{:}35a)$$

and

$$\left.\begin{aligned} \boldsymbol{\eta}\,|\,\eta'\,\rangle &= \eta'\,|\,\eta'\,\rangle \\ \boldsymbol{\nu}\,|\,\nu'\,\rangle &= \nu'\,|\,\nu'\,\rangle \end{aligned}\right\}, \qquad (1{:}35b)$$

that the basic eigenvectors $\{\,|\,\eta'\nu'\,\rangle\,\}$ of the η, ν-diagonal representation are formed by the *direct* products of the basic vectors $\{\,|\,\eta'\,\rangle\,\}$, $\{\,|\,\nu'\,\rangle\,\}$ of the η- and ν-representations, so that the dimensionality of the resultant space is the product of those of the constituent spaces. Moreover, the consistency of equations (1:35a, b) requires

$$|\,\eta'\nu'\,\rangle = |\,\eta'\,\rangle\,|\,\nu'\,\rangle = |\,\nu'\,\rangle\,|\,\eta'\,\rangle, \qquad (1{:}36)$$

or that the product satisfies the commutative axiom, and we infer that the distributive axiom also obtains. In terms of projection operators (§ 5) this development takes the form

$$\boldsymbol{\pi}_{\eta'\nu'} = \boldsymbol{\pi}_{\eta'}\boldsymbol{\pi}_{\nu'} = \boldsymbol{\pi}_{\nu'}\boldsymbol{\pi}_{\eta'}, \qquad (1{:}37)$$

which is an equivalent statement of the condition that $\boldsymbol{\eta}$, $\boldsymbol{\nu}$ commute. As will be seen in the next chapter, the formalism of the projection operators affords a very direct correlation of experimental findings with the mathematical theory, leading to the general interpretation of the quantum mechanics.

§ 7. General Comments

There is an additional point to be made concerning the labelling of matrix elements as regards order of occurrence. Though this matter is of no consequence in general theoretical considerations, it has considerable importance in actual cal-

[28] The $|\,\rangle$'s are completely determined except for an arbitrary factor of unit modulus, say $e^{i\gamma'}$; $\gamma' = \gamma'(\eta', \nu', \xi', \ldots)$.

culations, and it is desirable to avoid any possible confusion. Let us consider, as an example, a typical representative $\langle \xi_1'\xi_2'\xi_3' \mid \boldsymbol{\alpha} \mid \xi_1''\xi_2''\xi_3'' \rangle$ of some operator $\boldsymbol{\alpha}$ in a complete representation; the corresponding complete set of operators being $\boldsymbol{\xi}_1, \boldsymbol{\xi}_2, \boldsymbol{\xi}_3$.[29] This same question of multiple labelling of a matrix element in a given row and column arises frequently in group theory in connection with the Kronecker or direct matrix product, and we shall in this book usually adopt the convention used there, namely, we label in dictionary order. Thus the element in the $\xi_1'\xi_2'\xi_3'$ row and $\xi_1''\xi_2''\xi_3''$ column precedes the element in the $\xi_1'''\xi_2'''\xi_3'''$ row and $\xi_1^{\mathrm{IV}}\xi_2^{\mathrm{IV}}\xi_3^{\mathrm{IV}}$ column, e.g. if $\xi_1' < \xi_1'''$, or if $\xi_1' = \xi_1'''$, $\xi_2' < \xi_2'''$; and if also $\xi_2' = \xi_2'''$, then the precedence is established by $\xi_3' < \xi_3'''$, etc., and similarly for the sequence as to columns, $\xi_1'' < \xi_1^{\mathrm{IV}}$, etc. Any other consistent convention may be used just as well. In actual calculations it is often convenient to use some functionally related quantity (in the sense of a 1 : 1 correspondence), say $f(\xi_1')$, instead of the eigenvalue itself as label; and furthermore, the nature of a given physical problem will usually select the eigenvalues of some one of the operators to be given first consideration in the ordering process, i.e. correspond to ξ_1' in expressions like $\langle \xi_1'\xi_2'\xi_3' \mid \boldsymbol{\alpha} \mid \xi_1''\xi_2''\xi_3'' \rangle$, and likewise for $\mid \xi_1'\xi_2'\xi_3' \rangle$, etc. From the theoretical point of view, it can make no difference which operator is to be considered first, second, etc., since we may determine the same complete representation starting from the eigen-$\mid \rangle$'s of any one of the operators of a complete set; but in perturbation theory a careless choice can conceivably make a problem intractable.

The complete representation is the most important type in both practical calculation and work of a general theoretical nature. With regard to the latter it is rather inconvenient to carry all the symbols involved when we have a complete set of commuting operators $\boldsymbol{\xi}_1, \boldsymbol{\xi}_2, \ldots \boldsymbol{\xi}_n$. A typical eigenvector would be $\mid \xi_1'\xi_2' \ldots \xi_n' \rangle$, while typical representatives of an arbitrary $\mid \rangle$ and operator $\boldsymbol{\alpha}$ would be $\langle \xi_1'\xi_2' \ldots \xi_n' \mid \rangle$ and $\langle \xi_1'\xi_2' \ldots \xi_n' \mid \boldsymbol{\alpha} \mid \xi_1''\xi_2'' \ldots \xi_n'' \rangle$, respectively. When the meaning is clear from the text we may abbreviate these, as $\mid {}'\xi \rangle$, $\langle {}'\xi \mid \rangle$, and $\langle {}'\xi \mid \boldsymbol{\alpha} \mid {}''\xi \rangle$, using primes to the left of the symbols to indicate explicitly that the symbol stands for a complete set of commuting observables. A member of the set, $\boldsymbol{\xi}_n$, would then appear as

$$\langle {}'\xi \mid \boldsymbol{\xi}_n \mid {}''\xi \rangle = \xi_n' \delta({}'\xi, {}''\xi),$$

where $\delta({}'\xi, {}''\xi) = \delta(\xi_1', \xi_1'')\, \delta(\xi_2', \xi_2'') \ldots$, etc.

It has been pointed out that every representation, complete or not, has a degree of arbitrariness in the sense that the basic $\mid \rangle$'s are undetermined to the extent of a factor of unit modulus. Thus, the multiplication of each $\mid \xi_1'\xi_2' \ldots \xi_n' \rangle$ by a numeric of the form $e^{i'\gamma}$, where ${}'\gamma = {}'\gamma({}'\xi)$, will not affect any of the general conclusions which we have derived thus far, but the selection of phase factors, as such numerics are termed, must be made consistently in a given problem; and though the selection is arbitrary, it is by no means trivial. As we shall see, a judicious choice has a decided influence on the specific form which the representatives of operators and vectors take in a given representation. For the moment we merely note that multiplying each *basic* $\mid \rangle$ by such a factor necessitates the changes listed in tabular form below.

[29] We take the complete set as involving only 3 operators merely for simplicity and convenience.

		$\longrightarrow$	
Basic $\mid\ \rangle$'s	$\mid {}'\xi \rangle$	$e^{i\,'\gamma} \mid {}'\xi \rangle$	
Representative of arbitrary $\mid\ \rangle$	$\langle {}'\xi \mid\ \rangle$	$\langle {}'\xi \mid\ \rangle e^{-i\,'\gamma}$	(1:38)
Representative of arbitrary $\langle\ \mid$	$\langle\ \mid {}'\xi \rangle$	$\langle\ \mid {}'\xi \rangle e^{i\,'\gamma}$	
Representative of arbitrary operator	$\langle {}'\xi \mid \boldsymbol{\alpha} \mid {}''\xi \rangle$	$\langle {}'\xi \mid \boldsymbol{\alpha} \mid {}''\xi \rangle e^{i({}''\gamma - {}'\gamma)}$	

§ 8. Functions of Hermitian Operators

In the case of operators expressible as power series in terms of a given operator, there is no question of a functional definition. However, to cover all the cases of interest to us, it is desirable to make the following generalization:

If $\boldsymbol{\gamma}(\boldsymbol{\xi})$ is to be a function of a Hermitian operator $\boldsymbol{\xi}$, we require that the equation $\boldsymbol{\xi} \mid \xi'a' \rangle = \xi' \mid \xi'a' \rangle$ implies $\boldsymbol{\gamma}(\boldsymbol{\xi}) \mid \xi'a' \rangle = \gamma(\xi') \mid \xi'a' \rangle$, and conversely.[30] Thus we require that there be a unique $1:1$ correspondence between the eigenvalues of $\boldsymbol{\xi}$ and $\boldsymbol{\gamma}$, and necessarily that $\gamma(\xi')$ be a real function of ξ', the Hermitian character of $\boldsymbol{\gamma}(\boldsymbol{\xi})$ being implicit in the reality condition on $\gamma(\xi')$. In terms of the projection operators for this space, our requirement takes the form

$$\left.\begin{aligned} \boldsymbol{\xi} &= \sum_{\xi'a'} \xi' \boldsymbol{\pi}_{\xi'a'}, \\ \boldsymbol{\gamma}(\boldsymbol{\xi}) &= \sum_{\xi'a'} \gamma(\xi')\, \boldsymbol{\pi}_{\xi'a'}. \end{aligned}\right\} \qquad (1:39)$$

A somewhat less direct expression of the conditions imposed on a function of a Hermitian operator is implicit in two important theorems:

Theorem 5.—*If $\boldsymbol{\gamma}$ is a function of $\boldsymbol{\xi}$, then an operator which commutes with $\boldsymbol{\xi}$ necessarily commutes with $\boldsymbol{\gamma}$.*

Let the arbitrary operator be $\boldsymbol{\eta}$, then, by hypothesis,

$$\langle \xi'a' \mid \boldsymbol{\eta} \mid \xi''a'' \rangle = 0, \qquad (1:40)$$

unless $\xi' = \xi''$ (cf. eqn. 1:31); and

$$\langle \xi'a' \mid \boldsymbol{\gamma} \mid \xi''a'' \rangle = \gamma(\xi')\, \delta(\xi', \xi'')\, \delta(a', a''). \qquad (1:41)$$

Expressing $\boldsymbol{\gamma\eta} - \boldsymbol{\eta\gamma} = 0$ in representative form, we have

$$[\gamma(\xi') - \gamma(\xi'')] \langle \xi'a' \mid \boldsymbol{\eta} \mid \xi''a'' \rangle = 0, \qquad (1:42)$$

i.e. $\langle \xi'a' \mid \boldsymbol{\eta} \mid \xi''a'' \rangle = 0$, unless $\gamma(\xi') = \gamma(\xi'')$, which is a direct consequence of (1:40), and proves the theorem.

Theorem 6.—*If an operator $\boldsymbol{\gamma}$ is such that any operator which commutes with $\boldsymbol{\xi}$ necessarily commutes with $\boldsymbol{\gamma}$, then $\boldsymbol{\gamma}$ is a function of $\boldsymbol{\xi}$.*

The proof of this theorem, which is essentially the converse of the preceding one, involves somewhat more subtle considerations. Let us work with a representation defined by $\boldsymbol{\xi}$, and such other variables $\boldsymbol{\alpha}$, $\boldsymbol{\beta}$, . . . as are required to form a

[30] In dealing with operators whose eigenvalues take on discrete values only, the question of analyticity or continuity obviously has no meaning.

complete commuting set, and let $\boldsymbol{\eta}$ denote an operator which commutes with $\boldsymbol{\xi}$, and by hypothesis necessarily commutes with $\boldsymbol{\gamma}$. It suffices to take $\boldsymbol{\eta}$ of the form $\boldsymbol{\eta}(\boldsymbol{\xi}, \boldsymbol{\alpha}, \boldsymbol{\beta}, \ldots)$ to prove that $\boldsymbol{\gamma}$ is also of the form $\boldsymbol{\gamma}(\boldsymbol{\xi}, \boldsymbol{\alpha}, \boldsymbol{\beta}, \ldots)$, since

$$\boldsymbol{\eta\gamma} - \boldsymbol{\gamma\eta} = 0, \qquad (1{:}43a)$$

or

$$[\eta(\xi'\alpha'\beta'\ldots) - \eta(\xi''\alpha''\beta''\ldots)]\langle \xi'\alpha'\beta'\ldots | \boldsymbol{\gamma} | \xi''\alpha''\beta''\ldots\rangle = 0. \qquad (1{:}43b)$$

The theorem will be established if we can show that $\boldsymbol{\gamma}$ actually depends *only* on $\boldsymbol{\xi}$, and this follows immediately if there exist one or more operators which commute with $\boldsymbol{\xi}$ but not with $\boldsymbol{\alpha}, \boldsymbol{\beta}, \ldots$. We define an operator $\mathbf{O}_\alpha$ such that for any eigenvector $|\xi'\alpha'\beta'\ldots\rangle$

$$\mathbf{O}_\alpha |\xi'\alpha'\beta'\ldots\rangle = \sum_{\alpha'' \neq \alpha'} |\xi'\alpha''\beta'\ldots\rangle, \qquad (1{:}44a)$$

or

$$\langle \xi'\alpha''\beta'\ldots | \mathbf{O}_\alpha | \xi'\alpha'\beta'\ldots\rangle = 1 - \delta(\alpha', \alpha''). \qquad (1{:}44b)$$

$\mathbf{O}_\alpha$ is seen to be Hermitian,[31] and clearly does not commute with $\boldsymbol{\alpha}$, since

$$\langle \xi'\alpha'\beta'\ldots | \boldsymbol{\alpha}\mathbf{O}_\alpha - \mathbf{O}_\alpha\boldsymbol{\alpha} | \xi'\alpha''\beta'\ldots\rangle = \alpha' - \alpha''. \qquad (1{:}45)$$

Hence, the operator $\mathbf{O}_\alpha\mathbf{O}_\beta\ldots$, which commutes only with $\boldsymbol{\xi}$, forces $\boldsymbol{\gamma} = \boldsymbol{\gamma}(\boldsymbol{\xi})$.[32]

It is readily demonstrated that these same theorems obtain in the general case where the single operator $\boldsymbol{\xi}$ is replaced by a complete set of commuting operators $\boldsymbol{\xi}_1, \boldsymbol{\xi}_2, \ldots \boldsymbol{\xi}_n$.

If $\boldsymbol{\gamma}$ is a Hermitian operator which commutes with one of the $\boldsymbol{\xi}$'s, say $\boldsymbol{\xi}_m$, then from (1:40) $\langle {}'\xi | \boldsymbol{\gamma} | {}''\xi\rangle$ vanishes except for $\xi_m' = \xi_m''$; and should $\boldsymbol{\gamma}$ commute with every operator of the complete set, then

$$\langle {}'\xi | \boldsymbol{\gamma} | {}''\xi\rangle = \gamma({}'\xi)\,\delta({}'\xi, {}''\xi), \qquad (1{:}46)$$

or $\boldsymbol{\gamma}$ is represented by a diagonal Hermitian matrix and represents a function of the $\boldsymbol{\xi}$'s. This leads to the important theorem:

Theorem 7.—*The completeness of a set of commuting Hermitian operators implies that an operator which commutes with each of the operators of the set is necessarily a function of the operator set.*

We close our discussion of operators with a few simple examples of practical importance. If two operators $\boldsymbol{\eta}$ and $\boldsymbol{\xi}$ anticommute, $[\boldsymbol{\eta}, \boldsymbol{\xi}]_+ = 0$; then expressing this condition in the ξ-representation and making the appropriate reductions,

$$(\xi' + \xi'')\langle \xi'a' | \boldsymbol{\eta} | \xi''a''\rangle = 0, \qquad (1{:}47)$$

i.e. $\langle \xi'a' | \boldsymbol{\eta} | \xi''a''\rangle = 0$, unless $\xi' = -\xi''$.[33]

[31] Alternatively, $\mathbf{O}_\alpha$ can be written in the explicit form

$$\mathbf{O}_\alpha = \sum_{\alpha', \alpha''} \mathbf{P}_{\alpha', \alpha''} \qquad (\alpha' < \alpha''),$$

where $\mathbf{P}_{\alpha', \alpha''}$ denotes the permutation interchanging the attached (umbral) eigenvalue pair, and the Hermitian character of $\mathbf{O}_\alpha$ follows by virtue of the same property of the interchanges (cf. §§ 44, 50, 86).

[32] If $\boldsymbol{\xi}, \boldsymbol{\alpha}, \boldsymbol{\beta}, \ldots$ have continuous eigenvalue spectra, the Hermitian differential operators (cf. § 24) corresponding to $\boldsymbol{\alpha}, \boldsymbol{\beta}, \ldots$ serve the same purpose.

[33] A particular case of this is the so-called odd-even selection rule.

Of the various types of operator functions, two of the most useful are the inverse and square root operators.

The inverse operator is defined by the statement that $\boldsymbol{\xi} \mid \xi'a' \rangle = \xi' \mid \xi'a' \rangle$ implies, and is implied by, $\boldsymbol{\xi}^{-1} \mid \xi'a' \rangle = \xi'^{-1} \mid \xi'a' \rangle$. Obviously $\boldsymbol{\xi}$ and $\boldsymbol{\xi}^{-1}$ commute, and, since $\boldsymbol{\xi}\boldsymbol{\xi}^{-1} \mid \xi'a' \rangle = \mid \xi'a' \rangle$, we see that $\boldsymbol{\xi}^{-1}$ satisfies the usual conditions expected of a well-behaved inverse, viz.

$$\boldsymbol{\xi}\boldsymbol{\xi}^{-1} = \boldsymbol{\xi}^{-1}\boldsymbol{\xi} = \mathbf{I}. \qquad (1{:}48)$$ [34]

The inverse of an operator, properly speaking, can only be expected to exist provided the original operator does not have the eigenvalue zero (in certain cases, as will be seen, it is possible to extend this condition to include somewhat *improper* inverse operators).

The Hermitian square root of an operator exists only when the eigenvalue spectrum of the operator is non-negative. Then we have the defining equations

$$\left.\begin{aligned} \boldsymbol{\xi} \mid \xi'a' \rangle &= \xi' \mid \xi'a' \rangle, \\ \boldsymbol{\xi}^{\frac{1}{2}} \mid \xi'a' \rangle &= \pm\, \xi'^{\frac{1}{2}} \mid \xi'a' \rangle. \end{aligned}\right\} \qquad (1{:}49)$$

It is obvious that we must avoid the ambiguity of sign by specifying a particular sign for each eigenvalue of $\boldsymbol{\xi}^{\frac{1}{2}}$, and it is evident that $\boldsymbol{\xi}^{\frac{1}{2}}$ will satisfy the conditions required of a Hermitian operator function even if the sign prefixed to $\xi'^{\frac{1}{2}}$ varies in any manner whatever for successive eigenvalues. However, we must require that the same sign be used for all values of a' corresponding to a degenerate eigenvalue. The usual sign convention in practice is to assign the positive root to all the eigenvalues.

We have now completed the essential mathematical framework for operators with discrete eigenvalues, and further development consists largely of rather straightforward *formal* generalization to include continuous eigenvalue spectra and associated operators. At this point we shall find it useful to consider the physical concepts, and let further mathematical work be more explicitly conditioned by the requirements of physical interpretation.

[34] The Hermiticity of $\boldsymbol{\xi}$ guarantees the equivalence of the right and left inverses, which is not necessary for operators in general. Note that $(\boldsymbol{\alpha\beta})^{-1} = \boldsymbol{\beta}^{-1}\boldsymbol{\alpha}^{-1}$ as usual.

CHAPTER II

Physical Principles

§ 9. The Concept of State

Of all the underlying physical ideas which distinguish the quantal viewpoint from the classical, probably the most characteristic is that of indeterminacy. In the classical description of any arbitrary dynamical system of f degrees of freedom we may describe the state of the system *at a given time* by specifying the values of, say, the $2f$ conjugate momenta and coordinates at that time,[1] and it is assumed that this knowledge at one time determines the future behaviour of the system as it executes the classical equations of motion. The essential point, however, is the implicit assumption that we can in actual experiment determine a set of values of these variables with a precision limited only by our ingenuity, and that the experimental values obtained at a future time will agree with those predicted by our equations. Otherwise expressed, this implies that the internal structure of classical theory does not, *a priori*, take into consideration the subjective relation between the *observed* and the *observing mechanism*, and is to this extent a rather gross description [2] of natural phenomena. The quantal viewpoint on the other hand recognizes *ab initio* that there is a definite scale of large and small phenomena relative to observing mechanisms, determined by the *extent* to which an observation (measurement of a physical quantity) *disturbs* the observed system; and in particular, that there is an inherent natural limitation on the precision (quite aside from the ordinary concept of experimental error) of our measurements. In this sense it may be termed the theory of small (atomic) phenomena with the above definite meaning of *small.*

This basic concept is incorporated as an integral part of the general quantum theory, and the direct consequence thereof is an indeterminacy in the quantal specification of an arbitrary dynamical system as compared to the corresponding classical description given above. Specifically, the indeterminacy of specification manifests itself in that, for a system such as the above, precise values of only f of the dynamical variables [3] may be assigned or determined, while the values of the remaining variables are expressed in terms of probability considerations. Thus, we have a radically new concept in which determinations of certain related physical quantities (specifically, conjugate variables in the quantal sense) are mutually exclusive, i.e. the precise knowledge of the values of one quantity excludes the possibility of a definite determination for the other. Thus the domain of the quantum theory in a broad

[1] We are not concerned with the question of whether or not a solution can be obtained, but rather with what we understand by a *description* of the system.

[2] Which is not to imply that the classical theory does not describe correctly the larger aspects of nature for which it was explicitly developed.

[3] The quantal sense of this expression is somewhat different from the classical. See the discussion of Observables, § 10.

sense becomes the determination of conditional probabilities, i.e. a set of quantities is assumed to have given values, and we ask the probability that certain other quantities have specified values.

In keeping with the above discussion we define a state of a system as a specification or description of a system, at a given time, with the maximum number of mutually non-exclusive conditions of data.[4] Further, the states of a system will be represented as vectors radiating from a common origin in a linear vector space. The above definition of the state of a system is not relativistic, referring as it does to a three-dimensional cut of space-time corresponding to a particular time, and as such it is analogous to what in classical theory would be a set of numerical values of the dynamical variables.

We have rather casually indicated that states are to be represented by vectors in a suitable vector space, and it may appear that the correlation of states with this particular mathematical construct is a purely *ad hoc* assumption. As a matter of fact, the existence of such a correspondence is neither trivial nor self-evident; rather it is in the nature of a corollary of the general discipline called the Superposition Principle, which itself may be termed the *distillate* of a great many facts and inferences accumulated in the course of the development of quantal concepts. In brief, the Superposition Principle postulates that any state can be considered to be formed by the superposition of two or more other states, and conversely that two or more states may be superposed to form a new state. Thus, in effect, there exists a sort of *Fourier resolution* of physical description, in the sense that a system which is described as being in a given state can be pictured as being concomitantly in two or more other states, and conversely. There is in this description an indeterminateness or vagueness which on the one hand is incomprehensible in terms of classical theory, and on the other may even cause misgivings as to its philosophical implications. As to the former we must simply discard all preconceived notions based on the rigidly determinate nature of classical concepts, and for the latter we must avoid a too literal interpretation of the superposition process.

There are some who consider the Superposition Principle as the most fundamental concept in quantum theory; and, in fact, the whole theory can be constructed on this principle and a minimum of additional postulates, although such is not the usual course adopted. Whatever one's opinion as to its relative importance in the theory, this principle unquestionably presents the difference between the classical and quantal viewpoint in its most acute form. The vagueness which is so alien to classical theory is just that indeterminate element of quantum theory which is necessary to reconcile the wave-particle aspects of physical phenomena. The concept of superposition or addition of states does not imply that a dynamical system objectively co-exists in two or more mutually exclusive states (which has no invariant meaning), but rather that the maximal information (specification of a state) is necessarily delimited or incomplete, in such a way that a system in a definite state can be regarded as distributed in a certain way over a number of accessible,

[4] Note that this specification, which is sometimes termed a maximal set of conditions, is always less complete than in the classical sense. It may be added that the criterion of "maximal" specification is not entirely free of logical difficulties, particularly in the quantum mechanics of continua and relativistic fields. Cf. Chapter XII, § 101.

mutually exclusive states. As a result the given state takes on the properties of each component state in proportion to its weight factor in the superposition process.

It happens that many apparently paradoxical physical situations can only be resolved by *speaking* of the systems involved as though they existed in two or more states in the literal sense, as for example the interpretation of polarization and interference in terms of a single photon as so clearly analysed by Dirac.[5] It is shown (by analysing suitable *thought* experiments) that to understand the passage through an analyser of a single photon whose initial state of polarization is known to be oblique, it is necessary that the specified state of the photon be regarded as a superposition of two mutually perpendicular states of polarization—the weight factors determining the relative probability of transmission such as to give the correct value of the transmitted intensity. Similarly, interference experiments are intelligible in terms of the photon picture, only if a photon whose state is given as being in the initial beam (which for monochromatic light determines the momentum and approximate position of the photon) is regarded as existing partially in each of the two or more resultant beams, and hence interferes only with itself.[6] Lest this picture cause confusion we may note that in the case of two resultant beams, for example, an observation, at least conceptually, would tell us definitely which beam the photon is in. In effect, the added information forces it to jump from being partly in each beam to being entirely in one or the other. Thus it should be clear that the answer to the question of whether or not the photon *really* exists partly in each beam is in the affirmative, *if* this picture is understood as being equivalent to the indeterminateness of our *a priori* information as to its eventual whereabouts.

A further example is the interpretation of the Stern-Gerlach experiment in terms of a single atom. In the simplest case of two resultant beams the state of polarization, so to speak, must be interpreted as a superposition of two mutually anti-parallel states. A further observation with the same field direction does not affect either resultant state, but with another field direction again causes a splitting. This example also clearly illustrates the destruction of prior information by successive observation of incompatible quantities, which in this instance are the magnetic moments in different directions. We must proceed cautiously in the use of such pictures, using them as helpful descriptive constructs insofar as they are consistent with theory, but without expecting that the *ultimate* details of individual processes can be made meaningful in terms of more familiar macroscopic concepts. The logical difficulty lies in the attempt to trace the course of a single photon (particle) to a degree of detail which is operationally meaningless, as it is hopelessly beyond any possible experimental realization.

It has already been noted that in the composition or decomposition process (depending on how we view the superposition) the composite state in question inherits, so to speak, certain characteristics of the component states. In the simplest case this will mean that if a given observation of some physical quantity yields a definite, mutually exclusive aggregate of values, one for each component state,

[5] DIRAC, P. A. M.: *Quantum Mechanics* (Oxford). Referred to as *Q.M.*

[6] The conservation of energy requires that we consider only the probability of occurrence or non-occurrence of a single photon, rather than the probable number of photons, as is easily verified (cf. DIRAC, *ibid*).

then the same observation for the system in the composite state will yield some one of these values; which one we cannot *in general* predict. However, it is a physical fact that in a large number of observations each of the values belonging to the aggregate will be obtained with a definite frequency, and it is postulated that the probability of each value is determined by the weight factor of the corresponding component state in the superposition process. Hence, the *definite* and uniquely determined result of classical theory is replaced by a *definite* probability law—the result of a single observation remaining, in general, indeterminate.

It is clear that whatever mathematical construct is chosen to represent states, the equations relating them must be linear, and it is only in this respect that the quantum Superposition Principle has casual kinship to the classical superposition concept.

That the indicated representation by vectors is the correct one can readily be inferred from the preceding considerations, keeping in mind our illustrative examples. Thus, we may try to represent a state of a dynamical system by some symbol Ψ from which we are to be able to obtain the values, or probable values (as correlated with suitable experiments), of all physically meaningful quantities pertaining to the system in this state. Considering for simplicity a single property or characteristic, α, of the system, the superposition principle implies that Ψ can be regarded as composed of states $\Psi_{\alpha'}$, $\Psi_{\alpha''}$, . . . in which the quantity α *has* values α', α'', ... A measurement on α which gives the value α' may be stated to *project* the state Ψ into a state $\Psi_{\alpha'}$ *with respect to* α, or symbolically

$$O_{\alpha'}\Psi = \Psi_{\alpha'}. \qquad (2:1)$$

Clearly, if the measurement is to be meaningful, a second observation must give the same value, so that

$$\left.\begin{aligned} O_{\alpha'}\Psi_{\alpha'} &= \Psi_{\alpha'} \\ O_{\alpha''}\Psi_{\alpha'} &= 0 \end{aligned}\right\}, \qquad (2:2a)$$

or

$$\left.\begin{aligned} O_{\alpha'}O_{\alpha'}\Psi &= O_{\alpha'}\Psi \\ O_{\alpha''}O_{\alpha'}\Psi &= 0 \end{aligned}\right\}. \qquad (2:2b)$$

Moreover, if simultaneous measurement on a second quantity β is compatible, the sequence of the observations is immaterial, i.e.

$$\left.\begin{aligned} O_{\alpha'}\Psi &= \Psi_{\alpha'} \\ O_{\beta'}\Psi &= \Psi_{\beta'} \end{aligned}\right\}, \qquad (2:3a)$$

$$O_{\alpha'}O_{\beta'}\Psi = O_{\beta'}O_{\alpha'}\Psi = O_{\alpha'\beta'}\Psi. \qquad (2:3b)$$

These are just the properties of projection operators, so that the connection with the work of the last chapter immediately suggests the description of states by vectors, and therefore of physical variables by operators. Further, the reality of measurable values restricts the type of operator, and the fact that Ψ may be *any* state shows physically the necessity for the assumption of a general expansion theorem. From our preceding discussion one might expect, as is the case, that in contrast to the classical case, compounding of a state with itself does not result in a new state. This also suggests the use of vectors, and in particular that only the direction of these vectors shall be relevant. We need not consider the details of the argument here, but it is also possible to infer that complex coefficients must be admitted in the mathematical description of superposition, which fact conditions the choice of a suitable vector space.

§ 10. Observations and Observables

Every physical observation of a quantal (atomic) system consists in the determination, at a particular time, of the value of some dynamical quantity, e.g. coordinates, momenta, functions of these, etc. (there are other quantities having no classical analogue which we neglect at the moment). In the quantum theory, physically measurable quantities form a rather restricted class with certain special properties, and are termed *observables*.

The fundamental operator postulate is:

Every observable is represented by a linear operator in the mathematical formalism, which is further required to be Hermitian and satisfy the Expansion Theorem.

To this we add the general assumption that if the measurement of the observable represented by the operator $\boldsymbol{\alpha}$, for a system in the *normalized* state represented by $| \beta' \rangle$ say,[7] be repeated a large number of times, then the average of all results obtained will be

$$\langle \boldsymbol{\alpha} \rangle_{\beta'} = \langle \beta' | \boldsymbol{\alpha} | \beta' \rangle, \qquad (2:4)$$

where $\langle \boldsymbol{\alpha} \rangle$ signifies the average value of $\boldsymbol{\alpha}$ and $\langle \beta' | \beta' \rangle = 1$. If we expand $| \beta' \rangle$ in terms [8] of eigen-$| \rangle$'s of $\boldsymbol{\alpha}$, then

$$\langle \boldsymbol{\alpha} \rangle_{\beta'} = \sum_{\alpha', \alpha''} \langle \beta' | \alpha' \rangle \langle \alpha' | \boldsymbol{\alpha} | \alpha'' \rangle \langle \alpha'' | \beta' \rangle \qquad (2:5)$$

$$= \sum_{\alpha'} |\langle \beta' | \alpha' \rangle|^2 \alpha'. \qquad (2:6)$$

The form of (2:6) implies that every possible result of the measurement of an observable is one of its eigenvalues. We see that this is indeed true since, if $P(\alpha')$ is the probability of obtaining the result α' for a measurement of the observable, then the average value of the observable will be $\sum_{\alpha'} P(\alpha')\alpha'$ summed over all possible results of the measurement; and from previous work we know that

$$\sum_{\alpha'} |\langle \beta' | \alpha' \rangle|^2 = 1, \qquad (2:7)$$

as it must be if the interpretation is correct. In particular we have the important result that the probability of $\boldsymbol{\alpha}$ having the specified value α' (i.e. as a result of a measurement) for a given state is equal to the square of the modulus of the expansion coefficient (corresponding to this specified value) of the normalized $| \rangle$ representing that state, in the α-representation. This gives a direct physical meaning

[7] We write $| \beta' \rangle$ merely for definiteness, and might just as well have left it unspecified, i.e. $| \rangle$. In the following discussion the notation, strictly speaking, conforms to the case of non-degenerate discrete eigenvalues, but there is no loss of generality thereby since we may consider the results in the light of the general index convention in which we use but one symbol for a complete set of observables.

[8] In the expansion we take $\boldsymbol{\alpha}$ to be a non-degenerate operator for simplicity.

to the modulus of the representative of a normalized $| \rangle$ in a representation in which an observable is diagonal. This is a simple case of a more general theorem to be developed below, and explains the fundamental importance of such representations. With this probability interpretation the diagonality of an observable in its own representation simply means that the state under observation is an eigenstate of the observable; a measurement of this observable must necessarily give the eigenvalue belonging to the state. In the general case, however, the predicted probability is neither zero nor unity, and hence cannot be verified on the basis of a single decisive experiment. Indeed, the statement that a given quantity has a certain probability or expectation is *per se* meaningless unless it is capable of physical realization in terms of a large number of experimental measurements of the quantity in question. As indicated in the discussion of the Superposition Principle, the necessity of many repeated *identical* experiments is in the nature of a fundamental postulate, and the calculated probabilities (probability amplitudes) for a given property are to be correlated with experiment on the basis of the frequency of occurrence of the various possible values.[9]

Probability amplitudes are ordinarily calculated for a system executing its motion under the influence of known forces, exclusive of those introduced in the act of observation, and since a measurement usually modifies the state of the system, it is necessary, at least conceptually, to use an assemblage of a large number of identical copies, each executing its own motion independently of the others.[10] It would be impracticably tedious, if at all possible, to attempt to prepare the individual system in the same original state prior to each determination. Furthermore, the probability amplitude is generally a function of time (cf. § 26), and we are again forced to use a large ensemble of identical systems on which observations can be made at corresponding times.

§ 11. General Transformation Theory

(*a*) *Discrete Eigenvalue Spectra.*

Let us now consider two *distinct* complete sets of commuting observables $\boldsymbol{\xi}_1, \boldsymbol{\xi}_2, \ldots; \boldsymbol{\eta}_1, \boldsymbol{\eta}_2, \ldots;$ which we abbreviate as $\{\boldsymbol{\xi}\}, \{\boldsymbol{\eta}\}$, respectively, in accordance with the convention previously mentioned. In the ξ-representation we have

$$\langle\, `\xi \mid \boldsymbol{\xi}_k \mid {}``\xi\,\rangle = \xi_k{}'\,\delta\,(`\xi, {}``\xi), \qquad (2{:}8)$$

and we inquire as to the relation between the representatives of $\boldsymbol{\xi}_k$, say, in the different representations, ξ-, η-diagonal. Invoking the expansion theorem, we may immediately write the desired relations:

$$\langle\, `\eta \mid \boldsymbol{\xi}_k \mid {}``\eta\,\rangle = \sum_{`\xi,\, ``\xi} \langle\, `\eta \mid `\xi\,\rangle \langle\, `\xi \mid \boldsymbol{\xi}_k \mid {}``\xi\,\rangle \langle\, ``\xi \mid {}``\eta\,\rangle \qquad (2{:}9)$$

and, in particular,

$$\langle\, \boldsymbol{\xi}_k \,\rangle_{`\eta} = \langle\, `\eta \mid \boldsymbol{\xi}_k \mid `\eta\,\rangle = \sum_{`\xi} |\langle\, `\eta \mid `\xi\,\rangle|^2\, \xi_k{}' = \sum_{`\xi} P\,(`\xi\,)\, \xi_k{}', \qquad (2{:}10)$$

[9] I.e. the ratio of the number of favourable cases to the total. We purposely neglect the question of the intrinsic and proper interpretation of probability, which is still a rather undecided question. However, it appears that quantum theory is rather committed to the *frequency* school of thought.

[10] I.e. a Gibbsian ensemble.

i.e. the generalization of the probability interpretation to the case where the average of $\boldsymbol{\xi}_k$ is computed for a state in which each of a complete set of commuting observables $\{\boldsymbol{\eta}\}$ is known to be diagonal, or equivalently, is known to have specified values. Correspondingly, if we compute the average of a member of the complete set $\{\boldsymbol{\eta}\}$, $\boldsymbol{\eta}_k$ say, for the state for which it is known that the complete set $\{\boldsymbol{\xi}\}$ has specified values, we obtain

$$\langle \boldsymbol{\eta}_k \rangle_{{}'\xi} = \langle {}'\xi \mid \boldsymbol{\eta}_k \mid {}'\xi \rangle = \sum_{{}'\eta} |\langle {}'\xi \mid {}'\eta \rangle|^2 \, \eta_k{}' = \sum_{{}'\eta} P({}'\eta)\, \eta_k{}' . \quad (2:11)$$

From (2:10) and (2:11) we see that $P({}'\xi) = P({}'\eta)$, which constitutes the very important theorem of the reciprocity of quantal probabilities, viz.

The probability of a complete set of observables $\{\boldsymbol{\xi}\}$ *having values* ${}'\xi$ *for the state for which it is certain that the complete set of observables* $\{\boldsymbol{\eta}\}$ *have the values* ${}'\eta$, *is equal to the probability of the* $\boldsymbol{\eta}$*'s having the values* ${}'\eta$ *for the state for which it is certain that the* $\boldsymbol{\xi}$*'s have the values* ${}'\xi$.

It is customary to call the transformation functions $\langle {}'\xi \mid {}'\eta \rangle$ probability amplitudes, since it is the squared moduli of these quantities which are physically meaningful as probabilities. The determination of these probability amplitudes is one of the most important problems of quantum mechanics, and the general method has already been implicitly obtained in our previous work.[11] Thus, expressing the equation $\boldsymbol{\eta}_k \mid {}'\eta \rangle = \eta_k{}' \mid {}'\eta \rangle$ in the ξ-representation, viz.

$$\boldsymbol{\eta}_k \sum_{{}''\xi} \mid {}''\xi \rangle \langle {}''\xi \mid {}'\eta \rangle = \eta_k{}' \sum_{{}''\xi} \mid {}''\xi \rangle \langle {}''\xi \mid {}'\eta \rangle, \quad (2:12)$$

and pre-multiplying by $\langle {}'\xi \mid$, we obtain the familiar secular equation

$$\sum_{{}''\xi} \langle {}'\xi \mid \boldsymbol{\eta}_k \mid {}''\xi \rangle \langle {}''\xi \mid {}'\eta \rangle = \eta_k{}' \langle {}'\xi \mid {}'\eta \rangle. \quad (2:13)$$

This same equation results if we introduce the concept of a mixed representative of an observable, i.e. a form in which the rows and columns refer to two *distinct* diagonal representations, e.g.

$$\langle {}'\xi \mid \boldsymbol{\eta}_k \mid {}'\eta \rangle = \langle {}'\xi \mid \cdot \boldsymbol{\eta}_k \cdot \mid {}'\eta \rangle. \quad (2:14)$$

The right-hand side of (2:14) may be written either as $\eta_k{}' \langle {}'\xi \mid {}'\eta \rangle$ or as $\sum_{{}''\xi} \langle {}'\xi \mid \boldsymbol{\eta}_k \mid {}''\xi \rangle \langle {}''\xi \mid {}'\eta \rangle$, and equating these again gives (2:13). The equation (2:13) should properly be called the *eigenvalue-eigenfunction* equation.

We have considered so far the case when both complete sets $\{\boldsymbol{\xi}\}, \{\boldsymbol{\eta}\}$ had eigenvalue spectra of discrete values, and we must now consider the generalization to cases in which one or both sets have a continuous or mixed (discrete plus continuous) eigenvalue spectrum.

(*b*) *Continuous Eigenvalue Spectra.*

Let us first consider an observable $\boldsymbol{\xi}$ which has a continuous eigenvalue spectrum, and assume for simplicity that there exists but one independent eigen-$\mid \rangle$ belonging to any eigenvalue. Inasmuch as every real number is now by hypothesis an eigen-

[11] See § 6.

value, we see that the total number of eigen-$|\,\rangle$'s of $\boldsymbol{\xi}$ is non-denumerably infinite, as is the number of axes in the basis or representation formed by the eigenvectors $\{\,|\,\xi'\,\rangle\,\}$—*if such a basis exists.* Strictly speaking, the eigenvectors of such an observable cannot form a basis in the sense of the previous work since we run into difficulty on two counts: the expansion theorem is not satisfied in the usual sense, nor can we apply the usual normalization to unity.

Assuming that the $\{\,|\,\xi'\,\rangle\,\}$ can form a basis, we should expect the expansion of an arbitrary vector in terms of them to appear formally as

$$|\,\rangle = \int |\,\xi'\,\rangle\, d\xi' \,\langle\, \xi'\,|\,\rangle, \qquad (2{:}15)$$ [12]

where the integration is understood to extend over the whole eigenvalue spectrum of $\boldsymbol{\xi}$. However, if $\langle\,\xi''\,|\,\rangle$ is expressed as in the discrete case, we have

$$\langle\,\xi''\,|\,\rangle = \int \langle\,\xi''\,|\,\xi'\,\rangle\, d\xi' \,\langle\, \xi'\,|\,\rangle, \qquad (2{:}16)$$

and it is evident that no matter what value $\langle\,\xi''\,|\,\xi'\,\rangle$ may be given, there exists no ordinary function in the analytic sense which can satisfy (2:16). Furthermore, if we attempt to expand one of the basic eigen-$|\,\rangle$'s, say $|\,\xi''\,\rangle$, we have the same difficulty as regards the representative $\langle\,\xi'\,|\,\xi''\,\rangle$ in the equation

$$|\,\xi''\,\rangle = \int |\,\xi'\,\rangle\, d\xi' \,\langle\, \xi'\,|\,\xi''\,\rangle. \qquad (2{:}17)$$

The problem becomes more involved if we try to express the differential coefficient $\dfrac{d}{d\xi''}\,|\,\xi''\,\rangle$ in a form similar to (2:17), assuming $|\,\xi''\,\rangle$ involves the parameter ξ'' in sufficiently continuous manner for the differential coefficient to exist at all. Aside from the mathematical questions involved there is a physical reason for the appearance of these difficulties in the continuous case. Implicit in the eigenvalue-eigenvector equation $\boldsymbol{\xi}\,|\,\xi'\,\rangle = \xi'\,|\,\xi'\,\rangle$ is the basic assumption that a measurement on a system in the eigenstate $|\,\xi'\,\rangle$ will result in the value ξ' for $\boldsymbol{\xi}$ with certainty. As a matter of fact, it is clear that if an observable such as $\boldsymbol{\xi}$ with a continuous eigenvalue spectrum is measured for any actual state, the result must be distributed according to some definite probability law over a finite region which may be made as small as we please, but cannot be reduced to a point. Thus, in the strict sense, a state represented by $|\,\xi'\,\rangle$ is a hyper-idealized type of state which cannot actually exist; but, viewed as the limit of actual states, it serves as a very convenient abstraction. From this point of view we should not be surprised, but rather expect certain peculiarities to appear in the mathematics of such states.

A number of methods have been developed specifically to handle the continuous case, ranging from a more general formulation of the eigenvalue problem [13] to various formal processes of manipulation. Of these, we employ the formalism of Dirac, primarily because it affords a treatment of the continuous case which parallels closely the theory of discrete spectra already developed, and is exceptionally well adapted

[12] This follows from $\mathbf{I} = \int |\,\xi'\,\rangle\, d\xi' \,\langle\,\xi'\,|$, which is the formal transcription to the continuous case of the operator form of the expansion theorem, equation (1:20). The differential $d\xi'$ is inserted between the $|\,\xi'\,\rangle$ and $\langle\,\xi'\,|$ for convenience only.

[13] See von Neumann, J.: *Quantenmechanik,* Dover (1943).

to vigorous theoretical development. In general, physical reasonableness of results constitutes a sufficient check on the method.[14]

We introduce a function $\delta(\xi)$ defined by the conditions:

$$\int_{-\infty}^{\infty} \delta(\xi)\, d\xi = 1,\ \delta(\xi) = 0 \text{ for } \xi \neq 0; \quad . \quad . \quad . \quad (2{:}18a)$$

$$\int_{-\alpha}^{\infty} f(\xi)\,\delta(\xi)\, d\xi = f(0), \quad . \quad . \quad . \quad . \quad . \quad . \quad (2{:}18b)$$ [15]

where $f(\xi)$ is continuous, and we list some of its properties which will be useful in our further work. These may be demonstrated by treating $\delta(\xi)$ as though it were an ordinary function—continuous, differentiable and, in particular, assumed to be even.

$$\delta(\xi) = \delta(-\xi). \quad . \quad . \quad . \quad . \quad . \quad . \quad . \quad (2{:}19a)$$

$$\frac{d}{d\xi}\delta(-\xi) = \delta'(-\xi) = -\delta'(\xi). \quad . \quad . \quad . \quad . \quad (2{:}19b)$$

$$\xi\,\delta(\xi) = 0. \quad . \quad . \quad . \quad . \quad . \quad . \quad . \quad . \quad . \quad (2{:}19c)$$

$$\xi\,\delta'(\xi) = -\delta(\xi). \quad . \quad . \quad . \quad . \quad . \quad . \quad . \quad . \quad (2{:}19d)$$

$$f(\xi)\,\delta'(\xi - a) = -f'(\xi)\,\delta(\xi - a). \quad . \quad . \quad . \quad (2{:}19e)$$

$$\delta(a\xi) = \frac{1}{a}\delta(\xi) \qquad (a > 0). \quad . \quad . \quad . \quad . \quad . \quad (2{:}19f)$$

These equations appear far less objectionable if we recall that it is implied that both sides are multiplied by an analytic function and integrated.

With this formalism, the expansion of a basic $|\ \rangle$, say $|\ \xi''\rangle$, and its first differential coefficient, appear as

$$|\ \xi''\rangle = \int |\ \xi'\rangle\, d\xi' \langle \xi' \mid \xi''\rangle; \qquad \langle \xi' \mid \xi''\rangle = \delta(\xi' - \xi''); \quad (2{:}20a)$$

and

$$\frac{d}{d\xi''}|\ \xi''\rangle = -\int |\ \xi'\rangle\, d\xi'\, \delta'(\xi' - \xi'') \qquad \text{[cf. (2:19e) above]}. \quad (2{:}20b)$$

Now whatever the form of $\delta(\xi' - \xi'')$, it must evidently behave as an impulse function near the origin (i.e. at $\xi' = \xi''$) and there tend to infinity. The equation (2:20a) thus corresponds to normalization to infinity, and may be interpreted as showing that the *relative* probability of finding a system in any finite region is vanishingly small. This corresponds to the fact that the continuous eigenvalue spectrum is the quantal analogue of the unbound motions of classical theory. If we now take another observable $\boldsymbol{\eta}$, we have the following possibilities, assuming $\boldsymbol{\xi}$ to be as before:

η Eigenvalue spectrum	Orthogonality conditions	ξ Representative	
discrete	$\langle \eta'' \mid \eta'\rangle = \delta(\eta'', \eta')$	$\int \langle \eta'' \mid \xi''\rangle\, d\xi'' \langle \xi'' \mid \eta'\rangle$	(2:21a)
continuous	$\langle \eta'' \mid \eta'\rangle = \delta(\eta'', -\eta')$		(2:21b)

[14] The more rigorous formulation of von Neumann is not treated, but it may be stated that it appears to give the same result as the δ formalism in all cases.

[15] E.g. in the sense of the Dirichlet integral $\lim\limits_{a\to\infty} \int_{-\infty}^{\infty} f(\xi)\,d\xi \int_{-a}^{a} d\eta\, e^{i\eta\xi} = 2\pi f(0)$, which permits the *formal* equality $\int_{-\infty}^{\infty} d\eta\, e^{i\eta\xi} = 2\pi\,\delta(\xi)$, cf. DIRAC, *op cit.*

It is of course not essential that the concept of eigenvectors be introduced into the general quantal formulation at all, and the entire theory can be developed from the point of view of representation theory alone. This latter approach, however, lacks the unity and economy of form of the present treatment, and avoids explicit use of the δ function only in the sense that the normalization conditions (2:21a, b) might be written, respectively, as

$$\sum_{\eta''}\int\langle\,\eta''\mid\xi''\,\rangle\,d\xi''\,\langle\,\xi''\mid\eta'\,\rangle=1, \quad . \quad . \quad . \quad . \quad . \qquad (2{:}22a)$$

$$\int d\eta''\int\langle\,\eta''\mid\xi''\,\rangle\,d\xi''\,\langle\,\xi''\mid\eta'\,\rangle=1. \quad . \quad . \quad . \quad . \quad . \qquad (2{:}22b)$$

This result again merely emphasizes the formal aspect of the notation, and we should always be forced to consider limiting processes to establish rigorous proofs. Equations (2:21a) and (2:22a), in which $\boldsymbol{\xi}$ has a continuous eigenvalue spectrum, are the exact analogues to equation (1:7a). The probability interpretation developed for the discrete case strongly suggests that in (2:22a) $|\langle\,\xi'\mid\eta'\,\rangle|^2\,d\xi'$ be interpreted as the probability of $\boldsymbol{\xi}$ having a value within the range ξ' to $\xi'+d\xi'$ for the state for which $\boldsymbol{\eta}$ is known to have the value η', i.e. $|\langle\,\xi'\mid\eta'\,\rangle|^2$ is the probability per unit length[16] in the neighbourhood of ξ'. A strict reciprocity of probabilities cannot now hold since the states $\{|\,\xi'\,\rangle\}$ are not properly normalized, but we expect that $|\langle\,\xi'\mid\eta'\,\rangle|^2$ will be proportional to the probability of $\boldsymbol{\eta}$ having the value η' for the state for which $\boldsymbol{\xi}$ certainly has the value $\boldsymbol{\xi}'$.

If both $\boldsymbol{\xi}$ and $\boldsymbol{\eta}$ have continuous spectra, $|\langle\,\xi'\mid\eta'\,\rangle|^2$ will be proportional to the probability of $\boldsymbol{\xi}$ having a value in the range $d\xi'$ at ξ' for the state for which $\boldsymbol{\eta}$ is known to have the value η', and conversely. Thus the reciprocity holds in a strict sense when the observables in question are all discrete or all continuous, but not in the mixed case. With this interpretation the average value of any function $\mathbf{f}(\boldsymbol{\xi})$ of $\boldsymbol{\xi}$ for the normalized state $|\,\eta'\,\rangle$ will be[17]

$$\langle\,\mathbf{f}\,\rangle_{\eta'}=\int f(\,\xi'\,)\,|\langle\,\xi'\mid\eta'\,\rangle|^2\,d\xi'. \quad . \quad . \quad . \quad . \quad . \qquad (2{:}23)$$

The general assumption (2:4) requires that $\langle\,\mathbf{f}\,\rangle_{\eta'}=\langle\,\eta'\mid\mathbf{f}\mid\eta'\,\rangle$, which is seen to agree with (2:23), viz.

$$\begin{aligned}\langle\,\eta'\mid\mathbf{f}\mid\eta'\,\rangle&=\int\langle\,\eta'\mid\xi'\,\rangle\,d\xi'\,\langle\,\xi'\mid\mathbf{f}\int|\,\xi''\,\rangle\,d\xi''\,\langle\,\xi''\mid\eta'\,\rangle\\&=\int|\langle\,\xi'\mid\eta'\,\rangle|^2 f(\,\xi'\,)\,d\xi'. \quad . \quad . \quad . \quad . \quad . \quad . \quad . \qquad (2{:}24)\end{aligned}$$

In the general case, $\boldsymbol{\eta}$ and $\boldsymbol{\xi}$ will each stand for a complete set of commuting observables, and the members of each set may have eigenspectra which are all continuous, all discrete, or mixed.

The important point to keep in mind is that the concept of the average of an observable for a given state obtains in the strict sense of average, when the eigen-

[16] This is in accord with the previous discussion of states of observables with continuous eigenvalue spectra, since the probability of $\boldsymbol{\xi}$ having *exactly* the value ξ' for any physically observable state would be zero.

[17] Here $\boldsymbol{\xi}$ is continuous, η discrete, as indicated by the statement that $|\,\eta'\,\rangle$ is normalized. We shall generally use the word "normalized" in the sense-proper, normalization to unity.

vector representing the state in question is properly normalized to unity. Thus, for arbitrary observables $\boldsymbol{\alpha}$, $\boldsymbol{\beta}$, the formally computed averages $\langle \boldsymbol{\alpha} \rangle_{\xi'}$, $\langle \boldsymbol{\beta} \rangle_{\xi'}$, for the state $| \xi' \rangle$ of the continuous observable $\boldsymbol{\xi}$, will be infinitely larger[18] than the true averages; but in general for such states we shall only be interested in the ratio $\langle \boldsymbol{\alpha} \rangle / \langle \boldsymbol{\beta} \rangle$, and this will be correct since both contain the same large factors. It should now be clear that, in this formalism, the essential change in dealing with the continuous case is to introduce integrals instead of sums, and the δ function instead of the Kronecker δ in the appropriate places. The scalar product of two vectors $| \eta' \rangle$, $| \zeta' \rangle$, say, becomes

$$\langle \eta' | \zeta' \rangle = \int \langle \eta' | \xi' \rangle d\xi' \langle \xi' | \zeta' \rangle. \quad \quad (2:25)$$

The definition of the representative of a linear operator becomes

$$\boldsymbol{\alpha} | \xi'' \rangle = \int | \xi' \rangle d\xi' \langle \xi' | \boldsymbol{\alpha} | \xi'' \rangle, \quad \quad (2:26)$$

and we term functions like $\langle \xi' | \boldsymbol{\alpha} | \xi'' \rangle$ generalized matrix elements, even though it is obviously impossible to write down the matrix array. However, the name is appropriate since the usual rules of matrix manipulation hold, e.g.

$$\begin{aligned} \boldsymbol{\alpha\beta} | \xi'' \rangle &= \boldsymbol{\alpha} \int | \xi' \rangle d\xi' \langle \xi' | \boldsymbol{\beta} | \xi'' \rangle \\ &= \iint | \xi''' \rangle d\xi''' \langle \xi''' | \boldsymbol{\alpha} | \xi' \rangle d\xi' \langle \xi' | \boldsymbol{\beta} | \xi'' \rangle, \quad \quad (2:27) \end{aligned}$$

therefore

$$\langle \xi''' | \boldsymbol{\alpha\beta} | \xi'' \rangle = \int \langle \xi''' | \boldsymbol{\alpha} | \xi' \rangle d\xi' \langle \xi' | \boldsymbol{\beta} | \xi'' \rangle. \quad \quad (2:28)$$

In particular it is clear that the generalized continuous analogue of the unit matrix is $\delta(\xi' - \xi'')$, and correspondingly we define a diagonal matrix as one whose (ξ', ξ'') element is some function of ξ' or ξ'' multiplied into $\delta(\xi' - \xi'')$. The functional multiplier will then be called the diagonal element, although, as already explained, a diagonal element $\langle \xi' | \boldsymbol{\alpha} | \xi' \rangle$ of the observable is not just the average for the basic state represented by $| \xi' \rangle$. The representative of $\boldsymbol{\xi}$ is the diagonal matrix

$$\langle \xi' | \boldsymbol{\xi} | \xi'' \rangle = \xi' \delta (\xi' - \xi''), \quad \quad (2:29)$$

and we see that choosing a representation in which the basic vectors are eigen-$| \rangle$'s of $\boldsymbol{\xi}$ is equivalent to choosing a representation in which $\boldsymbol{\xi}$ is diagonal in the case of continuous eigenvalues just as in the discrete case, and the diagonal elements are in both cases just the eigenvalues of $\boldsymbol{\xi}$. Corresponding to (2:21*a*) we also have, if $\boldsymbol{\eta}$ is an observable with a discrete spectrum,

$$\langle \xi' | \xi'' \rangle = \delta (\xi' - \xi'') = \sum_{\eta'} \langle \xi' | \eta' \rangle \langle \eta' | \xi'' \rangle. \quad \quad (2:30)$$

(*c*) *Continuous and Mixed Eigenvalue Spectra.*

The generalization to include a complete set of commuting observables with continuous or mixed spectra[19] is largely a matter of simple extension of notation.

[18] Such states are represented by vectors of infinite length as indicated by equation (2:20*a*).

[19] Some of the members of the set may have a discrete and continuous spectrum of eigenvalues, or perhaps more commonly, one has in addition to this certain operators of the set which are pure discrete.

As in the discrete case, we take the basic $|\,\rangle$'s to be simultaneous eigen-$|\,\rangle$'s of a complete set of commuting observables, say $\boldsymbol{\xi}_1, \boldsymbol{\xi}_2, \ldots \boldsymbol{\xi}_n$, and for the moment assume that each has a continuous spectrum. Then,

$$| \xi_1''\xi_2'' \ldots \xi_n'' \rangle =$$

$$\int \cdots \int | \xi_1'\xi_2' \ldots \xi_n' \rangle d\xi_1' d\xi_2' \ldots d\xi_n' \, \delta(\xi_1' - \xi_1'') \ldots \delta(\xi_n' - \xi_n''), \quad (2{:}31a)$$

or, with the abbreviation agreed upon, we write this simply as

$$| {}''\xi \rangle = \int | {}'\xi \rangle d'\xi \, \delta({}'\xi - {}''\xi), \quad . \quad . \quad . \quad . \quad . \quad (2{:}31b)$$

and similarly,

$$\frac{\partial}{\partial \xi_m''} | {}''\xi \rangle = -\int | {}'\xi \rangle d'\xi \, \delta(\xi_1' - \xi_1'') \ldots \delta'(\xi_m' - \xi_m'') \ldots \delta(\xi_n' - \xi_n''). \quad (2{:}32)$$

Again, for a suitably normalized $|\,\rangle$, the probability of a simultaneous observation of all the $\boldsymbol{\xi}$'s, for the state represented by this $|\,\rangle$, yielding for each $\boldsymbol{\xi}_m$ a result in the region $d\xi_m'$ at ξ_m', will be

$$|\langle {}'\xi \,|\, \rangle|^2 \, d'\xi. \quad . \quad . \quad . \quad . \quad . \quad . \quad . \quad . \quad . \quad (2{:}33)$$

Thus all the results in the preceding section obtain if we take these to represent, in abbreviated form, the complete set. Equation (2:29) becomes

$$\langle {}'\xi \,|\, \boldsymbol{\xi}_m \,|\, {}''\xi \rangle = \xi_m' \, \delta({}'\xi - {}''\xi) \quad . \quad . \quad . \quad . \quad . \quad (2{:}34)$$

for every member of the set.

The remaining question of our formalism is to include the possibility of mixed eigenvalue spectra. For simplicity of writing, consider a single observable $\boldsymbol{\xi}$ with discrete eigenvalues denoted by $\xi', \xi'', \ldots$, and continuous eigenvalues denoted by $\xi^a, \xi^b, \ldots$. Then, expanding an arbitrary $|\,\rangle$ vector, we have

$$|\,\rangle = \sum_{\xi'} | \xi' \rangle \langle \xi' \,|\, \rangle + \int | \xi^a \rangle d\xi^a \langle \xi^a \,|\, \rangle. \quad . \quad . \quad . \quad (2{:}35)$$

The representatives of this $|\,\rangle$, i.e. $\langle \xi' \,|\, \rangle$ and $\langle \xi^a \,|\, \rangle$, have the meaning that if $|\,\rangle$ is properly normalized, then $|\langle \xi' \,|\, \rangle|^2$ is the probability of $\boldsymbol{\xi}$ having[20] the value ξ', and $|\langle \xi^a \,|\, \rangle|^2 \, d\xi^a$ is the probability of $\boldsymbol{\xi}$ having the value in $d\xi^a$ at ξ^a.

We list in tabular form various important quantities and relations defined over this type of basic $|\,\rangle$, which are readily derived from (2:35) and the definitions.

Orthogonality conditions:

$$\left.\begin{aligned} \langle \xi' \,|\, \xi'' \rangle &= \delta(\xi', \xi''), \\ \langle \xi^a \,|\, \xi' \rangle &= 0, \\ \langle \xi^a \,|\, \xi^b \rangle &= \delta(\xi^a - \xi^b). \end{aligned}\right\} \quad . \quad . \quad . \quad . \quad . \quad . \quad (2{:}36a)$$

[20] The eigen-$|\,\rangle$'s of $\boldsymbol{\xi}$ belonging to the discrete part of the spectrum can be normalized properly to give the usual interpretation of the discrete case.

Operator representatives:

$$\left.\begin{aligned} \boldsymbol{\alpha} \mid \xi'' \rangle &= \sum_{\xi'} \mid \xi' \rangle \langle \xi' \mid \boldsymbol{\alpha} \mid \xi'' \rangle + \int \mid \xi^a \rangle \, d\xi^a \, \langle \xi^a \mid \boldsymbol{\alpha} \mid \xi'' \rangle, \\ \boldsymbol{\alpha} \mid \xi^c \rangle &= \sum_{\xi'} \mid \xi' \rangle \langle \xi' \mid \boldsymbol{\alpha} \mid \xi^c \rangle + \int \mid \xi^a \rangle \, d\xi^a \, \langle \xi^a \mid \boldsymbol{\alpha} \mid \xi^c \rangle, \\ \langle \xi' \mid \boldsymbol{\alpha\beta} \mid \xi'' \rangle &= \sum_{\xi'''} \langle \xi' \mid \boldsymbol{\alpha} \mid \xi''' \rangle \langle \xi''' \mid \boldsymbol{\beta} \mid \xi'' \rangle + \int \langle \xi' \mid \boldsymbol{\alpha} \mid \xi^a \rangle \, d\xi^a \langle \xi^a \mid \boldsymbol{\beta} \mid \xi'' \rangle, \\ &\text{etc.} \end{aligned}\right\} \quad (2:36b)$$

§ 12. Point Transformations

A particularly simple type of transformation is the quantal point-transformation from a representation $\{ \mid {}'q \rangle \}$, which need not in general correspond to coordinate observables, to a functionally related representation $\{ \mid {}'Q \rangle \}$, where

$$Q_i' = Q_i'(q_1', q_2', \ldots q_n').$$

In certain problems such as arise in the theory of scattering and the closely related S-matrix theory,[21] the representation $\{ \mid {}'Q \rangle \}$ may be literally defined by the diagonality of a set of proper observables $\{ \mathbf{Q} \}$ which are simple functions of the set $\{ \mathbf{q} \}$. However, quite frequently the transformation is of a more trivial kind which is introduced for reasons of obtaining more symmetrical expressions or more convenient interpretation of physical results as, for example, in transforming to orthogonal curvilinear coordinates. In such cases the representation $\{ \mid {}'Q \rangle \}$ is of a purely formal character,[22] since there do not exist proper observables $\{ \mathbf{Q} \}$ which can be said to be diagonal. This latter type of transformation may be discussed from the point of view of introducing a weight factor [23] as a matter of convenience; but both cases are, in fact, simply examples of point transformations, differing only in the manner described above.

Let us then consider in general the relation between the representations $\{ \mid {}'q \rangle \}$ and $\{ \mid {}'Q \rangle \}$ where $Q_i' = Q_i'({}'q)$. For an arbitrary observable $\boldsymbol{\alpha}$ we may write, at least formally, the relation

$$\langle {}'q \mid \boldsymbol{\alpha} \mid {}''q \rangle = \int \ldots \int \langle {}'q \mid {}'Q \rangle \, d{}'Q \, \langle {}'Q \mid \boldsymbol{\alpha} \mid {}''Q \rangle \, d{}''Q \, \langle {}''Q \mid {}''q \rangle. \quad (2:37)$$

It is clear that when $Q_i' = Q_i'({}'q)$, the eigenvector $\mid {}'q \rangle$ is also an eigenvector of the *observables* $\{ \mathbf{Q} \}$, provided the latter exist and the functional relationship is of the simple type which can be uniquely defined [24] in the quantal sense. Furthermore, we can still write the relation (2:37) even when the $\mathbf{Q}$'s do not constitute a proper set of observables; although the relation in this case has only a formal significance, since the eigenvalue labelling $\mid {}''Q \rangle$ cannot be interpreted literally. In any event it is clear that for any state $\mid \rangle$, the wave-functions $\langle {}'q \mid \rangle$ and $\langle {}'Q \mid \rangle$, or equivalently the probability densities $|\langle {}'q \mid \rangle|^2$ and $|\langle {}'Q \mid \rangle|^2$, must convey the same physical information; thus the problem is the rather trivial one of determining proper normalization.

[21] Cf. Chap. XII.

[22] E.g. there are no operators which can be said to represent the angular coordinates.

[23] Cf. DIRAC, *op. cit.*

[24] Cf. Chaps. I and IV.

The relationship between the two systems is easily obtained from the requirement that

$$\int |\langle `q \mid \rangle|^2 \, d`q = \int |\langle `Q \mid \rangle|^2 \, d`Q$$
$$= \int |\langle `Q \mid \rangle|^2 \, J\,(`Q/`q)\, d`q, \quad . \quad . \quad . \quad . \quad (2{:}38)$$

where $J(`Q/`q)$ is the usual Jacobian determinant. Hence, we have the relation

$$|\langle `q \mid \rangle|^2 = |\langle `Q \mid \rangle|^2 J\,(`Q/`q), \quad . \quad . \quad . \quad . \quad . \quad (2{:}39a)$$

or, symbolically,

$$\langle `q \mid = J^{\frac{1}{2}}\,(`Q/`q)\,\langle `Q \mid. \quad . \quad . \quad . \quad . \quad . \quad . \quad (2{:}39b)$$ [25]

This leads to

$$\langle `q \mid ``Q \rangle = J^{\frac{1}{2}}\,(`Q/`q)\,\delta\,(`Q - ``Q)\,, \quad . \quad . \quad . \quad . \quad (2{:}40)$$

which combined with (2:37) gives

$$\langle `q \mid \alpha \mid ``q \rangle = J^{\frac{1}{2}}\,(`Q/`q)\,\langle `Q \mid \alpha \mid ``Q \rangle\, J^{\frac{1}{2}}\,(``Q/``q). \quad . \quad . \quad (2{:}41)$$

The relations (2:39–41) obviously require that the phases be unaffected by the transformation, and this is seen to be generally the case.

If we now consider the scalar product of any two vectors, we have

$$\langle `\alpha \mid `\beta \rangle = \int \langle `\alpha \mid `q \rangle\, d`q\, \langle `q \mid `\beta \rangle$$
$$= \int \langle `\alpha \mid `Q \rangle\, J\,(`Q/`q)\, d`q\, \langle `Q \mid `\beta \rangle$$
$$= \int \langle `\alpha \mid `Q \rangle\, d`Q\, \langle `Q \mid `\beta \rangle, \quad . \quad . \quad . \quad . \quad . \quad (2{:}42)$$

so that the usual transformation relations obtain for both representations. The previously mentioned interpretation in terms of a weight function follows by noting that the intermediate step in the above transformation corresponds to introducing $J(`Q/`q)$ as factor to each differential $d`q$, and multiplying each basic $\mid `q \rangle$ and $\langle ``q \mid$ by $J^{-\frac{1}{2}}(`Q/`q)$ and $J^{-\frac{1}{2}}(``Q/``q)$, respectively.

[25] Clearly the same holds for the adjoint vectors, and we write $\mid `q \rangle = \mid `Q \rangle\, J^{\frac{1}{2}}\,(`Q\,/\,`q)$ to conform with our general mode of writing.

CHAPTER III

Physical Principles—Observables

§ 13. Introduction

Since operators representing observables do not in general commute, we have to determine the conditions which permit us to decide this for any given pair of operators. Stated otherwise, we wish to know the value of the commutator $\boldsymbol{\alpha\beta} - \boldsymbol{\beta\alpha} = [\boldsymbol{\alpha}, \boldsymbol{\beta}]_-$ for arbitrary observables $\boldsymbol{\alpha}$, $\boldsymbol{\beta}$; as the introduction of these quantum conditions (as the commutator relations are called) makes the connection between the mathematical formalism of the quantum theory and experiment.

The usual procedure is to introduce formally the corresponding quantal analogues of the classical Poisson Brackets (P.B.'s),

$$[\alpha, \beta]_{q,p} = \sum_r \left\{\frac{\partial\alpha}{\partial q_r}\frac{\partial\beta}{\partial p_r} - \frac{\partial\alpha}{\partial p_r}\frac{\partial\beta}{\partial q_r}\right\}, \quad \ldots\ldots \quad (3:1)$$

in which α, β are dynamical variables which are functions of the generalized coordinates q_r and their canonically conjugate momenta p_r. As is well known the P.B.'s satisfy the conditions

$$[\alpha, \beta] = -[\beta, \alpha], \quad \ldots\ldots\ldots\ldots \quad (3:2a)$$

$$[\alpha_1 + \alpha_2, \beta] = [\alpha_1, \beta] + [\alpha_2, \beta], \quad \ldots\ldots\ldots \quad (3:2b)$$

$$[\alpha_1\alpha_2, \beta] = \alpha_1[\alpha_2, \beta] + [\alpha_1, \beta]\alpha_2, \quad \ldots\ldots \quad (3:2c)$$

$$\big[[\alpha, \beta], \gamma\big] + \big[[\beta, \gamma], \alpha\big] + \big[[\gamma, \alpha], \beta\big] = 0 \quad \text{(Jacobi identity)}; \quad (3:2d)$$

and Hamilton's canonical equations of motion are given by

$$\left.\begin{aligned} \dot{q}_r &= \frac{\partial H}{\partial p_r} = [q_r, H], \\ \dot{p}_r &= -\frac{\partial H}{\partial q_r} = [p_r, H], \end{aligned}\right\} \quad \ldots\ldots \quad (3:3a)$$

with the *basic* P.B.'s

$$\left.\begin{aligned} &[q_r, q_s] = [p_r, p_s] = 0, \\ &[q_r, p_s] = \delta_{rs}. \end{aligned}\right\} \quad \ldots\ldots \quad (3:3b)$$

We shall briefly consider the nature of the above-mentioned correspondence for reason of the insight thus obtained into the general structure and, in particular, certain invariantive aspects of quantum mechanics.

§ 14. Classical Contact Transformations

The essence of a classical contact transformation is the passage from one canonical system [e.g. (3:3)] to a new set of canonical coordinates and momenta $q_{r\tau}$, $p_{r\tau}$, such that Hamilton's canonical equations again obtain, viz.

$$\left.\begin{aligned} \dot{q}_{r\tau} &= \frac{\partial K}{\partial p_{r\tau}} = [\, q_{r\tau}, K\,], \\ \dot{p}_{r\tau} &= -\frac{\partial K}{\partial q_{r\tau}} = [\, p_{r\tau}, K\,], \end{aligned}\right\} \qquad (3{:}4)$$

with the new Hamiltonian $K(q_\tau, p_\tau)$. The necessary and sufficient condition is that the action expressed in the new variables again satisfies Hamilton's principle

$$\delta \int (\, \Sigma p_{r\tau}\dot{q}_{r\tau} - K\,)\, dt = 0, \qquad (3{:}5a)$$

but, more generally, it is clearly sufficient that the two action integrands differ by the total time derivative of some function U, i.e.

$$\Sigma\,(\, p_r\dot{q}_r - p_{r\tau}\dot{q}_{r\tau}\,) - (\, H - K\,) = \frac{dU}{dt}. \qquad (3{:}5b)$$

If we take $U = U(q, q_\tau, t)$, we find on comparing coefficients that

$$\left.\begin{aligned} \frac{\partial U}{\partial q_r} &= p_r, \\ \frac{\partial U}{\partial q_{r\tau}} &= -p_{r\tau}, \\ K &= H + \frac{\partial U}{\partial t}, \end{aligned}\right\} \qquad (3{:}6a)$$

which, in principle, permit us to obtain the transformation relations determining the new variables for a given assumed function U, which is said to *generate* the transformation. In particular, for the special transformation which makes $K \equiv 0$, all the new coordinates and momenta are constants of the motion, and in this case the above conditions give the equation for Hamilton's principle function:

$$H\left(q, \frac{\partial U}{\partial q}, t\right) + \frac{\partial U}{\partial t} = 0. \qquad (3{:}6b)$$

§ 15. Infinitesimal Contact Transformations

The Poisson Bracket is especially important because of its invariance under contact transformations, i.e. independence of the particular set of canonically conjugate coordinates and momenta. Thus,

$$[\, \alpha, \beta\,]_{q,p} = [\, \alpha, \beta\,]_{q_\tau, p_\tau}, \qquad (3{:}7a)$$

since

$$[\, \alpha, \beta\,]_{q,p} = [\, \alpha, \beta\,]_{q_\tau, p_\tau} [\, q_\tau, p_\tau\,]_{q,p}, \qquad (3{:}7b)$$

in general, and $[q_\tau, p_\tau]_{q,p} = 1$ for a contact transformation.[1]

[1] Cf. WHITTAKER, E. T.: *Analytical Dynamics*, Cambridge University Press (1937).

Let us now consider an infinitesimal contact transformation

$$\left.\begin{aligned} q_{r\tau} &= q_r + \delta q_r = q_r + \epsilon\phi_r(q_1 \ldots p_n), \\ p_{r\tau} &= p_r + \delta p_r = p_r + \epsilon\Psi_r(q_1 \ldots p_n), \end{aligned}\right\} \quad . \quad . \quad . \quad (3{:}8)$$

where ϵ is a small parameter whose square is negligible. Then the condition (3:5b) becomes

$$-\Sigma(p_r\, d\,\delta q_r + \delta p_r\, dq_r) - (H - K)\, dt = dU, \quad . \quad . \quad (3{:}9a)$$

or, putting

$$U = \epsilon S - \Sigma p_r\, \delta q_r,$$

$$\Sigma(dp_r\, \delta q_r - \delta p_r\, dq_r) - (H - K)\, dt = \epsilon\, dS. \quad . \quad . \quad . \quad (3{:}9b)$$

Hence

$$\left.\begin{aligned} \delta q_r &= \epsilon\frac{\delta S}{\delta p_r} = \epsilon[q_r, S], \\ \delta p_r &= -\epsilon\frac{\delta S}{\delta q_r} = \epsilon[p_r, S], \end{aligned}\right\} \quad . \quad . \quad . \quad . \quad . \quad (3{:}10)$$

which are the defining equations of the infinitesimal transformation generated by S. Under the transformation (3:8), a function $\alpha(q, p)$ goes over into $\alpha_\tau(q_\tau, p_\tau) = \alpha(q, p)$, so that

$$\alpha_\tau(q_\tau, p_\tau) = \alpha_\tau(q, p) + \epsilon\Sigma\left(\frac{\partial\alpha}{\partial q_r}\frac{\partial S}{\partial p_r} - \frac{\partial\alpha}{\partial p_r}\frac{\partial S}{\partial q_r}\right) + O(\epsilon^2)$$

$$= \alpha_\tau(q, p) + \epsilon[\alpha, S],$$

or

$$\delta\alpha = \alpha(q, p) - \alpha_\tau(q, p) = \epsilon[\alpha, S]. \quad . \quad . \quad . \quad . \quad . \quad (3{:}11)$$

§ 16. Examples of Infinitesimal Contact Transformations

I. *Hamiltonian as generator of time displacement.*

If we take $S = H$, $\epsilon = dt$, we find (cf. 3:10, 3:3a)

$$\left.\begin{aligned} \delta q_r &= dt[q_r H] = dq_r, \\ \delta p_r &= dt[p_r, H] = dp_r, \end{aligned}\right\} \quad . \quad . \quad . \quad . \quad . \quad (3{:}12)$$

or that the development of a system in time is given by a succession of infinitesimal contact transformations.

II. *Angular momentum as generator of angular displacement.*

We consider Cartesian coordinates and a positive azimuthal rotation through an angle ϵ, so that

$$\left.\begin{aligned} x_{r\tau} &= x_r + \epsilon y_r, \\ y_{r\tau} &= -\epsilon x_r + y_r, \end{aligned}\right\} \quad . \quad . \quad . \quad . \quad . \quad . \quad . \quad (3{:}13a)$$

and, inversely,

$$\left.\begin{aligned} x_r &= x_{r\tau} - \epsilon y_{r\tau}, \\ y_r &= \epsilon x_{r\tau} + y_{r\tau}. \end{aligned}\right\} \quad . \quad . \quad . \quad . \quad . \quad . \quad (3{:}13b)$$

Hence,

$$\left.\begin{aligned}\delta x_r &= \epsilon y_r = \epsilon\,[\,x_r, S\,],\\ \delta y_r &= -\epsilon x_r = \epsilon\,[\,y_r, S\,],\end{aligned}\right\} \qquad (3{:}14)$$ [2]

which are readily seen to be satisfied if the generator S is the negative total z-component of angular momentum $-L_z = \Sigma(y_r p_{x_r} - x_r p_{y_r})$, and similarly for the δp_r. More generally, the preceding development shows that for any vector function $N_{x,y,z}$, $[L_z, N_x] = N_y$ (cyclically); the familiar P.B.'s $[L_z, x] = y$, $[L_z, p_x] = p_y$, $[L_z, L_x] = L_y$, etc., being special cases.

III. *Linear momentum as generator of space displacement.*

With the same coordinate system, a displacement of amount ϵ in the x-direction, for example, gives

$$\delta x_r = \epsilon = \epsilon\frac{\partial S}{\partial p_{x_r}}, \qquad (3{:}15)$$

which is satisfied by $S = \Sigma p_{x_r}$.

§ 17. Form Invariance of the Hamiltonian—Constants of the Motion

If the Hamiltonian H is *form*-invariant under the transformation generated by S, then by (3:11)

$$\delta H = \epsilon\,[\,H, S\,] = 0, \qquad (3{:}16)$$

or the generator S is a constant of the motion. Hence, for a classical n-particle Hamiltonian, mere inspection of the interaction terms (with regard to invariance under translations and rotations) immediately permits one to conclude as to the constancy of the total linear and angular momenta, and components. As will be seen, essentially the same condition obtains in the quantal case.

§ 18. Quantal Contact Transformations—Quantum Conditions

When two dynamical variables $\boldsymbol{\alpha}$ and $\boldsymbol{\alpha}_\tau$ are related by an equation of the form

$$\boldsymbol{\alpha}_\tau = \mathbf{U}\boldsymbol{\alpha}\mathbf{U}^{-1}, \qquad (3{:}17)$$

then we say that $\boldsymbol{\alpha}_\tau$ is the transform of $\boldsymbol{\alpha}$ under the similarity or collineatory transformation generated by the operator $\mathbf{U}$. If, furthermore, $\mathbf{U}$ is unitary, i.e. $\mathbf{U}^* = \mathbf{U}^{-1}$, then the transformation is termed unitary or conjunctive. The similarity transformation has the important property that two operators so related have the same eigenvalue spectrum, with the transformed eigenvectors given by

$$|\,\alpha_\tau'\,\rangle = \mathbf{U}\,|\,\alpha'\,\rangle. \qquad (3{:}18)$$

Thus

$$\left.\begin{aligned}\boldsymbol{\alpha}\,|\,\alpha'\,\rangle &= \alpha'\,|\,\alpha'\,\rangle,\\ \boldsymbol{\alpha}_\tau\mathbf{U}\,|\,\alpha'\,\rangle &= \mathbf{U}\boldsymbol{\alpha}\mathbf{U}^{-1}\mathbf{U}\,|\,\alpha'\,\rangle = \alpha'\mathbf{U}\,|\,\alpha'\,\rangle,\end{aligned}\right\} \qquad (3{:}19)$$

[2] These follow from (3:10) *or* (3:11); e.g. $\alpha(x_r, y_r) = x_r = x_{r\tau} - \epsilon y_{r\tau} = \alpha_\tau(x_{r\tau}, y_{r\tau})$, so that $\alpha_\tau(x_r, y_r) = x_r - \epsilon y_r$, and $\delta\alpha = \epsilon y_r$, etc.

showing that $\mathbf{U} \mid \alpha' \rangle$ is an eigen-$\mid \rangle$ of $\boldsymbol{\alpha}_\tau$ belonging to the eigenvalue [3] α_τ' $(=\alpha')$, and conversely, we can show that any eigenvalue of $\boldsymbol{\alpha}_\tau$ is also an eigenvalue of $\boldsymbol{\alpha}$. If $\boldsymbol{\alpha}$ is real, then its transform $\boldsymbol{\alpha}_\tau$ can only be real provided $\mathbf{U}$ is unitary, and in addition all algebraic relations between operators and vectors are invariant under unitary transformation. To verify these properties we note first that for $\boldsymbol{\alpha}$ and $\boldsymbol{\alpha}_\tau$ real,

$$\boldsymbol{\alpha}_\tau^* = \mathbf{U}^{-1*}\boldsymbol{\alpha}\mathbf{U}^* = \boldsymbol{\alpha}_\tau = \mathbf{U}\boldsymbol{\alpha}\mathbf{U}^{-1}; \qquad (3{:}20a)$$

and hence

$$\boldsymbol{\alpha}\mathbf{U}^*\mathbf{U} = \mathbf{U}^*\mathbf{U}\boldsymbol{\alpha}, \qquad (3{:}20b)$$

which shows that $\mathbf{U}^*\mathbf{U}$ commutes with *any* linear operator, since any linear operator can be expressed as the sum of a Hermitian and an anti-Hermitian operator. It follows that $\mathbf{U}^*\mathbf{U}$ is at most a scalar multiple of the identity, and without loss of generality we may take $\mathbf{U}^*\mathbf{U} = \mathbf{I}$, which condition defines unitary operators. Similarly,

$$\left.\begin{aligned}(\boldsymbol{\alpha} + \boldsymbol{\beta})_\tau &= \mathbf{U}(\boldsymbol{\alpha} + \boldsymbol{\beta})\mathbf{U}^{-1} = \boldsymbol{\alpha}_\tau + \boldsymbol{\beta}_\tau,\\ (\boldsymbol{\alpha}\boldsymbol{\beta})_\tau &= \mathbf{U}(\boldsymbol{\alpha}\boldsymbol{\beta})\mathbf{U}^{-1} = \mathbf{U}\boldsymbol{\alpha}\mathbf{U}^{-1}\mathbf{U}\boldsymbol{\beta}\mathbf{U}^{-1} = \boldsymbol{\alpha}_\tau\boldsymbol{\beta}_\tau,\end{aligned}\right\} \qquad (3{:}21)$$

and in particular for $\boldsymbol{\xi} = \boldsymbol{\xi}(\boldsymbol{\alpha}, \boldsymbol{\beta})$, $\boldsymbol{\xi}_\tau = \mathbf{U}\boldsymbol{\xi}\mathbf{U}^{-1} = \boldsymbol{\xi}(\boldsymbol{\alpha}_\tau, \boldsymbol{\beta}_\tau)$, which may be readily verified using the general definition of observables.

If now we take $\mathbf{U}$ of the form

$$\mathbf{U} = e^{i\epsilon\mathbf{S}/\hbar} \approx 1 + \frac{i\epsilon}{\hbar}\mathbf{S}, \qquad (3{:}22)\ [4]$$

with $\mathbf{S}$ Hermitian, we have

$$\boldsymbol{\alpha}_\tau = \boldsymbol{\alpha} + \frac{\epsilon}{i\hbar}(\boldsymbol{\alpha}\mathbf{S} - \mathbf{S}\boldsymbol{\alpha}), \qquad (3{:}23)$$

and applied to $\mathbf{q}$ and $\mathbf{p}$,

$$\mathbf{q}_\tau = \mathbf{q} + \frac{\epsilon}{i\hbar}[\mathbf{q}, \mathbf{S}]_-, \qquad (3{:}24a)$$

$$\mathbf{p}_\tau = \mathbf{p} + \frac{\epsilon}{i\hbar}[\mathbf{p}, \mathbf{S}]_-. \qquad (3{:}24b)$$

These are all very similar to the preceding classical relations, and suggest that we define a quantal Poisson Bracket for any two observables as

$$[\boldsymbol{\alpha}, \boldsymbol{\beta}] = \frac{[\boldsymbol{\alpha}, \boldsymbol{\beta}]_-}{i\hbar}. \qquad (3{:}25)$$

Moreover, we know that coordinates and momenta have continuous eigenvalue spectra, so that, if $\mathbf{q}$, $\mathbf{p}$ are to be canonically conjugate in the quantal sense, we

[3] We shall adopt the convention that α and α_τ with the same number of primes denote the same number, e.g. $\alpha' = \alpha_\tau'$; but it is necessary to retain both symbols for this common eigenvalue to preserve the properties and meaning of symbols such as $\langle \alpha' \mid \alpha_\tau' \rangle$, $\langle \alpha' \mid \boldsymbol{\beta} \mid \alpha_\tau'' \rangle$, etc.

[4] The usual constant $\hbar$ is, in principle, as yet undefined. Its value becomes fixed on comparison of the equations of motion (cf. Chap. IV) with the experimental Bohr frequency relation.

should expect by analogy with the classical results that *translations* in their respective eigenvalues of amount ϵ would result from the above transforms with $\mathbf{S} = \mathbf{p}, -\mathbf{q}$, respectively, viz.

$$\mathbf{q}_\tau = \mathbf{q} + \epsilon [\, \mathbf{q}, \mathbf{p} \,], \qquad (3{:}26a)$$

$$\mathbf{p}_\tau = \mathbf{p} + \epsilon [\, \mathbf{q}, \mathbf{p} \,]. \qquad (3{:}26b)$$

The analogy is complete if $\mathbf{qp} - \mathbf{pq} = i\hbar$, which is to say that the *basic* quantal P.B. has the same value as the classical, and we assume this in general, at least when an analogous classical P.B. exists. Thus, the basic quantal P.B.'s are

$$\left.\begin{aligned} [\, \mathbf{q}_r, \mathbf{q}_s \,] &= [\, \mathbf{p}_r, \mathbf{p}_s \,] = 0, \\ [\, \mathbf{q}_r, \mathbf{p}_s \,] &= \mathbf{I}\, \delta_{rs}, \end{aligned}\right\} \qquad (3{:}27)$$ [5]

and it is readily seen that quantal P.B.'s also satisfy the relations (3:2).

A quantal contact transformation is also defined as a transformation from one set of canonical coordinates and momenta $\mathbf{q}_r$, $\mathbf{p}_r$, say, to another set $\mathbf{q}_{r\tau}$, $\mathbf{p}_{r\tau}$, and is thus simply a unitary transformation of the type considered above. Clearly, the basic P.B.'s are again invariant under such transformations. The quantal condition for a set of variables to be canonical is the commutator, and being algebraic is much simpler than its classical counterpart. We shall further extend these results to include dynamical systems for which canonical coordinates and momenta do not exist—defining such transformations simply as unitary. This generalization corresponds to the fact that the invariant properties of unitary transformations give them importance in their own right, while true contact transformations in quantum mechanics are an important but special case.

The equations (3:27) show the basic source of non-commutativity and provide the method of calculating commutators between other observables. The commutators of all observables with classical analogues may be obtained either by direct transcription or by application of one or more of the now algebraic relations (3:2). Before considering the derivation of commutators of more general observables in this manner, we shall consider briefly the consequences of non-commutativity of observables from the physical point of view. We have already found (§ 6) that a necessary condition for the existence of a simultaneous eigenstate of two or more observables, or equivalently that they be simultaneously diagonal, is that the observables must commute. This mathematical condition is often stated as *the compatibility of observables*, by which is meant that the measurements (at least conceptually) of commuting observables are not exclusive in the sense that the determination of a value for one precludes a precise determination for the others.

As indicated in the discussion of § 9, this fundamental emphasis on experimental correlation and compatibility finds its full expression in the Indeterminacy Principle. In a general sense, the Indeterminacy Principle and the Quantum conditions (3:27) are equivalent statements of one and the same aspect of natural phenomena; the latter giving explicit quantitative form to the Principle. To illustrate more fully, let us take a pair of observables $\mathbf{q}$, $\mathbf{p}$ whose classical analogues are the canonically conjugate coordinate and momentum of an electron (one-dimensional picture), say,

[5] Usually the unit operator is omitted, but must always be understood.

and by hypothesis satisfy the quantal relation $[\mathfrak{q}, \mathfrak{p}]_- = i\hbar$. Both of these observables are known to have continuous spectra of eigenvalues and, for an arbitrary normalized state $|\,\rangle$, a measurement for these will give, respectively, as probable or expected mean values

$$\left.\begin{aligned}\langle\, \mathfrak{q}\,\rangle &= \langle\, |\, \mathfrak{q}\, |\,\rangle = \int |\langle\, |\, q'\,\rangle|^2\, q'\, dq', \\ \langle\, \mathfrak{p}\,\rangle &= \langle\, |\, \mathfrak{p}\, |\,\rangle = \int |\langle\, |\, p'\,\rangle|^2\, p'\, dp',\end{aligned}\right\} \quad . \quad . \quad . \quad (3{:}28a)$$

in accord with the general probability interpretation.

We may now inquire as to the explicit expression of the effect which the commutator implies in simultaneous measurements of $\mathfrak{q}$ and $\mathfrak{p}$ for the arbitrary state $|\,\rangle$. In general, the measured values of $\mathfrak{q}$ and $\mathfrak{p}$ have a certain spread about the expected mean values, and a measure of precision of determination is given by the dispersion or mean square deviation of the measured values about the mean, i.e.

$$\left.\begin{aligned}\langle\, (\,\Delta\mathfrak{q}\,)^2\,\rangle &= \int |\langle\, |\, q'\,\rangle|^2\, dq'(q' - \langle\, \mathfrak{q}\,\rangle)^2, \\ \langle\, (\,\Delta\mathfrak{p}\,)^2\,\rangle &= \int |\langle\, |\, p'\,\rangle|^2\, dp'(p' - \langle\, \mathfrak{p}\,\rangle)^2,\end{aligned}\right\} \quad . \quad . \quad . \quad (3{:}28b)$$

and we are interested in the correlation between these two quantities in the form of the product

$$\langle\, (\,\Delta\mathfrak{q}\,)^2\,\rangle\langle\, (\,\Delta\mathfrak{p}\,)^2\,\rangle. \quad . \quad . \quad . \quad . \quad . \quad . \quad . \quad . \quad (3{:}28c)$$

From the point of view of classical theory, there is nothing in the nature of things to prevent either or both $\langle\, (\,\Delta\mathfrak{q}\,)^2\,\rangle, \langle\, (\,\Delta\mathfrak{p}\,)^2\,\rangle$ from being zero, depending upon the degree of precision of the measuring apparatus, real or hypothetical. We shall now show that in quantum theory the commutator gives a physical restriction on (3:28*c*).

For arbitrary vectors $|\, a\,\rangle$, $|\, b\,\rangle$ in a unitary space, we have the Schwarz inequality

$$\langle\, a\, |\, a\,\rangle\langle\, b\, |\, b\,\rangle \geqslant \tfrac{1}{4}\{\langle\, a\, |\, b\,\rangle + \langle\, b\, |\, a\,\rangle\}^2. \quad . \quad . \quad . \quad (3{:}28d)$$

Now, $i(\mathfrak{q} - \langle\, \mathfrak{q}\,\rangle)$ and $(\mathfrak{p} - \langle\, \mathfrak{p}\,\rangle)$ operating on $|\,\rangle$ generate new vectors which we may denote as $|\, a\,\rangle$ and $|\, b\,\rangle$, respectively; applying (3:28*d*), we obtain

$$\{\langle\, |(\mathfrak{q} - \langle\, \mathfrak{q}\,\rangle)^* (\mathfrak{q} - \langle\, \mathfrak{q}\,\rangle)|\,\rangle\}\, \{\langle\, |(\mathfrak{p} - \langle\, \mathfrak{p}\,\rangle)^* (\mathfrak{p} - \langle\, \mathfrak{p}\,\rangle)|\,\rangle\}$$
$$\geqslant \tfrac{1}{4}\{-i\langle\, |(\,\mathfrak{q} - \langle\, \mathfrak{q}\,\rangle)^* (\mathfrak{p} - \langle\, \mathfrak{p}\,\rangle)\,|\,\rangle + i\langle\, |(\,\mathfrak{p} - \langle\, \mathfrak{p}\,\rangle)^* (\mathfrak{q} - \langle\, \mathfrak{q}\,\rangle)|\,\rangle\}^2. \quad (3{:}28e)$$

Since $\mathfrak{q}$ and $\mathfrak{p}$ are Hermitian by the definition of observable, and $\langle\, \mathfrak{q}\,\rangle$, $\langle\, \mathfrak{p}\,\rangle$ are just numbers, this simplifies to

$$\{\langle\, |(\mathfrak{q} - \langle\, \mathfrak{q}\,\rangle)^2\,|\,\rangle\}\, \{\langle\, |(\,\mathfrak{p} - \langle\, \mathfrak{p}\,\rangle)^2\,|\,\rangle\} \geqslant -\tfrac{1}{4}\{\langle\, |\mathfrak{q}\mathfrak{p} - \mathfrak{p}\mathfrak{q}|\,\rangle\}^2, \qquad (3{:}28f)$$

and we find

$$\langle\, (\,\Delta\mathfrak{q}\,)^2\,\rangle\langle\, (\,\Delta\mathfrak{p}\,)^2\,\rangle \geqslant \hbar^2/4. \quad . \quad . \quad . \quad . \quad . \quad . \quad . \quad (3{:}28g)$$

The root-mean-square deviation is often called the *uncertainty* (Standard Deviation), e.g. $\delta_p = \sqrt{\langle\, (\,\Delta\mathfrak{p}\,)^2\,\rangle}$; and we can write (3:28*g*) as

$$\delta_p\,\delta_q \geqslant \hbar/2. \quad . \quad . \quad . \quad . \quad . \quad . \quad . \quad . \quad (3{:}28h)$$

Thus, the more accurately we determine $\mathbf{q}$, the wider is the spread in the values obtained for $\mathbf{p}$, and conversely. In particular, if the arbitrary state $|\rangle$ is an eigenstate of $\mathbf{q}$, then we see that $\delta_q = 0$, and the value of $\mathbf{p}$ is completely indeterminate, i.e. all eigenvalues of $\mathbf{p}$ are equally probable, and conversely. Physically, this means that if a specific position for the electron is known, then the value of the momentum is completely indefinite,[6] and vice versa.

From the fundamental commutator we obtain the relation

$$\mathbf{q}^n\mathbf{p} - \mathbf{p}\mathbf{q}^n = ni\hbar\mathbf{q}^{n-1}, \qquad (3:29a)$$

which is readily proved by induction with respect to n, showing that if it holds for 1 and n, it holds for $n + 1$, and hence in general. We can write (3:29a), for arbitrary n, as

$$\mathbf{q}^n\mathbf{p} - \mathbf{p}\mathbf{q}^n = i\hbar\frac{d\mathbf{q}^n}{d\mathbf{q}}, \qquad (3:29b)$$

from which it follows that any operator function $\mathbf{f}(\mathbf{q})$, expressible in a power series, satisfies the relation

$$\mathbf{f}\mathbf{p} - \mathbf{p}\mathbf{f} = i\hbar\frac{d\mathbf{f}}{d\mathbf{q}}. \qquad (3:29c)$$

It is evident from symmetry that the corresponding equations in $\mathbf{p}$ are

$$\mathbf{p}^n\mathbf{q} - \mathbf{q}\mathbf{p}^n = -\, i\hbar\frac{d\mathbf{p}^n}{d\mathbf{p}}, \qquad (3:30a)$$

and

$$\mathbf{f}(\mathbf{p})\mathbf{q} - \mathbf{q}\mathbf{f}(\mathbf{p}) = -\, i\hbar\frac{d\mathbf{f}(\mathbf{p})}{d\mathbf{p}}. \qquad (3:30b)$$

The operator function of particular interest to us in a future connection (Chap. XI) is the exponential, defined as usual by

$$e^{i\gamma\mathbf{q}} = \sum_{n=0}^{\infty}\frac{(i\gamma\mathbf{q})^n}{n!} \quad (\gamma \text{ any real number}). \qquad (3:31a)$$

Substituting this function in (3:29c), we obtain

$$e^{i\gamma\mathbf{q}}\,\mathbf{p} - \mathbf{p}e^{i\gamma\mathbf{q}} = -\,\gamma\hbar e^{i\gamma\mathbf{q}}, \qquad (3:31b)$$

i.e. $\mathbf{p}e^{i\gamma\mathbf{q}} = e^{i\gamma\mathbf{q}}(\mathbf{p} + \gamma\hbar)$.

If we operate on an eigen-$|\rangle$ of $\mathbf{p}$ belonging to the eigenvalue p', we find

$$\mathbf{p}e^{i\gamma\mathbf{q}}\,|\,p'\rangle = (p' + \gamma\hbar)\,e^{i\gamma\mathbf{q}}\,|\,p'\rangle, \qquad (3:31c)$$

which shows that $e^{i\gamma\mathbf{q}}\,|\,p'\rangle$ is an eigen-$|\rangle$ of $\mathbf{p}$ belonging[7] to the eigenvalue $p' + \gamma\hbar$. Thus, since the real number γ is arbitrary, it follows that if $\mathbf{p}$ has any eigenvalues they form a continuous spectrum from $-\infty$ to ∞; and by symmetry the same result obviously holds for the spectrum of $\mathbf{q}$. Hence, the class of canonically conjugate observables is at once very severely restricted. If the above argument were

[6] Of course it is clear that the extreme limits are not actually realizable for physical reasons.

[7] Cf. equations (3:22), (3:24b), (3:26b).

to be carried through for γ complex, one would arrive at an apparent difficulty in the appearance of inadmissible complex eigenvalues; but this objection can be ruled out on the grounds that, for γ complex, the exponential operator becomes improper (in particular non-convergent),[8] and hence itself inadmissible. It should be noted that there exist pairs of quantities which apparently satisfy the fundamental commutator, and at a casual glance might be taken for canonically conjugate observables in the quantal sense. The term *pairs of quantities* is intentionally noncommittal because, ordinarily, one or other of the variables involved is not an operator in the sense of general theory; although, with this understanding, we may refer to them as pseudo-canonical variables. Examples of such pairs of variables are the time (t), which cannot be properly defined as an operator, and the negative of the Hamiltonian operator **H**, which admits a discrete spectrum.[9] The Heisenberg relation $\delta_t \delta_E \sim h$ is inferred from $\delta_q \delta_p$ by a hybridization of classical and quantal ideas, and cannot be rigorously derived along the lines of (3:28). Although there is by definition a correlation between time and energy (cf. § 26) in the sense that a variable energy (time-dependent Hamiltonian) cannot be specified at all; and in contrast, for definite energies (eigenstates of the Hamiltonian), the time is essentially irrelevant; still, the δ_t above can be described as an uncertainty in a metaphorical sense only. Similarly, the formal relation $[\phi, -i\hbar\partial/\partial\phi]_- = i\hbar$, involving the **q**-diagonal representative of the z component of angular momentum (transformed to spherical coordinates), is sometimes quoted as showing the conjugacy of this component and the polar angle ϕ. The momentum component is a proper operator, but admits of a discrete spectrum while there exists no operator corresponding to ϕ, which in any case is not uniquely defined.

There is another type of pseudo-commutator involving formally defined operators, such as the action **J** and angle variable $\boldsymbol{\omega}$ associated with the problem of the harmonic oscillator.[10] The action variable has by definition a discrete spectrum, while the angle variable cannot be defined at all except through the related *step* operators $e^{\pm i\omega}$, so that the commutator $[\boldsymbol{\omega}, \mathbf{J}] = 1$ is meaningless in the strict sense. Nonetheless, operators of this latter type are extremely important in general theory, as for example in the second quantization (cf. § 93a); so much so, that it is more or less customary to refer to them simply as canonically conjugate, and they are manipulated as such. Nevertheless, no difficulty will arise through their use if one is careful to avoid drawing general inferences too casually.

The theoretical specification of "minimum uncertainty" for canonically conjugate operators rests solely on the quantum conditions (3:27), and clearly contains no reference to the experimental technique or mechanism involved in observation. An important corollary is the fact that in combining two or more systems, the canonical commutators of the individual component systems retain their original value despite interactions, as evidenced by the agreement of theory and experiment on this basis. This constitutes the most striking proof that the mathematical for-

[8] The argument is still not sufficiently rigorous, but the conclusion as to the necessity of a continuous spectrum has been demonstrated by von Neumann on more general grounds.

[9] Even in the classical case the energy plays the role of momentum conjugate to the time only for a special type of canonical transformation.

[10] Cf. DIRAC, *Q.M.*

malism of uncertainty must be independent of the *nature* of the observing mechanism, since in the last analysis all quantal observations reduce to controlled interactions of pairs of systems.

§ 19. General Commutators

It will be useful in our later work to have available certain fundamental commutators which we now derive. The picture of a single electron moving in a central field of force [11] is fundamental to all theoretical physics, and the commutators pertaining thereto are the prototypes of all more general types.

Taking Cartesian coordinates of the electron referred to the force centre as origin, the coordinates $\mathbf{x}$, $\mathbf{y}$, $\mathbf{z}$ and momenta $\mathbf{p}_x$, $\mathbf{p}_y$, $\mathbf{p}_z$ satisfy the quantum conditions

$$[\mathbf{x}, \mathbf{y}] = 0; \quad [\mathbf{x}, \mathbf{p}_x] = 1; \quad [\mathbf{x}, \mathbf{p}_y] = 0; \quad \text{etc.} \qquad (3{:}32a)$$

The angular momentum is defined, as in classical theory, by

$$\underline{\mathbf{l}} = \underline{\mathbf{r}} \times \underline{\mathbf{p}}, \text{ i.e. } \mathbf{l}_x = \mathbf{y}\mathbf{p}_z - \mathbf{z}\mathbf{p}_y, \text{ etc.}; \qquad (3{:}32b)$$

and from (3:32*b*) we obtain the further useful result

$$\underline{\mathbf{l}} \cdot \underline{\mathbf{r}} = \mathbf{l}_x\mathbf{x} + \mathbf{l}_y\mathbf{y} + \mathbf{l}_z\mathbf{z} = 0. \qquad (3{:}32c)$$

The commutator relations between coordinates, linear momenta, and angular momenta are obtained from the Poisson Bracket expressions, using (3:32*a*, *b*), e.g.

$$\left.\begin{aligned} [\mathbf{l}_z, \mathbf{x}] &= \mathbf{y}, \\ [\mathbf{l}_z, \mathbf{y}] &= -\mathbf{x}, \\ [\mathbf{l}_z, \mathbf{z}] &= 0; \end{aligned}\right\} \qquad (3{:}33a)$$ [12]

$$[\mathbf{l}_z, \mathbf{p}_x] = \mathbf{p}_y; \qquad (3{:}33b)$$

$$[\mathbf{l}_z, \mathbf{l}_x] = \mathbf{l}_y; \qquad (3{:}33c)$$

all others being obtainable by cyclic interchange.

It is convenient at this point to introduce the central operator of the whole quantum theory, i.e. the Hamiltonian $\mathbf{H}$. This linear Hermitian operator is the operator transcription of the analogous Hamiltonian of classical theory, and is assumed to be identical in form with the latter, when it exists.[13] $\mathbf{H}$ is an observable *by definition*, and in a closed (conservative) system represents the energy. We leave the important question of the eigenvalues and eigenstates of the Hamiltonian for a later section, but consider here its commutator relations with other observables.

The simplest Hamiltonian for atomic systems is in our one electron case, and is given as in the classical theory by

$$\mathbf{H} = \frac{1}{2m}\underline{\mathbf{p}}^2 + \mathbf{V}(|\underline{\mathbf{r}}|).$$

[11] I.e. potential $\mathbf{V}$ as a function only of $(\mathbf{x}^2 + \mathbf{y}^2 + \mathbf{z}^2)$.

[12] The analogue of (3:13*a*), for example, is readily seen to be $\mathbf{x}_\tau = \mathbf{U}\mathbf{x}\mathbf{U}^{-1}$, with $\mathbf{U} = 1 - \frac{i\epsilon}{\hbar}\mathbf{l}_z$.

[13] There will, of course, in the general case be terms of a purely quantal origin, since there are operators without classical analogue.

It is clear from (3:32*a*) that none of the coordinate observables can commute with $\mathbf{H}$; but we shall show that each component of angular momentum does and, by the same token, the total angular momentum, since it is a function of them (Theorem 5, § 8). Thus

$$[\,\mathbf{l}_z, \mathbf{x}^2 + \mathbf{y}^2 + \mathbf{z}^2\,] = \mathbf{x}\,[\,\mathbf{l}_z, \mathbf{x}\,] + [\,\mathbf{l}_z, \mathbf{x}\,]\,\mathbf{x} + \mathbf{y}\,[\,\mathbf{l}_z, \mathbf{y}\,] + [\,\mathbf{l}_z, \mathbf{y}\,]\,\mathbf{y} = 0, \quad (3:34a)$$ [14]

and

$$[\,\mathbf{l}_z, \mathbf{p}_x{}^2 + \mathbf{p}_y{}^2 + \mathbf{p}_z{}^2\,] = 0. \quad (3:34b)$$

From symmetry, it is clear that these equations also hold for $\mathbf{l}_x$ and $\mathbf{l}_y$, and we find that the angular momentum commutes with the Hamiltonian in the particular case when it is simply a function [15] of $|\,\underline{\mathbf{r}}\,|$ and $\underline{\mathbf{p}}^2$.

For a system of many electrons, neglecting interactions of a specifically quantal character,[16] the Hamiltonian will be of the classical form

$$\mathbf{H} = \sum_i \frac{1}{2m}\,\underline{\mathbf{p}}_i{}^2 + \sum_i \mathbf{u}\,(\,|\,\underline{\mathbf{r}}_i\,|\,) + \sum_{i<j} \mathbf{v}\,(\,|\,\underline{\mathbf{r}}_{ij}\,|\,).$$

The observables referring to a particular electron will commute with those referring to any other, since the quantum conditions place restrictions only on the operators belonging to one particle or individual subsystem;[17] and if $\underline{\mathbf{l}}_i$ denotes the vector orbital angular momentum of the electron, we have

$$\underline{\mathbf{l}}_i \times \underline{\mathbf{l}}_j + \underline{\mathbf{l}}_j \times \underline{\mathbf{l}}_i = 0 \qquad (\,i \neq j). \quad (3:35a)$$

The total angular momentum $\underline{\mathbf{L}} = \sum_i \underline{\mathbf{l}}_i$ will then have the commutator expressed as

$$\underline{\mathbf{L}} \times \underline{\mathbf{L}} = \sum_{i,j} \underline{\mathbf{l}}_i \times \underline{\mathbf{l}}_j = i\hbar\underline{\mathbf{L}}. \quad (3:35b)$$

In the particular approximation mentioned above, it is clear that $\underline{\mathbf{L}}$ commutes with $\mathbf{H}$.[18] We may further note (in passing) the important fact that since in this case $\mathbf{H}$, $\underline{\mathbf{L}}^2$ and $\mathbf{L}_z$ commute, they may be simultaneously diagonalized. The result (3:35*b*) shows that the components of total angular momentum $\underline{\mathbf{L}}$ of any number of particles obey the same commutation rule as those of a single particle, and we adopt the general hypothesis that any angular momentum $\underline{\mathbf{J}}$ satisfies the commutator

$$\underline{\mathbf{J}} \times \underline{\mathbf{J}} = i\hbar\underline{\mathbf{J}}. \quad (3:35c)$$

We have already mentioned that there are quantal operators without classical analogue, and among these is the intrinsic electronic angular momentum, or briefly, electron spin observable $\underline{\mathbf{s}}$. In accord with the assumption above we require $\underline{\mathbf{s}}$ to have the commutator $\underline{\mathbf{s}} \times \underline{\mathbf{s}} = i\hbar\underline{\mathbf{s}}$. In our further work it will sometimes be more convenient to consider, instead of $\underline{\mathbf{s}}$, the operator $\underline{\boldsymbol{\sigma}}$ defined by $\underline{\boldsymbol{\sigma}} = \frac{2}{\hbar}\underline{\mathbf{s}}$, whose commutator is, therefore, given by

$$\underline{\boldsymbol{\sigma}} \times \underline{\boldsymbol{\sigma}} = 2i\underline{\boldsymbol{\sigma}}, \text{ i.e. } \boldsymbol{\sigma}_y\boldsymbol{\sigma}_z - \boldsymbol{\sigma}_z\boldsymbol{\sigma}_y = 2i\boldsymbol{\sigma}_x, \text{ etc.}$$

[14] In particular, $\mathbf{l}_z$ and $\underline{\mathbf{r}}$ commute, since we know that an operator $\boldsymbol{\eta}$ which commutes with the operator $\boldsymbol{\xi}$, say, commutes with $\mathbf{f}(\boldsymbol{\xi})$.

[15] This, of course, follows quite trivially from the evident invariance of $\mathbf{H}$ under all rotations.

[16] I.e. involving spin, etc.

[17] Observables corresponding to different degrees of freedom commute.

[18] This approximation forms the starting point of an important perturbation problem.

§ 20. Elements of Non-commutative Algebra

(*a*) *Introduction.*

The basic quantal postulate [19] that all angular momenta satisfy the commutator $\underline{\mathbf{J}} \times \underline{\mathbf{J}} = i\hbar\underline{\mathbf{J}}$ is one of the most attractive features of quantum mechanics, inasmuch as this simple rule combined with elementary non-commutative analysis leads to a vast array of fundamental theorems on angular momenta. We shall now obtain a few of the more important results which will be of special use to us in our further work. From the preceding discussion it follows that the squared magnitude $\underline{\mathbf{J}}^2$ of the vector $\underline{\mathbf{J}}$ commutes with each component of $\underline{\mathbf{J}}$, and hence with $\underline{\mathbf{J}}$ itself. Thus

$$[\,\mathbf{J}_x, \underline{\mathbf{J}}^2\,] = [\,\mathbf{J}_x, \mathbf{J}_y\,]\,\mathbf{J}_y + \mathbf{J}_y\,[\,\mathbf{J}_x, \mathbf{J}_y\,] + [\,\mathbf{J}_x, \mathbf{J}_z\,]\,\mathbf{J}_z + \mathbf{J}_z\,[\,\mathbf{J}_x, \mathbf{J}_z\,] = 0, \quad (3{:}36)$$

and correspondingly for the other components, by symmetry.

Therefore, we may introduce a $\underline{\mathbf{J}}^2$, $\mathbf{J}_z$, $\boldsymbol{\beta}$-diagonal representation where $\boldsymbol{\beta}$ denotes such other observables as may be required to form a complete commuting set with $\underline{\mathbf{J}}^2$ and $\mathbf{J}_z$. By a previous result, any function $\boldsymbol{\Gamma}$ of the components $\mathbf{J}_x$, $\mathbf{J}_y$, $\mathbf{J}_z$ commutes with $\underline{\mathbf{J}}^2$, i.e. $\boldsymbol{\Gamma}\underline{\mathbf{J}}^2 - \underline{\mathbf{J}}^2\boldsymbol{\Gamma} = 0$, or in representative form

$$(\,\underline{J}^{2\prime\prime} - \underline{J}^{2\prime}\,)\,\langle\, \beta'\underline{J}^{2\prime}J_z' \mid \boldsymbol{\Gamma} \mid \beta''\underline{J}^{2\prime\prime}J_z''\,\rangle = 0, \quad . \quad . \quad . \quad . \quad (3{:}37)$$

so that only those matrix elements of $\boldsymbol{\Gamma}$ for which $\underline{J}^{2\prime} = \underline{J}^{2\prime\prime}$ can be non-zero. Correspondingly, if we require that the $\boldsymbol{\beta}$'s commute with $\mathbf{J}_x$ and $\mathbf{J}_y$ as well as J_z (which is usually possible), then it follows from $\boldsymbol{\Gamma\beta} - \boldsymbol{\beta\Gamma} = 0$ (all $\boldsymbol{\beta}$'s), that

$$\langle\, \beta'\underline{J}^{2\prime}J_z' \mid \boldsymbol{\Gamma} \mid \beta''\underline{J}^{2\prime}J_z''\,\rangle = 0, \qquad (\text{unless } \beta' = \beta''). \quad . \quad . \quad (3{:}38)$$

The significance of the result (3:37) is simply that any equation between functions of the angular momentum components, when expressed in representative form, is decomposed into relations between finite block matrices (sub-matrices), each characterized by a given eigenvalue $\underline{J}^{2\prime}$ of $\underline{\mathbf{J}}^2$, i.e. matrices defined over the finite subspace belonging to $\underline{J}^{2\prime}$. This circumstance is often described by the statement that the non-vanishing matrix elements of $\boldsymbol{\Gamma}$ are diagonal in $\underline{\mathbf{J}}^2$, so that in such equations $\underline{\mathrm{J}}^2$ plays the part of a number $\underline{J}^{2\prime}$ (within each subspace). It is for this same reason that the requirement (3:38) is introduced, since then the matrices are also diagonal in the $\boldsymbol{\beta}$'s, and the non-vanishing elements $\langle\, \beta'\underline{J}^{2\prime}J_z' \mid \boldsymbol{\Gamma} \mid \beta'\underline{J}^{2\prime}J_z''\,\rangle$ for any given eigenvalue set β', $\underline{J}^{2\prime}$ (β', $\underline{J}^{2\prime}$ subspace) form a square matrix labelled essentially by the eigenvalues of $\mathbf{J}_z$; $\underline{\mathbf{J}}^2$ and the $\boldsymbol{\beta}$'s remain fixed and are considered as just the numbers $\underline{J}^{2\prime}$, β'.

(*b*) *Vertical Communication—Shift Operators.*[20]

The symbolic determination of the simultaneous eigenvalues of $\underline{\mathbf{J}}^2$ and $\mathbf{J}_z$ depends on a process which may be termed *vertical communication* and involves the *shift operators* $\mathbf{J}^{\pm} = \mathbf{J}_x \pm i\mathbf{J}_y$. The reason for these descriptive terms is the following:

[19] This must be termed a postulate, since the spin commutator is independent of the fundamental coordinate-momentum commutator.

[20] SCHROEDINGER, E.: *Proc. Roy. Irish Acad.*, **47**, 39 (1941).

From the commutation rules, we find that

$$\mathbf{J}_z(\mathbf{J}_x \pm i\mathbf{J}_y) = (\mathbf{J}_x \pm i\mathbf{J}_y)(\mathbf{J}_z \pm \hbar), \quad . \quad . \quad . \quad . \quad (3{:}39a)$$

or, in representative form,

$$\langle \beta' \underline{J}^{2\prime} J_z' \mid \mathbf{J}_x \pm i\mathbf{J}_y \mid \beta' J^{2\prime} J_z'' \rangle (J_z' - J_z'' \mp \hbar) = 0, \quad . \quad (3{:}39b)$$

from which the matrix elements of $\mathbf{J}_x \pm i\mathbf{J}_y$ vanish unless $J_z'' = J_z' \mp \hbar$, respectively. In other words, $\mathbf{J}^{\pm}$ operating on the eigenvector $\mid \beta' \underline{J}^{2\prime} J_z' \mp \hbar \rangle$, respectively, converts it into $\mid \beta' \underline{J}^{2\prime} J_z' \rangle$; or operating on $\mid \beta' \underline{J}^{2\prime} J_z' \rangle$, produces an eigenvector of $\mathbf{J}_z$ belonging to $J_z' \pm \hbar$, *or the zero vector*. This interpretation is, of course, just that implicit in (3:39*a*) where the role of the eigenvectors $\mid \beta' \underline{J}^{2\prime} J_z' \rangle$ has been suppressed. The operators $\mathbf{J}^{\pm}$ in equation (3:39*a*) are just a particular example of *shift operators*, which are characterized in general by the fact that the shift operator on commutation with another operator ($\mathbf{J}_z$ here) reproduces itself up to a constant multiplier ($\pm \hbar$ here); the constant multiplier is the resultant shift in the eigenvalue of the *other* operator. In view of the above discussion, it is evident that the eigenvectors $\mid \beta' \underline{J}^{2\prime} J_z' \rangle$ spanning the $\underline{J}^{2\prime}$ subspace form a chain or ladder of eigenvectors (eigenvalues), the steps of the ladder being labelled by successive eigenvalues of $\mathbf{J}_z$, and hence the shift operators do indeed establish a vertical communication. This result, incidentally, justifies our previous reference to the finite subspace characterized by the eigenvalue $\underline{J}^{2\prime}$, since the ladder steps have been shown to be discrete of length $\hbar$, and clearly[21] $\mid J_z' \mid \leqslant \sqrt{\underline{J}^{2\prime}}$ so that the eigenvalues of $\mathbf{J}_z$ corresponding to $J^{2\prime}$ form a discrete bounded set. We determine the upper and lower limits in $\mathbf{J}_z$ eigenvalues (top and bottom of the ladder) for a given $J^{2\prime}$, essentially from the conditions

$$\left.\begin{aligned} \mathbf{J}^{+} \mid \beta' \underline{J}^{2\prime} J_z{}^{t} \rangle &= 0, \\ \mathbf{J}^{-} \mid \beta' \underline{J}^{2\prime} J_z{}^{b} \rangle &= 0, \end{aligned}\right\} \quad . \quad . \quad . \quad . \quad . \quad . \quad . \quad . \quad (3{:}40)$$

which follow from the known boundedness of the J_z' set and the described properties of the shift operators. However, in the following we shall again largely suppress the eigenvectors, although, as in the discussion of equation (3:39*a*), they may be introduced explicitly at any point or from the start, if so desired.

We consider the equations

$$\mathbf{J}^{-}\mathbf{J}^{+} = \underline{\mathbf{J}}^2 - \mathbf{J}_z{}^2 - \hbar\mathbf{J}_z, \quad . \quad . \quad . \quad . \quad . \quad . \quad (3{:}41a)$$

$$\mathbf{J}^{+}\mathbf{J}^{-} = \underline{\mathbf{J}}^2 - \mathbf{J}_z{}^2 + \hbar\mathbf{J}_z, \quad . \quad . \quad . \quad . \quad . \quad . \quad (3{:}41b)$$

and equating diagonal elements on each side of the representative form, we find[22]

$$\sum_{J_z''} \langle J_z' \mid \mathbf{J}^{-} \mid J_z'' \rangle \langle J_z'' \mid \mathbf{J}^{+} \mid J_z' \rangle = J^{2\prime} - J_z{}^{2\prime} - \hbar J_z', \quad . \quad (3{:}42a)$$

$$\sum_{J_z''} \langle J_z' \mid \mathbf{J}^{+} \mid J_z'' \rangle \langle J_z'' \mid \mathbf{J}^{-} \mid J_z' \rangle = J^{2\prime} - J_z{}^{2\prime} + \hbar J_z'. \quad . \quad (3{:}42b)$$

[21] Since $(J_x{}^2 + J_y{}^2)' = J^{2\prime} - J_z{}^{2\prime} \geqslant 0$ from the Hermiticity of $\mathbf{J}_x{}^2, \mathbf{J}_y{}^2$; but note that the possibility of determining the eigenvalues of $(\mathbf{J}_x{}^2 + \mathbf{J}_y{}^2)$ does not imply the same for $\mathbf{J}_x$ and $\mathbf{J}_y$ individually.

[22] The fixed indices β', $J^{2\prime}$ in the representatives are suppressed for brevity.

From the result (3:39*b*) it follows that all terms in the summations vanish except, at most, that one for which $J_z'' = J_z' + \hbar$ in (3:42*a*), and $J_z'' = J_z' - \hbar$ in (3:42*b*). Considering first (3:42*a*), we see [23] that $\underline{J}^{2\prime} - J_z^{2\prime} - \hbar J_z' \geqslant 0$, and if J_z^t labels the top of the ladder, then $J_z^t + \hbar$ is not an eigenvalue (in the set corresponding to $\underline{J}^{2\prime}$), and hence

$$\underline{J}^{2\prime} - J_z^t(J_z^t + \hbar) = 0. \quad \ldots\ldots \quad (3:43a)$$

By the same token, if in (3:42*b*) J_z^b labels the bottom of the ladder, then $J_z^b - \hbar$ is not an eigenvalue (in the set corresponding to $\underline{J}^{2\prime}$), and hence

$$\underline{J}^{2\prime} - J_z^b(J_z^b - \hbar) = 0. \quad \ldots\ldots \quad (3:43b)$$

Combining these results, we find that

$$(J_z^t + J_z^b)(J_z^b - J_z^t - \hbar) = 0, \quad \ldots\ldots \quad (3:44)$$

or $J_z^b = -J_z^t$, since $J_z^t \geqslant J_z^b$ by hypothesis. Furthermore, the maximum minus the minimum value, i.e. $2J_z^t$, must be an integral multiple of $\hbar$ greater than or equal to zero, which we shall denote by $2j$ with j obviously restricted to integral and half-odd integral values, zero included. Hence

$$J_z^t = j\hbar, \; J_z^b = -j\hbar, \quad \ldots\ldots \quad (3:45)$$

and from equations (3:43),

$$\underline{J}^{2\prime} = j(j+1)\hbar^2; \;\; j = (0, \tfrac{1}{2}, 1, \tfrac{3}{2}, \ldots). \quad \ldots \quad (3:46)$$

Corresponding to a given eigenvalue of $\underline{\mathbf{J}}^2$, it is convenient to denote the $2j + 1$ associated eigenvalues of $\mathbf{J}_z$ by

$$J_z' = m_j\hbar; \; m_j = (j, j-1, \ldots -j). \quad \ldots \quad (3:47)$$ [24]

We may conveniently summarize all of the conclusions obtained by means of the ladder diagram on p. 46, which is self-explanatory.

The preceding results must be qualified when the angular momentum in question is expressible in terms of the coordinates and linear momenta, i.e. the so-called orbital angular momentum, since it is well known that the eigenvalues of the components in this case must all be integral multiples [25] of $\hbar$. Hence, denoting the orbital vector by $\underline{\mathbf{l}}$, we have in the customary notation

$$\left.\begin{aligned} \underline{l}^{2\prime} &= l(l+1)\hbar^2, & l &= 0, 1, 2, \ldots \\ l_z' &= m_l\hbar, & m_l &= l, l-1 \ldots -l. \end{aligned}\right\} \quad \ldots \quad (3:48)$$

The more general result (3:46) occurs physically only because of the existence of spin angular momentum, which is not expressible in terms of the coordinates

[23] The terms on the left are conjugate elements; $\langle J_z' | \mathbf{J}^- | J_z'' \rangle = \langle J_z'' | \mathbf{J}^+ | J_z' \rangle^*$, which is implicit in the remarks of Footnote 22.

[24] $\mathbf{J}_x$ and $\mathbf{J}_y$ obviously take on the same eigenvalues as $\mathbf{J}_z$, since all three enter the commutation rules symmetrically.

[25] In the contrary case, the operator $\mathbf{U} = e^{-(2\pi i/\hbar)\mathbf{l}_z}$ (which generates a rotation of 2π in coordinate space) applied to a state of definite $\mathbf{l}_z$ leads to multiple-valued eigenvectors, implying a spatial distinction which is not physically realized.

and linear momenta of the particle, and hence is free of the above-mentioned restriction (cf. § 53). For essentially the same reason, the squared magnitude of the spin vector may be postulated to have but a single eigenvalue $\underline{s}^{2\prime} = s(s+1)\hbar^2$ ($\underline{s}$-fixed),[26] since by definition there are no variables with which $\underline{\mathbf{s}}^2$ does not commute, which means that $\underline{\mathbf{s}}^2$ is at most a scalar multiple of the identity.

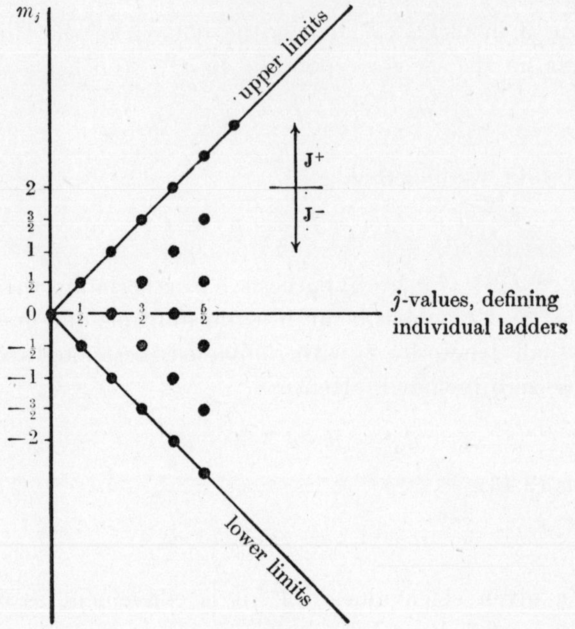

Fig. 3.1

(c) *Angular Momentum—Magnitude.*

It is evident that we may introduce a dynamical variable $+\sqrt{\underline{\mathbf{J}}^2}$ with the meaning of the magnitude of the vector, but its eigenvalues $\sqrt{j(j+1)}\hbar$ are not especially convenient to handle. For this reason, it is sometimes useful to describe the magnitude by a closely related variable $\mathbf{K}$, defined by

$$\mathbf{K} = (\underline{\mathbf{J}}^2 + \tfrac{1}{4}\hbar^2)^{\frac{1}{2}} - \tfrac{1}{2}\hbar, \quad . \quad . \quad . \quad . \quad . \quad . \quad . \quad . \quad . \qquad (3{:}49)$$

from which it follows that

$$\mathbf{K}(\mathbf{K} + \hbar) = \underline{\mathbf{J}}^2. \quad . \quad . \quad . \quad . \quad . \quad . \quad . \quad . \qquad (3{:}50)$$

The eigenvalues of $\mathbf{K}$ are readily seen to be integral or half-integral multiples of $\hbar$, including zero; and for each eigenvalue K' $(= j\hbar)$ of $\mathbf{K}$, the eigenvalues of $\mathbf{J}_z$ are $K', K' - \hbar, \ldots -K'$, so that $\mathbf{K}$ does give a convenient description of the magnitude of $\underline{\mathbf{J}}^2$.

[26] For example, $s = \frac{1}{2}$ for electrons, protons, neutrons, etc.

§ 21. The Addition Theorem

A fundamental question which occurs in one form or other in virtually all quantal problems is that concerning the addition of commuting angular momentum vectors.[27] If we once obtain the general results for two such vectors, then the addition properties of any number of vectors obviously follow by simple repetition. Let us then consider two commuting vectors $\underline{\mathbf{J}}_1$, $\underline{\mathbf{J}}_2$ and their resultant $\underline{\mathbf{J}} = \underline{\mathbf{J}}_1 + \underline{\mathbf{J}}_2$, and determine the simultaneous eigenvalues of $\underline{\mathbf{J}}^2$ and $\mathbf{J}_z$ which obviously commute. Again introducing such observables $\boldsymbol{\beta}$ as are required to form a complete commuting set, we note that our system may be described in two alternative ways: either by the complete[28] set $\{ \boldsymbol{\beta}, \underline{\mathbf{J}}_1^2, \underline{\mathbf{J}}_2^2, \mathbf{J}_{1z}, \mathbf{J}_{2z} \}$, or $\{ \boldsymbol{\beta}, \underline{\mathbf{J}}_1^2, \underline{\mathbf{J}}_2^2, \underline{\mathbf{J}}^2, \mathbf{J}_z \}$, which we shall refer to as the A and B representations, respectively. In the A representation, the subspace characterized by the magnitude (units of $\hbar$) eigenvalues j_1, j_2 is $(2j_1 + 1)(2j_2 + 1)$-dimensional according to (3:47), corresponding to the number of independent ways[29] of choosing m_{j_1} and m_{j_2}. Furthermore, it is evident that the eigenvalues of $\mathbf{J}_z = \mathbf{J}_{1z} + \mathbf{J}_{2z}$ are common to both representations A and B, i.e. the basic vectors of both are eigenstates[30] of $\mathbf{J}_z$. With this observation, the determination of the eigenvalues of $\mathbf{J}_z$ is trivial, and the corresponding eigenvalues of $\underline{\mathbf{J}}^2$ are obtained by simple enumeration. Thus from A, the $2(j_1 + j_2) + 1$ distinct eigenvalues of $\mathbf{J}_z$ and their multiplicities[31] (assuming $j_2 \leqslant j_1$ for definiteness) are

$$\begin{array}{lccccccccc} m_j: & j_1+j_2, & j_1+j_2-1, & \ldots & j_1-j_2, & j_1-j_2-1, & \ldots & j_2-j_1, & j_2-j_1-1, & \ldots & -j_2-j_1, \\ \text{multiplicity:} & 1, & 2 & ,\ldots & 2j_2+1, & 2j_2+1 & ,\ldots & 2j_2+1, & 2j_2 & ,\ldots & 1 \end{array} \qquad (3:51)$$

In the B representation we have [cf. (3:47)] $m_j = (j, j-1, \ldots -j)$, where $j_{\max} = j_1 + j_2$ from the above, and one may readily verify that the eigenvalue range $j = (j_1 + j_2, j_1 + j_2 - 1, \ldots j_1 - j_2)$ with $j_{\min} = j_1 - j_2$ ($|j_1 - j_2|$ in general) gives the same distribution and multiplicity of $\mathbf{J}_z$ eigenvalues as above.[32]

The preceding work may again be schematically presented, but we must obviously take some specific condition such as $j_1 \geqslant j_2$ (both integral), since the eigenvalue pair (j_1, j_2) may be any combination of integers or half-odd integers so that the

[27] Two vectors are said to *commute* when the nine distinct commutators formed by taking their components in pairs all vanish. From our previous discussions this is evidently the case for angular momenta of distinct particles or independent vectors, such as spin and orbital momentum corresponding to a single particle.

[28] We shall denote the corresponding eigenvectors by $|\,\beta j_1 j_2 m_{j_1} m_{j_2}\rangle$ and $|\,\beta j_1 j_2 j m_j\rangle$, which are here more convenient than $|\,\beta \underline{J}_1^{2\prime} \underline{J}_2^{2\prime} J_{1z}{}' J_{2z}{}'\rangle$ and $|\,\beta \underline{J}_1^{2\prime} \underline{J}_2^{2\prime} \underline{J}^{2\prime} J_z{}'\rangle$.

[29] Equivalently, the number of independent eigenvectors $|\,\beta j_1 j_2 m_{j_1} m_{j_2}\rangle$ spanning this subspace.

[30] The operators $\mathbf{U}_1 = e^{-(i/\hbar)\mathbf{J}_{1z}\varphi}$, $\mathbf{U}_2 = e^{-(i/\hbar)\mathbf{J}_{2z}\varphi}$ generate the coordinate rotation ϕ for each of two particles or systems. Clearly, $\mathbf{U} = \mathbf{U}_1\mathbf{U}_2 = e^{-(i/\hbar)\mathbf{J}_z\varphi}$ generates the rotation of the combined system, from which it follows that $\underline{\mathbf{J}} \times \underline{\mathbf{J}} = i\hbar\underline{\mathbf{J}}$, etc.

[31] Multiplicity = number of repetitions. There are $(2j_1 + 1)(2j_2 + 1)$ possible $\mathbf{J}_z$ eigenvalues, but only $2(j_1 + j_2) + 1$ of them are distinct.

[32] It is evident that the number of *distinct* m_j values is $2(j_1 + j_2) + 1$, and with the stated j range, $\sum_{=j_1-j_2}^{j_1+j_2} (2j + 1) = (2j_1 + 1)(2j_2 + 1)$. Hence, the total number of values and the individual multiplicities are the same as before.

general case without restriction is not presentable in a single diagram. However, our chosen condition evidently involves no loss of generality.

In fig. 3.2 we have taken as ordinates and abscissa the eigenvalues of $\mathbf{J}_{1z}$ and $\mathbf{J}_{2z}$, respectively, corresponding to the $(2j_1 + 1)(2j_2 + 1)$-dimensional subspace belonging to the eigenvalue pair (j_1, j_2), and the entries at the intersections are the resultant J_z' $(= m_j\hbar)$ values. The various equal m_j's fall on the level lines which

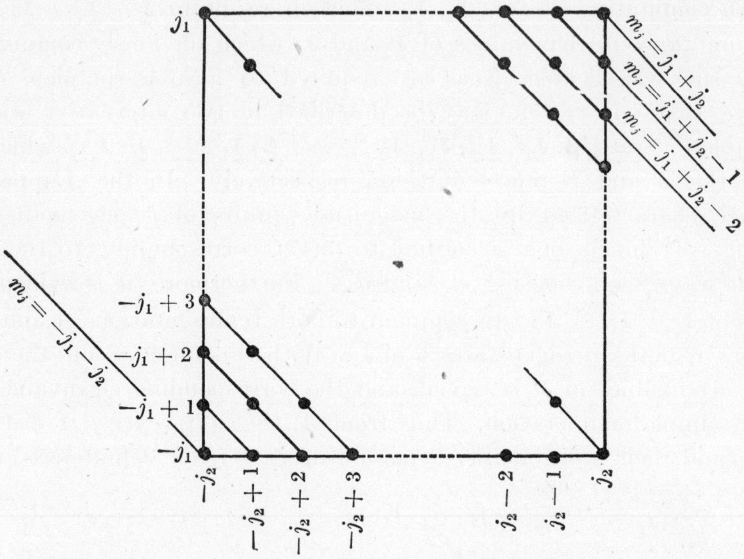

Fig. 3.2.—Resultant $\mathbf{J}_z$ eigenvalues and multiplicities. *A* representation

run from left to right at $-45°$ as indicated; the multiplicity of a given m_j being equal to the number of entries (points) along that given level line. From the diagram we may infer that the $2j_2$ values

$$m_j = (j_1 + j_2, j_1 + j_2 - 1, \ldots j_1 - j_2 + 1)$$

have multiplicities 1, 2, . . . $2j_2$, respectively, and that the same applies to the symmetrically located set of $2j_2$ values

$$m_j = (-j_1 - j_2, -j_1 - j_2 + 1, \ldots j_2 - j_1 - 1).$$

Between them lies a set of $2(j_1 - j_2) + 1$ values

$$m_j = (j_1 - j_2, j_1 - j_2 - 1, \ldots j_2 - j_1 + 1, j_2 - j_1),$$

each of multiplicity $2j_2 + 1$. This breakdown of eigenvalues and multiplicities is seen to be correct since we have found

$$4j_2 + 2(j_1 - j_2) + 1 = 2(j_1 + j_2) + 1$$

distinct eigenvalues whose multiplicities add up to

$$2\sum_{1}^{2j_2} 1 + (2j_2 + 1)[2(j_1 - j_2) + 1] = (2j_1 + 1)(2j_2 + 1).$$

Fig. 3.3 is the corresponding ladder diagram appropriate to the B representation, but it differs from fig. 3.1 in that we have plotted the resultant K' $(= j\hbar)$ values as abscissa *decreasing* from left to right as indicated. This reversal is necessary if we do not wish to assign particular numerical values to j_1, j_2, which would otherwise be required, since it is obvious that the diagram must now form a trapezoid (unless $j_1 = j_2$) whose shorter side is labelled by $j = |j_1 - j_2|$. The correlation between the two diagrams is of course very simple, namely, that all entries or points in a given horizontal row in fig. 3.3 are obtained from a particular level line, or as we may say, diagonal row in fig. 3.2. These diagrams are important *per se*, but would be of limited interest for our purposes were it not for the generalization of

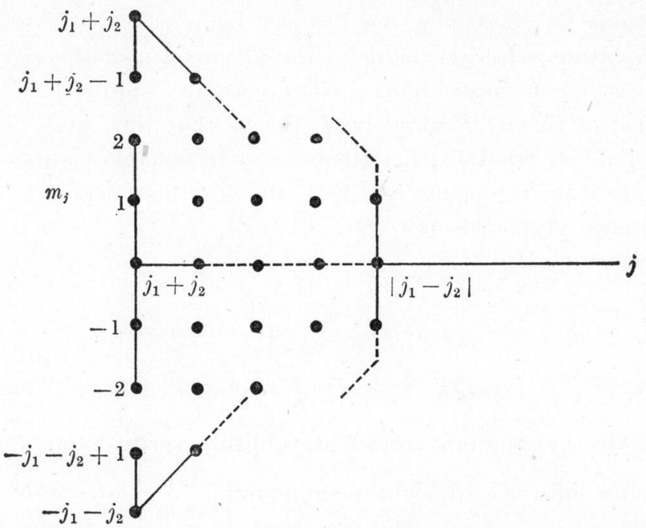

Fig. 3.3.—Ladder diagram for vector addition, (j_1, j_2) subspace, (j_1, j_2) integral and $j_1 \geqslant j_2$. B representation

the communication process which is suggested by them. In the process of vertical communication, the shift operators $\mathbf{J}^{\pm}$ commute with $\underline{\mathbf{J}}^2$ so that on commutation with $\mathbf{J}_z$ they can only result in a shift up or down on a particular j ladder; they do not lead to transitions from one ladder to another, nor is there any other shift operator in the case of a single vector $\underline{\mathbf{J}}$ which can effect such a transition. However, when we add two or more angular momentum vectors and consider the ladder diagrams (e.g. fig. 3.3) of the resultant, we find that such transition processes can exist. In the general case, as we shall now show, there are also *diagonal* and *horizontal* communications such that starting from any point in the diagram (fig. 3.3) a suitable shift operator moves us to any one of eight neighbouring points,[33] i.e. in eight *signed* directions, unless the move takes us outside the diagram, in which case we obtain a zero resultant. Considering just the two vectors $\underline{\mathbf{J}}_1$, $\underline{\mathbf{J}}_2$ and their resultant $\underline{\mathbf{J}}$ as before, the necessary conditions on the six new shift operators (omitting $\mathbf{J}^{\pm} = \mathbf{J}_1{}^{\pm} + \mathbf{J}_2{}^{\pm}$) are quite evident. The two operators establishing a horizontal communication (i.e. between adjacent ladders $j \to j \pm 1$ and $m_j \to m_j$) must commute

[33] The vertical process accounts for two adjacent points.

with $\mathbf{J}_z = \mathbf{J}_{1z} + \mathbf{J}_{2z}$, but reproduce themselves up to a factor $\left\{\begin{matrix} 2(j+1)\hbar^2 \\ -2j\hbar^2 \end{matrix}\right\}$ on commutation [34] with $\underline{\mathbf{J}}^2$. Similarly, the four operators establishing a diagonal communication (i.e. between adjacent ladders $j \to j \pm 1$ and $m_j \to m_j \pm 1$ in all combinations) must reproduce themselves up to a factor $\pm\hbar$ on commutation with $\underline{\mathbf{J}}_z$, in addition to the above relation with $\underline{\mathbf{J}}^2$. From the form of the required shift in the eigenvalues of $\underline{\mathbf{J}}^2$, it follows that these new shift operators on commutation with $\underline{\mathbf{J}}^2$ cannot simply reproduce themselves up to a constant multiplier in the literal sense, but rather to a function of $\underline{\mathbf{J}}^2$. The functions must obviously involve the magnitude variable $\mathbf{K}$, specifically in the forms $2\hbar(\mathbf{K} + \hbar)$ and $-2\hbar\mathbf{K}$, which, however, are equivalent to constant multipliers according to a previous result. The determination of the proper expressions for these new operators is by no means obvious, but we have *a priori* an important criterion, namely, the given form of the eigenvalue shift for both $\underline{\mathbf{J}}^2$ and $\mathbf{J}_z$, which suggests the correct direction of approach. In particular, the postulated effect of these operators on $\mathbf{J}_z$ means that they must somehow be very similar to the familiar triad $\mathbf{J}^{\pm}$, $\mathbf{J}_z$. Hence, it is reasonable to first try to construct independent operators analogous to these, and for this purpose it is convenient to list here the known properties of $\mathbf{J}^{\pm}$, $\mathbf{J}_z$.

$$[\mathbf{J}_z, \mathbf{J}^+]_- = \hbar\mathbf{J}^+. \qquad (3{:}52a)$$

$$[\mathbf{J}_z, \mathbf{J}^-]_- = -\hbar\mathbf{J}^-. \qquad (3{:}52b)$$

$$[\underline{\mathbf{J}}^2, \mathbf{J}^{\pm}]_- = [\underline{\mathbf{J}}^2, \mathbf{J}_z]_- = 0. \qquad (3{:}52c)$$

We note again that the operators $\mathbf{J}^{\pm}$ establish a vertical communication sending every eigenvector into its adjacent neighbour $\left\{\begin{matrix}\text{above}\\ \text{below}\end{matrix}\right\}$, respectively, in the same column (cf. fig. 3.3), if one exists. There are only a limited number of simple operators which may be constructed from the component vectors $\underline{\mathbf{J}}_1$, $\underline{\mathbf{J}}_2$ forming $\underline{\mathbf{J}}$, and we consider the vector operator defined by the symbolic vector product $\underline{\mathbf{J}}_1 \times \underline{\mathbf{J}}_2$, i.e.

$$\boldsymbol{\alpha}_x = \mathbf{J}_{1y}\mathbf{J}_{2z} - \mathbf{J}_{1z}\mathbf{J}_{2y}, \text{ etc.} \qquad (3{:}53)$$

By analogy with (3:52) we form the operators

$$\boldsymbol{\alpha}^{\pm} = \boldsymbol{\alpha}_x \pm i\boldsymbol{\alpha}_y, \qquad (3{:}54)$$

and we may readily verify that corresponding to (3:52) these have the commutators:

$$[\mathbf{J}_z, \boldsymbol{\alpha}^+]_- = \hbar\boldsymbol{\alpha}, \qquad (3{:}35a)$$

$$[\mathbf{J}_z, \boldsymbol{\alpha}^-]_- = -\hbar\boldsymbol{\alpha}, \qquad (3{:}55b)$$

$$[\mathbf{J}_z, \boldsymbol{\alpha}_z]_- = 0. \qquad (3{:}55c)$$

Hence, they have the same effect, respectively, on the eigenvalue of $\mathbf{J}_z$ as do $\mathbf{J}^{\pm}$, $\mathbf{J}_z$, but they do not affect $\underline{\mathbf{J}}^2$ in any simple way. However, we may take the two

[34] Since $j \to j + 1$ means $j(j+1)\hbar^2 \to [j(j+1) + 2(j+1)]\hbar^2$ and $j \to j - 1$ means $j(j+1)\hbar^2 \to [j(j+1) - 2j]\hbar^2$. Formally, we may say that the shift operators must reproduce themselves up to a factor $\pm\hbar$ on commutation with $\mathbf{K}$, where $\mathbf{K}(\mathbf{K} + \hbar) = \underline{\mathbf{J}}^2$.

triads and try to construct six new operators that do. For this purpose we require the 15 commutators which can be formed from $\mathbf{J}^\pm$, $\mathbf{J}_z$, $\boldsymbol{\alpha}^\pm$, $\boldsymbol{\alpha}_z$, of which we have already given 5. The remaining ones are:

$$[\mathbf{J}^+, \mathbf{J}^-]_- = 2\hbar \mathbf{J}_z. \quad (3{:}56a)$$

$$[\mathbf{J}^+, \boldsymbol{\alpha}^+]_- = 0. \qquad [\mathbf{J}^-, \boldsymbol{\alpha}^-]_- = 0. \quad (3{:}56b)$$ [35]

$$[\mathbf{J}^+, \boldsymbol{\alpha}^-]_- = 2\hbar \boldsymbol{\alpha}_z. \qquad [\mathbf{J}^-, \boldsymbol{\alpha}^+]_- = -2\hbar \boldsymbol{\alpha}_z. \quad (3{:}56c)$$

$$[\mathbf{J}^+, \boldsymbol{\alpha}_z]_- = -\hbar \boldsymbol{\alpha}^+. \qquad [\mathbf{J}^-, \boldsymbol{\alpha}_z]_- = \hbar \boldsymbol{\alpha}^-. \quad (3{:}56d)$$

$$[\boldsymbol{\alpha}^+, \boldsymbol{\alpha}^-]_- = 2\hbar \mathbf{J}_z\,(\underline{\mathbf{J}}_1\cdot\underline{\mathbf{J}}_2). \quad (3{:}56e)$$

$$[\boldsymbol{\alpha}^+, \boldsymbol{\alpha}_z]_- = -\hbar \mathbf{J}^+\,(\underline{\mathbf{J}}_1\cdot\underline{\mathbf{J}}_2). \quad (3{:}56f)$$

$$[\boldsymbol{\alpha}^-, \boldsymbol{\alpha}_z]_- = \hbar \mathbf{J}^-\,(\underline{\mathbf{J}}_1\cdot\underline{\mathbf{J}}_2). \quad (3{:}56g)$$

These relations are obtained by straightforward, though tedious, calculation, and the work is simplified somewhat (particularly in the last three entries) by use of the relations

$$\left.\begin{aligned}\mathbf{J}^+\mathbf{J}^- + \mathbf{J}_z(\mathbf{J}_z - \hbar) &= \underline{\mathbf{J}}^2,\\ \mathbf{J}^-\mathbf{J}^+ + \mathbf{J}_z(\mathbf{J}_z + \hbar) &= \underline{\mathbf{J}}^2;\end{aligned}\right\} \quad (3{:}57a)$$

$$\mathbf{J}^+\boldsymbol{\alpha}^- + \mathbf{J}^-\boldsymbol{\alpha}^+ + 2\mathbf{J}_z\boldsymbol{\alpha}_z = 0. \quad (3{:}57b)$$

We can now supply the missing commutators of $\boldsymbol{\alpha}^\pm$, $\boldsymbol{\alpha}_z$ with $\underline{\mathbf{J}}^2$ (cf. 3:52*d*), which are found to be

$$[\underline{\mathbf{J}}^2, \boldsymbol{\alpha}^+]_- = 2\hbar(\boldsymbol{\alpha}^+\mathbf{J}_z - \mathbf{J}^+\boldsymbol{\alpha}_z), \quad (3{:}58a)$$

$$[\underline{\mathbf{J}}^2, \boldsymbol{\alpha}^-]_- = -2\hbar(\boldsymbol{\alpha}^-\mathbf{J}_z - \mathbf{J}^-\boldsymbol{\alpha}_z), \quad (3{:}58b)$$

$$[\underline{\mathbf{J}}^2, \boldsymbol{\alpha}_z]_- = \hbar(\mathbf{J}^+\boldsymbol{\alpha}^- - \boldsymbol{\alpha}^+\mathbf{J}^-), \quad (3{:}58c)$$

showing explicitly that the $\boldsymbol{\alpha}$ triad does not reproduce itself with respect to $\underline{\mathbf{J}}^2$ as required of shift operators. However, we do obtain essentially the desired result if we again commute the resultants on the right above [36] with $\underline{\mathbf{J}}^2$, viz.

$$[\underline{\mathbf{J}}^2, \boldsymbol{\alpha}^+\mathbf{J}_z - \mathbf{J}^+\boldsymbol{\alpha}_z]_- = 2\hbar\{\boldsymbol{\alpha}^+(\mathbf{J}^2 + \mathbf{J}_z\hbar) - \hbar\mathbf{J}^+\boldsymbol{\alpha}_z\}, \quad (3{:}59a)$$

$$[\underline{\mathbf{J}}^2, \boldsymbol{\alpha}^-\mathbf{J}_z - \mathbf{J}^-\boldsymbol{\alpha}_z]_- = 2\hbar\{\boldsymbol{\alpha}^-(-\underline{\mathbf{J}}^2 + \mathbf{J}_z\hbar) - \hbar\mathbf{J}^-\boldsymbol{\alpha}_z\}, \quad (3{:}59b)$$

$$[\underline{\mathbf{J}}^2, \mathbf{J}^+\boldsymbol{\alpha}^- - \boldsymbol{\alpha}^+\mathbf{J}^-]_- = 2\hbar\{2\boldsymbol{\alpha}_z\mathbf{J}^2 + \hbar(\mathbf{J}^+\boldsymbol{\alpha}^- - \boldsymbol{\alpha}^+\mathbf{J}^-)\}. \quad (3{:}59c)$$

These again are obviously not shift operators (with respect to $\underline{\mathbf{J}}^2$), but the importance of the result is that in each case we obtain a linear combination of the operator quantities which were commuted with $\underline{\mathbf{J}}^2$, e.g. $\boldsymbol{\alpha}^+(\underline{\mathbf{J}}^2 + \mathbf{J}_z\hbar) - \hbar\mathbf{J}^+\boldsymbol{\alpha}_z$ in (3:59*a*).[37] It follows that, by taking a suitable linear combination of *corresponding* commutators

[35] The double entries under (*b*), (*c*), and (*d*) indicate that only one of each pair is independent, which follows from the observation that $\mathbf{J}^- = (\mathbf{J}^+)^*$, $\boldsymbol{\alpha}^- = (\boldsymbol{\alpha}^+)^*$ and $\boldsymbol{\alpha}_z = \boldsymbol{\alpha}_z^*$.

[36] This device is also employed in the derivation of the well-known "radiation" selection rules. Cf. Dirac, *Q.M.*, Chap. VII.

[37] As previously discussed, any function of $\underline{\mathbf{J}}^2$ and $\mathbf{J}_z$ appearing in such equations is equivalent to a constant multiplier.

in (3:58) and (3:59) (i.e. of the operators appearing therein), we can form operators which *are* reproduced on commutation with $\underline{\mathbf{J}}^2$. Knowing the required shift in $\mathbf{J}^2$ eigenvalues, it is readily seen that there are two such operators which can be formed in each set, i.e. from (3:58*a*), (3:59*a*) . . . (3:58*c*), (3:59*c*). These operators and their commutators with $\underline{\mathbf{J}}^2$ are:

$$\left.\begin{aligned} \overset{\nwarrow}{\bigcirc} &= \boldsymbol{\alpha}^+(\mathbf{J}_z + \mathbf{K}) - \mathbf{J}^+\boldsymbol{\alpha}_z. & [\mathbf{J}^2, \overset{\nwarrow}{\bigcirc}]_- &= 2\hbar\overset{\nwarrow}{\bigcirc}(\mathbf{K} + \hbar). \\ \overset{\nearrow}{\bigcirc} &= \boldsymbol{\alpha}^+(\mathbf{J}_z - \mathbf{K} - \hbar) - \mathbf{J}^+\boldsymbol{\alpha}_z. & [\mathbf{J}^2, \overset{\nearrow}{\bigcirc}]_- &= -2\hbar\overset{\nearrow}{\bigcirc}\mathbf{K}. \end{aligned}\right\} \quad (3{:}60a)$$

$$\left.\begin{aligned} \underset{\swarrow}{\bigcirc} &= \boldsymbol{\alpha}^-(\mathbf{J}_z - \mathbf{K}) - \mathbf{J}^-\boldsymbol{\alpha}_z. & [\mathbf{J}^2, \underset{\swarrow}{\bigcirc}]_- &= 2\hbar\underset{\swarrow}{\bigcirc}(\mathbf{K} + \hbar). \\ \underset{\searrow}{\bigcirc} &= \boldsymbol{\alpha}^-(\mathbf{J}_z + \mathbf{K} + \hbar) - \mathbf{J}^-\boldsymbol{\alpha}_z. & [\mathbf{J}^2, \underset{\searrow}{\bigcirc}]_- &= -2\hbar\underset{\searrow}{\bigcirc}\mathbf{K}. \end{aligned}\right\} \quad (3{:}60b)$$

$$\left.\begin{aligned} \overset{\leftarrow}{\ominus} &= \mathbf{J}^+\boldsymbol{\alpha}^- - \boldsymbol{\alpha}^+\mathbf{J}^- + 2\boldsymbol{\alpha}_z\mathbf{K}. & [\mathbf{J}^2, \overset{\leftarrow}{\ominus}]_- &= 2\hbar\overset{\leftarrow}{\ominus}(\mathbf{K} + \hbar). \\ \overset{\rightarrow}{\ominus} &= \mathbf{J}^+\boldsymbol{\alpha}^- - \boldsymbol{\alpha}^+\mathbf{J}^- - 2\boldsymbol{\alpha}_z(\mathbf{K} + \hbar). & [\mathbf{J}^2, \overset{\rightarrow}{\ominus}]_- &= -2\hbar\overset{\rightarrow}{\ominus}\mathbf{K}. \end{aligned}\right\} \quad (3{:}60c)$$

Their respective commutators with $\mathbf{J}_z$ can be obtained from (3:52) and (3:55) by inspection, and we have:

$$\left.\begin{aligned} [\mathbf{J}_z, \overset{\nwarrow}{\bigcirc}]_- &= \hbar\overset{\nwarrow}{\bigcirc}. \\ [\mathbf{J}_z, \overset{\nearrow}{\bigcirc}]_- &= \hbar\overset{\nearrow}{\bigcirc}. \end{aligned}\right\} \quad . \; . \; . \; . \; . \; . \; . \; . \; . \; . \quad (3{:}61a)$$

$$\left.\begin{aligned} [\mathbf{J}_z, \underset{\swarrow}{\bigcirc}]_- &= -\hbar\underset{\swarrow}{\bigcirc}. \\ [\mathbf{J}_z, \underset{\searrow}{\bigcirc}]_- &= -\hbar\underset{\searrow}{\bigcirc}. \end{aligned}\right\} \quad . \; . \; . \; . \; . \; . \; . \; . \; . \quad (3{:}61b)$$

$$\left.\begin{aligned} [\mathbf{J}_z, \overset{\leftarrow}{\ominus}]_- &= 0. \\ [\mathbf{J}_z, \overset{\rightarrow}{\ominus}]_- &= 0. \end{aligned}\right\} \quad . \; . \; . \; . \; . \; . \; . \; . \; . \; . \quad (3{:}61c)$$

According to (3:60*a*) the operator $\overset{\nwarrow}{\bigcirc}$ increases the eigenvalue of $\underline{\mathbf{J}}^2$ by $2\hbar(\mathbf{K} + \hbar)$, whereas $\overset{\nearrow}{\bigcirc}$ decreases it by $2\hbar\mathbf{K}$; or equivalently, the eigenvector represented by a point in our diagram is shifted into the adjacent column at the left and right, respectively, and according to (3:61*a*) both operators lead to the next higher row.[38] Hence, $\overset{\nwarrow}{\bigcirc}$ and $\overset{\nearrow}{\bigcirc}$ do establish "diagonal" communication to the left and right upward as suggested by the arrow notation. By the same reasoning we see that $\underset{\swarrow}{\bigcirc}$ and $\underset{\searrow}{\bigcirc}$ are diagonal shift operators to the left and right downward, respectively; while $\overset{\leftarrow}{\ominus}$ and $\overset{\rightarrow}{\ominus}$ are left and right horizontal shift operators, since by (3:61*c*) they leave the eigenvalues of $\mathbf{J}_z$ unaffected. Thus, if we consider any point (eigenvector) in fig. 3.3, we have the following diagram (fig. 3.4) of the shifts, assuming that the neighbouring points (eigenvectors) exist.[39]

It is now evident that the whole family of vectors can be generated by repeated operation of the shift operators on any one of them, and in a great variety of ways. Moreover, it follows that all operations or sets of operations connecting the same two points in the diagram above must differ one from the other by, at most, a function [40] of $\underline{\mathbf{J}}^2$, $\mathbf{J}_z$. Examples of the simpler of these interrelations are the commutators:

[38] E.g., $\overset{\nwarrow}{\bigcirc}\,|\,j, m_j\,\rangle \rightarrow |\,j + 1, m_j + 1\,\rangle$, $\overset{\nearrow}{\bigcirc}\,|\,j, m_j\,\rangle \rightarrow |\,j - 1, m_j + 1\,\rangle$, where we have suppressed all indices in the eigenvectors $|\,j, m_j\,\rangle$ other than j, m_j (i.e. of $\mathbf{K}$, $\mathbf{J}_z$, respectively).

[39] The eigenvector is annihilated by the shift operator in the contrary case.

[40] In the general quantal sense of function.

$$[\overrightarrow{\ominus}, \mathbf{J}^{+}]_{-} = 2\hbar\,\overset{\nearrow}{\oslash}. \qquad [\overrightarrow{\ominus}, \mathbf{J}^{-}]_{-} = 2\hbar\,\underset{\searrow}{\oslash}. \quad \ldots \quad (3{:}62a)$$

$$[\overleftarrow{\ominus}, \mathbf{J}^{+}]_{-} = 2\hbar\,\overset{\nwarrow}{\oslash}. \qquad [\overleftarrow{\ominus}, \mathbf{J}^{-}]_{-} = 2\hbar\,\underset{\swarrow}{\oslash}. \quad \ldots \quad (3{:}62b)$$

$$[\overset{\nwarrow}{\oslash}, \mathbf{J}^{+}]_{-} = 0. \qquad [\overset{\nwarrow}{\oslash}, \mathbf{J}^{-}]_{-} = \hbar\overleftarrow{\ominus}. \quad \ldots \quad (3{:}62c)$$

$$[\overset{\nearrow}{\oslash}, \mathbf{J}^{+}]_{-} = 0. \qquad [\overset{\nearrow}{\oslash}, \mathbf{J}^{-}]_{-} = \hbar\overrightarrow{\ominus}. \quad \ldots \quad (3{:}62d)$$

$$[\underset{\swarrow}{\oslash}, \mathbf{J}^{+}]_{-} = \hbar\overleftarrow{\ominus}. \qquad [\underset{\swarrow}{\oslash}, \mathbf{J}^{-}]_{-} = 0. \quad \ldots \quad (3{:}62e)$$

$$[\underset{\searrow}{\oslash}, \mathbf{J}^{+}]_{-} = \hbar\overrightarrow{\ominus}. \qquad [\underset{\searrow}{\oslash}, \mathbf{J}^{-}]_{-} = 0. \quad \ldots \quad (3{:}62f)$$

The interpretation of these relations is quite clear from the diagram (fig. 3.4), e.g. the commutator $[\overset{\nwarrow}{\oslash}, \mathbf{J}^{+}]_{-}$ must be equal to zero since there exists no *primitive* shift

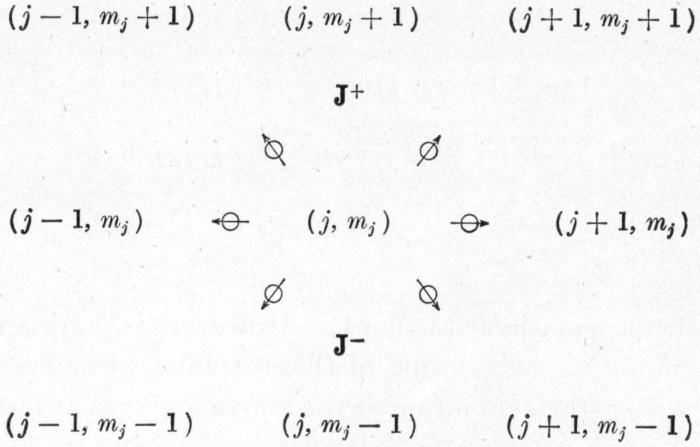

Fig. 3.4—Communication diagram

operator which connects the same two points $(j, m_j;\ j+1, m_j+2)$. Of more value in computation are the products of shift operators, such as

$$\mathbf{J}^{+}\overrightarrow{\ominus} = 2\overset{\nearrow}{\oslash}(\mathbf{K} + \mathbf{J}_z), \quad \ldots \quad (3{:}63a)$$

$$\mathbf{J}^{+}\overleftarrow{\ominus} = -2\overset{\nwarrow}{\oslash}(\mathbf{K} - \mathbf{J}_z + \hbar), \quad \ldots \quad (3{:}63b)$$

$$2\mathbf{J}^{-}\overset{\nwarrow}{\oslash} = -\overleftarrow{\ominus}(\mathbf{K} + \mathbf{J}_z + 2\hbar), \quad \ldots \quad (3{:}63c)$$

which are readily obtained with the help of the commutators of $\mathbf{K}$ with the shift operators, e.g. $[\mathbf{K}, \overrightarrow{\ominus}]_{-} = -\hbar\overrightarrow{\ominus}$. The products of the type $\overrightarrow{\ominus}\underset{\swarrow}{\oslash}$ are extremely difficult to handle by purely symbolic methods, and hence we defer consideration of them for the moment.

§ 22. Normalization of Shift Operators

The application of the shift operators to a normalized eigenvector $|jm\rangle$ does not directly give normalized resultants, so that we must now evaluate the normalization factors involved. The operators $\mathbf{J}^{\pm}$ are particularly simple, and here the well-known result is

$$\mathbf{J}^{+}|j\ m\rangle = A(j,m)\,|j\ m+1\rangle = \hbar[(j-m)(j+m+1)]^{\frac{1}{2}}\,|j\ m+1\rangle, \quad (3{:}64a)\text{[41]}$$

$$\mathbf{J}^{-}|j\ m\rangle = B(j,m)\,|j\ m-1\rangle = \hbar[(j+m)(j-m+1)]^{\frac{1}{2}}\,|j\ m-1\rangle. \quad (3{:}64b)$$

[41] These follow immediately from (3:57*a*, *b*) and the fact that $(\mathbf{J}^{\pm}|\,\rangle)^{*} = \langle\,|\mathbf{J}^{\mp}$.

However, this is a special case, and the factors for the other shift operators cannot be easily evaluated by symbolical calculation entirely within the $\underline{\mathbf{J}}_1^2$, $\underline{\mathbf{J}}_2^2$, $\underline{\mathbf{J}}^2$, $\mathbf{J}_z$-diagonal representation. Of course, the commutation rules (3:62) permit us to set up difference equations in the normalization factors of the six shift operators; but since these equations involve only $A(j, m)$, $B(j, m)$, they give only that part of the factors which depends only on j, m, whereas it is clear that there must also be multipliers in $(j - j_1 - j_2)$, $(j - j_1 + j_2)\,(j + j_1 - j_2)$, etc., since our operators cannot lead outside the diagram. The simplest procedure is to evaluate the necessary matrix elements in the defining equations

$$\langle j-1\ m \mid \ominus\!\!\rightarrow \mid j\ m \rangle = D\,(j_1 j_2 j\ m), \quad . \quad . \quad . \quad (3{:}65a)$$

$$\langle j+1\ m+1 \mid \obslash \mid j\ m \rangle = E\,(j_1 j_2 j\ m), \quad . \quad . \quad . \quad (3{:}65b)$$

$$\langle j+1\ m \mid \leftarrow\!\!\ominus \mid j\ m \rangle = F\,(j_1 j_2 j\ m), \quad . \quad . \quad . \quad (3{:}65c)$$

$$\langle j+1\ m-1 \mid \oslash \mid j\ m \rangle = G\,(j_1 j_2 j\ m), \quad . \quad . \quad . \quad (3{:}65d)$$

etc., which follow from equations (3:60–61). However, it is also clear from (3:62–63) that the determination of any one of these suffices to determine all,[42] at least in principle. In any case, the evaluation of the above involves at most the determination of the corresponding matrix elements of $\boldsymbol{\alpha}_z$, $\boldsymbol{\alpha}^+$, which are conveniently taken in the form

$$\boldsymbol{\alpha}_z = i\,(\mathbf{J}_1^+\mathbf{J}_2^- - \underline{\mathbf{J}}_1\cdot\underline{\mathbf{J}}_2 + \mathbf{J}_{1z}\mathbf{J}_{2z}), \quad . \quad . \quad . \quad . \quad (3{:}66a)$$

$$\boldsymbol{\alpha}^+ = i\,(\mathbf{J}_2^+\mathbf{J}_{1z} - \mathbf{J}_1^+\mathbf{J}_{2z}). \quad . \quad . \quad . \quad . \quad . \quad . \quad . \quad . \quad (3{:}66b)$$

The calculation of the elements follows simply from the relations:

$$\mathbf{J}_{1z}\mid j\ m\rangle = m\,(j\,\vdots\,J_1\,\vdots\,j)\mid j\ m\rangle + [\,(j-m)\,(j+m)\,]^{\frac{1}{2}}\,(j-1\,\vdots\,J_1\,\vdots\,j)\mid j-1\ m\rangle$$
$$+\,[\,(j-m+1)\,(j+m+1)\,]^{\frac{1}{2}}\,(j+1\,\vdots\,J_1\,\vdots\,j)\mid j+1\ m\rangle. \quad (3{:}67a)$$

$$\mathbf{J}_1^+\mid j\ m\rangle = -\,[\,(j+m+1)\,(j+m+2)\,]^{\frac{1}{2}}\,(j+1\,\vdots\,J_1\,\vdots\,j)\mid j+1\ m+1\rangle$$
$$+\,[\,(j-m)\,(j+m+1)\,]^{\frac{1}{2}}\,(j\,\vdots\,J_1\,\vdots\,j)\mid j\ m+1\rangle$$
$$+\,[\,(j-m)\,(j-m-1)\,]^{\frac{1}{2}}\,(j-1\,\vdots\,J_1\,\vdots\,j)\mid j-1\ m+1\rangle. \quad (3{:}67b)$$

$$\mathbf{J}_1^-\mid j\ m\rangle = [\,(j-m+1)\,(j-m+2)\,]^{\frac{1}{2}}\,(j+1\,\vdots\,J_1\,\vdots\,j)\mid j+1\ m-1\rangle$$
$$+\,[\,(j+m)\,(j-m+1)\,]^{\frac{1}{2}}\,(j\,\vdots\,J_1\,\vdots\,j)\mid j\ m-1\rangle$$
$$-\,[\,(j+m)\,(j+m-1)\,]^{\frac{1}{2}}\,(j-1\,\vdots\,J_1\,\vdots\,j)\mid j-1\ m-1\rangle. \quad (3{:}67c)$$

[42] Actually, the determination of one only determines the normalization factors of the other shift operators on the same side of the vertical [i.e. which operate in the same half-plane relative to the vertical, cf. (3:62–63)], unless we also evaluated at least one product of the general type $\ominus\!\!\rightarrow\ \oslash$.

$$(j:J_1:j)=(j_1j_2j:J_1:j_1j_2j)=\frac{j_1(j_1+1)-j_2(j_2+1)+j(j+1)}{2j\,(j+1)}\hbar. \quad (3{:}67d)$$ [43]

$$(j:J_1:j-1)=(j-1:J_1:j)=-(j:J_2:j-1)$$
$$=\hbar\left[\frac{(j-j_1+j_2)(j+j_1-j_2)(j_1+j_2+1+j)(j_1+j_2+1-j)}{4j^2\,(2j-1)\,(2j+1)}\right]^{\frac{1}{2}}. \quad (3{:}67e)$$ [44]

Then from (3:65–67) we find that

$$D=-\frac{\hbar^3}{2}\Big[\frac{(2j+1)}{(2j-1)}\,(j+m)\,(j-m)\,(j-j_1+j_2)\,(j+j_1-j_2)\,(j_1+j_2+1+j)\,(j-j_1-j_2-1)\Big]^{\frac{1}{2}}, \quad (3{:}68a)$$

$$E=\frac{\hbar^3}{2}\Big[\frac{(2j+1)}{(2j+3)}(j+m+1)\,(j+m+2)\,(j-j_1+j_2+1)\,(j+j_1-j_2+1)\,(j_1+j_2+2+j)\,(j-j_1-j_2)\Big]^{\frac{1}{2}}, \quad (3{:}68b)$$

$$F=-2\,\left[\frac{(j-m+1)}{(j+m+2)}\right]^{\frac{1}{2}}E, \quad (3{:}68c)$$

$$G=\left[\frac{(j-m+1)\,(j-m+2)}{(j+m+1)\,(j+m+2)}\right]^{\frac{1}{2}}E, \quad (3{:}68d)$$

and similarly for the other shift operators. We note that, as previously remarked, only one of the last three is required to determine the other two, e.g. (3:68*c*) follows from (3:68*a*) and (3:63*b*). We can now derive more general operator products than given in (3:63). Thus, with (3:68*a*, *d*), we find

$$\ominus\,\varnothing=\mathbf{J}^-(\mathbf{K}-\mathbf{J}_z+2\hbar)\,\{\,\underline{\mathbf{J}}_1{}^2\,\underline{\mathbf{J}}_2{}^2-(\underline{\mathbf{J}}_1\cdot\underline{\mathbf{J}}_2)^2-(\underline{\mathbf{J}}_1\cdot\underline{\mathbf{J}}_2)\,(\mathbf{K}+\hbar)\,\hbar\,\}, \quad (3{:}68')$$

which is most difficult to obtain directly in symbolic form. Nonetheless, an important corollary of (3:68′) is that if we evaluate the products of this type symbolically, then, in conjunction with the relations of the type (3:62–63), we can set up difference equations from which the normalization factors may be inferred (up to a phase of unit modulus) without appeal to the foregoing matrix calculations.

§ 23. Transformation Amplitudes

The transformation amplitudes $\langle j_1j_2m_1m_2\,|\,j_1j_2j\ m\rangle$, or simply $\langle m_1m_2\,|\,j\ m\rangle$, between the representations A and B are determined by the above choice of relative phases (preceding footnote), the specification $|\,j_1j_2\ j_1j_2\rangle=|\,j_1j_2\ j_1+j_2\ j_1+j_2\rangle$ for

[43] The indices 1, 2 are interchanged in the corresponding expression for $(j:J_2:j)$.

[44] These equations (3:67) are essentially as given by CONDON-SHORTLEY, *Theory of Atomic Spectra*, to which we refer the reader for the detailed derivation, which is not difficult, but too lengthy to warrant development here since, as will be seen, it is not of primary importance to the final conclusion. We may note that the difference in sign of $(j:J_1:j-1)$, $(j:J_2:j-1)$ above corresponds to a definite choice of relative phase of states of different j. See CONDON-SHORTLEY for an excellent discussion of the whole question of phases.

the B state of highest j, m, and the recursion formulæ obtained by pre-multiplying (3:64a, b, and 3:67a) by $\langle m_1 m_2 |$, namely:

$$\begin{aligned}
&[(j_1+m_1)(j_1-m_1+1)]^{\frac{1}{2}}\langle m_1-1\ m_2 | j\ m\rangle \\
&\qquad + [(j_2+m_2)(j_2-m_2+1)]^{\frac{1}{2}}\langle m_1 m_2-1 | j\ m\rangle \\
&\qquad = [(j-m)(j+m+1)]^{\frac{1}{2}}\langle m_1 m_2 | j\ m+1\rangle. \quad . \quad . \qquad (3{:}69a)
\end{aligned}$$

$$\begin{aligned}
&[(j_1-m_1)(j_1+m_1+1)]^{\frac{1}{2}}\langle m_1+1\ m_2 | j\ m\rangle \\
&\qquad + [(j_2-m_2)(j_2+m_2+1)]^{\frac{1}{2}}\langle m_1 m_2+1 | j\ m\rangle \\
&\qquad = [(j+m)(j-m+1)]^{\frac{1}{2}}\langle m_1 m_2 | j\ m-1\rangle. \quad . \quad . \qquad (3{:}69b)
\end{aligned}$$

$$\begin{aligned}
&[(j-m)(j+m)]^{\frac{1}{2}}(j-1 \vdots J_1 \vdots j)\langle m_1 m_2 | j-1\ m\rangle \\
&\quad = [m_1 - m(j \vdots J_1 \vdots j)]\langle m_1 m_2 | j\ m\rangle \\
&\qquad - [(j-m+1)(j+m+1)]^{\frac{1}{2}}(j+1 \vdots J_1 \vdots j)\langle m_1 m_2 | j\ m-1\rangle. \quad (3{:}70)
\end{aligned}$$

Similarly, from the equations $\overset{\nwarrow}{\oslash}\, | j\ m\rangle = E(j_1 j_2 j\ m)\,| j+1\ m+1\rangle$, etc., we obtain six more recursion formulæ which are useful in practical calculation, since the general solution for $\langle m_1 m_2 | j\ m\rangle$ is so complex as to be almost unmanageable for all but the smallest values. Nonetheless, for completeness and further application, we shall determine [45] this general expression for these coefficients from (3:69a, b) and (3:70) by comparatively simple algebraic manipulation as contrasted with the rather complex (though more unified) group-theoretical derivation originally given by Wigner.[46] The solution is obtained from difference equations by induction as follows:

We avoid the irrational factors in (3:69a, b) and (3:70) by setting

$$\langle m_1 m_2 | j m\rangle = (-)^{j_1-m_1} f(m_1 m_2; j m)\left[\frac{(j_1+m_1)!\,(j_2+m_2)!\,(j+m)!}{(j_1-m_1)!\,(j_2-m_2)!\,(j-m)!}\right]^{\frac{1}{2}}, \qquad (3{:}71)$$

with which our equations become

$$(j-m)(j+m+1)f(m_1 m_2; j\ m+1) = f(m_1 m_2-1; j\ m) - f(m_1-1\ m_2; j\ m), \quad (3{:}69a')$$

$$\begin{aligned}
f(m_1 m_2; j\ m-1) &= (j_2-m_2)(j_2+m_2+1)f(m_1 m_2+1; j\ m) \\
&\quad - (j_1-m_1)(j_1+m_1+1)f(m_1+1\ m_2; j\ m). \quad (3{:}69b')
\end{aligned}$$

If we now set $m = j$ in (3:69a') we find that $f(m_1 m_2; j\ j)$ is independent of m_1 and m_2, so that we may write

$$f(m_1 m_2; j\ j) = A_j, \quad . \quad . \quad . \quad . \quad . \quad . \quad . \qquad (3{:}72a)$$

which, combined with (3:69b') for $m = j$, gives

$$f(m_1 m_2; j\ j-1) = [(j_2-m_2)(j_2+m_2+1) - (j_1-m_1)(j_1+m_1+1)]A_j. \quad (3{:}72b)$$

[45] See* RACAH, G.: *Phys. Rev.*, **62**, 438 (1942).
[46] WIGNER, E.: *Gruppentheorie* (Vieweg, 1931).

Repeating again with $m = j - 1$ in (3:69b'), we get

$$f(m_1m_2\,;j\,j-2) = [(j_2-m_2)(j_2-m_2-1)(j_2+m_2+1)(j_2+m_2+2) \\ -2(j_1-m_1)(j_1+m_1+1)(j_2-m_2)(j_2+m_2+1) \\ +(j_1-m_1)(j_1-m_1-1)(j_1+m_1+1)(j_1+m_1+2)]A_j. \quad (3{:}72c)$$

From these we may infer that the general expression will be [47]

$$f(m_1m_2\,;j\,j-u) \\ = A_j \sum_t (-)^t \binom{u}{t} \frac{(j_2-m_2)!\,(j_2+m_2+u-t)!\,(j_1-m_1)!\,(j_1+m_1+t)!}{(j_2-m_2-u+t)!\,(j_2+m_2)!\,(j_1-m_1-t)!\,(j_1+m_1)!}, \quad (3{:}73)$$

which may be easily verified by showing that it satisfies (3:69b'). Just as we have omitted the indices j_1j_2 in $\langle j_1j_2m_1m_2 \,|\, j_1j_2j\,m \rangle$ because both sets of $|\,\rangle$'s are eigenstates of $\mathbf{J}_1^2$, $\mathbf{J}_2^2$, and the expansion of $|\,j_1j_2j\,m\rangle$ in terms of the former includes only those states of the same j_1, j_2; so it is obvious that the summation over m_1, m_2 in the expression

$$|\,j_1j_2j\,m\rangle = \sum_{m_1m_2} |\,j_1j_2m_1m_2\rangle\langle j_1j_2m_1m_2\,|\,j_1j_2jm\rangle \quad . \quad . \quad (3{:}74)$$

will include only terms for which $m_1 + m_2 = m$, since the basic states $|\,j_1j_2m_1m_2\rangle$ are also eigenstates of $\mathbf{J}_z = \mathbf{J}_{1z} + \mathbf{J}_{2z}$. With this observation we obtain the dependence of $\langle m_1m_2\,|\,j\,m\rangle$ on m_1, m_2 and m by introducing (3:73) into (3:71), i.e.

$$\langle m_1m_2\,|\,j\,m\rangle = \delta(m_1+m_2,m)\,A_j \left[\frac{(j_2-m_2)!\,(j_1-m_1)!\,(j-m)!\,(j+m)!}{(j_1+m_1)!\,(j_2+m_2)!}\right]^{\frac{1}{2}} \\ \sum (-)^{j_1-m_1+t} \frac{(j_1+m_1+t)!\,(j_2+j-m_1-t)!}{t!\,(j-m-t)!\,(j_1-m_1-t)!\,(j_2-j+m_1+t)!}. \quad (3{:}75)$$

The difference equation (3:70) now permits us to determine the dependence of A_j on j. Thus, noting (3:67d, e) and setting $m = j$, so that the left side vanishes, we obtain

$$0 = A_j - 2(j+1)(2j+1)(j+1:J_1:j)\,A_{j+1}, \quad . \quad . \quad (3{:}76a)$$

or

$$A_j = \left[(j_1+j_2+j+2)(j_1+j_2-j)(j+j_1-j_2+1)(j+j_2-j_1+1)\frac{(2j+1)}{(2j+3)}\right]^{\frac{1}{2}} A_{j+1}, \quad (3{:}76b)$$

which is satisfied by

$$A_j = A\left[\frac{(2j+1)\,(j_1+j_2-j)!}{(j_1+j_2+j+1)!\,(j+j_1-j_2)!\,(j+j_2-j_1)!}\right]^{\frac{1}{2}}, \quad . \quad (3{:}77)$$

with A a constant equal to 1 according to (3:75), (3:77), and the initial condition $\langle j_1j_2\,|\,j_1+j_2\;j_1+j_2\rangle = 1$ for the highest B state.

[47] The summation is over all integral values consistent with the factorial notation; the factorial of a negative number being meaningless.

Thus, finally,[48]

$$\langle m_1 m_2 | j\ m \rangle$$
$$= \delta(m_1 + m_2, m) \left[\frac{(2j+1)(j_1+j_2-j)!(j_1-m_1)!(j_2-m_2)!(j-m)!(j+m)!}{(j_1+j_2+j+1)!(j+j_1-j_2)!(j+j_2-j_1)!(j_1+m_1)!(j_2+m_2)!}\right]^{\frac{1}{2}}$$
$$\Sigma\, (-)^{j_1-m_1+t} \frac{(j_1+m_1+t)!\,(j+j_2-m_1-t)!}{t!\,(j-m-t)!\,(j_1-m_1-t)!\,(j_2-j+m_1+t)!}. \quad (3{:}78a)$$

This may be transformed to the more symmetrical and useful form (cf. RACAH, *loc. cit.*)

$$\langle m_1 m_2 | j\ m \rangle$$
$$= \delta(m_1+m_2,m)\,[(2j+1)(j_1+j_2-j)!\,(j+j_1-j_2)!\,(j+j_2-j_1)!/(j_1+j_2+1)!]^{\frac{1}{2}}$$
$$\sum_z (-)^z \frac{[(j_1+m_1)!\,(j_1-m_1)!\,(j_2+m_2)!\,(j_2-m_2)!\,(j+m)!\,(j-m)!]^{\frac{1}{2}}}{z!(j_1+j_2-j-z)!(j_1-m_1-z)!(j_2+m_2-z)!(j-j_2+m_1+z)!(j-j_1-m_2+z)!}$$
$$(3{:}78b)$$

TABLE 3.1.—TRANSFORMATION COEFFICIENTS

$\langle j_1\ \tfrac{1}{2}\ m_1 m_2 | j_1\ \tfrac{1}{2}\ j\ m \rangle$

$j=$	$j_1+\frac{1}{2}$	$j_1-\frac{1}{2}$
$m_2=\frac{1}{2}$	$\left[\frac{j_1+m+\frac{1}{2}}{2j_1+1}\right]^{\frac{1}{2}}$	$-\left[\frac{j_1-m+\frac{1}{2}}{2j_1+1}\right]^{\frac{1}{2}}$
$m_2=-\frac{1}{2}$	$\left[\frac{j_1-m+\frac{1}{2}}{2j_1+1}\right]^{\frac{1}{2}}$	$\left[\frac{j_1+m+\frac{1}{2}}{2j_1+1}\right]^{\frac{1}{2}}$

$\langle j_1\ 1\ m_1 m_2 | j_1\ 1\ j\ m \rangle$

$j=$	j_1+1	j_1	j_1-1
$m_2=1$	$\left[\frac{(j_1+m)(j_1+m+1)}{(2j_1+1)(2j_1+2)}\right]^{\frac{1}{2}}$	$-\left[\frac{(j_1+m)(j_1-m+1)}{2j_1(j_1+1)}\right]^{\frac{1}{2}}$	$\left[\frac{(j_1-m)(j_1-m+1)}{2j_1(2j_1+1)}\right]^{\frac{1}{2}}$
$m_2=0$	$\left[\frac{(j_1-m+1)(j_1+m+1)}{(2j_1+1)(j_1+1)}\right]^{\frac{1}{2}}$	$\frac{m}{[j_1(j_1+1)]^{\frac{1}{2}}}$	$-\left[\frac{(j_1-m)(j_1+m)}{j_1(2j_1+1)}\right]^{\frac{1}{2}}$
$m_2=-1$	$\left[\frac{(j_1-m)(j_1-m+1)}{(2j_1+1)(2j_1+2)}\right]^{\frac{1}{2}}$	$\left[\frac{(j_1-m)(j_1+m+1)}{2j_1(j_1+1)}\right]^{\frac{1}{2}}$	$\left[\frac{(j_1+m+1)(j_1+m)}{2j_1(2j_1+1)}\right]^{\frac{1}{2}}$

[48] This equation is equivalent to, but not identical in form with Wigner's (cf. WIGNER, *loc. cit.*, or *T.A.S.*, p. 75). It may be transformed to the same form, but, as Racah notes, neither form recommends itself particularly to practical computation. Tables are also available in *T.A.S.*

CHAPTER IV

Physical Representation Theory

§ 24. Introduction—The Canonical Representations

The solution of physical problems in the quantal sense consists, in part, of the determination of conditional probabilities; which is to say, that we take a set of commuting observables $\boldsymbol{\alpha}$ to be diagonal ($\boldsymbol{\alpha}$-diagonal representation), and inquire as to the probable values for another commuting set $\boldsymbol{\beta}$, where in most cases the sets denoted by $\boldsymbol{\alpha}$ and $\boldsymbol{\beta}$ are complete. The choice of the sets $\boldsymbol{\alpha}$, $\boldsymbol{\beta}$ depends on the nature of the problem and the particular information desired. When the coordinate observables or linear momenta form the set $\boldsymbol{\alpha}$, we shall describe the representation as one of the *canonical* type.

Let us consider a one-dimensional system described by canonical coordinate and momentum $\mathfrak{q}$, $\mathfrak{p}$, and introduce a representation in which the coordinate is diagonal. This representation will not be uniquely defined unless $\mathfrak{q}$ by itself forms a complete set, which we assume to be the case. We shall find that this assumption leads to a self-consistent determination of the representatives of $\mathfrak{q}$ and $\mathfrak{p}$ satisfying the quantum conditions, and is therefore correct. We know that $\mathfrak{q}$ has a continuous eigenspectrum, and we introduce the linear operator $d/d\mathfrak{q}$ which, operating on any $|\,\rangle$, is equivalent to differentiating its $\mathfrak{q}$-representative $\langle q' \,|\,\rangle$ with respect to q'. Thus, $d/d\mathfrak{q}$ is defined by the *mixed* representative

$$\langle q' \,|\, \frac{d}{d\mathfrak{q}} \,|\,\rangle = \frac{d}{dq'} \langle q' \,|\,\rangle, \qquad (4{:}1a)$$

or equivalently,

$$\langle q' \,|\, \frac{d}{d\mathfrak{q}} = \frac{d}{dq'} \langle q' \,|, \qquad (4{:}1b)$$

which shows the effect of $d/d\mathfrak{q}$ on a *basic* $\langle\,|$. Moreover, we have the companion equations

$$\mathfrak{q} \,|\, q' \rangle = q' \,|\, q' \rangle, \qquad (4{:}2a)$$

$$\langle q' \,|\, q'' \rangle = \delta(q' - q''), \qquad (4{:}2b)$$

with the help of which we determine the effect of $d/d\mathfrak{q}$ on a *basic* $|\,\rangle$, viz.

$$\langle q' \,|\, \frac{d}{d\mathfrak{q}} \,|\, q'' \rangle = \frac{d}{dq'} \langle q' \,|\, q'' \rangle = -\frac{d}{dq''} \langle q' \,|\, q'' \rangle, \qquad (4{:}3a)$$

or equivalently (cf. § 11*b*)

$$\frac{d}{d\mathbf{q}} \mid q'' \rangle = -\frac{d}{dq''} \mid q'' \rangle. \qquad (4:3b)$$ [1]

We can now readily obtain the commutator $\left[\frac{d}{d\mathbf{q}}, \mathbf{q}\right]_-$, e.g.

$$\langle q' \mid \frac{d}{d\mathbf{q}} \mathbf{q} = \frac{d}{dq'} \langle q' \mid \mathbf{q} = \langle q' \mid + q' \frac{d}{dq'} \langle q' \mid, \qquad (4:4a)$$

and

$$\langle q' \mid \mathbf{q} \frac{d}{d\mathbf{q}} = q' \langle q' \mid \frac{d}{d\mathbf{q}} = q' \frac{d}{dq'} \langle q' \mid, \qquad (4:4b)$$

whence

$$\langle q' \mid \left(\frac{d}{d\mathbf{q}} \mathbf{q} - \mathbf{q} \frac{d}{d\mathbf{q}}\right) = \langle q' \mid, \qquad (4:5a)$$

or

$$\frac{d}{d\mathbf{q}} \mathbf{q} - \mathbf{q} \frac{d}{d\mathbf{q}} = \mathbf{I}. \qquad (4:5b)$$

Furthermore, we have

$$\langle q' \mid \frac{d^*}{d\mathbf{q}} \mid q'' \rangle = \langle q'' \mid \frac{d}{d\mathbf{q}} \mid q' \rangle^* = \delta'(q'' - q')$$

$$= -\delta'(q' - q'') = -\langle q' \mid \frac{d}{d\mathbf{q}} \mid q'' \rangle, \qquad (4:6)$$

showing that $d/d\mathbf{q}$ is anti-Hermitian and therefore $\pm i d/d\mathbf{q}$ Hermitian. It follows that $-i\hbar d/d\mathbf{q}$ and $\mathbf{p}$ have the same commutator with $\mathbf{q}$ and, since their difference commutes with $\mathbf{q}$, which we have assumed to form a complete set by itself, it follows that

$$\mathbf{p} + i\hbar \frac{d}{d\mathbf{q}} = \mathbf{f}(\mathbf{q}), \qquad (4:7)$$

where $\mathbf{f}$ must also be Hermitian.[2]

It is desirable to eliminate $\mathbf{f}$ so as to be able to identify linear momentum variables as differential operators (in canonical coordinate representations), and it can readily be shown [3] that this may always be arranged by selecting a $\mathbf{q}$-representation with

[1] Alternatively, from (4:1*a*) we have

$$\langle q' \mid \frac{d}{d\mathbf{q}} \mid \rangle = \int \langle q' \mid \frac{d}{d\mathbf{q}} \mid q'' \rangle \, dq'' \langle q'' \mid \rangle = \frac{d}{dq'} \langle q' \mid \rangle,$$

showing that

$$\langle q' \mid \frac{d}{d\mathbf{q}} \mid q'' \rangle = -\frac{d}{dq''} \delta(q' - q'').$$

[2] Of course the same conclusion follows directly from the basic commutator which in representative form gives

$$(q' - q'') \langle q' \mid \mathbf{p} \mid q'' \rangle = i\hbar \, \delta(q' - q''),$$

from which [cf. (2:19*c*, *d*)]

$$\langle q' \mid \mathbf{p} \mid q'' \rangle = -i\hbar \frac{d}{dq'} \delta(q' - q'') + f(q') \delta(q' - q'').$$

[3] Cf. DIRAC, *Q.M.*

properly chosen phases. The preceding work applies immediately to a complete set $\mathbf{q}_1, \mathbf{q}_2, \ldots \mathbf{q}_n$ of n degrees of freedom [4] if we take the previous $\mathbf{q}$ to be the abbreviated notation for a complete set. For each $\mathbf{q}_r$, we now have a differentiation operator $\partial/\partial\mathbf{q}_r$ given by

$$\langle\, 'q \mid \partial/\partial\mathbf{q}_r \mid\, \rangle = \frac{\partial}{\partial q_r'} \langle\, 'q \mid\, \rangle,$$

$$\langle\, 'q \mid \partial/\partial\mathbf{q}_r \mid ''q\, \rangle = \delta(q_1' - q_1'') \ldots \delta(q_{r-1}' - q_{r-1}'')\, \delta'(q_r' - q_r'')\, \delta(q_{r+1}' - q_{r+1}'') \ldots, \tag{4:8}$$

and with proper choice of phases each $\mathbf{p}_r$ will be given by $-i\hbar\partial/\partial\mathbf{q}_r$. With this identification all the commutators in $\mathbf{q}$, $\mathbf{p}$ are identically satisfied, as is easily seen, and in particular we obtain the important relations [cf. (3:29*c*)]:

$$\mathbf{f}\mathbf{p}_r - \mathbf{p}_r\mathbf{f} = i\hbar \frac{\partial \mathbf{f}}{\partial \mathbf{q}_r} \quad . \quad . \quad . \quad . \quad . \quad . \quad . \quad . \tag{4:9}$$

for any function $\mathbf{f}$ of the $\mathbf{q}$'s, and

$$\langle\, 'q \mid \mathbf{p}_r\boldsymbol{\xi} \mid ''q\, \rangle = -i\hbar \frac{\partial}{\partial q_r'} \langle\, 'q \mid \boldsymbol{\xi} \mid ''q\, \rangle, \quad . \quad . \quad . \tag{4:10a}$$

$$\langle\, 'q \mid \boldsymbol{\xi}\mathbf{p}_r \mid ''q\, \rangle = i\hbar \frac{\partial}{\partial q_r''} \langle\, 'q \mid \boldsymbol{\xi} \mid ''q\, \rangle, \quad . \quad . \quad . \quad . \tag{4:10b}$$

for any linear operator $\boldsymbol{\xi}$.

This type of representation is doubtless the most useful in practice. Thus, if we consider the Hamiltonian operator $\mathbf{H}(\mathbf{q}_1, \mathbf{q}_2, \ldots \mathbf{q}_n, \mathbf{p}_1, \ldots \mathbf{p}_n)$ in the $\mathbf{q}$-diagonal representation, it becomes the symbolic differential operator

$$\mathbf{H}\left(\mathbf{q}, -i\hbar \frac{d}{d\mathbf{q}}\right) \quad . \quad . \quad . \quad . \quad . \quad . \quad . \quad . \tag{4:11}$$

in the abbreviated notation.[5] The eigenvalue-eigenvector equation for $\mathbf{H}$ is

$$\mathbf{H} \mid H'\alpha'\, \rangle = H' \mid H'\alpha'\, \rangle. \quad . \quad . \quad . \quad . \quad . \quad . \tag{4:12}$$ [6]

In the canonical $\mathbf{q}$-representation (4:12) becomes (pre-multiplying by $\langle\, 'q \mid\,)$

$$\langle\, 'q \mid \mathbf{H} \mid H'\alpha'\, \rangle = \int \ldots \int \langle\, 'q \mid \mathbf{H} \mid ''q\, \rangle\, d''q\, \langle\, ''q \mid H'\alpha'\, \rangle = H' \langle\, 'q \mid H'\alpha'\, \rangle, \tag{4:13}$$

which is the equation for the determination of the eigenvalues of $\mathbf{H}$ and the transformation coefficients (probability amplitudes) between the $\mathbf{q}$-diagonal representation and the representation in which $\mathbf{H}$ is one of a complete set of commuting operators $\mathbf{H}, \boldsymbol{\alpha}_1, \boldsymbol{\alpha}_2, \ldots$. Because of the physical importance of $\mathbf{H}$ as the energy

[4] $3n$ degrees if $\mathbf{q}$ denotes the coordinate triple.

[5] When acting as pre-multiplier to a symbolic $|\, \rangle$. In replacing each $\mathbf{p}_r$ by $-i\hbar\partial/\partial\mathbf{q}_r$ we must preserve the order of factors, and this, in general, can only be done correctly in Cartesian coordinates.

[6] We include the symbol α' to indicate that $\mathbf{H}$ is ordinarily not a complete set by itself, so that there usually exists some degeneracy.

in conservative systems, this latter type of representation is generally called the $\mathbf{H}$-diagonal or energy representation. Equation (4:13) is, formally, a linear integral equation and is the most general form of the first Schroedinger wave equation.[7] In more familiar differential operator form, equation (4:13) appears as

$$H(\grave{}q, -i\hbar\partial/\partial\grave{}q)\langle\grave{}q \mid H'\alpha'\rangle = H'\langle\grave{}q \mid H'\alpha'\rangle, \quad . \quad . \quad . \quad (4{:}14)$$

which, however, is entirely equivalent to (4:13) since in this particular case the kernel $\langle\grave{}q \mid \mathbf{H} \mid \grave{}\grave{}q\rangle$ of the integral equation is singular, i.e. expressible in terms of δ functions and their derivatives, and therefore reduces to (4:14).[8]

In considering the canonical representations we could, as noted, just as well have taken $\mathbf{p}$ diagonal, and determined the corresponding symbolic form of $\mathbf{q}$. This procedure is practically identical with the work in the $\mathbf{q}$-representation, with the exception that each $\mathbf{q}_r$ would be represented by the operator $\pm i\hbar\partial/\partial\mathbf{p}_r$ depending on whether $\mathbf{q}_r$ operates to the right on a symbolic $\mid\,\rangle$ or to the left on a $\langle\,\mid$, or conversely with respect to the basic $\mathbf{p}$-eigenvectors. This sign relation is just opposite to that obtained before, and is readily seen to fit the fundamental commutator. Generally speaking, the $\mathbf{p}$-representation is not so useful, because $\mathbf{H}$ is ordinarily expressed as a simple power series in the momentum operators, but not in the coordinate operators. However, there are special problems, in particular the theory of scattering and the closely related $\mathbf{S}$-matrix theory,[9] for which the $\mathbf{p}$-representation is especially suited, and it is important to obtain the transformation coefficients $\langle q' \mid p'\rangle$ connecting the $\mathbf{q}$-diagonal and the $\mathbf{p}$-diagonal representations. If these functions are known, we can immediately transcribe the representatives of operators and vectors given in the $\mathbf{q}$-representation to the $\mathbf{p}$-representation, and conversely, according to the general theory.

The eigenvector equation for $\mathbf{p}$, where we take the one-dimensional problem again for simplicity, is

$$\mathbf{p} \mid p' \mid\rangle = p' \mid p'\rangle, \quad . \quad . \quad . \quad . \quad . \quad . \quad . \quad (4{:}15)$$

and in the $\mathbf{q}$-representation we have

$$\langle q' \mid \mathbf{p} \mid p'\rangle = \int \langle q' \mid \mathbf{p} \mid q''\rangle dq'' \langle q'' \mid p'\rangle = -i\hbar\frac{d}{dq'}\langle q' \mid p'\rangle = p'\langle q' \mid p'\rangle. \quad (4{:}16)$$

The solution of this equation is

$$\langle q' \mid p'\rangle = c(p')\,e^{iq'p'/\hbar}, \quad . \quad . \quad . \quad . \quad . \quad . \quad (4{:}17)$$

[7] The amplitudes $\langle\grave{}q \mid H'\alpha'\rangle$ are more familiarly termed wave- or eigen-functions and commonly denoted by the symbol Ψ, which, of course, must not be confused with the symbolic eigenvectors.

[8] Thus, considering $\mathbf{U}(\mathbf{q}) = \mathbf{U}(\mathbf{q}_1, \mathbf{q}_2, \ldots)$ the potential energy term in $\mathbf{H}$, as a function of the coordinates only, we have

$$\langle\grave{}q \mid \mathbf{U} \mid \grave{}\grave{}q\rangle = U(\grave{}q)\,\delta(\grave{}q - \grave{}\grave{}q),$$

and similarly,

$$\langle\grave{}q \mid \partial^2/\partial\mathbf{q}_r^2 \mid \grave{}\grave{}q\rangle = \delta(q_1' - q_1'') \ldots \delta''(q_r' - q_r'') \ldots \delta(q_n' - q_n'').$$

[9] Cf. Chap. XII.

and the modulus of c is determined from the normalization condition

$$\langle p' \mid p'' \rangle = \int_{-\infty}^{\infty} \langle p' \mid q' \rangle \, dq' \, \langle q' \mid p'' \rangle = \delta(p' - p''), \quad . \quad (4{:}18a)$$

or

$$\bar{c}'c'' \int_{-\infty}^{\infty} e^{iq'(p''-p')/\hbar} \, dq' = \delta(p' - p''). \quad . \quad . \quad . \quad . \quad (4{:}18b)$$

The left side of (4:18b) gives[10] $2\pi \mid c' \mid^2 \delta\{(p''-p')/\hbar\} = \mid c' \mid^2 h\,\delta(p''-p')$, whence

$$\langle q' \mid p' \rangle = h^{-\frac{1}{2}} e^{iq'p'/\hbar}. \quad . \quad . \quad . \quad . \quad . \quad . \quad . \quad . \quad (4{:}19)$$

Accordingly the $\mathbf{q}$- and $\mathbf{p}$-representatives of a $\mid \rangle$ are related by

$$\left.\begin{aligned} \langle q' \mid \rangle &= h^{-\frac{1}{2}} \int_{-\infty}^{\infty} e^{iq'p'/\hbar} \, dp' \, \langle p' \mid \rangle, \\ \langle p' \mid \rangle &= h^{-\frac{1}{2}} \int_{-\infty}^{\infty} e^{-iq'p'/\hbar} \, dq' \, \langle q' \mid \rangle, \end{aligned}\right\} \quad . \quad . \quad . \quad . \quad (4{:}20)$$

showing that either representative is, apart from a numerical factor, the Fourier transform of the other.[11]

Before we can extend the result (4:19) to the general case of, say, $3n$ degrees of freedom, we must develop further the theorem on constituent systems which was briefly noted in Chap. I, § 6, in connection with projection operators. Namely, that in many problems of quantum mechanics, as in the present case, it is convenient (or indeed necessary) to combine two distinct dynamical systems and consider them as one, or conversely, to break up a system into non-interacting separate units. This procedure is implicitly a basic part of most perturbation calculations in which we consider systems as separate and *a posteriori* introduce an interaction as perturbation. As has already been emphasized, the quantum conditions are such that dynamical variables referring to different degrees of freedom commute. On this basis we can see how separate dynamical systems can be counted as one, since all the dynamical variables of any one of the constituent systems will commute with those of any other which by definition is distinct and has its own degrees of freedom.

If we take a complete commuting set $\boldsymbol{\xi}$ for the first constituent system, $\boldsymbol{\eta}$ for the second, etc., then it is evident that the $\boldsymbol{\xi}$'s, $\boldsymbol{\eta}$'s, etc., together form a complete commuting set for the combined system. Further, the basic $\mid \rangle$'s, $\mid {}'\xi'\eta \ldots \rangle$ in the $\boldsymbol{\xi}, \boldsymbol{\eta}, \ldots$-representation may be considered as the *direct* products of the constituent basic $\mid \rangle$'s, $\mid {}'\xi \rangle$, $\mid {}'\eta \rangle$, etc.—the total space being considered as the product of the vector spaces of the constituent systems. The product of representatives of $\mid \rangle$'s for the constituent systems will give the representative of a $\mid \rangle$ for the whole system, e.g. (cf. § 6)

$$\langle {}'\xi'\eta \ldots \mid \rangle = \langle {}'\xi \mid \rangle \langle {}'\eta \mid \rangle \ldots, \quad . \quad . \quad . \quad . \quad . \quad (4{:}21a)$$

although a general $\mid \rangle$ corresponds to a sum or integral of terms of this type. Similarly, if we take other commuting sets for the constituent systems, e.g. $\boldsymbol{\alpha}, \boldsymbol{\beta}, \ldots$

[10] Cf. Footnote 15, p. 26.

[11] If we take $\hbar = 1$, these equations assume the familiar Fourier form, and in practice this is often a convenient choice of unit since the factor can always be restored in the final results by dimensional considerations.

instead of ξ, η, . . . , respectively, then the transformation functions for the whole system will be the products of the individual transformations, viz.

$$\langle\, `\xi`\eta \ldots \mid `\alpha`\beta \ldots \rangle = \langle\, `\xi \mid `\alpha \rangle \langle\, `\eta \mid `\beta \rangle \ldots . \quad . \quad . \quad (4{:}21b)$$

Applying this result to our particular case, the generalization of (4:19) is given by

$$\langle\, `q_1`q_2 \ldots \mid `p_1`p_2 \ldots \rangle = h^{-3n/2}\, e^{i(`q_1 \cdot `p_1 + `q_2 \cdot `p_2 + \ldots)/\hbar}. \quad . \quad . \quad (4{:}22)$$ [12]

§ 25. Fixed and Moving Operators and Representations

The quantum theory developed thus far dealt exclusively with the determination of the relations obtaining between states, operators, and their respective representatives at one particular time. Of course we cannot derive the equations of motion on purely epistemological grounds, but we can show that the invariance of the symbolic equations under unitary transformations leads to several equivalent and equally fundamental formulations. In classical theory the physical equations of motion are relations between dynamical variables at different times, while in quantum theory they must be expected ultimately to be relations between the average values of the variables at different times, since the symbolic scheme is given physical meaning by virtue of the basic postulate that the number $\langle\, \xi \,\rangle = \langle \mid \xi \mid \rangle$ is the expectation or average value of the observable ξ for the state $\mid \rangle$, provided the latter is suitably normalized. In particular, we observe that states and dynamical variables are not given by uniquely determined vectors since we may pass from any original set to the transforms $\mid \rangle \to \mathbf{U} \mid \rangle$, $\xi \to \mathbf{U}\xi\mathbf{U}^{-1}$ obtaining the same physical results. Hence, what we must ultimately determine is the value of the expression $\frac{d}{dt}\langle\, \xi \,\rangle$, and we must not impute any absolute significance to the equations of motion in so far as this term usually refers to the *pictured intrinsic* motion of states and observables.

As regards the development of operators in time, the classical analogue indicates that here, too, we may expect a gradual unfolding of successive infinitesimal contact transformations now generated by the time-displacement operator $e^{i\mathbf{H}\,\delta t/\hbar}$, where t is the time and $\mathbf{H}$ the Hamiltonian operator, which at present is assumed not to depend explicitly on t. More generally, we may consider the finite time-displacement operator $\mathbf{U} = e^{i\mathbf{H}t/\hbar}$, so that if the $\mathbf{q}$'s and their eigenvectors $\mid `q \,\rangle$ are constant,[13] satisfying the equations

$$\left.\begin{aligned} \frac{d}{dt}\,\mathbf{q} &= 0, \\ \frac{d}{dt} \mid `q \,\rangle &= 0, \end{aligned}\right\} \quad . \quad . \quad . \quad . \quad . \quad . \quad . \quad . \quad (4{:}23)$$

[12] $\mathbf{q}$ indicates $\mathbf{x}$, $\mathbf{y}$, $\mathbf{z}$, and correspondingly $\mathbf{p}$ indicates the vector with components $\mathbf{p}_x$, $\mathbf{p}_y$, $\mathbf{p}_z$.

[13] In this chapter time-dependent vectors, operators, etc., will be so indicated by suitable subscript or index, although zero subscripts corresponding to initial values are by custom omitted as the sense will always be clear from the equations; and it will be seen that in most cases the index t can be used as *transformed* with equal meaning. Obviously an eigenvalue *per se*, with index, merely identifies the observable in question in accord with the convention of Footnote 3, p. 36, and does not imply time dependence.

their transforms $\mathfrak{q}_t = \mathbf{U}\mathfrak{q}\mathbf{U}^*$ and $| {}'q_t \rangle = \mathbf{U} \, | {}'q \rangle$ must satisfy the equations

$$\left.\begin{aligned} i\hbar \frac{dt}{d} \mathfrak{q}_t &= \mathfrak{q}_t\mathbf{H} - \mathbf{H}\mathfrak{q}_t, \\ i\hbar \frac{d}{dt} | {}'q_t \rangle &= -\mathbf{H} \, | {}'q_t \rangle, \end{aligned}\right\} \quad . \; . \; . \; . \; . \; . \quad (4{:}24)$$

since

$$\frac{d}{dt}\mathbf{U} = \frac{i}{\hbar}\mathbf{H}\mathbf{U} \quad \text{and} \quad \frac{d}{dt}\mathbf{U}^* = -\frac{i}{\hbar}\mathbf{U}^*\mathbf{H}. \quad . \; . \; . \; . \; . \quad (4{:}25)$$

For algebraic functions of non-commuting observables [14] we can readily verify that $\boldsymbol{\xi}(\mathfrak{q}_t, \mathfrak{p}_t) = \boldsymbol{\xi}_t = \mathbf{U}\boldsymbol{\xi}\mathbf{U}^{-1}$, and if $\boldsymbol{\xi}$ does not explicitly depend on the time, it follows that $\boldsymbol{\xi}_t$ satisfies the equation

$$i\hbar \frac{d}{dt} \boldsymbol{\xi}_t = \boldsymbol{\xi}_t\mathbf{H} - \mathbf{H}\boldsymbol{\xi}_t. \quad . \; . \; . \; . \; . \; . \; . \; . \quad (4{:}26)$$ [15]

This result may also be derived by noting that if the *basic* vectors obey the relation $i\hbar \frac{d}{dt} | \rangle = -\mathbf{H} \, | \rangle$, then an observable attached to this *moving* system of co-ordinates may be characterized by the equation

$$\boldsymbol{\xi}_t \, | a \rangle = | b \rangle, \quad . \; . \; . \; . \; . \; . \; . \; . \quad (4{:}27)$$

where $| a \rangle$ and $| b \rangle$ are vectors embedded in the moving representation. From this equation we obtain

$$i\hbar \left(\frac{d}{dt}\boldsymbol{\xi}_t\right) | a \rangle - \boldsymbol{\xi}_t\mathbf{H} \, | a \rangle = -\mathbf{H} \, | b \rangle = -\mathbf{H}\boldsymbol{\xi}_t \, | a \rangle, \quad . \; . \quad (4{:}28)$$

from which (4:26) follows since $| a \rangle$ is arbitrary. Both systems (4:23) and (4:24) constitute proper representations, and it is convenient (and descriptive) to refer to these coordinate systems and attached operators as *fixed* and *moving*, respectively.[16] We may note that $\mathbf{H}$ has at any time the same functional form in terms of the dynamical variables of either system (4:23) or (4:24), but in the latter, as in equations (4:26–28), these dynamical variables are represented by moving linear operators. However, for the operator $\mathbf{H}$ this distinction is, in general, of a trivial nature owing to the special form of $\mathbf{U}$.

[14] So far it has been possible to define only algebraic well-ordered functions unambiguously in quantum theory. This limitation has greatly hampered further development of theory. See, however, DIRAC: *Rev. Mod. Phys.*, **17**, 195 (1945).

[15] When $\boldsymbol{\xi}$ involves t explicitly, the above equation must be generalized to

$$i\hbar \frac{d}{dt} \boldsymbol{\xi}_t = i\hbar \frac{\partial}{\partial t} \boldsymbol{\xi}_t + \boldsymbol{\xi}_t\mathbf{H} - \mathbf{H}\boldsymbol{\xi}_t,$$

which again closely parallels the classical equation of motion in Hamiltonian mechanics.

[16] As will be seen, these are representations in the Schroedinger (S) and Born-Heisenberg-Jordan ($B.H.J.$) pictures of quantum mechanics. The systems (4:23) and (4:24), respectively, can be appropriately termed the S and $B.H.J.$ *operator equations of motion.*

§ 26. Change of State in Time

In the preceding section we introduced an ordinary time variable in an indirect and somewhat incidental way as a parameter in a particular unitary transformation, and it thus appears that the time plays a rather subsidiary parametric role in quantum theory. Broadly speaking, this is the case, since it is not possible to introduce an observable (operator) in the usual sense, which would represent the time.[17] The remaining point which we must consider to round off the essential structure of quantum theory is the relation between states, or equivalently the vectors which represent them, at successive instants in time.

The close correspondence between the classical and quantal equations of motion for dynamical variables suggests that the intrinsic equation (4:26) derives its physical meaning in the sense

$$\frac{d}{dt}\langle \mid \xi_t \mid \rangle = \langle \mid [\,\xi_t, \mathbf{H}\,] \mid \rangle, \qquad (4{:}29)$$

that is, as an average value transcription of the classical form—the *physical states* satisfying what may be termed the *B.H.J. vector equation of motion*

$$\frac{d}{dt} \mid \rangle = 0. \qquad (4{:}30)$$

Alternatively, we may write (4:29) in the form

$$\frac{d}{dt}\langle \mid \mathbf{U}\xi\mathbf{U}^* \mid \rangle = \langle \mid \mathbf{U}[\,\xi, \mathbf{H}\,]\,\mathbf{U}^* \mid \rangle, \qquad (4{:}31a)$$

or

$$\frac{d}{dt}\langle ;t \mid \xi \mid ;t \rangle = \langle ;t \mid [\,\xi, \mathbf{H}\,] \mid ;t \rangle, \qquad (4{:}31b)$$

with

$$\mid ;t \rangle = \mathbf{U}^* \mid \rangle = \mathbf{U}^* \mid ;0 \rangle. \qquad (4{:}32)$$

The transformed state vector $\mid ;t \rangle$ therefore satisfies the equation

$$i\hbar\frac{d}{dt} \mid ;t \rangle = \mathbf{H} \mid ;t \rangle, \qquad (4{:}33)$$

which may be termed the Schroedinger *vector equation of motion* for states, although it is more familiar in representative form as the second Schroedinger wave-equation.[18]

[17] This remains true in the relativistic formulation even though the space and time variables are essentially on a mathematically equal footing. In particular, as noted in § 18, the time variable and the negative Hamiltonian are not canonically conjugate.

[18] In the above development we have approached the time dependence of physical states through the correspondence afforded by the equations of motion for dynamical variables; passing then from the equation (4:30) to (4:33) by appeal to the unitary invariance of the equations. Alternatively, we could proceed from the opposite direction, so to speak, by extension of the usual three-dimensional sense of superposition of states on the assumption that the principle also holds in four dimensions; which, from the former point of view, simply means that states that are linear combinations of other states at one instant of time remain so at all times. This requires that all states of a system vary with time, if at all, according to a law of the form

$$\mid ;t + \delta t \rangle = \mathbf{G}\,(t + \delta t) \mid ;t \rangle,$$

where $\mathbf{G}$ is a linear operator which from our discussion of unitary invariance may be assumed to be of the form $\exp -i\mathbf{H}\,\delta t/\hbar$. The full development of this viewpoint is given by DIRAC, *Q.M.* See also Chap. XII, § 101.

The laws (4:30) and (4:33), combined with the results of the preceding section, define equivalent quantum mechanical equations of motion. In tabular form:

	S picture	*B.H.J. picture*
States as vectors	IA: moving $i\hbar \frac{d}{dt} \mid ; t \rangle = \mathbf{H} \mid ; t \rangle$	IIA: fixed $i\hbar \frac{d}{dt} \mid \rangle = 0$
Dynamical variables as linear operators	IB: fixed $i\hbar \frac{d}{dt} \xi = 0$	IIB: moving $i\hbar \frac{d}{dt} \xi_t = [\, \xi_t, \mathbf{H} \,]_-$

To these we might properly add the corresponding equations governing representations in these pictures, namely (4:24) and (4:23), but it is customary to find only IA and IIB mentioned as equations of motion. We may quite literally say that quantities fixed in the *S* picture are moving in the *B.H.J.* picture, and conversely;[19] the correspondence being such that if $\mid 1 \rangle$, $\mid 2 \rangle$ denote states satisfying the equations of motion, and ξ denotes any dynamical variable not explicitly dependent on t, then

$$i\hbar \frac{d}{dt} \langle 1 \mid \xi \mid 2 \rangle = \langle 1 \mid \xi \mathbf{H} - \mathbf{H} \xi \mid 2 \rangle; \quad . \quad . \quad . \quad . \quad (4:34)$$

and in particular [20]

$$i\hbar \frac{d}{dt} \langle \xi \rangle = \langle [\, \xi, \mathbf{H} \,]_- \rangle,$$

which is the *invariant form* of the equations of motion, being independent of the picture used. Equations (4:34) simply express the fact that in consequence of the linear and invariant properties of equations in quantum mechanics, the development or behaviour of a system in time may be described as a development of the states themselves, the observables remaining constant—equal to the value of the dynamical variables corresponding to the initial time, or conversely. The practical way of writing equations (4:33) and (4:30) is in terms of representations and, as we have shown, they must lead to identical physical results. If, for example, we take a representation in which the coordinates are diagonal, this means taking the representation (4:23) together with (4:33), or (4:24) with (4:30). These lead to the familiar form of Schroedinger's second wave-equation.

[19] This must be qualified in certain special cases, e.g. when comparing systems with different Hamiltonians (see fig. 4.2).

[20] Here we might have written $\mid 1 ; t \rangle$, ξ_t, etc. (the meaning of the index t depending on the picture), but as in the greater part of this book, the present chapter excepted, no distinguishing subscripts are used since, strictly speaking, ξ and ξ_t represent the same observable, and similarly for the vector $\mid \rangle$. The spirit of quantum theory permits no rigid distinction, and it is not uncommon to use ξ with both meanings in a single equation, the distinction being clear from the context.

S picture:

$$i\hbar \frac{d}{dt}\langle\, 'q \mid ; t\,\rangle = \int \langle\, 'q \mid \mathbf{H} \mid ''q\,\rangle\, d\,''q\,\langle\, ''q \mid ; t\,\rangle. \quad . \quad . \quad (4{:}35a)$$

B.H.J. picture:

$$i\hbar \frac{d}{dt}\langle\, 'q_t \mid \rangle = \int \langle\, 'q_t \mid \mathbf{H} \mid ''q_t\,\rangle\, d\,''q_t\,\langle\, ''q_t \mid \rangle. \quad . \quad . \quad . \quad (4{:}35b)$$ [21]

We may also write $\langle\, 'q\,; t \mid \rangle$ instead of $\langle\, 'q_t \mid \rangle$ in (4:35*b*) if we observe that $\langle\, 'q_t \mid \rangle$ is a function of the n variables $q_{1t}', \ldots q_{nt}'$, and therefore of the $n + 1$ variables $q_1', q_2', \ldots q_n', t$, where $q_1', \ldots q_n'$ are no longer considered as depending on the variable t. The difference in viewpoint in the above derivations of the wave-equation is perhaps best seen in a geometrical picture:

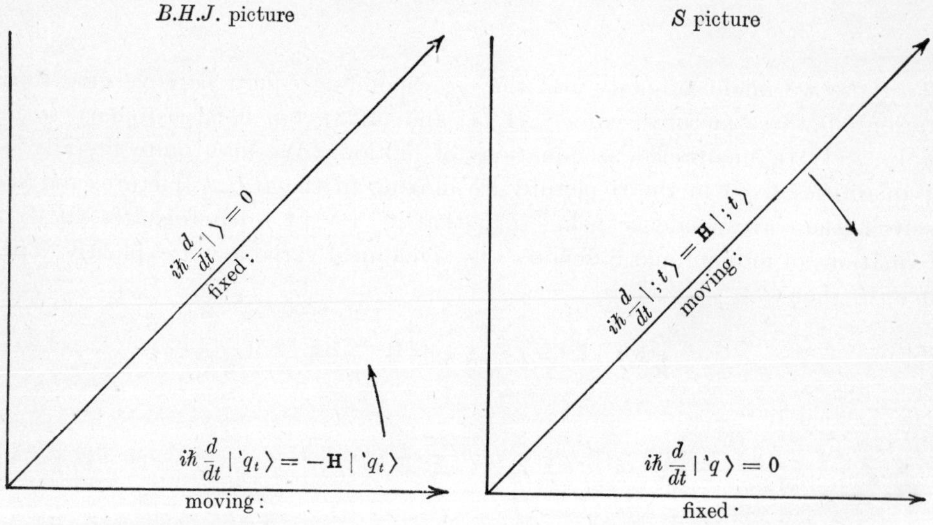

Fig. 4.1.—Geometrical picture of different formulations of the wave-equation. The moving vectors in the diagram are indicated as though rotating, although this is admittedly a rather loose description.

It is thus permissible to speak of the wave-equations in the *S* and *B.H.J.* pictures (which are of course identical) as differing geometrically in the sense that the time enters the generalized direction cosine (probability amplitude) from the right and left respectively, i.e. in the former it is introduced through the time dependence of the states themselves, while in the latter the time dependence is put into the representation.

It is important to understand that the $\mathfrak{q}$-diagonal Schroedinger representation is only a special case, though unquestionably the most important, of a whole class of representations which have the common property of being fixed, and lead to wave-equations of the form (4:35*a*). Whether or not the right-hand side of the wave-equations involves a sum or integral, or both, depends on the eigenvalue spectrum of the observables defining the representation. The Schroedinger equation (4:35*a*)

[21] Logically, this may be called Schroedinger's equation in either picture, but it is customary to reserve this term for the former fixed representation.

is perfectly general, and we now wish to specialize to the case of a dynamical system for which **H** is constant, i.e. in which there are no exterior forces varying with time. Then there are solutions of the form [22]

$$\langle\, `q \mid `\alpha\,;t\,\rangle = \langle\, `q \mid `\alpha\,\rangle\, e^{-iH't/\hbar}, \quad . \quad . \quad . \quad . \quad . \qquad (4{:}36a)$$

with

$$\int \langle\, `q \mid \mathbf{H} \mid ``q\,\rangle\, d``q\, \langle\, ``q \mid `\alpha\,\rangle = H' \langle\, `q \mid `\alpha\,\rangle. \quad . \quad . \quad . \qquad (4{:}36b)$$

Here $\boldsymbol{\alpha}$ indicates **H** and such other observables which combine with **H** to form a complete commuting set of which $\mid `\alpha\,\rangle$ is an eigenvector. According to a previous result, a function of the dynamical variables not explicitly dependent on the time is a *constant of the motion* if it commutes with **H**. Since such variables must commute with **H** at all times, this usually requires that **H** be a constant too. The constancy of **H** in the Born-Heisenberg-Jordan picture means that $\partial\mathbf{H}/\partial t = 0$, or that **H** itself does not involve t explicitly and, hence, is also a constant in the Schroedinger picture. Since constants of the motion satisfy the condition $d\boldsymbol{\alpha}/dt = 0$ in either picture ($\boldsymbol{\alpha}_t = \mathbf{U}\boldsymbol{\alpha}\mathbf{U}^{-1} = \boldsymbol{\alpha}$), there is in this case a certain redundancy in notation. We retain the subscript in this chapter, however, to conform with the general scheme of presentation. Equation (4:36*b*) is the standard equation for determining the eigenvalues of **H**, and hence when **H** does not involve t explicitly there exist solutions, periodic in time, of the above form with H' an eigenvalue of **H**. This special kind of state is such that the average value of an observable is independent of time, since

$$\langle\, \boldsymbol{\xi}\,\rangle = \langle\, `\alpha\,;t \mid \boldsymbol{\xi} \mid `\alpha\,;t\,\rangle = \iint \langle\, `\alpha\,;t \mid `q\,\rangle\, d`q\, \langle\, `q \mid \boldsymbol{\xi} \mid ``q\,\rangle\, d``q\, \langle\, ``q \mid `\alpha\,;t\,\rangle, \qquad (4{:}37)$$ [23]

which according to (4:36*a*) is independent of t. Thus, the probability of obtaining any particular result when we make an observation is independent of the time, and such a state is called a *stationary state*.

Let us now consider what theory of representation we get when we take the stationary states to be the basic states of the representation. From the respective equations of motion we obtain the following geometrical picture (fig. 4.2) of the various representations possible when the basic states are all eigenstates of the Hamiltonian.

Representation (*c*), with the constants of the motion diagonal, is moving in the *S* picture and is, therefore, fixed in the *B.H.J.* picture (*d*). Alternatively, we can introduce a representation with the $\boldsymbol{\alpha}$'s diagonal which is fixed in the *S* picture (*e*), and is thus moving in the *B.H.J.* picture (*f*). In this special case there is, as indicated above, a duplicity of notation, since (*c*) is related to (*e*) and (*d*) by the same phase factor, and likewise (*f*) to (*e*) and (*d*). We prefer to keep the notation

[22] We consider only (4:35*a*) to avoid unnecessary repetition, since (4:35*b*) leads to the same conclusions with slight change of notation.

[23] In the *B.H.J.* picture

$$\langle\, `\alpha \mid \boldsymbol{\xi}_t \mid `\alpha\,\rangle = \iint \langle\, `\alpha \mid `q_t\,\rangle\, d`q_t\, \langle\, `q_t \mid \boldsymbol{\xi}_t \mid ``q_t\,\rangle\, d``q_t\, \langle\, ``q_t \mid `\alpha\,\rangle,$$

which gives the same result. Indeed $\langle\, `q_t \mid \boldsymbol{\xi}_t \mid ``q_t\,\rangle$ is constant, and this condition characterizes a moving basis in this picture, just as the constancy of $\langle\, `q \mid \boldsymbol{\xi} \mid ``q\,\rangle$ characterizes a fixed basis in the *S* picture.

consistent within each picture, but this should cause no difficulty. The fixed representations in the two pictures differ only in that the basic vectors of the *B.H.J.* representation satisfy the equation of motion (IIA). Nevertheless, in the equation $\langle\, `\alpha \mid ; t \,\rangle = \langle\, `\alpha \mid \,\rangle_\tau\, e^{-iH't/\hbar}$ the left- and right-hand representatives are sometimes referred to as the *S* and *B.H.J.* representatives of the *same* state. (The two representations do not differ in phase, except as a figure of speech, since the phase difference arises from the fact that $\mid ; t\,\rangle$ and $\mid\,\rangle_\tau = \mathbf{U} \mid ; t\,\rangle$ represent the same state, but in different pictures.) It will be observed that the representative of an observable [24] ξ in (*c*) and (*d*) varies according to the law—constant $e^{i(H'-H'')t/\hbar}$—the con-

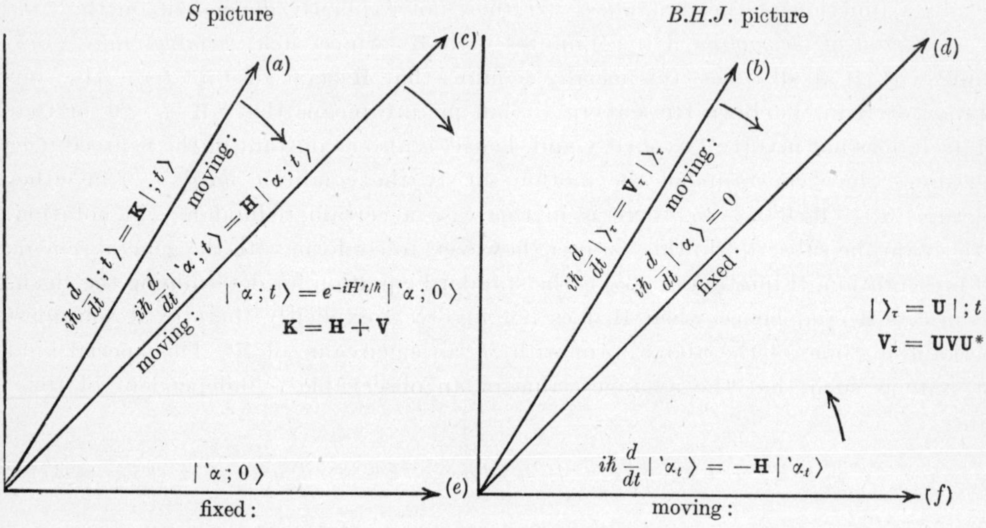

Fig. 4.2.—Geometrical picture of the possible representations when the basic states are all eigenstates of the Hamiltonian

stant being the representative of ξ in (*e*) and (*f*) respectively. The above diagram also illustrates the exception to the fixed-moving parallelism between the two pictures which arises when we compare systems with different Hamiltonians, e.g. **H** and **K** above. The equation of state (*a*) when expressed in the fixed representation (*e*) leads to the Schroedinger wave-equation

$$i\hbar \frac{d}{dt} \langle\, `\alpha \mid ; t\,\rangle = \sum_{''\alpha} \langle\, `\alpha \mid \mathbf{K} \mid ''\alpha\,\rangle \langle\, ''\alpha \mid ; t\,\rangle$$

$$= H' \langle\, `\alpha \mid ; t\,\rangle + \sum_{''\alpha} \langle\, `\alpha \mid \mathbf{V} \mid ''\alpha\,\rangle \langle\, ''\alpha \mid ; t\,\rangle, \quad . \quad (4{:}38)$$

when

$$\mathbf{K} = \mathbf{H} + \mathbf{V},$$

assuming a discrete spectrum for definiteness; and the same result with appropriate change of notation is obtained for the transformed vector $\mid\,\rangle_\tau$ (*b*) relative to the moving representation (*f*). This equation may be described as giving the variation with time of the direction cosine between (*a*) and (*e*) or, equivalently, (*b*) and (*f*),

[24] Cf. Footnote 20.

due to **K**. Whichever picture we adopt to obtain (4:38), the matrix of **V** appearing therein is constant except in so far as **V** itself involves t explicitly.

In perturbation problems one is usually more interested in the separate effect of the perturbing potential **V** when considered from the point of view of the unperturbed system defined by the Hamiltonian **H**. Or as we may say, we consider only the variation in the direction cosine between (a) and (c), or (b) and (d), owing to the added potential **V**. In the *B.H.J.* picture we have

$$i\hbar \frac{d}{dt}\langle\, '\alpha \mid \rangle_\tau = \sum_{''\alpha} \langle\, '\alpha \mid \mathbf{V}_\tau \mid {''\alpha} \rangle \langle\, ''\alpha \mid \rangle_\tau, \quad . \quad . \quad . \quad . \quad . \quad (4{:}39)$$

and in the S picture

$$i\hbar \frac{d}{dt}\langle\, '\alpha\, ; t \mid ; t \rangle = \sum_{''\alpha} \langle\, '\alpha\, ; t \mid \mathbf{V} \mid {''\alpha}\, ; t \rangle \langle\, ''\alpha\, ; t \mid ; t \rangle. \quad . \quad . \quad . \quad (4{:}40)$$

These equations are, of course, identical, and the essential point to notice is that in both the matrix of **V** varies rapidly according to the law $\sim e^{i(H'-H'')t/\hbar}$, aside from any explicit dependence of **V** on t. In theoretical work we use one or other general picture as convenience dictates, and it is not ordinarily necessary to use distinguishing indices or subscripts. A note of caution may be added pertinent to the fact that, although it is customary to give the laws of motion in the previously mentioned limited form, and we may for reasons of convenience pass back and forth from S to *B.H.J.* pictures, they do not hold simultaneously. Thus, as an illustration,

$$\langle \mid \xi_t \mid \rangle = \iint \langle \mid {'q_t} \rangle\, d'q_t \langle\, 'q_t \mid \xi_t \mid {''q_t} \rangle\, d''q_t \langle\, ''q_t \mid \rangle$$

$$= \iint \langle\, ; t \mid {'q} \rangle\, d'q \langle\, 'q \mid \xi \mid {''q} \rangle\, d''q \langle\, ''q \mid ; t \rangle = \langle\, ; t \mid \xi \mid ; t \rangle.$$

§ 27. The Density Matrix

In our later work we shall at times be interested in dynamical systems whose specification is less complete than those heretofore considered, in the sense that it may be unnecessary or even impossible to know that the dynamical system is in a specified state at a given time. Instead, the available information may consist solely of the knowledge that the system is to be found in one or another of a number of accessible states according to a given probability distribution. The problem thus stated is essentially a statistical one, and in classical theory leads to the concepts of the Gibbs ensemble, phase space, and density in phase, which we shall consider later in more detail, together with the quantal analogues in so far as they exist. Here we need only recall the well-known fact that the concept of phase space has, strictly speaking, no meaning in quantum mechanics owing to the non-commutation of canonical coordinates and momenta, which precludes the simultaneous assignment of values required to satisfy a phase space. Nonetheless, there exists a close quantal analogue to the classical *density in phase*, and it is primarily the mathematics of this *quantum density* which we wish to consider here. We introduce the density operator here because it has, in consequence of its definition, certain apparently anomalous properties which can cause confusion, and seem best disposed of while we are considering the general equations of motion. An acquaintance with the classical statistical mechanics is helpful, but not a necessary prerequisite to an understanding of the few simple physical concepts involved in the present discussion.

Let us now suppose that it is given that P_n is the probability that a dynamical system under study is at a certain time in the nth state $| n ; t \rangle$ of a certain set of states accessible to it. Here we are implicitly assuming that the set of states cover a discrete range as indicated by the ordinal parameter n, the extension to the case of a continuous or mixed range being trivial. We are evidently considering the S picture (states as moving vectors) and, in an arbitrary representation determined by the fixed operators $\boldsymbol{\xi}$ whose eigenvalue spectrum may be taken as continuous for definiteness, a wave-function will be written as $\langle {}'\xi | n ; t \rangle$ in keeping with the notation of this chapter. For a single state, the probability that the $\boldsymbol{\xi}$'s have values in the range $d'\xi$ at $'\xi$ is $| \langle {}'\xi | \rangle |^2$, and hence for the given distribution in the present case the corresponding probability will be

$$\sum_n |\langle {}'\xi | n ; t \rangle|^2 P_n. \qquad (4:41)$$

This expression can be formally interpreted as a diagonal element of the quantum density operator $\boldsymbol{\rho}$, defined directly by the operator product

$$\boldsymbol{\rho} = \sum_n | n ; t \rangle P_n \langle n ; t | = \sum_n \mathbf{U}^* | n \rangle P_n \langle n | \mathbf{U}, \qquad (4:42)$$

or by its representative,

$$\langle {}'\xi | \boldsymbol{\rho} | {}''\xi \rangle = \sum_n \langle {}'\xi | n ; t \rangle P_n \langle n ; t | {}''\xi \rangle, \qquad (4:43)$$

which is actually more general.[25] The density operator is a rather exceptional, if not hybrid, construct, since its representative in a fixed S-type representation, as defined by (4:43), obviously varies with time. This is simply because $\boldsymbol{\rho}$ spans a set of moving physical states, and hence itself varies with time [cf. (4:46) below] in the S picture in contrast to the more familiar observables which do not *explicitly* depend on the time. The transform of (4:42) defines the density operator in the *B.H.J.* picture as

$$\boldsymbol{\rho}_t = \mathbf{U}\boldsymbol{\rho}\mathbf{U}^* = \sum_n | n \rangle P_n \langle n |, \qquad (4:44)$$

or by its representative,

$$\langle {}'\xi_t | \boldsymbol{\rho}_t | {}''\xi_t \rangle = \sum_n \langle {}'\xi_t | n \rangle P_n \langle n | {}''\xi_t \rangle, \qquad (4:45)$$

which will also depend unusually on the time, since $\langle {}'\xi_t | \boldsymbol{\rho}_t | {}''\xi_t \rangle$ varies with the time instead of being constant as it would be for a simply moving observable. In fact, we shall find that $\boldsymbol{\rho}_t$ itself is constant.

[25] Since in the approximate treatment of many-particle problems, $\boldsymbol{\rho}$ can always be defined through (4:43), even when the form (4:42) cannot be written explicitly.

The equation of motion of the density operators is most easily obtained by differentiating (4:42), which gives

$$i\hbar \frac{\partial}{\partial t} \boldsymbol{\rho} = \mathbf{H}\boldsymbol{\rho} - \boldsymbol{\rho}\mathbf{H} = -[\boldsymbol{\rho}, \mathbf{H}]_-, \quad . \quad . \quad . \quad . \quad . \quad (4:46)$$

since P_n is constant as long as the system is undisturbed.[26] It immediately follows that

$$i\hbar \frac{d}{dt} \boldsymbol{\rho}_t = 0, \quad . \quad . \quad . \quad . \quad . \quad . \quad . \quad . \quad . \quad . \quad (4:47)$$

which is also quite obvious from the constancy of $| n \rangle$ in the definition (4:44). The formal definition of the density operator is especially convenient since from (4:42) it is trivially evident that $\boldsymbol{\rho}$ is Hermitian.[27] Further, it is readily seen that $\boldsymbol{\rho}$ has only positive eigenvalues, thus paralleling the non-negative character of the classical density in phase. This follows simply because the eigenvectors and eigenvalues of $\boldsymbol{\rho}$ are $| n\,; t \rangle$ and P_n in accord with the physical meaning of $\boldsymbol{\rho}$, viz.

$$\boldsymbol{\rho} \,| n\,; t \rangle = \sum_m | m\,; t \rangle P_m \langle m\,; t \,|\, n\,; t \rangle = P_n \,| n\,; t \rangle. \quad . \quad . \quad (4:48)$$ [28]

For a system distributed over the various states in this manner, the average value of an observable $\boldsymbol{\alpha}$ will be

$$\begin{aligned} \langle \boldsymbol{\alpha} \rangle &= \sum_n P_n \langle n\,; t \,|\, \boldsymbol{\alpha} \,|\, n\,; t \rangle \\ &= \iint \sum_n P_n \langle n\,; t \,|\, {}'\xi \rangle \, d'\xi \, \langle {}'\xi \,|\, \boldsymbol{\alpha} \,|\, {}''\xi \rangle \, d''\xi \, \langle {}''\xi \,|\, n\,; t \rangle \\ &= \iint \langle {}'\xi \,|\, \boldsymbol{\alpha} \,|\, {}''\xi \rangle \, d''\xi \, \langle {}''\xi \,|\, \boldsymbol{\rho} \,|\, {}'\xi \rangle \, d'\xi \\ &= \int \langle {}'\xi \,|\, \boldsymbol{\alpha\rho} \,|\, {}'\xi \rangle \, d'\xi, \quad . \quad . \quad . \quad . \quad . \quad . \quad . \quad . \quad . \quad . \quad . \quad . \quad (4:49) \end{aligned}$$

or, the average value of an observable is given by summing or integrating the product $\boldsymbol{\alpha\rho}$ along the diagonal, over the eigenvalue spectrum of the observables defining the representation.

This diagonal sum or integral (or both) is called the *spur* ($\mathscr{S}p$) of the operator product, and for any representation satisfies the conditions

$$\left.\begin{aligned} \mathscr{S}p\,(\boldsymbol{\alpha\beta}) &= \mathscr{S}p\,(\boldsymbol{\beta\alpha}), \\ \mathscr{S}p\,(\boldsymbol{\alpha\beta\gamma}) &= \mathscr{S}p\,(\boldsymbol{\beta\gamma\alpha}) = \mathscr{S}p\,(\boldsymbol{\gamma\alpha\beta}). \end{aligned}\right\} \quad . \quad . \quad . \quad . \quad (4:50)$$

[26] This result may also be obtained somewhat less directly from the definition (4:43); thus,

$$\begin{aligned} i\hbar \frac{d}{dt} \langle {}'\xi \,|\, \boldsymbol{\rho} \,|\, {}''\xi \rangle &= \langle {}'\xi \,|\, i\hbar \frac{\partial}{\partial t} \boldsymbol{\rho} \,|\, {}''\xi \rangle = \sum_n \{ \langle {}'\xi \,|\, \mathbf{H} \,|\, n\,; t \rangle P_n \langle n\,; t \,|\, {}''\xi \rangle - \langle {}'\xi \,|\, n\,; t \rangle P_n \langle n\,; t \,|\, \mathbf{H} \,|\, {}''\xi \rangle \} \\ &= \langle {}'\xi \,|\, \mathbf{H}\boldsymbol{\rho} - \boldsymbol{\rho}\mathbf{H} \,|\, {}''\xi \rangle, \end{aligned}$$

and similarly for the result (4:47). The equation of motion (4:46) is identical in form with that of the classical density.

[27] Noting that $\{ | a \rangle \langle b | \}^* = | b \rangle \langle a |$, and that P_n as a probability is a positive number.

[28] If the system is in a definite state, then clearly $\boldsymbol{\rho}^2 = \boldsymbol{\rho}$, i.e. $\boldsymbol{\rho}$ is idempotent and has eigenvalues zero or one, in accord with the available information.

The spur of a product of operators is invariant under cyclic interchange and, in particular, under unitary transformations. Thus

$$\langle \boldsymbol{\alpha} \rangle = \mathcal{S}p\,(\boldsymbol{\rho\alpha}), \qquad (4{:}51)$$

and

$$i\hbar \frac{d}{dt} \langle \boldsymbol{\alpha} \rangle = \mathcal{S}p\,(i\hbar\dot{\boldsymbol{\rho}}\boldsymbol{\alpha})$$
$$= \mathcal{S}p\{\boldsymbol{\rho}(\boldsymbol{\alpha}\mathbf{H} - \mathbf{H}\boldsymbol{\alpha})\} = \langle \boldsymbol{\alpha}\mathbf{H} - \mathbf{H}\boldsymbol{\alpha} \rangle. \qquad (4{:}52)$$ [29]

The above-mentioned invariance of the spur under transformation of representation is especially useful in perturbation theory (cf. §§ 32, 83) where for discrete eigenvalue spectra (and $P_n = 1$ in the preceding) it is known as the Spur Theorem, which states in addition that the spur equals the sum of the eigenvalues weighted by their degeneracies, viz. taking $\boldsymbol{\xi}$-, $\boldsymbol{\eta}$-, and $\boldsymbol{\alpha}$-representations as discrete,

$$\mathcal{S}p_\xi \boldsymbol{\alpha} = \sum_{\xi'} \langle \xi' \,|\, \boldsymbol{\alpha} \,|\, \xi' \rangle = \sum_{\xi'\eta'\eta''} \langle \xi' \,|\, \eta' \rangle \langle \eta' \,|\, \boldsymbol{\alpha} \,|\, \eta'' \rangle \langle \eta'' \,|\, \xi' \rangle$$
$$= \sum_{\eta'} \langle \eta' \,|\, \boldsymbol{\alpha} \,|\, \eta' \rangle = \mathcal{S}p_\eta \boldsymbol{\alpha}. \qquad (4{:}53)$$

Hence, as above, the spur requires no identifying subscript, and for the $\boldsymbol{\alpha}$-representation itself,

$$\mathcal{S}p\,\boldsymbol{\alpha} = \sum_{\alpha',\alpha'} \alpha' = \sum_{\alpha'} \alpha' g(\alpha'), \qquad (4{:}54)$$

where $g(\alpha')$ is the degeneracy (or multiplicity) of the eigenvalue α'. The variations of this theorem for various types of eigenspectra are obvious, but of less practical import.

[29] In particular, note that $\boldsymbol{\rho}$ is a constant of the motion for stationary states, in which case it commutes with the Hamiltonian by definition.

CHAPTER V

Fundamentals of Perturbation Theory

§ 28. Introduction

Most problems which arise in quantum mechanics are of such a complex nature that a solution for the eigenvalues and eigenvectors of the associated operators cannot be obtained in closed form. All problems involving the study of many particles, as in the theory of atomic spectra, solid state, etc., fall in this category. Even if the analytical difficulties could be overcome, it is doubtful that an exact solution would be particularly useful because of its complicated mathematical nature, and the consequent difficulty in physical interpretation. Thus, for both mathematical and physical reasons, we must resort to various methods of approximation, which need not be considered as an ugly feature, since, in the last analysis, all of physics is successive approximation in the attempt to describe natural phenomena.

Aside from certain special methods to be considered later, the basis of most approximate developments is the simple idea of relating the actual problem, which we shall call problem A, to one for which we can obtain an exact and manageable solution, problem B. The difference between the operators of the two problems is considered as a *weak* perturbation, and for the moment we can qualify a weak perturbation only in a general way as one causing but a small [1] change in the eigenvalues and eigenvectors of the unperturbed problem. In the following discussion of perturbation methods we shall take these operators to be the respective Hamiltonians **K** and **H**, since this is the most important case, and correspondingly we shall be working in the energy representations [2] of the two problems.

It should be noted at this point that in practice we may classify perturbation problems according to two types, although the distinction is one of viewpoint rather than physical or mathematical kind. In the first and perhaps simpler type we take the viewpoint that the unperturbed Hamiltonian **H** and the perturbation are determined *a priori* by the physical conditions defining the preparation of states with Hamiltonian **K**, and in this sense we have just two related problems. The second and more general approach starts directly with the Hamiltonian **K** of the perturbed problem, leaving us free to choose that part of **K** which we wish to define our unperturbed states, the remanent part being the perturbation; consequently the number of related problems is, at least in principle, infinite. Hence, it is important to realize that in many cases the success of the approximate methods will depend in large measure on a proper choice of the unperturbed comparison problem, i.e.

[1] A more exact meaning of *small* will be clear from the subsequent discussion.

[2] However, the transformation to differential operators and wave-functions for the equations developed here is of a trivial nature.

the perturbation, and this selection depends primarily on the nature of the particular problem under consideration.

The basic assumption of the present method is that the eigenvectors and eigenvalues of the perturbed problem reduce in a continuous way to the solutions of the unperturbed problem as the perturbation potential tends to zero. This continuity hypothesis will certainly not hold if, for example, the eigenvalue spectrum of problem A is continuous while that of problem B is pure-discrete, since a discontinuous change obviously occurs in the limit of vanishing perturbation. Similarly, the perturbation may introduce new singularities which invalidate the above hypothesis but, since no general rule can be given, we shall proceed on this hypothesis with the observation that each individual problem should be examined to see that it satisfies the requisite conditions.

With regard to the behaviour of the perturbing term we note that quite generally there occurs a perturbation parameter, κ say, which may appear as a natural physical parameter, as for applied electric or magnetic fields, or may be entirely artificial. In either case it is possible to define a κ such that $0 \leqslant \kappa \leqslant 1$, the outer bounds corresponding to the unperturbed and perturbed problem respectively, and in the sense of the second viewpoint above we thus define on κ a one-parameter continuous series of related problems. Under the continuity hypothesis we then expand the eigenvectors and eigenvalues of problem A in power series in κ, the zero-order terms being, by definition, the corresponding quantities belonging to problem B. However, it is not especially convenient to have formulæ involving κ in various complicated ways, and we therefore suppress it, indicating the various orders of magnitude by suitable indices.

§ 29. Discrete Spectrum—Non-degenerate

We denote the eigenvectors of $\mathbf{H}$ and $\mathbf{K}$ by $|H'\rangle$ and $|K'\rangle$ respectively, and we assume that $\mathbf{H}$ by itself forms a complete commuting set so that the unperturbed problem is non-degenerate. Suppose $\mathbf{K}$ and $\mathbf{H}$ are related by the equation

$$\mathbf{K} = \mathbf{H} + \mathbf{V}_1 + \mathbf{V}_2 + \ldots, \qquad (5{:}1)$$

where $\mathbf{V}_1$, $\mathbf{V}_2$, etc., are considered as small perturbing terms of first, second, etc., order, i.e. their respective representatives in the unperturbed *B.H.J.* representation are small, of these orders of magnitude. We have the exact equations:

$$\mathbf{H}\,|H'\rangle = H'\,|H'\rangle, \qquad (5{:}2a)$$

$$|K'\rangle = \sum_{H''} |H''\rangle\langle H''|K'\rangle, \qquad (5{:}2b)$$

$$\sum_{H''} \langle H'|\mathbf{K}|H''\rangle\langle H''|K'''\rangle = K'''\langle H'|K'''\rangle; \qquad (5{:}2c)$$

and introduce the approximate series development

$$|K'\rangle = |0\rangle + |1\rangle + |2\rangle + \ldots = |K';0\rangle + |K';1\rangle + \ldots, \qquad (5{:}3a)$$

where obviously the zero-order approximation $| K'; 0 \rangle$, corresponding to the vanishing of the perturbation and the actual coincidence of **K** and **H**, must be an eigenvector of **H**. It is sometimes more convenient to write this expansion in terms of wave-functions (transformation amplitudes), e.g.

$$\langle H'' \mid K' \rangle = \delta (H'', H') + \langle H'' \mid K' ; 1 \rangle + \langle H'' \mid K' ; 2 \rangle + \ldots , \quad (5:3b)$$

where $\delta(H'', H')$ arises since $| K';\ 0 \rangle$ is the eigenvector $| H' \rangle$ belonging to H', if we agree to label corresponding perturbed and unperturbed states by the same number of primes—which we may do since, by hypothesis, each perturbed state approximates closely to one and only one unperturbed state. The added indices as in the first-order term $\langle H'' \mid K' ; 1 \rangle$, for example, also serve to indicate that these amplitudes are not exact since $\langle H'' \mid K' ; 1 \rangle = \langle H'' \mid 1 \rangle$ and $| 1 \rangle$ is not an eigenvector of **K**. This notation is adopted because it permits us to indicate more precisely the particular perturbed and unperturbed states under discussion, and the order of approximation by the added subscript. Further, we assume that K''' can be expressed in the series

$$K''' = H''' + \Delta_1 H''' + \Delta_2 H''' + \ldots . \quad . \quad . \quad . \quad . \quad (5:3c)$$

Substituting (5:3*b*, *c*) in (5:2*c*), and equating terms of the same order of magnitude, we obtain the following series of equations.

Zero order:

$$(H' - H''') \, \delta (H', H''') = 0, \quad . \quad . \quad . \quad . \quad . \quad (5:4)$$

which merely expresses the known fact that $| 0 \rangle$ is an eigenvector of **H**.

First order:

$$H' \langle H' | K''' ; 1 \rangle + \langle H' \mid \mathbf{V}_1 \mid H''' \rangle = H''' \langle H' \mid K''' ; 1 \rangle + \Delta_1 H''' \, \delta (H', H'''). \quad (5:5a)$$

For $H' = H'''$, we find

$$\Delta_1 H' = \langle H' \mid \mathbf{V}_1 \mid H' \rangle, \quad . \quad . \quad . \quad . \quad . \quad . \quad (5:5b)$$

i.e. the first-order correction is the average of the first-order perturbation potential taken over the unperturbed state. Further,

$$\langle H' \mid K''' ; 1 \rangle = - \frac{\langle H' \mid \mathbf{V}_1 \mid H''' \rangle}{H' - H'''} \qquad (H' \neq H'''). \quad . \quad (5:5c)$$

This does not determine $\langle H' \mid K' ; 1 \rangle$, which we find from normalization, viz.

$$\begin{aligned} & \sum_{H''} \langle K' \mid H'' \rangle \langle H'' \mid K''' \rangle \\ & \quad = \delta (K', K''') \\ & \quad = \delta (H', H''') + \{ \langle H' \mid K''' ; 1 \rangle + \langle K' ; 1 \mid H''' \rangle \} \\ & \qquad + \{ \langle H' \mid K''' ; 2 \rangle + \langle K' ; 2 \mid H''' \rangle \\ & \qquad\qquad + \sum_{H''} \langle K' ; 1 \mid H'' \rangle \langle H'' \mid K''' ; 1 \rangle \} + \ldots , \end{aligned} \quad (5:5d)$$

where terms of the same order are bracketed together. Hence, since

$$\langle H' \mid K' ; 1 \rangle = \langle K' ; 1 \mid H' \rangle^*, \text{ etc.},$$

we find

$$\left.\begin{aligned} \mathscr{Re} \langle H' \mid K' ; 1 \rangle &= 0, \\ \mathscr{Re} \langle H' \mid K' ; 2 \rangle &= -\tfrac{1}{2} \sum_{H'' \neq H'} |\langle H'' \mid K' ; 1 \rangle|^2. \end{aligned}\right\} \quad . \quad . \quad (5{:}5e)$$

We may choose the imaginary part of $\langle H' \mid K' ; 1 \rangle$ arbitrarily, which corresponds to the arbitrariness in phase of $\mid K' \rangle$. The most convenient procedure is to set the imaginary part equal to zero, and we shall take $\mathscr{Im} \langle H' \mid K' ; j \rangle = 0$, for all j.

Second order:

$$\langle H' \mid \mathbf{V}_2 \mid H''' \rangle + \sum_{H''} \langle H' \mid \mathbf{V}_1 \mid H'' \rangle \langle H'' \mid K''' ; 1 \rangle + H' \langle H' \mid K''' ; 2 \rangle$$
$$= \Delta_2 H''' \,\delta (H', H''') + \Delta_1 H''' \langle H' \mid K''' ; 1 \rangle + H''' \langle H' \mid K''' ; 2 \rangle. \quad (5{:}6a)$$

For $H''' = H'$ (and correspondingly $K''' = K$),

$$\begin{aligned} \Delta_2 H' &= \langle H' \mid \mathbf{V}_2 \mid H' \rangle + \sum_{H'' \neq H'} \langle H' \mid \mathbf{V}_1 \mid H'' \rangle \langle H'' \mid K' ; 1 \rangle \\ &= \langle H' \mid \mathbf{V}_2 \mid H' \rangle + \sum_{H'' \neq H'} \frac{|\langle H' \mid \mathbf{V}_1 \mid H'' \rangle|^2}{H' - H''}. \quad . \quad . \quad . \quad . \quad (5{:}6b) \end{aligned}$$

For $H' \neq H'''$,

$$\langle H' \mid K''' ; 2 \rangle = \sum_{H'' \neq H'''} \frac{\langle H' \mid \mathbf{V}_1 \mid H'' \rangle \langle H'' \mid \mathbf{V}_1 \mid H''' \rangle}{(H' - H''') (H'' - H''')}$$
$$- \frac{\langle H' \mid \mathbf{V}_2 \mid H''' \rangle}{(H' - H''')} - \frac{\langle H''' \mid \mathbf{V}_1 \mid H''' \rangle \langle H' \mid \mathbf{V}_1 \mid H''' \rangle}{(H' - H''')^2}, \quad (5{:}6c)$$

and $\langle H' \mid K' ; 2 \rangle$ is given in (5:5*e*). The higher-order approximations are readily obtained in the same manner, but it is practically useless to go beyond the second (except for a few special cases), because of the increasing complexity of terms.

§ 30. Mixed Spectrum—Non-degenerate

The foregoing treatment deals specifically with the perturbation problem for the case of a pure *discrete* spectrum of the unperturbed Hamiltonian. We can readily extend this to include the case of a mixed unperturbed spectrum, and we shall show that in many cases the continuous part of the spectrum may be neglected so that the preceding results remain essentially correct.

Denoting eigenvalues in the continuous spectrum by letters, e.g. H^c as before, then equation (5:2*c*) which determines the shift in the discrete levels is replaced by the more general equations

$$\sum_{H''} \langle H' | \mathbf{K} | H'' \rangle \langle H'' | K''' \rangle + \int \langle H' | \mathbf{K} | H^c \rangle dH^c \langle H^c | K''' \rangle = K''' \langle H' | K''' \rangle, \quad (5{:}7a)$$

$$\sum_{H''} \langle H^b | \mathbf{K} | H'' \rangle \langle H'' | K''' \rangle + \int \langle H^b | \mathbf{K} | H^c \rangle dH^c \langle H^c | K''' \rangle = K''' \langle H^b | K''' \rangle. \quad (5{:}7b)$$

Equation (5:3b) must now be replaced by the equations

$$\langle H'' \mid K''' \rangle = \delta(H'', H''') + \langle H'' \mid K''' ; 1 \rangle + \langle H'' \mid K''' ; 2 \rangle + \ldots, \quad (5:8a)$$

$$\langle H^c \mid K''' \rangle = \quad 0 \quad + \langle H^c \mid K''' ; 1 \rangle + \langle H^c \mid K''' ; 2 \rangle + \ldots, \quad (5:8b)$$

where the expansion for $\langle H^c \mid K''' \rangle$ begins with a first-order term since

$$\langle H^c \mid H''' \rangle = 0,$$

which simply indicates that we are at present interested in the shift in the discrete spectrum, and by hypothesis $\mid K''' \rangle$ has no component in the continuous spectrum in the limit of vanishing perturbation. From (5:7a and 8a) we again obtain the first-order result

$$\left.\begin{aligned} \langle H' \mid \mathbf{V}_1 \mid H' \rangle &= \Delta_1 H', \\ \langle H' \mid K''' ; 1 \rangle &= -\frac{\langle H' \mid \mathbf{V}_1 \mid H''' \rangle}{H' - H'''}; \end{aligned}\right\} \quad . \quad . \quad . \quad . \quad (5:9a)$$

and as we might have anticipated, equations (5:7b and 8b) give

$$\langle H^b \mid K''' ; 1 \rangle = -\frac{\langle H^b \mid \mathbf{V}_1 \mid H''' \rangle}{H^b - H'''}. \quad . \quad . \quad . \quad . \quad (5:9b)$$

In like manner, the second-order terms from (5:7a and 8a) are

$$\Delta_2 H' = \langle H' \mid \mathbf{V}_2 \mid H' \rangle + \sum_{H'' \neq H'} \frac{|\langle H' \mid \mathbf{V}_1 \mid H'' \rangle|^2}{H' - H''} + \int \frac{|\langle H' \mid \mathbf{V}_1 \mid H^c \rangle|^2}{H' - H^c} dH^c, \quad (5:10a)$$

$$\langle H' | K''' ; 2 \rangle = \sum_{H'' \neq H'''} \frac{\langle H' | \mathbf{V}_1 | H'' \rangle \langle H'' | \mathbf{V}_1 | H''' \rangle}{(H' - H''')(H'' - H''')} + \int \frac{\langle H' | \mathbf{V}_1 | H^c \rangle \, dH^c \langle H^c | \mathbf{V}_1 | H''' \rangle}{(H' - H''')(H^c - H''')}$$

$$- \frac{\langle H' \mid \mathbf{V}_2 \mid H''' \rangle}{H' - H'''} - \frac{\langle H' \mid \mathbf{V}_1 \mid H''' \rangle \langle H''' \mid \mathbf{V}_1 \mid H''' \rangle}{(H' - H''')^2}. \quad (5:10b)$$

From (5:7b and 8b) the amplitude $\langle H^b \mid K''' ; 2 \rangle$ is given by

$$\langle H^b | K''' ; 2 \rangle = \sum_{H'' \neq H'''} \frac{\langle H^b | \mathbf{V}_1 | H'' \rangle \langle H'' | \mathbf{V}_1 | H''' \rangle}{(H^b - H''')(H'' - H''')} + \int \frac{\langle H^b | \mathbf{V}_1 | H^c \rangle \, dH^c \langle H^c | \mathbf{V}_1 | H''' \rangle}{(H^b - H''')(H^c - H''')}$$

$$- \frac{\langle H^b \mid \mathbf{V}_2 \mid H''' \rangle}{H^b - H'''} - \frac{\langle H^b \mid \mathbf{V}_1 \mid H''' \rangle \langle H''' \mid \mathbf{V}_1 \mid H''' \rangle}{(H^b - H''')^2}. \quad (5:10c)$$

Again $\langle H' \mid K' ; 2 \rangle$ is determined by normalization, which now gives

$$\mathcal{R}e \langle H' \mid K' ; 2 \rangle = -\tfrac{1}{2} \Big\{ \sum_{H'' \neq H'} |\langle H'' \mid K' ; 1 \rangle|^2 + \int |\langle H^c \mid K' ; 1 \rangle|^2 dH^c \Big\}. \quad (5:11)$$

We observe from (5:10a) that in this approximation each eigenvalue or level is displaced upward by those below it, and downward by those above; and the displacements are proportional to the square of the coupling as given by the matrix elements of $\mathbf{V}_1$, and inversely proportional to the corresponding energy difference. It is this dependence, plus the fact that ordinarily the coupling between distant levels is very small, that often permits us to neglect the continuous part of the eigenspectrum. However, it must be emphasized that here again there is no general rule and each case must be considered on its own merits.

We may note that the expansion (5:3*a*) as it stands can be applied in a manner which corresponds literally to Born's method of treating collision problems. Thus, taking the perturbing potential as **V** for simplicity, we introduce (5:3*a* and 3*c*) into the exact equation

$$\mathbf{K} \mid K' \rangle = K' \mid K' \rangle, \qquad (5{:}12)$$

and obtain the following system of recursion equations for the jth approximation $| j \rangle$ in terms of the lower-order approximations.

$$\left.\begin{aligned}
(\mathbf{H} - H') \mid H' \rangle &= 0. \\
(\mathbf{H} - H') \mid 1 \rangle &= -(\mathbf{V} - \Delta_1 H') \mid H' \rangle. \\
(\mathbf{H} - H') \mid 2 \rangle &= -(\mathbf{V} - \Delta_1 H') \mid 1 \rangle + \Delta_2 H' \mid H' \rangle. \\
&\vdots \\
(\mathbf{H} - H') \mid n+1 \rangle &= -(\mathbf{V} - \Delta_1 H') \mid n \rangle + \Delta_2 H' \mid n-1 \rangle + \\
&\qquad \ldots \Delta_{n+1} H' \mid H' \rangle.
\end{aligned}\right\} \qquad (5{:}13)$$

Here we invoke the theorem [3] that if $(\mathbf{H} - H') \mid a \rangle = \mid b \rangle$ then $\langle H' \mid b \rangle = 0$, as follows from the Hermiticity of **H** when we pre-multiply by $\langle H' \mid$. Applied to equation (5:13) we again obtain the previous results. These recursion formulæ are, of course, precisely identical with those obtained before, the only difference being that we do not eliminate the symbolic vectors in the approximate development (5:3*a*) of $\mid K' \rangle$ until a later stage in the calculation.

§ 31. Perturbed Representatives of General Operators

It is sometimes of interest to determine the approximate effect produced by a perturbation on the matrix representative of some operator $\boldsymbol{\alpha}$. We have the exact equation

$$\langle K' \mid \boldsymbol{\alpha} \mid K'' \rangle = \sum_{H''', H^{\mathrm{IV}}} \langle K' \mid H''' \rangle \langle H''' \mid \boldsymbol{\alpha} \mid H^{\mathrm{IV}} \rangle \langle H^{\mathrm{IV}} \mid K'' \rangle, \qquad (5{:}14)$$

which combined with our previous calculations gives

$$\langle K' \mid \boldsymbol{\alpha} \mid K'' \rangle = \langle H' \mid \boldsymbol{\alpha} \mid H'' \rangle + \Big\{ \sum_{H^{\mathrm{IV}}} \langle H' \mid \boldsymbol{\alpha} \mid H^{\mathrm{IV}} \rangle \langle H^{\mathrm{IV}} \mid K'' ; 1 \rangle$$
$$+ \sum_{H'''} \langle K' ; 1 \mid H''' \rangle \langle H''' \mid \boldsymbol{\alpha} \mid H'' \rangle \Big\} + \ldots, \qquad (5{:}15a)$$

or

$$\langle K' \mid \boldsymbol{\alpha} \mid K'' \rangle = \langle H' \mid \boldsymbol{\alpha} \mid H'' \rangle + \Delta_1 \langle H' \mid \boldsymbol{\alpha} \mid H'' \rangle + \Delta_2 \langle H' \mid \boldsymbol{\alpha} \mid H'' \rangle + \ldots; \qquad (5{:}15b)$$

[3] The equation transcribed to a coordinate representation is known as the orthogonality property of non-homogeneous differential equations, i.e. $(\Lambda - \lambda) g = h$, with Λ a self-adjoint differential operator.

and from (5:15a),

$$\Delta_1 \langle H' \mid \boldsymbol{\alpha} \mid H'' \rangle = \sum_{H'''} \left\{ \frac{\langle H' \mid \boldsymbol{\alpha} \mid H''' \rangle \langle H''' \mid \mathbf{V}_1 \mid H'' \rangle}{(H'' - H''')} + \frac{\langle H' \mid \mathbf{V}_1 \mid H''' \rangle \langle H''' \mid \boldsymbol{\alpha} \mid H'' \rangle}{(H' - H''')} \right\}, \quad (5:16)$$

where $H''' \neq H''$, H' in the respective sums above. The diagonal term is

$$\Delta_1 \langle H' \mid \boldsymbol{\alpha} \mid H' \rangle = \sum_{H''' \neq H'} \left\{ \frac{\langle H' \mid \boldsymbol{\alpha} \mid H''' \rangle \langle H''' \mid \mathbf{V}_1 \mid H' \rangle + \langle H' \mid \mathbf{V}_1 \mid H''' \rangle \langle H''' \mid \boldsymbol{\alpha} \mid H' \rangle}{H' - H'''} \right\}. \quad (5:16a)$$

In particular, if $\boldsymbol{\alpha} = \mathbf{V}_1$, then

$$\Delta_1 \langle H' \mid \mathbf{V}_1 \mid H' \rangle = 2 \sum_{H''' \neq H'} \frac{|\langle H' \mid \mathbf{V}_1 \mid H''' \rangle|^2}{H' - H'''}, \quad . \quad . \quad (5:16b)$$

and comparing with (5:6b) when $\mathbf{V}_1$ is the only non-zero perturbing term (as is often the case) we find

$$\Delta_2 H' \doteq \tfrac{1}{2}\Delta_1 \langle H' \mid \mathbf{V}_1 \mid H' \rangle, \quad . \quad . \quad . \quad . \quad . \quad . \quad (5:17a)$$

and in general,

$$\Delta_n H' = \frac{1}{n} \Delta_{n-1} \langle H' \mid \mathbf{V}_1 \mid H' \rangle. \quad . \quad . \quad . \quad . \quad . \quad (5:17b)$$

§ 32. Degenerate Case

The case of true or *absolute* degeneracy is characterized by the fact that to a given eigenvalue H' of the unperturbed Hamiltonian there belong a number g' of independent states, where in general $g' = g'(H')$. In order to distinguish the independent eigenvectors of a g'-fold degenerate set we must as usual introduce a set of operators which together with **H** form a complete commuting set, and whose eigenvalues label the states, e.g. $\mid H'\alpha' \rangle$. The perturbation potential will, in general, cause some splitting of the g' coincident eigenvalues (states), i.e. remove the degeneracy to some extent at least, and since we must label the g' states belonging to **K** which correspond to the original degenerate eigenvalue H', the prime notation is no longer especially convenient. For our present purpose it is more convenient to label the states as $\mid H^{r,p} \rangle$, where H^r replaces H' as prototype eigenvalue, and $p = 1, 2, \ldots g_r$; the ordering of the states of a degenerate set being dictated by convenience in the particular problem under consideration.

The selection of a degenerate set of g_r vectors belonging to H^r is an arbitrary matter, and indeed there are an infinite number of possibilities. If we choose any initial orthonormal set denoted by $\{ \mid \underline{H^{r,p}} \rangle \}$, these are determined only to within a unitary transformation since the set given by the linear combinations

$$\mid H^{r,s} \rangle = \sum_p \mid \underline{H^{r,p}} \rangle \langle \underline{H^{r,p}} \mid H^{r,s} \rangle = \sum_p c\,(rs, rp) \mid \underline{H^{r,p}} \rangle, \quad . \quad (5:18a)$$

with

$$\sum_p \langle H^{r,t} \mid \underline{H^{r,p}} \rangle \langle \underline{H^{r,p}} \mid H^{r,s} \rangle = \sum_t \bar{c}\,(rp, rt)\, c\,(rs, rp) = \delta\,(t, s), \quad (5:18b)$$

is also orthonormal.

It follows from our previous work that, as the perturbing term tends to zero, $| K^{l,m} \rangle$ (for each m) will reduce to one of the eigenstates of the original unperturbed problem, but this eigenstate, barring special cases, will be a linear combination of our arbitrarily chosen initial set—the particular combination depending on the perturbing potential $\mathbf{V}$. Hence, the degenerate case differs only in the respect that we must first determine the correct zero-order approximation to the eigenvectors of $\mathbf{K}$, since we cannot in general identify this limit with the members of our arbitrarily chosen set. The proper linear combinations correspond to selecting the coefficients in (5:18*a*) so that the matrix of $\mathbf{V}$ is diagonal in the subspace of the $\{ | H^{r,s} \rangle \}$, i.e.

$$\langle H^{r,t} | \mathbf{V} | H^{r,s} \rangle = \epsilon^{r,s} \delta(s,t). \quad . \quad . \quad . \quad . \quad . \quad (5{:}19)$$

This particular choice of the $| H^{r,s} \rangle$ is not an *ad hoc* assumption as it might appear, but a straightforward consequence of the fact that in the degenerate case (5:5*c*), (5:6*b*), etc., acquire resonance denominators owing to the coincidence of eigenvalues, and these infinite terms are removed by our special choice. The diagonal elements of $\mathbf{V}$ are found from the general equation

$$\mathbf{V} | H^{r,s} \rangle = \epsilon^{r,s} | H^{r,s} \rangle + \sum_{j,k}^{j \neq r} | H^{j,k} \rangle \langle H^{j,k} | \mathbf{V} | H^{r,s} \rangle. \quad . \quad . \quad . \quad (5{:}20)$$

Pre-multiplying (5:20) by $\langle \underline{H^{r,q}} |$, and using (5:18), we obtain the secular equation

$$\sum_p \langle \underline{H^{r,q}} | \mathbf{V} | \underline{H^{r,p}} \rangle c(rs, rp) = \epsilon^{r,s} c(rs, rq). \quad . \quad . \quad . \quad . \quad (5{:}21)$$

Noting that all quantities refer to the rth degenerate level, we may drop the index r, and write this as

$$\sum_p \langle \underline{q} | \mathbf{V} | \underline{p} \rangle c(s,p) = \epsilon^s c(s,q). \quad . \quad . \quad . \quad . \quad . \quad . \quad (5{:}22)^4$$

This set of g_r equations has a non-trivial solution for the c's only if the determinant of the coefficients vanishes, i.e.

$$\begin{vmatrix} \langle 1 | \mathbf{V} | 1 \rangle - \epsilon^s & \langle 1 | \mathbf{V} | 2 \rangle \ldots & \langle 1 | \mathbf{V} | g_r \rangle \\ \langle 2 | \mathbf{V} | 1 \rangle & \langle 2 | \mathbf{V} | 2 \rangle - \epsilon^s \ldots & \langle 2 | \mathbf{V} | g_r \rangle \\ \cdot & \cdot & \cdot \\ \cdot & \cdot & \cdot \\ \cdot & \cdot & \cdot \\ \langle g_r | \mathbf{V} | 1 \rangle & \langle g_r | \mathbf{V} | 2 \rangle \ldots & \langle g_r | \mathbf{V} | g_r \rangle - \epsilon^s \end{vmatrix} = 0. \quad (5{:}23)^5$$

The g_r values of ϵ^s give the diagonal elements of $\mathbf{V}$ referring to the subspace of H^r, and each value of ϵ^s substituted in (5:22) gives the ratio of the expansion coefficients c, which are then completely determined by the unitary condition (5:18*a*).

[4] This equation may obviously also be written as

$$\sum_p \langle \underline{q} | \mathbf{K} | \underline{p} \rangle c(s,p) = \sum_p \langle \underline{q} | \mathbf{H} + \mathbf{V} | \underline{p} \rangle c(s,p) = (H^r + \epsilon^{r,s}) c(s,q) = Wc(s,q),$$

which is sometimes more convenient.

[5] We may note that if the initial vectors are *not* orthogonal the secular determinant differs in that one computes matrix elements of $\mathbf{V} - \epsilon\mathbf{I}$, instead of $\mathbf{V}$ alone. Or, if convenience dictates, we may equivalently compute the elements of $\mathbf{K} - W\mathbf{I}$ according to the preceding footnote.

It should be noted here, that the value of the Spur Theorem [§ 27, equations (4:53–54)] lies in the fact that if the secular determinant factors into a number of small block determinants along the diagonal, as is often the case,[6] then, from a knowledge of certain of the roots, the others can be obtained from the spur by simple subtraction.

Having determined the correct "zero-order" approximation we may now proceed essentially as in the previous non-degenerate case. Thus,

$$\langle H^{j,k} \mid K^{r,s} \rangle = \delta(j,r)\,\delta(k,s) + \langle H^{j,k} \mid K^{r,s};1 \rangle + \langle H^{j,k} \mid K^{r,s};2 \rangle + \ldots, \quad (5:24)$$

$$K^{r,s} = H^r + \Delta_1^{(s)} H^r + \Delta_2^{(s)} H^r + \ldots, \quad (5:25a)$$

$$\Delta_1^{(s)} H^r = \epsilon^{r,s} = \langle H^{r,s} \mid \mathbf{V} \mid H^{r,s} \rangle. \quad (5:25b)$$

Note that the process of determining the correct zero-order approximation permits us to begin the expansion (5:24) with δ's, and also determines the first-order energy corrections $\epsilon^{r,s}$. In the expressions (5:23–25) we have implicitly assumed that $\epsilon^{r,s}$ is different for each s, and this is practically the only important case.

From the equation

$$\sum_{j,k} \langle H^{l,m} \mid \mathbf{K} \mid H^{j,k} \rangle \langle H^{j,k} \mid K^{r,s} \rangle = K^{r,s} \langle H^{l,m} \mid K^{r,s} \rangle, \quad (5:26)$$

we obtain

$$(H^l - H^r)\,\delta(l,r)\,\delta(m,s) = 0, \quad (5:27)$$

and

$$(H^l - H^r)\langle H^{l,m} \mid K^{r,s};1 \rangle + \langle H^{l,m} \mid \mathbf{V} \mid H^{r,s} \rangle - \Delta_1^{(s)} H^r \,\delta(l,r)\,\delta(m,s) = 0, \quad (5:28)$$

i.e.

$$\langle H^{r,s} \mid \mathbf{V} \mid H^{r,s} \rangle = \Delta_1^{(s)} H^r,$$

$$\langle H^{l,m} \mid K^{r,s};1 \rangle = -\frac{\langle H^{l,m} \mid \mathbf{V} \mid H^{r,s} \rangle}{H^l - H^{jr}} \qquad (l \neq r).$$

This simple result for the first order is obtained because of the way in which we have determined our $\{ \mid H^{r,s} \rangle \}$. If we had not done so we would at this point obtain the secular equation (5:21). Equating second-order terms to zero, we obtain

$$(H^l - H^r)\langle H^{l,m} \mid K^{r,s};2 \rangle + \sum_{j,k}\{\langle H^{l,m} \mid \mathbf{V} \mid H^{j,k} \rangle - \Delta_1^{(s)} H^r \delta(l,r)\,\delta(m,s)\}\langle H^{j,k} \mid K^{r,s};1 \rangle$$
$$- \Delta_2^{(s)} H^r \,\delta(l,r)\,\delta(m,s) = 0, \quad (5:29)$$

i.e.

$$\Delta_2^{(s)} H^r = \sum_{j,k} \frac{|\langle H^{r,s} \mid \mathbf{V} \mid H^{j,k} \rangle|^2}{H^r - H^j} \qquad (j \neq r),$$

$$\langle H^{r,m} \mid K^{r,s};1 \rangle = \sum_{j,k} \frac{\langle H^{r,m} \mid \mathbf{V} \mid H^{j,k} \rangle \langle H^{j,k} \mid \mathbf{V} \mid H^{r,s} \rangle}{(H^r - H^j)(\epsilon^{r,s} - \epsilon^{r,m})} \qquad (j \neq r, m \neq s).$$

We have now determined $\mid K^{r,s} \rangle$ to terms of the first order except for the coefficient $\langle H^{r,s} \mid K^{r,s};1 \rangle$, which as before is determined by normalization and has

[6] Cf. § 83. Certain simplifying conditions noted there greatly increase the utility of this result.

zero real part; and again for simplicity we take the imaginary part to be zero also. We observe that the determination of the correction to the eigenvalues is always one order ahead of the expansion coefficients. Higher approximations, as listed below, are readily obtained, but the computations are rarely carried beyond the first or second order.

TABLE 5.1.—PERTURBATION FORMULÆ

$\{ | H^{r,s} \rangle \}$ chosen such that $\langle H^{r,t} | \mathbf{V} | H^{r,s} \rangle = \epsilon^{r,s}\, \delta(s,t)$, and the g_r values of $\epsilon^{r,s}$ assumed to be distinct.

I. $\langle H^{j,k} | K^{r,s} \rangle = \delta(j,r)\,\delta(k,s) + \langle H^{j,k} | K^{r,s}; 1 \rangle + \langle H^{j,k} | K^{r,s}; 2 \rangle + \cdots.$

II. $K^{r,s} = H^r + \Delta_1^{(s)} H^r + \Delta_2^{(s)} H^r + \cdots.$

III. $\Delta_1^{(s)} H^r = \epsilon^{r,s} = \langle H^{r,s} | \mathbf{V} | H^{r,s} \rangle.$

IV. $$\Delta_2^{(s)} H^r = \sum_{j,k} \frac{|\langle H^{r,s} | \mathbf{V} | H^{j,k} \rangle|^2}{H^r - H^j} \qquad (j \neq r).$$

V. $$\Delta_3^{(s)} H^r = \sum_{j,k} \langle H^{r,s} | \mathbf{V} | H^{j,k} \rangle \langle H^{j,k} | K^{r,s}; 2 \rangle \qquad (j \neq r).$$

VI. $$\Delta_n^{(s)} H^r = \sum_{j,k} \langle H^{r,s} | \mathbf{V} | H^{j,k} \rangle \langle H^{j,k} | K^{r,s}; n-1 \rangle - \sum_{\nu=2}^{n-2} \Delta_\nu^{(s)} H^r \langle H^{r,s} | K^{r,s}; n-\nu \rangle \qquad (j \neq r).$$

VII. $$\langle H^{l,m} | K^{r,s}; 1 \rangle = \frac{\langle H^{l,m} | \mathbf{V} | H^{r,s} \rangle}{H^r - H^l} \qquad (l \neq r).$$

VIII. $$\langle H^{r,m} | K^{r,s}; 1 \rangle = \sum_{j,k} \frac{\langle H^{r,m} | \mathbf{V} | H^{j,k} \rangle \langle H^{j,k} | \mathbf{V} | H^{r,s} \rangle}{(H^r - H^j)(\epsilon^{r,s} - \epsilon^{r,m})} \qquad (j \neq r,\ m \neq s).$$

IX. $\langle H^{r,m} | K^{r,m}; 1 \rangle = 0.$

X. $$\langle H^{l,m} | K^{r,s}; 2 \rangle = -\sum_{j,k} \frac{\langle H^{l,m} | \mathbf{V} | H^{j,k} \rangle \langle H^{j,k} | K^{r,s}; 1 \rangle}{(H^l - H^r)} - \frac{\langle H^{l,m} | \mathbf{V} | H^{r,s} \rangle \langle H^{r,s} | \mathbf{V} | H^{r,s} \rangle}{(H^l - H^r)^2} \qquad (l \neq r).$$

XI. $$\langle H^{r,m} | K^{r,s}; 2 \rangle = \sum_{j,k} \frac{\langle H^{r,m} | \mathbf{V} | H^{j,k} \rangle \langle H^{j,k} | K^{r,s}; 2 \rangle}{\epsilon^{r,s} - \epsilon^{r,m}} - \frac{\Delta_2^{(s)} H^r \langle H^{r,m} | K^{r,s}; 1 \rangle}{\epsilon^{r,s} - \epsilon^{r,m}} \qquad (j \neq r,\ m \neq s).$$

XII. $$\langle H^{r,m} | K^{r,m}; 2 \rangle = -\tfrac{1}{2} \sum_{j,k} |\langle H^{j,k} | K^{r,m}; 1 \rangle|^2.$$

XIII. $$\langle H^{l,m} | K^{r,s}; n \rangle = -\sum_{j,k} \frac{\langle H^{l,m} | \mathbf{V} | H^{j,k} \rangle \langle H^{j,k} | K^{r,s}; n-1 \rangle}{H^l - H^r} + \sum_{\nu=1}^{n-1} \frac{\Delta_\nu^{(s)} H^r \langle H^{l,m} | K^{r,s}; n-\nu \rangle}{H^l - H^r} \qquad (l \neq r).$$

$$\text{XIV.}\quad \langle H^{r,m} \mid K^{r,s}; n \rangle = \sum_{j,k} \frac{\langle H^{r,m} \mid \mathbf{V} \mid H^{j,k} \rangle \langle H^{j,k} \mid K^{r,s}; n \rangle}{\epsilon^{r,s} - \epsilon^{r,m}} - \sum_{\nu=1}^{n-1} \frac{\Delta_{\nu+1}^{(s)} H^r \langle H^{r,m} \mid K^{r,s}; n-\nu \rangle}{\epsilon^{r,s} - \epsilon^{r,m}} \qquad (j \neq r,\ m \neq s).$$

$$\text{XV.}\quad \langle H^{r,m} \mid K^{r,m}; n \rangle = -\tfrac{1}{2} \sum_{\nu=1}^{n-1} \sum_{j,k} \langle K^{r,m}; \nu \mid H^{j,k} \rangle \langle H^{j,k} \mid K^{r,m}; n-\nu \rangle.$$

§ 33. Reduction of Degenerate Case to Non-degenerate

If in the degenerate case we add to the matrix of $\mathbf{H}$ the diagonal elements of $\mathbf{V}$, computed with the eigenvectors $\mid H^{r,s} \rangle$ as defined above, then we have a problem for which we know the eigenvalues $H^r + \epsilon^{r,s}$ and the corresponding eigenvectors, and which by hypothesis is non-degenerate. In other words, we take the Hamiltonian of the unperturbed problem to be $\mathbf{H}_1 = \mathbf{H} + \mathbf{V}_a$ by formally separating $\mathbf{V}$ into the parts $\mathbf{V}_a$ and $\mathbf{V}_b$, where the operators $\mathbf{V}_a$ and $\mathbf{V}_b$ are defined by their matrix elements as

$$\langle H^{j,k} \mid \mathbf{V}_a \mid H^{r,s} \rangle = \epsilon^{r,s} \delta(j,r)\,\delta(k,s); \qquad \epsilon^{r,s} = \langle H^{r,s} \mid \mathbf{V} \mid H^{r,s} \rangle;$$

$$\langle H^{j,k} \mid \mathbf{V}_b \mid H^{r,s} \rangle = \begin{cases} \langle H^{j,k} \mid \mathbf{V} \mid H^{r,s} \rangle, & j \neq r \\ 0 & j = r \end{cases}.$$

Since the newly defined unperturbed problem is no longer degenerate, the simpler notation of § 29 applies, but for our present purpose we retain the notation of the degenerate case with the understanding that the vectors $\{ \mid H^{r,s} \rangle \} = \{ \mid H_1^{r,s} \rangle \}$, $s = 1, 2, \ldots g_r$, etc., are no longer considered as members of a degenerate set. We may note that the definition of the operators by their representatives, as above, is no less general than an explicit operator form, which here cannot be obtained except for special cases such as the anomalous Zeeman effect.[7] Using the above device, equations I, II, etc. (Table 5.1) are replaced by

$$\langle H^{j,k} \mid K^{r,s} \rangle = \delta(j,r)\,\delta(k,s) + \langle H^{j,k} \mid K^{r,s}; 1 \rangle + \langle H^{j,k} \mid K^{r,s}; 2 \rangle + \ldots \qquad \text{I}a.$$

$$K^{r,s} = (H^r + \epsilon^{r,s}) + \Delta_2^{(s)} H^r + \ldots \qquad \text{II}a.$$

$$(H^l + \epsilon^{l,m} - H^r - \epsilon^{r,s})\,\delta(l,r)\,\delta(m,s) = 0. \qquad \text{III}a.$$

$$(H^l + \epsilon^{l,m} - H^r - \epsilon^{r,s}) \langle H^{l,m} \mid K^{r,s}; 1 \rangle = - \langle H^{l,m} \mid \mathbf{V}_b \mid H^{r,s} \rangle, \qquad \text{IV}a.$$

i.e.

$$\langle H^{l,m} \mid K^{r,s}; 1 \rangle = - \frac{\langle H^{l,m} \mid \mathbf{V}_b \mid H^{r,s} \rangle}{H^l + \epsilon^{l,m} - H^r - \epsilon^{r,s}} \qquad (l \neq r). \qquad \text{IV}b.$$

$$(H^l + \epsilon^{l,m} - H^r - \epsilon^{r,s}) \langle H^{l,m} \mid K^{r,s}; 2 \rangle + \sum_{j,k} \langle H^{l,m} \mid \mathbf{V}_b \mid H^{j,k} \rangle \langle H^{j,k} \mid K^{r,s}; 1 \rangle = \Delta_2^{(s)} H^r\,\delta(l,r)\,\delta(m,s), \qquad \text{V}a.$$

[7] Cf. DIRAC, *op. cit.* See also Chap. XI, § 99

i.e.

$$\Delta_2^{(s)}H^r = \sum_{j,k} \langle H^{r,s} \mid \mathbf{V}_b \mid H^{j,k} \rangle \langle H^{j,k} \mid K^{r,s} ; 1 \rangle$$

$$= \sum_{j,k} \frac{|\langle H^{r,s} \mid \mathbf{V}_b \mid H^{j,k} \rangle|^2}{H^r + \epsilon^{r,s} - H^j - \epsilon^{j,k}} \qquad (j \neq r). \quad . \quad . \quad . \quad \mathrm{V}b.$$

$$\langle H^{l,m} \mid K^{r,s} ; 2 \rangle = \sum_{j,k} \frac{\langle H^{l,m} \mid \mathbf{V}_b \mid H^{j,k} \rangle \langle H^{j,k} \mid K^{r,s} ; 1 \rangle}{H^r + \epsilon^{r,s} - H^l - \epsilon^{l,m}}, \quad . \quad . \quad . \quad \mathrm{VI}a.$$

etc.

For most problems, either of the two preceding methods may be used, but, in general, the convergence is apt to be slower for the latter.[8] As with most general questions of convergence in perturbation methods, a precise comparison is hardly possible because of the undetermined series occurring.[9]

§ 34. Relative Degeneracy

The procedure for the *true* degenerate case seems at first sight completely different from that of the non-degenerate case. However, by taking a group of well-separated levels (states) and bringing them closer and closer together until they coincide exactly, we have a continuous transition from non-degeneracy to absolute degeneracy. The question now is where the limit lies for the application of one method or the other. The answer is found by examining more closely equations (5:5*b*, *c*; 5:6*b*, *c*).

In order that the procedure of the perturbation calculus converge for a given state belonging to H', say, it is necessary that $|\langle H' \mid \mathbf{V} \mid H''' \rangle|$ be smaller than $|H' - H'''|$ for all H''' and, in order that the convergence be rapid, $\langle H' \mid \mathbf{V} \mid H''' \rangle$ should be *much* smaller—for we have assumed $\langle H' \mid K''' ; 1 \rangle$ to be small compared to unity, and this can only be realized under the above-mentioned conditions. If, for example, there are two levels H^1, H^2 which perturb each other and lie so close that the difference $H^2 - H^1 = \delta$ is of the same order of magnitude or smaller than the interaction coupling $\langle H^1 \mid \mathbf{V} \mid H^2 \rangle$, or V_{12} for brevity, then we can no longer treat them as non-degenerate. In such a case, $\langle H^1 \mid K^2 ; 1 \rangle$ is not small, but a slight modification of the method of the degenerate case will give the desired result. We shall restrict our considerations to the simplest case of a single pair of such *nearly* degenerate states, since this example will illustrate an interesting physical aspect of the perturbation problem in general, and the results are readily extended to include many interacting states. The present problem is essentially the converse of the one treated in § 33, since it may be described as a forcible reduction of the problem to a degenerate one by the obvious expedient of subtracting off the small differences in the unperturbed matrix of **H**, and adding these to the perturbation matrix. If this is done we indeed have a degenerate problem, and our first task is to determine the correct zero-order approximation to the eigenvectors, or equivalently, the eigenfunctions. Following the procedure of § 32, we write

[8] Cf. *T.A.S.* for further discussion and illustrative examples.
[9] However, see WILSON: *Proc. Roy. Soc.* A, **124**, 186 (1929).

$$|K^1\rangle = c(1,1)|H^1\rangle + c(1,2)|H^2\rangle + |K^1;1\rangle + |K^1;2\rangle + \dots, \quad (5:30)$$

$$|K^2\rangle = c(2,1)|H^1\rangle + c(2,2)|H^2\rangle + |K^2;1\rangle + |K^2;2\rangle, \quad (5:31)$$

$$H^2 - H^1 = \delta, \quad (5:32)$$

$$\left.\begin{aligned} K^1 &= H^1 + \epsilon^1 + \dots, \\ K^2 &= H^1 + \epsilon^2 + \dots \end{aligned}\right\} \quad (5:33)$$

The coefficients c are determined by the usual equations:

$$\left.\begin{aligned} \{\langle H^1|\mathbf{V}|H^1\rangle - \epsilon^n\}c(n,1) + \langle H^1|\mathbf{V}|H^2\rangle c(n,2) = 0, \\ \langle H^2|\mathbf{V}|H^1\rangle c(n,1) + \{\langle H^2|\mathbf{V}|H^2\rangle + \delta - \epsilon^n\}c(n,2) = 0, \end{aligned}\right\} \quad (n=1,2) \quad (5:34)$$

i.e.

$$\begin{vmatrix} V_{11} - \epsilon^n & V_{12} \\ V_{21} & V_{22} + \delta - \epsilon^n \end{vmatrix} = 0, \quad (5:35)$$

where the δ appears because of the way in which we have defined the perturbation. Then

$$\epsilon^{1,2} = \frac{\delta + V_{11} + V_{22}}{2} \mp \tfrac{1}{2}[(\delta + V_{22} - V_{11})^2 + 4|V_{12}|^2]^{\frac{1}{2}}. \quad (5:36)$$

Let us consider a few special cases:

If there is no interaction, $V_{12} = 0$ (or for $\delta \gg |V_{12}|$) and we find

$$\left.\begin{aligned} c(1,1) = c(2,2) = 1, \\ c(1,2) = c(2,1) = 0; \end{aligned}\right\} \quad (5:37)$$

$$\left.\begin{aligned} \epsilon^1 &= V_{11}, \\ \epsilon^2 &= V_{22} + \delta. \end{aligned}\right\} \quad (5:38)$$

The result (5:37) is just the usual non-degenerate zero-order, and (5:38), which is the shift of the two levels due to the average perturbation potential, is the ordinary non-degenerate first-order energy correction. The distance between the two levels is now $\delta + V_{22} - V_{11}$, which is the first term in the root (5:36), and in this approximation the mean of the two levels lies a distance $\frac{1}{2}(\delta + V_{11} + V_{22})$ (which is the first term of 5:36) above H^1. We see, therefore, that we can treat the two parts of the perturbation separately; first, the self-action of the states, V_{11} and V_{22}, and then we have the resultant states with only the interaction V_{12} between them.

If we wish to study the effect of the latter we can put $V_{11} = V_{22} = 0$, obtaining

$$\epsilon^{1,2} = \frac{\delta}{2} \mp \tfrac{1}{2}[\delta^2 + 4|V_{12}|^2]^{\frac{1}{2}}, \quad (5:39)$$

and for $\delta \ll |V_{12}|$ this gives

$$\left.\begin{aligned} \epsilon^1 &= -\frac{|V_{12}|^2}{\delta}, \quad K^1 \cong H^1 + \epsilon^1, \\ \epsilon^2 &= \delta + \frac{|V_{12}|^2}{\delta}, \quad K^2 \cong H^1 + \epsilon^2 \approx H^2 - \epsilon^1; \end{aligned}\right\} \quad (5:40)$$

which shows that we can regard the interaction as a repulsion between the levels which increases rapidly as the two interacting levels approach. The result (5:40), which is here obtained as a first approximation, will be recognized as the second-order term (5:6*b*) in the treatment for non-degenerate states, specialized to the present case. As we already know, the second-order approximation to the energy (5:6*b*) is nothing but the result of all possible interactions between the given level and all others. The significant point to notice is that while the results in the non-degenerate treatment were no longer valid for small δ, they now remain valid for all values of δ.

For $\delta = 0$, we have from the above,

$$\epsilon^1 = -\mid V_{12} \mid, \qquad \epsilon^2 = \mid V_{12} \mid; \quad . \quad . \quad . \quad . \quad . \quad (5:41)$$

$$c(1, 1) = c(1, 2) = c(2, 1) = -c(2, 2) = 1/\sqrt{2}. \quad . \quad (5:42)$$

The relations (5:37) show that when the two states do not perturb each other appreciably, the perturbed states (in the limit) are identical with the unperturbed ones; whereas, when the interaction is not negligible, each perturbed state acquires the properties of both unperturbed states, and in the limiting case (5:42), when $\delta = 0$, the properties are equally shared.

CHAPTER VI

Group Concepts and Symmetry Properties

§ 35. n-Particle Systems

We shall not consider the applications of the general quantum theory to the usual elementary systems, but pass directly to the more important questions which arise in the analysis of many-particle systems and, in particular, systems of identical particles. We are now in a better position to consider the method (noted in §§ 6, 27) of combining constituent systems which involves the multiplication of the constituent vector spaces. In general, for n systems, which are not necessarily identical, there will be a set of observables $\boldsymbol{\xi}_1$ describing the first system, $\boldsymbol{\xi}_2$ the second, etc., and it is assumed that the observables of the various systems commute (even when interactions are present), or symbolically

$$[\,\boldsymbol{\xi}_j,\ \boldsymbol{\xi}_k\,] = 0 \qquad (j \neq k). \qquad \text{(6:1)}$$

The individual systems will have the respective Hamiltonians $\mathbf{H}_1(\boldsymbol{\xi}_1)$, $\mathbf{H}_2(\boldsymbol{\xi}_2)$, . . . , and the equations of motion

$$\dot{\boldsymbol{\xi}}_k = [\,\boldsymbol{\xi}_k,\ \mathbf{H}_k\,], \qquad \text{(6:2)}$$

and since the variables of the distinct systems all commute, the equations of motion of the total system will be (neglecting interaction terms)

$$\dot{\boldsymbol{\xi}}_k = [\,\boldsymbol{\xi}_k,\ \mathbf{H}\,], \qquad \mathbf{H} = \sum_j \mathbf{H}_j\,(\,\boldsymbol{\xi}_j\,), \qquad \text{(6:3)}$$

which show that the equations of motion are unchanged. If now we take a complete set of observables $\mathbf{q}_1$ out of $\boldsymbol{\xi}_1$, $\mathbf{q}_2$ out of $\boldsymbol{\xi}_2$, etc., the constituent S equations are

$$i\hbar \frac{d}{dt} \langle\, q_k' \mid \rangle = \int \langle\, q_k' \mid \mathbf{H}_k \mid q_k'' \,\rangle\, dq_k'' \,\langle\, q_k'' \mid \rangle, \quad \text{for all } k. \qquad \text{(6:4)}$$

In the combined $\mathbf{q} = \{\, \mathbf{q}_1,\ \mathbf{q}_2,\ .\ .\ .\ \mathbf{q}_n \,\}$ representation, $\mathbf{H}_k$, for example, will have the representative

$$\langle\, {}'q \mid \mathbf{H}_k \mid {}''q \,\rangle = \langle\, q_k' \mid \mathbf{H}_k \mid q_k'' \,\rangle \prod_{j \neq k} \delta\,(\, q_j' - q_j'' \,), \qquad \text{(6:5)}$$

which result combined with equation (6:4) shows that the probability amplitude $\langle\, {}'q \mid \rangle = \langle\, q_1' \mid \rangle \langle\, q_2' \mid \rangle \ldots \langle\, q_n' \mid \rangle$ satisfies the S equation

$$i\hbar \frac{d}{dt} \langle\, {}'q \mid \rangle = \int \langle\, {}'q \mid \mathbf{H} \mid {}''q \,\rangle\, d''q \,\langle\, {}''q \mid \rangle. \qquad \text{(6:6)}$$

Thus, the S equation obtains for the resultant system, if we add the Hamiltonians of the constituent systems, and multiply their vector spaces. This result is not *a priori* self-evident or trivial, since it is only possible because the S equation is linear in d/dt.

§ 36. Supplementary Conditions

Aside from the basic quantum postulates discussed in Chapter III, there are in general additional restrictions on physical states, of the type

$$\mathbf{A} \mid \rangle = 0 \qquad (\mathbf{A} \text{ a linear operator}), \quad . \ . \ . \ . \ . \quad (6{:}7)$$

which are termed supplementary conditions, since they show that the vector space of all possible $\mid \rangle$'s is more general than necessary to represent physical states corresponding to our world.[1] In other words, such conditions restrict our $\mid \rangle$'s to a certain subspace of the whole vector space, and it is clear that if such a restriction is to be physically meaningful, the specified subspace must be invariant under all admissible linear operators, and in particular under the equations of motion, i.e. states corresponding to *our world* and *not our world* are exclusive, and there cannot be transitions from one to the other. Hence, if the $\mid \rangle$'s (states), moving according to the law

$$i\hbar \frac{d}{dt} \mid \rangle = \mathbf{H} \mid \rangle, \quad . \ . \ . \ . \ . \ . \ . \ . \quad (6{:}8)$$

initially lie in the selected subspace, they must remain in it; which means that if

$$\mathbf{A} \mid \rangle = 0, \quad . \ . \ . \ . \ . \ . \ . \ . \ . \ . \quad (6{:}9a)$$

then

$$\mathbf{A} \frac{d}{dt} \mid \rangle = 0. \quad . \ . \ . \ . \ . \ . \ . \ . \ . \quad (6{:}9b)$$

From these conditions it follows that

$$\langle \mid \mathbf{AH} - \mathbf{HA} \mid \rangle = 0, \quad . \ . \ . \ . \ . \ . \ . \ . \quad (6{:}10a)$$

which usually means that we must have

$$[\, \mathbf{A}, \mathbf{H} \,]_- = 0. \quad . \ . \ . \ . \ . \ . \ . \ . \ . \quad (6{:}10b)$$

These supplementary conditions must not be too restrictive, and if there are two or more such conditions they must of course be consistent. Thus, if

$$\mathbf{A} \mid \rangle = 0, \qquad \mathbf{B} \mid \rangle = 0, \quad . \ . \ . \ . \ . \ . \quad (6{:}11)$$

then

$$\left.\begin{aligned} [\, \mathbf{A}, \mathbf{B} \,]_- \mid \rangle &= 0, \\ \big[\, \mathbf{A}, [\, \mathbf{A}, \mathbf{B} \,]_- \big]_- \mid \rangle &= 0, \\ \big[\, \mathbf{B}, [\, \mathbf{A}, \mathbf{B} \,]_- \big]_- \mid \rangle &= 0, \end{aligned}\right\}, \quad . \ . \ . \ . \ . \ . \quad (6{:}12)$$

etc.,

[1] In the sense that there are many types of states which would correspond to a world based on different principles, and hence physically unobservable in our universe.

all of which must be consistent, and if after a certain number of these constructs no new conditions arise, then we may take it that our conditions are not redundant.[2] In the present theory the most important supplementary conditions are the symmetry restrictions on systems composed of identical units (particles), which we shall consider in some detail. Physically, these restrictions indicate a coupling between systems which, however, is radically different from the familiar type of *physical* interaction. Nonetheless, the analogy is so close that it is not uncommon to refer to them as interactions, even to the assignment of an interaction energy (cf. Chap. VII).

§ 37. Identical Systems

The problem of most general interest and importance is that of a system whose component parts are all *identical* units, such as electrons, photons, etc. The individual particles will, as before, be characterized by observables $\boldsymbol{\xi}_1, \boldsymbol{\xi}_2, \ldots \boldsymbol{\xi}_n$, but it is now necessary to reconsider the meaning of *observable* since, if we interchange any pair of particles, there will be no corresponding physically observable change, so that it is meaningless to speak of the observables $\boldsymbol{\xi}_1$ as *belonging* to particle [1], etc. In other words, such a literal characterization ascribes an unrealized individuality to each particle; hence, we cannot speak of the $\boldsymbol{\xi}$'s individually as observables. If, for example, we take a complete set of observables $\mathbf{q}$, as before, it is meaningless to ask the probability that a *specific* particle has *its* $\mathbf{q}$'s equal to (or in the neighbourhood of) q'. However, we may inquire as to the probability of a (any) particle being in a given region of space, or of two particles being simultaneously in two given regions, etc.; or how many particles have their momenta equal to (in the range of) a specified value, and similarly for more general observables.

The characteristic of this general type of observable is obviously that it must be symmetrical in the variables of all the particles. Thus, we may take any property or variable $\boldsymbol{\eta}$ pertaining to one of the constituent systems and form the variable $\sum_r \boldsymbol{\eta}_r$, i.e. the total $\boldsymbol{\eta}$ summed over all constituent systems, which property is evidently an observable. In the same way, more complicated quantities of the type $\sum_{r \neq s} \boldsymbol{\eta}_r \boldsymbol{\eta}_s$, etc., can be constructed, but observables of the type of the previous elementary sum appear to play the more important role in theory. From probability theory we know that from the average values of $\sum_r \boldsymbol{\eta}_r, \sum_r \boldsymbol{\eta}_r^2, \ldots$, and hence in general of $\sum_r \mathbf{f}(\boldsymbol{\eta}_r)$ for an arbitrary function of $\boldsymbol{\eta}$, the distribution function of the aggregate systems can, in principle, be inferred.[3] That is, we shall know the average number of particles having $\boldsymbol{\eta}$ equal to any specified value, a special case of importance being the average number of particles in a limited region of configuration space, or the probability of a (any) particle being in a specified region of space. Similarly, the average value of all quantities of the type $\sum_{r \neq s} \boldsymbol{\eta}_r \boldsymbol{\eta}_s$ interpreted for this special illus-

[2] An example of redundant conditions would be $\mathbf{p} | \rangle = 0$, $\mathbf{q} | \rangle = 0$, from which it follows that $[\mathbf{q}, \mathbf{p}]_- = 0$ or $\hbar = 0$, since $| \rangle = 0$ is not a state.

[3] Problem of moments, Tshebysheff-Markoff.

trative case permits us to determine the probability that two particles be found simultaneously in two specified regions of space, etc. The mathematical theory of such compound observables leads us naturally to the quantal analogue of the Gibbs ensemble in statistical mechanics, and ultimately to the theory of the second quantization (Chap. XI).

The total $\mathbf{q}$-representation previously mentioned must obviously be selected in such a way as to be symmetrical with respect to all the particles. For one particle the average value of an arbitrary observable $\boldsymbol{\eta}$ will be

$$\langle \boldsymbol{\eta} \rangle = \iint \langle \mid q' \rangle \, dq' \, \langle q' \mid \boldsymbol{\eta} \mid q'' \rangle \, dq'' \, \langle q'' \mid \rangle, \quad . \quad . \quad . \quad (6{:}13)$$

and for the combined system of, say, n particles, the average total is given by

$$\sum_r \iint \langle r \mid q' \rangle \, dq' \, \langle q' \mid \boldsymbol{\eta}_r \mid q'' \rangle \, dq'' \, \langle q'' \mid r \rangle, \quad . \quad . \quad . \quad (6{:}14)$$

where $\langle q' \mid r \rangle$ is the wave-function of the rth particle or constituent system. The matrix element $\langle q' \mid \boldsymbol{\eta}_r \mid q'' \rangle$ can obviously be taken outside the summation over r since the operators $\boldsymbol{\eta}_r$ are homologous; with the result that equation (6:14) becomes

$$\iint \langle q' \mid \boldsymbol{\eta} \mid q'' \rangle \, dq' \, dq'' \sum_r \langle q'' \mid r \rangle \langle r \mid q' \rangle$$
$$= \iint \langle q' \mid \boldsymbol{\eta} \mid q'' \rangle \, dq'' \, \langle q'' \mid \boldsymbol{\rho} \mid q' \rangle \, dq' = \mathscr{S}p \, (\boldsymbol{\eta\rho}). \quad . \quad (6{:}15)$$

This density $\boldsymbol{\rho}$, of course, satisfies the equation of motion (4:46) as may be readily verified, but the ensemble cannot be said to be completely described by $\boldsymbol{\rho}$ since the averages of quantities of the more general type $\sum_{r \neq s} \mathbf{f}(\boldsymbol{\eta}_r, \boldsymbol{\eta}_s)$, etc., are as yet outside the scope of the description afforded by $\boldsymbol{\rho}$. It is an awkward feature that we are thus limited to averages of quantities defined for the constituent systems individually as in $\sum_r \boldsymbol{\eta}_r$, which means that the theory as yet does not permit us to analyse or calculate correlations between the individual systems or particles. However, the theory so far has imposed no symmetry conditions on the state vectors or wave-functions describing the systems other than that the variables defining the systems enter symmetrically in physically admissible operators. The generalization of the ensemble analysis to include symmetry considerations is fairly detailed, though basically simple, and, as we shall see (Chaps. VII, VIII), permits us to take proper account of correlations.

The symmetry conditions are, as previously mentioned, an example of supplementary conditions; the two important cases being the restriction to wave-functions which are completely symmetrical (Bose-Einstein) or antisymmetrical (Fermi-Dirac) in the variables of all the particles or constituent systems.[4] As we shall see later, the restriction to states (equivalently, wave-functions) of one *or* other symmetry type does not actually constitute a postulate independent of previously stated

[4] It need hardly be mentioned that this restriction to the two extreme symmetry types, excluding intermediate cases, has yet to be precisely qualified. In particular, it is not true without reference to the variables defining the system, their completeness, and the sufficiency of the description afforded by them—as verified by experimental findings (cf. §§ 51, 52, 54).

quantum postulates.[5] These conditions, as we shall see, are of the linear form [equation (6:7)], and we must first show that the corresponding subspaces are invariant under the equations of motion. To this end it is convenient to introduce explicitly the concept of the symmetric (permutation) group into general theory.[6]

§ 38. Introductory Remarks on Group Theory

The theory of groups is to a large extent simply a theory of quantities which do not (in general) obey the commutative axiom of multiplication. The mathematical domain of group-theoretical consideration is essentially the same many-dimensional unitary space employed in quantum theory and, hence, we may say that the two theories are generically related. Group-theoretical methods (in the formal sense) are extremely useful in general and find ready application in quantum theory; but aside from space-symmetry groups in molecular and crystal theory, it is not usually necessary to apply full-fledged group-theoretical techniques. Indeed, as Dirac has shown, physical considerations permit the application of the equivalent of group methods to many atomic problems along rather informal, even heuristic, lines—so that oftentimes one need not invoke any of the formal results of group theory.[7] It is not our purpose to develop fully the group methods, which can be found elsewhere, but, inasmuch as group theory is not generally standard equipment, we shall briefly consider for orientation and comparison (with the Dirac method, cf. Chap. X) some of the more elementary group properties that are useful in the present problem. It is hoped that this device will establish a sufficient bridge so as to eliminate any seeming mystery from the more physical approach developed by Dirac. Moreover, we shall also wish to consider the very fruitful generalizations of this method, as developed by Van Vleck and Serber, which do depend in greater degree on formal group theory. The aspects of group theory which we consider could be developed entirely within the framework of the general symbolism of the quantum theory, but this would defeat the purpose, and neither improve the logical order of presentation nor simplify the development; the reason being that the symbolic method inherently leads in natural fashion to individual or prototype representatives (matrix elements) rather than to entire matrices (as entities) with which it now becomes convenient to work. Correspondingly, we use script letters to indicate matrices as distinct from elements and operators. This tends to put us in the position of ploughing with a mule and a bullock, but appears to be the lesser evil.[8]

[5] However, a theoretical basis for one or the other symmetry type for a *given* genus of particles (i.e. the connection between spin and statistics) can be obtained only through the relativistic ($\mathfrak{q}$-number) field theory. See Pauli, W.: *Phys. Rev.*, **58**, 716 (1940).

[6] We choose here a middle path between the completely formal group-theoretical approach and the simpler (in principle) physical approach. The former is much too general for most purposes, and the latter necessitates the introduction of various essentially *group-theoretic* concepts in somewhat *ad hoc* fashion, which detracts from the unity of treatment and may give rise to needless difficulties.

[7] In fact, the considerations of Chap. III on invariance under rotations, and the analysis of the addition of angular-momentum vectors, are essentially group-theoretical in nature. For the more formal consideration of these matters we may refer to the text by Wigner.

[8] Of necessity the discussion will be extremely brief, and omits some detailed proofs. Aside from its intrinsic beauty, the group theory is well worth study, and there are a variety of excellent treatises on the subject. As noted in the preface, our review draws largely on Murnaghan's treatment.

§ 39. The Group Postulates

A collection (or set) G of distinct elements $R, S, T, \ldots$, for which we have a rule for combining elements termed product,[9] is called a group if:

I. Given that R, S are elements[10] of G ($R, S \subset G$), then RS is also an element.

II. Given that R, S, T are elements of G, then the associative axiom holds and $R(ST) = (RS)T$.

III. The collection G contains a unique element E (the identity) such that for every element $S \subset G$, $SE = ES = S$. We need actually only postulate $ES = S$, since it is readily shown that such a *left* identity implies the *right* identity.[11]

IV. For each element $S \subset G$ there is a unique element $S^{-1} \subset G$ termed the inverse of S, such that $SS^{-1} = S^{-1}S = E$. Here, with (III) above, we need only require that $S^{-1}S = E$, since the left inverse implies the right.[11] For our immediate purpose it will suffice to consider exclusively finite groups, namely, those whose order or number of elements is finite.

§ 40. Isomorphism

Two groups G, H are termed *simply isomorphic*[12] if to each element S_1 $(=E)$, $S_2, \ldots$ of G there corresponds a unique element $T_1, T_2, \ldots$ of H, *and conversely*, such that S_iS_j corresponds to T_iT_j. Simply isomorphic groups are described as being equivalent, and in general if the elements of two such groups are abstract symbols without meaning other than as group elements, the groups are termed abstract and are obviously indistinguishable, i.e. they may be said to be the same group. However, in physical applications the elements are usually characterized by special properties, e.g. groups of matrices, permutations, rotations, etc., which are called special groups so that simply isomorphic special groups are distinguishable although they correspond to the same abstract group.

If to each element in H there correspond n elements in G, while to each element in G there correspond m elements in H, such that S_iS_j in G corresponds to T_iT_j in H with T_i, T_j *any* elements of H corresponding, respectively, to S_i and S_j—then the groups G, H are termed isomorphic. The group G is also said to have an (n, m) isomorphism with H. The case which is next in importance to the preceding *simple* isomorphism is that in which $n > 1$ and $m = 1$ (or $n = 1$ and $m > 1$). In the first instance, G is said to be *multiply isomorphic*[13] to H.

[9] We write the product of S by R as RS even though the law of combination may be addition rather than multiplication.

[10] The symbol $\subset$ reads *contained in* or *belonging to.*

[11] It follows that $SS^{-1} = ESS^{-1} = (S^{-1})^{-1}S^{-1}SS^{-1} = (S^{-1})^{-1}S^{-1} = E$ and $SE = SS^{-1}S = ES = S$. However, the alternative assumptions $SE = S$ and $S^{-1}S = E$, i.e. a right identity and a left inverse, are readily shown to be insufficient.

[12] In the group literature the terms *holomorphic* and *isomorphic* are also used.

[13] Note that the fact that G is multiply isomorphic (or homomorphic) to H does not imply that H is multiply isomorphic to G. A simple but important case (though an instance of non-finite groups) is the (2, 1) isomorphism of the binary unimodular unitary group U_2 to the 3-dimensional rotation group O_3 (cf. § 53). Here each element of the former corresponds to one element $O(U)$ of the latter, while, conversely, to each element $O(U)$ there correspond two elements $\pm U$, i.e. $U \to O(U)$ while $O(U) \to \pm U$ $[O(U) = O(-U)]$. Actually, this relation furnishes a representation (cf. § 45) $U \to O(U)$ of the group U_2 by O_3, and, conversely, the group U_2 furnishes the so-called spin representation (which is two-valued) $O(U) \to \pm U$ of O_3.

§ 41. Subgroups

A collection of h ($< g$) elements within a group G of order g, which themselves form a group, is called a *subgroup*. If we consider the series S, S^2, S^3, . . . arising from an element S in G, then since G is finite there must evidently be some $n \leqq g$ for which $S^n = E$. The least index n for which this is true is called the order of the element S, and the series S, S^2, . . . S^n ($=E$), the period of the element. This constitutes a cyclic subgroup and is clearly Abelian (i.e. commutative). It follows that every group which is not cyclic of prime order contains a cyclic subgroup.

§ 42. Cosets

Let H be a subgroup of order h of a group G of order g, and let H consist of the elements S_1, S_2, . . . S_h; denote the elements of G *not contained in* H by T_1, T_2, . . . T_{g-h}. The collection of elements HT or S_1T, S_2T, . . . S_hT is called a right coset of H. Clearly the coset does not constitute a subgroup since it does not contain E or indeed any other element [14] of H. Similarly, TH is a left coset. It is essentially evident that two right (or left) cosets of a subgroup either both contain the same elements or else have no common element. Thus, if for two cosets HT_1, HT_2 we have at least one common element $S_iT_1 = S_jT_2$, it follows that $T_2T_1^{-1} = S_j^{-1}S_i \subset H$. Then $HT_2T_1^{-1}$ is, except for order, identical with H, and $HT_2T_1^{-1}T_1$, which is just HT_2, is also, except for order, the coset HT_1. The subgroup H and its different right cosets, say $n - 1$ in number, clearly exhaust all the elements of the group G.

This gives the important result that $g = hn$, *or that the order of a subgroup is a divisor of the order of the group.*[15]

§ 43. Classes of Conjugate Elements

If S and T are any elements of a group G, the element TST^{-1} is called the conjugate of S with respect to T, or the transform of S by T. The set of elements which are conjugate (or similar) to a given element is called a *class of conjugate elements*, or simply a *class*. Let us now examine a group G of g elements, and consider an element S_1 of the class C_i of order n_i. In general, there will be h elements of G, say T_1, T_2, . . . T_h, which commute with S_1, i.e. transform S_1 into itself:

$$S_1 = T_iS_1T_i^{-1} \qquad (i = 1, 2, \ldots h). \qquad . \quad . \quad . \quad . \qquad (6:16a)$$

For any element S_j *similar* to S_1 there will be an element U which transforms S_1 into S_j ($US_1U^{-1} = S_j$). Therefore, each of the h elements UT_i transforms S_1 into S_j, since

$$(UT_i)S_1(UT_i)^{-1} = UT_iS_1T_i^{-1}U^{-1} = S_j. \qquad . \quad . \quad . \qquad (6:16b)$$

[14] In the contrary case we should have $S_iT = S_j$, or $T = S_i^{-1}S_j$, contrary to the assumption that T is not in H.

[15] In particular, the order of every element of a group is a divisor of the order of the group.

Furthermore, if V transforms S_1 into S_j,

$$(U^{-1}V)S_1(U^{-1}V)^{-1} = U^{-1}VS_1V^{-1}U = U^{-1}S_jU = S_1, \quad (6{:}17)$$

so that $U^{-1}V$ commutes with S_1, and is therefore one of the elements T_i. It follows that there are exactly h elements which transform S_1 into S_j or, in general, into any element of the class C_i. Since there are g elements of G by which S_1 may be transformed, we conclude that

$$g = hn_i, \quad (6{:}18)$$

or that the order of the class is a divisor of the order of the group. The point of this derivation which will be of particular value to us in later work is that for a fixed element $S_{(i)}$ of the class C_i, the elements $TS_{(i)}T^{-1}$ obtained by letting T run through the g elements of the group will consist of the class C_i repeated g/n_i times. In this connection it will be convenient to extend the meaning of the symbol C_i to denote also the *sum* of the elements in the class.

Finally, we may note that:

(i) The unit element is a class by itself, and no other class is a subgroup.
(ii) All elements of a class have the same order.
(iii) In an Abelian group every element is a class by itself.

§ 44. The Symmetric Group Π_n

(*a*) *Definition.*

The group of primary interest in the present connection is that of the $n!$ permutations on n letters or objects, and we shall briefly consider some of the group properties illustrated by this finite symmetric group Π_n of order $n!$. The members or elements of the symmetric group are the operations involved in passing from a standard sequence, e.g. $(1, 2, \ldots n)$, to any other. They *are not* the sets of letters thus obtained. Let us for the present denote a typical permutation P by

$$P = \uparrow \begin{pmatrix} p_1, p_2, \ldots p_n \\ 1, 2, \ldots n \end{pmatrix} = \uparrow \begin{pmatrix} p_j \\ j \end{pmatrix}, \quad (6{:}19)$$

i.e. the operation P replaces 1 by p_1, 2 by p_2, . . . , n by p_n (all p_j distinct).

If now we take another permutation

$$S = \uparrow \begin{pmatrix} s_j \\ j \end{pmatrix}, \quad (6{:}20a)$$

it is evident that S can also be written as

$$S = \uparrow \begin{pmatrix} s_{p_j} \\ p_j \end{pmatrix}, \quad (6{:}20b)$$

since 1 is in the set $(p_1, p_2, \ldots p_n)$, and the S process replaces p_1 by s_{p_1}, p_2 by s_{p_2}, etc., which amounts to replacing 1 by s_1, 2 by s_2, . . . , etc. In other words, we are merely rearranging or relabelling the standard set of numbers. The product SP

is understood in the sense that we first perform the operation P on the set $(1, 2, \ldots n)$, following with the operation S; and since P sends j into p_j, and S sends p_j into s_{p_j}, it follows that the product SP (sequential performance) sends j into s_{p_j}:

$$SP = \uparrow\binom{s_j}{j}\uparrow\binom{p_j}{j} = \uparrow\binom{s_{p_j}}{p_j}\uparrow\binom{p_j}{j} = \uparrow\binom{s_{p_j}}{j}. \quad . \quad . \quad (6{:}21)$$

(*b*) *Cycle Structure.*

Let us consider a typical permutation

$$P = \rightarrow\binom{254316}{123456}. \quad . \quad . \quad . \quad . \quad . \quad . \quad . \quad (6{:}22a)$$

This can also be written in *cycle form* as

$$P = (\,125\,)\,(\,43\,)\,(\,6\,) = (\,6\,)\;(\,34\,)\,(\,251\,),\text{ etc.,} \quad . \quad . \quad (6{:}22b)$$

which indicates that 1 goes into 2, 2 goes into 5, 5 goes into 1 closing the cycle, etc. Every permutation can thus be written in cycle form, each number or letter appearing but once in the cycle description. In general, there will be c_1 unary cycles or cycles on one fixed letter, c_2 binary cycles or cycles on two letters, c_3 ternary cycles or cycles on three letters, etc.; as indicated in (6:22*b*), the sequence of the different cycles is immaterial, as is the sequence of symbols within a cycle, provided the cyclic order in the latter is unaltered, e.g. $(125) = (251) \neq (521)$. The permutation P is then described as having the cycle structure c, i.e. it factors into c_1 unary cycles, c_2 binary, etc. It is clear that the reciprocal of P can be obtained from the cycle form of P by mere reversal, and hence P and P^{-1} have the same cycle structure.

(*c*) *The Classes of* Π_n.

The permutation $Q = SPS^{-1}$, which is the transform of P by S, is given by

$$SPS^{-1} = \uparrow\binom{s_j}{j}\uparrow\binom{p_j}{j}\uparrow\binom{j}{s_j} = \uparrow\binom{s_{p_j}}{p_j}\uparrow\binom{p_j}{j}\uparrow\binom{j}{s_j} = \uparrow\binom{s_{p_j}}{s_j}, \quad (6{:}23)$$

from which it is obvious that the cycle structure of Q is that of P, that of S being immaterial. Hence, the similar or conjugate permutations which by definition constitute a *class* C are the set of all permutations having a *common cycle structure*.

The *number of classes* is obviously the number of distinct solutions in positive integers (including zero) of the equation

$$c_1 + 2c_2 + 3c_3 + \ldots + nc_n = n, \quad . \quad . \quad . \quad . \quad . \quad (6{:}24)$$

which is also the number of partitions of n into positive integers, including zero. The partition notation is especially convenient in denoting the class of a permutation. Thus the partition of $n = 12$ given by 3, 2, 2, 2, 1, 1, 1, 0, 0, . . . is written as $\{\,1^3, 2^3, 3\,\}$ (omitting the zeros which occur at the end) and explicitly indicates 3 unary, 3 binary, and 1 ternary cycle. As an illustration, the symmetric group of order 3! has 3 classes which may be enumerated as follows:

The first class consists (as always) of the identity, which here has 3 unary cycles (1), (2), (3) corresponding to the partition $\{1^3\}$. The second class contains the three simple transpositions or interchanges (12), (13), (23), so that the class is characterized by one unary and one binary cycle, i.e. the partition $\{1, 2\}$. The third class consists of the ternary cycles (123), (132) belonging to the partition $\{3\}$. Similarly, one may readily verify that the symmetric group of order 4! has 5 classes corresponding to the partitions $\{1^4\}$, $\{1^2, 2\}$, $\{1, 3\}$, $\{4\}$, $\{2^2\}$ whose respective orders (= number of elements) are 1, 6, 8, 6, 3. We list here for future reference the partitions of n (for small n) and their respective number μ (= number of classes).[16]

TABLE 6.1.—PARTITIONS

n:		μ
1:	$\{1\}^+$	1
2:	$\{1^2\}^+, \{2\}^-$	2
3:	$\{1^3\}^+, \{1, 2\}^-, \{3\}^+$	3
4:	$\{1^4\}^+, \{1^2, 2\}^-, \{2^2\}^+, \{1, 3\}^+, \{4\}^-$	5
5:	$\{1^5\}^+, \{1^3, 2\}^-, \{1, 2^2\}^+, \{1^2, 3\}^+, \{2, 3\}^-, \{1, 4\}^-, \{5\}^+$	7
6:	$\{1^6\}^+, \{1^4, 2\}^-, \{1^2, 2^2\}^+, \{2^3\}^-, \{1^3, 3\}^+, \{1, 2, 3\}^-,$ $\{3^2\}^+, \{1^2, 4\}^-, \{2, 4\}^+, \{1, 5\}^+, \{6\}^-$	11

The counting procedure to determine the order of a given class is trivial for groups of low order, but it is important to have an explicit general expression for the number n_i of permutations in the class C_i (i.e. the order of the ith class $\{1^{c_1}, 2^{c_2}, \ldots\}$) of the general symmetric group of order $n!$. This number is readily obtained as follows:

If we take any permutation P of the class C_i, all permutations of this class will be found in the set obtained by applying each of the $n!$ elements of the symmetric group to the *numbers* in the cycle description of P. However, the order of appearance of the unary, binary, ternary, etc., cycles is immaterial and, hence, each permutation of the class will be found (at least) $c_1!\, c_2! \ldots c_n!$ times in the resultant set. Furthermore, each binary cycle may start off with either of its 2 letters, each ternary with any of its 3 letters, etc., without altering the permutation having the given cycle structure. Consequently, the *order* of the ith class C_i is

$$n_i = n!/c_1!\, 2^{c_2}c_2!\, 3^{c_3}c_3! \ldots n^{c_n}c_n! \qquad (6{:}25)$$

If any two *similar* permutations R, T are written in cycle form with the various factor cycles in the same order, then R is transformed into T by the permutation

$$S = \uparrow \binom{t_j}{r_j}, \quad T = SRS^{-1}, \qquad (6{:}26)$$

[16] The superscripts $\pm$ indicate the parity (evenness or oddness) of the class [cf. equation (6:31) *et seq.*].

since S^{-1} sends t_j into r_j, R sends r_j into r_{j+1}, after which S sends r_{j+1} into t_{j+1}, which means that SRS^{-1} sends t_j into t_{j+1}, as does T itself. Example:

$$\left.\begin{aligned} R &= (1234)(567) \\ T &= (3275)(146) \end{aligned}\right\} \quad S = \uparrow\begin{pmatrix}3275146\\1234567\end{pmatrix} = (137645). \qquad (6{:}27a)$$

However, it is evident that the generator S is not unique, for we can also write

$$\left.\begin{aligned} R &= (2341)(675) \\ T &= (3275)(146) \end{aligned}\right\} \quad S = \uparrow\begin{pmatrix}3275146\\2341675\end{pmatrix} = (23)(47)(156). \qquad (6{:}27b)$$

The resultants are obtained most directly by writing the product in factor cycles, e.g. for (6:27a)

$$SRS^{-1} = (137645)(1234)(567)(546731) = (146)(3275), \qquad (6{:}28a)$$

since in the successive cycles, starting at the right, we have $1 \to 5 \to 6 \to 4$, i.e. $1 \to 4$, etc., and similarly for (6:27b),

$$(23)(47)(156)(2341)(675)(32)(74)(651) = (146)(2753). \qquad (6{:}28b)$$

We may note that all these results are obtainable simply by applying the permutation S directly to the *numbers* in the cycle description of R. Thus, if we write

$$\left.\begin{aligned} S &= \uparrow\begin{pmatrix}s_j\\j\end{pmatrix}, \quad R = (123)\ldots(klm\ldots)(\ldots), \\ T &= SRS^{-1} = S(123\ldots)S^{-1}S(klm\ldots)S^{-1}S(\ldots), \end{aligned}\right\} \qquad (6{:}29a)$$

and

$$S(123\ldots)S^{-1} = \uparrow\begin{pmatrix}s_1s_2\ldots\\12\ldots\end{pmatrix}\uparrow\begin{pmatrix}234\ldots\\123\ldots\end{pmatrix}\uparrow\begin{pmatrix}123\ldots\\s_1s_2s_3\ldots\end{pmatrix} = (s_1s_2s_3\ldots),$$

then for (6:27a) and (6:27b) we have

$$\left.\begin{aligned} (137645)[(1234)(567)] &= (3275)(146), \\ (23)(47)(156)[(2341)(675)] &= (3275)(146), \end{aligned}\right\} \qquad (6{:}29b)^{17}$$

respectively. These results do not, however, indicate that $T = SR$, which is incorrect, since in (6:27–28) we considered the operations involved, whereas in (6:29) S operates on the cycle form of R. As a product, the results of (6:29b) would be (127) (345) and (137645) respectively, agreeing with (6:28a) and (6:28b) since the operation of sequential performance is associative.

Aside from the trivial case, the simplest type of permutation is the binary cycle, which is usually termed simple transposition or interchange; yet, despite its simplicity, the interchange plays a basic role in physical theory, and for this reason, if no other, it is necessary to consider its relation to the general permutation of arbitrary cycle structure. Actually, this question is rather trivial, since it is evident

[17] [ ] here means that we are operating directly on the numbers in the cycle factors.

from our considerations on products that any cycle of higher degree may be expressed as a product of interchanges, and moreover, in a variety of ways. Of necessity the product will contain the same letter or letters in two or more factors, since we are concerned with the composition of an arbitrary cycle in terms of interchange products, and not merely the cycle factorization of a single permutation. If a permutation P contains a cycle of degree $m \leqslant n$, i.e. a cycle on m letters, and in addition $(n - m)$ unary cycles, then P is of the form $(p_1, p_2, \ldots p_m)$. One way of expressing P is [cf. (6:28a) *et seq.*]:

$$P = (p_1 p_2 \ldots p_m) = (p_1, p_m)(p_1, p_{m-1}) \ldots (p_1, p_2), \quad . \quad (6:30a)$$

e.g.

$$(13245) = (15)(14)(12)(13) = (13)(32)(24)(45), \text{ etc.} \quad . \quad (6:30b)$$

A significant classification of the $n!$ permutations is obtained by considering the effect of each permutation on the signature product

$$\phi = \prod_{r<s}^{n} (\epsilon_r - \epsilon_s) = (\epsilon_1 - \epsilon_2)(\epsilon_1 - \epsilon_3) \ldots (\epsilon_{n-1} - \epsilon_n). \quad . \quad (6:31)$$

It is evident that any permutation of the subscripts of the ϵ's can at most affect the sign of ϕ, and since each of the interchanges in (6:30a) introduces a factor -1, it follows that P multiplies ϕ by $(-)^{m-1}$. Hence, a permutation of arbitrary cycle structure C will not affect ϕ if $c_2 + c_4 + \ldots$ is even, and changes its sign if $c_2 + c_4 + \ldots$ is odd. Thus, the permutations are divided into even and odd classes according as $c_2 + c_4 + c_6 + \ldots$ is even or odd. Correspondingly, each permutation P may be assigned a signature function $\delta_p = \pm 1$ according as P is $\left\{\begin{matrix}\text{even}\\ \text{odd}\end{matrix}\right\}$, i.e. relative to the resolution of P into a product of interchanges or, equivalently, relative to the effect of P on the signature product. The $n!/2$ even permutations clearly form a subgroup (called the alternating group), while the odd permutations do not, since the product of two odd permutations is even, and the odd class does not include the identity.

§ 45. Group Representations

Let us suppose that given a group G we can associate with every element $S \subset G$ a square non-singular matrix $\mathscr{D}(S)$ such that $\mathscr{D}(ST) = \mathscr{D}(S)\mathscr{D}(T)$ for every S, $T \subset G$. Then it follows that this set of matrices forms a group[18] relative to ordinary matrix multiplication, which is isomorphic to G. We should further note that isomorphism here does not necessarily imply *simple isomorphism*, since we have not specified that $T \neq S$ implies $\mathscr{D}(T) \neq \mathscr{D}(S)$. Thus in the most trivial case we could associate the one-dimensional unit matrix with every element of G. If *simple isomorphism* obtains, the representation is sometimes termed true or faithful.

[18] From $ES = S$ it follows that $\mathscr{D}(E)\mathscr{D}(S) = \mathscr{D}(S)$, and since the matrices are by hypothesis non-singular, $\mathscr{D}^{-1}(S)$ exists, and this implies that $\mathscr{D}(E)$ is the unit matrix. Furthermore, $S^{-1}S = E$ implies $\mathscr{D}(S^{-1})\mathscr{D}(S) = \mathscr{D}(E)$ so that the matrix set contains the reciprocal of each of its members.

Such a collection of $n \times n$ matrices is said to constitute an n-dimensional *representation* [19] of the isomorphic group G. A simple and useful illustration of these considerations is provided by the previously mentioned symmetric group on n letters. Let us again write as typical element $S = \uparrow \binom{s_j}{j}$, and take for $\mathscr{D}(S)$ the matrix of which all elements in the jth column are zero except the one in the s_jth row which is unity, i.e. $\mathscr{D}(s) = (\sigma_{kj})$ where $\sigma_{kj} = 0$ unless $k = s_j$, for all j. The matrices $\mathscr{D}(S)$ thus defined constitute an n-dimensional representation of the symmetric group since it is evident that $\mathscr{D}(T)\mathscr{D}(S) = \sum_l \tau_{kl}\sigma_{lj}$ will be zero unless k and j are such that $l = s_j$, $k = t_l = t_{s_j}$; and $\mathscr{D}(T)\mathscr{D}(S)$ is therefore the matrix associated with TS. This particular matrix group is described as the permutation matrix representation of the symmetric group. In the particular case of the symmetric group on 3 letters, the group elements are

$$\left.\begin{aligned} &E = (1)(2)(3); \\ &P_{12} = (12)(3), \quad P_{13} = (13)(2), \quad P_{23} = (1)(23); \\ &P_{123} = (123), \quad P_{123} = (132); \end{aligned}\right\} . \quad (6{:}32a)$$

where we have segregated the classes for convenience, and one can readily verify that the corresponding permutation matrices are

$$\left.\begin{aligned} &\mathscr{D}(E) = \begin{Vmatrix} 1 & 0 & 0 \\ 0 & 1 & 0 \\ 0 & 0 & 1 \end{Vmatrix}; \\ &\mathscr{D}(P_{12}) = \begin{Vmatrix} 0 & 1 & 0 \\ 1 & 0 & 0 \\ 0 & 0 & 1 \end{Vmatrix}; \quad \mathscr{D}(P_{13}) = \begin{Vmatrix} 0 & 0 & 1 \\ 0 & 1 & 0 \\ 1 & 0 & 0 \end{Vmatrix}; \quad \mathscr{D}(P_{23}) = \begin{Vmatrix} 1 & 0 & 0 \\ 0 & 0 & 1 \\ 0 & 1 & 0 \end{Vmatrix}; \\ &\mathscr{D}(P_{123}) = \begin{Vmatrix} 0 & 0 & 1 \\ 1 & 0 & 0 \\ 0 & 1 & 0 \end{Vmatrix}; \quad \mathscr{D}(P_{132}) = \begin{Vmatrix} 0 & 1 & 0 \\ 0 & 0 & 1 \\ 1 & 0 & 0 \end{Vmatrix}. \end{aligned}\right\} \quad (6{:}32b)$$

It is of considerable importance to have a multiplication table for a group; which simply means a square array bordered at the left and top by the group elements with the products of pairs of elements (row by column) entered at the intersections. Table (6:33) shows the results for the preceding example, and we note in passing that each element occurs but once in each row or column, which is of course a necessary consequence of the group postulates; and further, both groups (6:32*a*) and (6:32*b*) satisfy the table as required.

[19] This use of the term "representation" should not be confused with the specific meaning of the quantal terminology. However, a representation of a group (in general) arises in exactly the same way and with exactly the same intrinsic meaning as do the quantal representatives of operators.

MULTIPLICATION TABLE OF SYMMETRIC GROUP OF ORDER 3! (6:33)

	E	P_{123}	P_{132}	P_{23}	P_{13}	P_{12}
E	E	P_{123}	P_{132}	P_{23}	P_{13}	P_{12}
P_{123}	P_{123}	P_{132}	E	P_{12}	P_{23}	P_{13}
P_{132}	P_{132}	E	P_{123}	P_{13}	P_{12}	P_{23}
P_{23}	P_{23}	P_{13}	P_{12}	E	P_{123}	P_{132}
P_{13}	P_{13}	P_{12}	P_{23}	P_{132}	E	P_{123}
P_{12}	P_{12}	P_{23}	P_{13}	P_{123}	P_{132}	E

The matrix set (6:32*b*) is an example of what is termed a *reducible* representation, by which we mean the following: In general, any representation of a group G consists of a set of matrices $\{ \mathscr{D}(S_j) \}$, $j = 1, 2, \ldots g$, forming a group isomorphic to G. Now, if by some means we obtain a representation [20] of dimension n, say, it is often possible to introduce a new basis (i.e. a similitude transformation [21] of the type $\mathscr{Q}\mathscr{D}\mathscr{Q}^{-1}$) such that for every j, $\mathscr{D}(S_j)$ is reduced to the form

$$\begin{Vmatrix} \mathscr{D}_1 & 0^* \\ 0 & \mathscr{D}_2 \end{Vmatrix}, \quad . \quad . \quad . \quad . \quad . \quad . \quad . \quad . \qquad (6:34)$$

where $\mathscr{D}_1$ is an $m \times m$ matrix ($m < n$), $\mathscr{D}_2$ is an $n-m \times n-m$ matrix, and 0, 0* are the $n-m \times m$ zero matrix and its adjoint. This situation is described by the statement that the original set of matrices $\{ \mathscr{D} \}$ is the *direct sum* of the two sets $\{ \mathscr{D}_1 \}$ and $\{ \mathscr{D}_2 \}$, which is written as

$$\mathscr{D} (S_j) = \mathscr{D}_1 (S_j) \dot{+} \mathscr{D}_2 (S_j) \quad \text{(for every } j). \quad . \quad . \quad . \qquad (6:35)$$

In other words the representation $\Gamma = \{ \mathscr{D} \}$ is completely reduced, the reduction giving two representations of G, namely $\Gamma_1 = \{ \mathscr{D}_1 \}$ and $\Gamma_2 = \{ \mathscr{D}_2 \}$ of dimensions m and $n-m$ respectively. That Γ_1 and Γ_2 are actually representations of G follows simply from

$$\mathscr{D} (S_jS_k) = \mathscr{D} (S_j) \mathscr{D} (S_k) = \begin{Vmatrix} \mathscr{D}_1 (S_j) \mathscr{D}_1 (S_k) & 0^* \\ 0 & \mathscr{D}_2 (S_j) \mathscr{D}_2 (S_k) \end{Vmatrix}, \qquad (6:36)$$

which shows that $\mathscr{D}_1(S_jS_k) = \mathscr{D}_1(S_j)\mathscr{D}_1(S_k)$, etc., and the non-singularity of $\mathscr{D}_1(S_j)$

[20] In physical applications, representations obtain readily from the meaning of the *special* group, e.g. rotations, permutations, etc.

[21] See MURNAGHAN, *op. cit.*, especially Chaps. I–III. Representations differing by a *common* transform are said to be *equivalent*.

and $\mathscr{D}_2(S_j)$ as guaranteed by the non-singularity of $\mathscr{D}(S_j)$ and the relation[22] $\det \mathscr{D}(S_j) = \det \mathscr{D}_1(S_j) \det \mathscr{D}_2(S_j)$. Γ is then described as the sum of Γ_1 and Γ_2, i.e. $\Gamma = \Gamma_1 \dot{+} \Gamma_2$ where the sum obviously is not to be taken literally, but as a shorthand expression of (6:35) for the whole matrix set. We then proceed to analyse Γ_1 and Γ_2 in the same fashion until ultimately we arrive at a finite set of irreducible (non-completely reducible) component representations[23] $\Gamma_1, \Gamma_2, \ldots$. The complete analysis may be expressed as

$$\mathscr{Q}\mathscr{D}\mathscr{Q}^{-1} = \Gamma = \text{diag}\,[\,\Gamma_1, \Gamma_2, \ldots\,], \qquad (6:37)$$

or $\Gamma = \sum_j c_j \Gamma_j$ in the above sense of sum, and the coefficients are the multiplicities of the various irreducible representations. The latter implies that some representations may appear several times or not at all in the reduction process, so that it is not always possible to obtain all the irreducible representations from a single reducible set $\{\mathscr{D}\}$.

In the above discussion as in the remainder of our short survey of group methods we consider the *group representation* concept in the briefest possible way, since to develop here the techniques of determining the representations would carry us far afield of both the purpose of this book and our actual needs. In practice we shall require only a few special group representations in explicit form, for which we shall develop the method as the need arises. Our purpose here is to establish the general concepts and the flavour of group methods, so that when we come to deal with permutations as *quantal operators*, our manipulations will seem less mysterious, and we shall have available some simple guiding principles. As indicated in the preceding discussion, we do not ordinarily require the explicit form of the representations of a given group. The reason for this happy circumstance is simply that in most physical applications the quantities of importance are the *characters* of the representations, i.e. the sets of numbers $\chi(S_j) = \mathscr{S}p\, \mathscr{D}(S_j)$ corresponding to the representation $\Gamma = \{\mathscr{D}(S_j)\}$ of the group G, and these may be obtained without prior knowledge of the explicit form[24] of the matrices $\{\mathscr{D}(S_j)\}$. The determination of the characters for any finite group (aside from special methods) depends on what are known as the orthogonality relations of the characters of the irreducible representations of the group, which we shall proceed to establish.

We have already considered (in principle) one way of obtaining two or more matrix representations of a given group G, by the process of reduction of a supposedly

[22] One may easily carry the above argument through when the original representation is reducible, but not completely reducible, i.e. $\mathscr{D}(S_j)$ is brought to the form

$$\left\| \begin{matrix} \mathscr{D}_1(S_j) & \mu(S_j) \\ 0 & \mathscr{D}_1(S_j) \end{matrix} \right\|.$$

The only essential change is that (6:35) does not hold; but we shall not be interested in this case.

[23] The irreducibility of a representation of a group guarantees by definition that the linear space spanned by the vectors constituting the *basis* of the matrix representation is the *entire* space or the trivial zero space; reducibility of a representation being equivalent to the existence of a common proper invariant subspace of the collection of matrices.

[24] The term *character* corresponds to the well-known fact that the Spur of a matrix is invariant under similarity transformation, i.e. $\mathscr{S}p\,\mathscr{D} = \mathscr{S}p\,\mathscr{Q}\mathscr{D}\mathscr{Q}^{-1}$, so that the character is a property of the matrix, independent of the coordinate system in which the matrix is presented. Comparison of this matrical viewpoint with the results of Section 27 shows the essential similarity of the group and quantal theory.

known reducible representation Γ. Let us now suppose that we have two representations $\Gamma_1 = \{ \mathscr{D}_1(S_j) \}, \Gamma_2 = \{ \mathscr{D}_2(S_j) \}$, of dimensions m, n respectively, of a given group $G = \{ S_1, S_2, \ldots S_g \}$. For the moment it is immaterial whether these representations are irreducible or reducible. We shall show that from Γ_1 and/or Γ_2 we can construct other representations by means of the so-called direct or Kronecker matrix product.

§ 46. The Kronecker Product

Consider two arbitrary square matrices $\mathscr{A}$, $\mathscr{B}$ of dimensions m and n respectively. If we form the $(mn)^2$ products $\mathscr{A}_{jk}\mathscr{B}_{pq}$, then the resultant square array defines a matrix $\mathscr{C}$, termed the Kronecker product $\mathscr{A} \times \mathscr{B}$, which is of dimension mn and whose element in the (j, p) row and (k, q) column is $\mathscr{A}_{jk}\mathscr{B}_{pq}$. As mentioned in Chapter I, we arrange the row and column index pairs (j, p) and (k, q) in dictionary order so that (j, p) precedes (j', p') when $j < j'$, or if $j = j'$, when $p < p'$, etc. We may then write $\mathscr{A} \times \mathscr{B}$ in block form as

$$\mathscr{A} \times \mathscr{B} = \left\| \begin{matrix} \mathscr{A}_{11}\mathscr{B} & \mathscr{A}_{12}\mathscr{B} \ldots \\ \mathscr{A}_{21}\mathscr{B} & \mathscr{A}_{22}\mathscr{B} \ldots \\ \cdot & \cdot \\ \cdot & \cdot \\ \cdot & \cdot \end{matrix} \right\|, \quad \ldots\ldots \quad (6{:}38)$$

and in particular if $\mathscr{A}$ is the m-dimensional unit matrix $\mathscr{I}_m$,

$$\mathscr{I}_m \times \mathscr{B} = \text{diag}\,[\,\mathscr{B}^{(m)}\,] = \mathscr{B} \dotplus \mathscr{B} \dotplus \mathscr{B} \dotplus \ldots \quad (m \text{ terms}). \qquad (6{:}39)$$

The Kronecker product is in general non-commutative, but one may readily show that $\mathscr{B} \times \mathscr{A}$ is the transform of $\mathscr{A} \times \mathscr{B}$ by some permutation matrix, i.e. $\mathscr{B} \times \mathscr{A} = \mathscr{P}(\mathscr{A} \times \mathscr{B})\mathscr{P}^{-1}$. However, Kronecker multiplication is associative since for arbitrary matrices $\mathscr{A}$, $\mathscr{B}$, $\mathscr{C}$ the element in the (j_1, j_2, j_3) row and (k_1, k_2, k_3) column is $\mathscr{A}_{j_1k_1}\mathscr{B}_{j_2k_2}\mathscr{C}_{j_3k_3}$ in either $\mathscr{A} \times (\mathscr{B} \times \mathscr{C})$ or $(\mathscr{A} \times \mathscr{B}) \times \mathscr{C}$, and the resultant is clearly of the same dimension in both cases. The importance of the Kronecker product depends largely on the following property: If we take matrices $\mathscr{A}_1$, $\mathscr{A}_2$ of dimension m and $\mathscr{B}_1$, $\mathscr{B}_2$ of dimension n, then the *ordinary* matrix product of the two mn-dimensional matrices $\mathscr{A}_1 \times \mathscr{B}_1$ and $\mathscr{A}_2 \times \mathscr{B}_2$ is given by

$$(\mathscr{A}_1 \times \mathscr{B}_1)(\mathscr{A}_2 \times \mathscr{B}_2) = \mathscr{A}_1\mathscr{A}_2 \times \mathscr{B}_1\mathscr{B}_2, \quad \ldots \quad (6{:}40)$$

since

$$\sum_{\alpha}^{m}\sum_{\beta}^{n}(\mathscr{A}_1)_{j\alpha}(\mathscr{B}_1)_{p\beta}(\mathscr{A}_2)_{\alpha k}(\mathscr{B}_2)_{\beta q} = \sum_{\alpha}^{m}(\mathscr{A}_1)_{j\alpha}(\mathscr{A}_2)_{\alpha k}\sum_{\beta}^{n}(\mathscr{B}_1)_{p\beta}(\mathscr{B}_2)_{\beta q}.$$

We may note the following consequences of (6:40). If $\mathscr{A}$, $\mathscr{B}$ above are non-singular, then

$$(\mathscr{A} \times \mathscr{B})(\mathscr{A} \times \mathscr{B})^{-1} = (\mathscr{A} \times \mathscr{B})(\mathscr{A}^{-1} \times \mathscr{B}^{-1}) = \mathscr{I}_m \times \mathscr{I}_n = \mathscr{I}_{mn}, \quad (6{:}41a)$$

$$(\mathscr{A} \times \mathscr{B}) = (\mathscr{A} \times \mathscr{I}_n)(\mathscr{I}_m \times \mathscr{B}), \quad \ldots\ldots \quad (6{:}41b)$$

and

$$\det(\mathscr{A} \times \mathscr{B}) = (\det \mathscr{A})^n (\det \mathscr{B})^m. \quad \ldots\ldots \quad (6{:}41c)$$

Further, $(\mathscr{A} \times \mathscr{B})^* = (\mathscr{A}^* \times \mathscr{B}^*)$, since the (jp, kq) element of $(\mathscr{A} \times \mathscr{B})^*$ is given by $\overline{\mathscr{A}}_{kj}\overline{\mathscr{B}}_{qp} = \mathscr{A}_{jk}{}^*\mathscr{B}_{pq}{}^*$, i.e. the (jp, kq) element of $(\mathscr{A}^* \times \mathscr{B}^*)$, so that if $\mathscr{A}$ and $\mathscr{B}$ are unitary then $(\mathscr{A} \times \mathscr{B})$ is also unitary; thus

$$(\mathscr{A} \times \mathscr{B})^*(\mathscr{A} \times \mathscr{B}) = (\mathscr{A}^*\mathscr{A} \times \mathscr{B}^*\mathscr{B}) = (\mathscr{I}_m \times \mathscr{I}_n) = \mathscr{I}_{mn}. \quad (6{:}41d)$$

Returning now to the two representations $\Gamma_1 = \{ \mathscr{D}_1(S_j) \}$, $\Gamma_2 = \{ \mathscr{D}_2(S_j) \}$ of the group G, we see that the matrices $\mathscr{D}_1(S_j) \times \mathscr{D}_2(S_j)$ (for every j) are non-singular, and constitute an mn-dimensional representation of G, e.g.

$$\{\mathscr{D}_1(S_j) \times \mathscr{D}_2(S_j)\}\{\mathscr{D}_1(S_k) \times \mathscr{D}_2(S_k)\} = \mathscr{D}_1(S_jS_k) \times \mathscr{D}_2(S_jS_k). \quad (6{:}42)$$

This mn-dimensional representation is described as the Kronecker product representation and written as $\Gamma_1 \times \Gamma_2$, which is obviously *equivalent* to $\Gamma_2 \times \Gamma_1$, so that we have the result that Kronecker multiplication of group representations is commutative. As a special case of the above we may form the Kronecker product $\Gamma_1 \times \Gamma_1$ of the representation Γ_1 by itself, which yields an m^2-dimensional representation. We may obviously repeat this self-multiplication process to obtain representations derived from Γ_1 of dimensions $m^3, m^4, \ldots$, etc., but we shall not investigate this case since it is not especially relevant to the determination of the orthogonality relations.

§ 47. The Orthogonality Relations for Groups of Finite Order

Let us again consider any matrices $\mathscr{A}$, $\mathscr{B}$ of respective dimensions m and n, and further introduce an arbitrary $m \times n$ matrix $\mathscr{X}$. Then $\mathscr{X}$ may be regarded as a vector[25] in the mn-dimensional space of $\mathscr{A} \times \mathscr{B}$, the elements $\mathscr{X}_{rs}$ in the rth row and sth column of $\mathscr{X}$ being regarded as the (r, s) component of the vector $\mathscr{X}$. Then, $\mathscr{A} \times \mathscr{B}$ operating on the vector $\mathscr{X}$ produces a new vector $\mathscr{Y}$ whose (r, s) component is $\sum_{\alpha}^{m} \sum_{\beta}^{n} \mathscr{A}_{r\alpha}\mathscr{B}_{s\beta}\mathscr{X}_{\alpha\beta}$, i.e. $\mathscr{Y} = \mathscr{A}\mathscr{X}\tilde{\mathscr{B}}$, where $\tilde{\mathscr{B}}$ is the transposed matrix of $\mathscr{B}$, obtained by interchanging rows and columns. It follows that under $\mathscr{A} \times \overline{\mathscr{B}}$ the vector $\mathscr{X}$ is sent into $\mathscr{Y} = \mathscr{A}\mathscr{X}\mathscr{B}^*$, and when $\mathscr{Y} = \mathscr{X}$ the vector $\mathscr{X}$ is termed an invariant vector of $\mathscr{A} \times \overline{\mathscr{B}}$. From the previously mentioned n-dimensional representation $\Gamma_2 = \{ \mathscr{D}_2(S_j) \}$ we immediately obtain the representation $\overline{\Gamma}_2 = \{ \overline{\mathscr{D}}_2(S_j) \}$, and from Γ_1 and Γ_2 the mn-dimensional Kronecker product representation $\Gamma_1 \times \overline{\Gamma}_2 = \{ \mathscr{D}_1(S_j) \times \overline{\mathscr{D}}_2(S_j) \}$. It follows then that an $m \times n$ matrix $\mathscr{X}$, regarded as the vector with components $\mathscr{X}_{rs}$, is an invariant vector of the representation $\Gamma_1 \times \overline{\Gamma}_2$ if it is an invariant vector of $\mathscr{D}_1(S_j) \times \overline{\mathscr{D}}_2(S_j)$ for every j, i.e.

$$\mathscr{X} = \mathscr{D}_1(S_j)\mathscr{X}\mathscr{D}_2{}^*(S_j), \qquad \text{for all } j, \quad \ldots \quad (6{:}43)$$

or

$$\mathscr{X}\{\mathscr{D}_2{}^*(S_j)\}^{-1} = \mathscr{D}_1(S_j)\mathscr{X}.$$

[25] In general a linear vector space may be defined as an Abelian (= commutative) group $\{s_1, s_2, \ldots\}$ with addition (+) as the combination law instead of multiplication. The Abelian property is a consequence of associativity of addition; the unit element 0, such that $s_i + 0 = s_i$, and the inverse $s_i^{-1} = -s_i$, such that $s_i + s_i^{-1} = 0$. The set of all $m \times n$ matrices also constitutes an Abelian group under addition so that we may regard any $m \times n$ matrix as a vector in an mn-dimensional linear vector space; the mn different matrices, each of which has all of its elements zero except one, which is unity, being linearly independent and, hence, every $m \times n$ matrix being a linear combination of them.

The matrix set $\{ [\mathscr{D}_2^*(S_j)]^{-1} \}$ constitutes the so-called n-dimensional adjoint representation Γ_2^* of G, which follows from the fact that the set includes the unit matrix $\{ \mathscr{D}_2^*(E) \}^{-1} = (\mathscr{I}_n^*)^{-1} = \mathscr{I}_n$, the inverse $\{ \mathscr{D}_2^*(S_j^{-1}) \}^{-1}$ of each of its elements $\{ \mathscr{D}_2^*(S_j) \}^{-1}$, and

$$\{ \mathscr{D}_2^*(S_jS_k) \}^{-1} = [\{ \mathscr{D}_2(S_j) \mathscr{D}_2(S_k) \}^*]^{-1} = \{ \mathscr{D}_2^*(S_j) \}^{-1} \{ \mathscr{D}_2^*(S_k) \}^{-1}.$$

If both Γ_1 and Γ_2^* are irreducible then (6:43) leads to the simple alternatives (Schur's lemma, see Appendix I):

$$\mathscr{X} = 0, \qquad (6:44a)$$

i.e. the only invariant vector of $\Gamma_1 \times \bar{\Gamma}_2$ is the trivial zero vector,

$$m = n, \qquad (6:44b)$$

and Γ_2^* is equivalent to Γ_1 $(= \mathscr{X}\Gamma_2^*\mathscr{X}^{-1})$. The invariant vectors of any n-dimensional representation Γ of a finite group G are easily obtained if we observe that for any vector $\mathscr{X}$ ($n \times 1$ matrix) in the space of Γ, the average of $\mathscr{D}(S)\mathscr{X}$ over G is invariant, i.e. the vector $\mathscr{U} = \frac{1}{g}\sum_j^g \mathscr{D}(S_j)\mathscr{X}$ is invariant [26] since $\mathscr{D}(S_k)\mathscr{U} = \frac{1}{g}\sum_j^g \mathscr{D}(S_kS_j)\mathscr{X} = \mathscr{U}$. All invariant vectors of Γ are obviously obtained by taking $\mathscr{X} = \epsilon_k$, $k = 1, 2, \ldots n$, where the vectors ϵ_k form a basis in the space of Γ, e.g. ϵ_k may be taken as the $n \times 1$ matrix whose elements are all zero, save the one in the kth row, which is unity. The corresponding invariant vectors are $\mathscr{U}_k = \frac{1}{g}\sum_j^g \mathscr{D}(S_j)\epsilon_k$, which means that $\mathscr{U}_k$ is given by the average over the group of the kth columns of the matrices comprising Γ. We have seen (6:43) that for *irreducible, non-equivalent* representations Γ_1, Γ_2^*, the only invariant vector of the representation $\Gamma_1 \times \bar{\Gamma}_2$ is the zero vector, which from the above means that the average of $\mathscr{D}_1(S) \times \bar{\mathscr{D}}_2(S)$ over the group must be the mn-dimensional zero matrix, i.e.

$$\sum_{i=1}^{g} [\mathscr{D}_1(S_i)]_{jk} [\bar{\mathscr{D}}_2(S_i)]_{pq} = \sum_i^g [\mathscr{D}_2^*(S_i)]_{qp} [\mathscr{D}_1(S_i)]_{jk} = 0, \qquad (6:45a)$$

$\Gamma_1 = \{ \mathscr{D}_1(S_i) \}$, $\Gamma_2^* = \{ [\mathscr{D}_2^*(S_i)]^{-1} \}$, irreducible, non-equivalent representations. If Γ_1 and Γ_2^* are equivalent we can always arrange to have $\{ \mathscr{D}_2^*(S_j) \}^{-1} = \mathscr{D}_1(S_j)$ (by suitable transformation, cf. Appendix I), and from (6:43) we know that any invariant vector $\mathscr{X}$ of $\Gamma_1 \times \bar{\Gamma}_2$ is such that $\mathscr{X} = \mathscr{D}_1(S_j)\mathscr{X}\mathscr{D}_2^*(S_j)$ or $\mathscr{X}\mathscr{D}_1(S_j) = \mathscr{D}_1(S_j)\mathscr{X}$, which tells us that $\mathscr{X}$ is a scalar matrix (= multiple of unit matrix) since Γ_1 is irreducible.[27] From the above and the discussion of the determination of the invariant vectors it follows that the average over the group of the (k, q)th columns of $\mathscr{D}_1(S) \times \bar{\mathscr{D}}_2(S)$ is a scalar matrix, i.e. the average over G of $\mathscr{D}_1(S)_{jk}\bar{\mathscr{D}}_2(S)_{pq}$ is zero except for $j = p$, in which case its value is the same for all j. This common

[26] Recalling that the set of elements $\{S_kS_j\}$, S_k fixed and S_j variable over the g elements of G, is again the set $\{S_j\}$, and accordingly $\Sigma\, \mathscr{D}(S_kS_j) = \Sigma\, \mathscr{D}(S_j)$. This is known as a left-translation of the group G by S_k.

[27] See Appendix I, Theorem II.

value is readily seen to be $1/d$ where d is the dimension of the representation (common to both Γ_1 and Γ_2 in the present case), since, summing over j, we find

$$\sum_j \mathscr{D}_1(S)_{jk}\overline{\mathscr{D}}_2(S)_{jq} = \sum_j \mathscr{D}_2^*(S)_{qj}\mathscr{D}_1(S)_{jk} = \delta_{qk},$$

where we have used the fact that $\{\mathscr{D}_2^*(S)\}^{-1} = \mathscr{D}_1(S)$. We thus have the important result that for an irreducible d-dimensional representation $\Gamma = \{\mathscr{D}(S_j)\}$ for a finite group,

$$\sum_i^g \mathscr{D}^*(S_i)_{qp}\mathscr{D}(S_i)_{jk} = \frac{g}{d}\delta_{qk}\delta_{jp}. \qquad (6{:}45b)$$

Equations (6:45*a*) and (6:45*b*) are the required orthogonality conditions on irreducible representations of a finite group. Implicit in the above is the condition that the representations are unitary (i.e. unitary matrices) in which case $\mathscr{D}^*(S) = \mathscr{D}^{-1}(S) = \mathscr{D}(S^{-1})$. However, this is not an important restriction, since it may be shown that all representations of a finite group are equivalent to unitary representations (cf. Appendix I), and the latter are the only type which arise in quantum mechanics.

§ 48. Group Characters as Class Functions

Let us assume that the group G contains $p \leqslant g$ classes $C_1, C_2, \ldots C_p$, and denote the character of the kth class by χ_k where $\chi(S) = \chi_k$ for all $S \subset C_k$. The fact that all elements of G which belong to the class C_k have the same character leads to the description of the characters of a representation of a group as comprising a *class function.* If in (6:45*a*, *b*) we set $j = k$, $p = q$, and sum over j and q, we find corresponding orthogonality relations of the characters of irreducible, non-equivalent representations Γ_1, Γ_2 of the group G; namely,

$$\sum_S \overline{\chi}^{(2)}(S)\chi^{(1)}(S) = 0, \qquad (6{:}46a)$$

$$\sum_S \overline{\chi}(S)\chi(S) = g. \qquad (6{:}46b)$$

As a sum over the p classes, these relations take the form

$$\sum_{k=1}^{p} n_k\overline{\chi}_k^{(2)}\chi_k^{(1)} = 0, \qquad (6{:}47a)$$

$$\sum_{k=1}^{p} n_k\overline{\chi}_k\chi_k = g, \qquad (6{:}47b)$$

where n_k and χ_k are the order and character of the kth class C_k. These relations may be exhibited in particularly convenient form if we regard the p quantities $\chi_k\sqrt{\frac{n_k}{g}} = \nu_k$ as the components in a p-dimensional space of a vector ν which is termed the vector character of Γ. Then, equations (6:47) appear as the scalar products

$$\left.\begin{aligned}\overline{\nu}^{(2)}\cdot\nu^{(1)} &= 0,\\ \overline{\nu}\cdot\nu &= 1,\end{aligned}\right\} \qquad (6{:}48a)$$

which show that the vector characters of irreducible non-equivalent representations form an orthogonal set. This leads to the observation that the number of irreducible non-equivalent representations of a finite group is at most equal to the number p of classes, since there cannot be more than p linearly independent vectors in a p-dimensional space. A further consequence is that the resolution $\Gamma = \sum_i c_i \Gamma_i$ [cf. (6:37)] of a reducible representation Γ implies that the vector character $\nu^{(\Gamma)}$ of Γ is given by

$$\nu^{(\Gamma)} = \sum_i c_i \nu^{(i)}, \qquad (6{:}48b)$$

so that the multiplicities c_i are uniquely given by the scalar product

$$c_i = \bar{\nu}^{(i)} \cdot \nu^{(\Gamma)}. \qquad (6{:}48c)$$

The equations (6:48a, b, c) give a very simple criterion as to the reducibility of any representation Γ of a finite group in terms of its characters. Thus, if $\nu^{(\Gamma)}$ denotes the vector character of Γ, it follows that $\bar{\nu}^{(\Gamma)} \cdot \nu^{(\Gamma)} = \sum_i (c_i)^2$, which assumes its minimum value, unity, only when Γ is irreducible. From (6:46b) an equivalent condition for irreducibility is that the average of $|\chi(S)|^2$ over the group be unity.

§ 49. Class Multiplication

Let us consider any two classes C_j, C_k of G, and denote by C_jC_k the set of elements obtained by taking all products S_jS_k of elements $S_j \subset C_j$ and $S_k \subset C_k$. (S_j, S_k here, of course, merely indicate prototype elements of their respective classes.) It is essentially evident that the class product can be resolved into a sum of classes, since the whole class determined by S_jS_k appears with S_jS_k in the set C_jC_k, and moreover, each element of the class occurs equally often. Similarly, one may easily show that class multiplication is commutative, so that we may write

$$C_jC_k = C_kC_j = \sum_{l=1}^{p} c_{jk}{}^l C_l. \quad c_{jk}{}^l = c_{kj}{}^l. \qquad (6{:}49)$$

The unit class always consists of the simple identity element so that $C_1C_k = C_k$, which is expressed in terms of the class constants $c_{jk}{}^l$ as $c_{1k}{}^l = \delta_k{}^l$. Another immediate consequence of (6:49) is that C_jC_k does not include the unit class at all unless the class C_k contains the elements inverse to those in C_j, i.e. $c_{jk}{}^1 = 0$ unless $k = -j$, in which case $c^1_{j,-} = n_j$, where, for convenience, we indicate the class whose elements are inverse to those in C_j by C_{-j}, even though they coincide. Corresponding to the class sum C_j let us denote by $\mathscr{C}_j$ the sum of those matrices of a representation Γ which correspond to the elements $S_j \subset C_j$ of the group G. We know that for any $S \subset G$, SS_jS^{-1} appears with S_j in C_j for all $S_j \subset C_j$. Consequently, $\mathscr{D}(S)\mathscr{C}_j\mathscr{D}(S^{-1}) = \mathscr{C}_j$, showing that $\mathscr{C}_j$ commutes with every matrix in $\Gamma = \{ \mathscr{D}(S) \}$, and if Γ is a d-dimensional irreducible representation, $\mathscr{C}_j$ must be a scalar matrix[28] which we write

[28] Appendix I, Theorem II.

as $\lambda_j \mathscr{I}_d$ ($\mathscr{I}_d = d$-dimensional unit matrix). Since $\chi(S) = \chi_k$ for every $S \subset C_k$, it follows that

$$\mathscr{S}p\, \mathscr{C}_k = \lambda_k d = n_k \chi_k, \quad . \quad . \quad . \quad . \quad . \quad . \quad . \quad (6{:}50a)$$

and combined with (6:49) we obtain

$$\mathscr{C}_j \mathscr{C}_k = \sum_{l=1}^{p} c_{jk}{}^l \mathscr{C}_l, \quad . \quad . \quad . \quad . \quad . \quad . \quad . \quad (6{:}50b)$$

$$\lambda_j \lambda_k \mathscr{I}_d = \sum_{l=1}^{p} c_{jk}{}^l \lambda_l \mathscr{I}_d, \quad . \quad . \quad . \quad . \quad . \quad . \quad . \quad (6{:}50c)$$

or

$$n_j n_k \chi_j \chi_k = d \sum_{l=1}^{p} c_{jk}{}^l n_l \chi_l.$$

If we sum this last over the q ($\leqslant p$) irreducible representations Γ_h of G, we find

$$n_j n_k \sum_{h=1}^{q} \chi_j{}^h \chi_k{}^h = \sum_{l=1}^{p} c_{jk}{}^l n_l \sum_{h=1}^{q} d_h \chi_l{}^h. \quad . \quad . \quad . \quad . \quad . \quad (6{:}51)$$

In order to complete the analysis of equation (6:51), we need to consider the fundamental concept of the regular (permutation) representation of a group $G = \{ S_1, S_2, \ldots S_g \}$, of order g. If we form the product $S_p S_j$, keeping S_p fixed while S_j runs through the group G, then we know that $\{ S_p S_j \} = \{ S_j \} = G$, i.e. a left translation. Thus, multiplication by S_p amounts to applying a permutation $P = \uparrow \binom{p_j}{j}$, say, on the subscripts of the elements S, which we indicate explicitly by writing $S_p S_j = S_{p_j}$. Furthermore, if multiplication by S_p (in the translation process) corresponds to a permutation P, and S_q to the permutation Q, then $S_q S_p$ corresponds to QP. If $\mathscr{P}$ denotes the permutation matrix associated with P, i.e. the matrix all of those elements in the jth column are zero except the one in the p_jth row which is unity ($j = 1, 2, \ldots g$); then the g matrices $\{ \mathscr{D}(S_p) \} = \{ \mathscr{P} \}$ of dimension g constitute the so-called regular representation. We wish now to consider the relation of this regular representation Γ to the $q \leqslant p$ (p = number of classes) non-equivalent, irreducible representations $\Gamma_1, \Gamma_2, \ldots \Gamma_q$. It follows from the definition of the regular representation that $\mathscr{S}p\, \mathscr{D}(S) = 0$, except that $\mathscr{S}p\, \mathscr{D}(E) = \mathscr{S}p\, \mathscr{I}_g = g$ ($\mathscr{I}_g = g$-dimensional unit matrix), since only $\mathscr{D}(E)$ has non-zero elements along the principal diagonal. In other words, all the characters of the regular representation are zero, except that for the unit class, $\chi_1 = g$; or that only the unit-class component ($= \sqrt{g}$) of the vector character ν of Γ is non-vanishing [cf. (6:47, 48) *et seq.*]. From (6:48c) we then have $c_i = \bar{\nu}_1{}^{(i)} \sqrt{g}$, and since $\nu_1{}^{(i)}$ is the spur of $\mathscr{D}_i{}^*(E) = \mathscr{D}_i(E)$ (the unit matrix of the representation Γ_i) divided by $\sqrt{g}$, it follows that $c_i = d_i$, the dimension of the representation Γ_i. Hence for any finite group the regular representation contains every irreducible representation Γ_i a number of times equal to the dimension d_i of the latter. Resolving equation (6:48b) according to its components (classes) we find that for the unit class

$$g = \sum_{i=1}^{q} d_i{}^2 ; \quad . \quad . \quad . \quad . \quad . \quad . \quad . \quad . \quad (6{:}52a)$$

or the sum of the squared dimensions of the non-equivalent irreducible representations of G equals the order of G; while for any other class ($j = 2, \ldots p$)

$$\sum_{i=1}^{q} d_i \chi_j^{(i)} = 0. \qquad (6{:}52b)$$

With the above results, equation (6:51) reduces to

$$n_j n_k \sum_{h=1}^{q} \chi_j^h \chi_k^h = g c_{jk}^{\ 1} = g n_j \delta_{j,\,-k}, \qquad (6{:}53)$$

or

$$\sum_{h=1}^{q} \chi_j^h \chi_k^h = \frac{g}{n_j} \delta_{j,\,-k}.$$

From this result we may also easily infer that $q \geqslant p$, just as before we found $q \leqslant p$, so that it follows that the number of non-equivalent, irreducible representations of any finite group equals the number of its classes. Now, for any representation of a finite group we have the relation [29] $\chi_{-j} = \bar{\chi}_j$, and applying this to (6:53), we may summarize the orthogonality relations for finite groups as

$$\sum_{h=1}^{p} \chi_j^h \bar{\chi}_k^h = \frac{g}{n_j} \delta_{jk}, \qquad (6{:}54a)$$

$$\sum_{i=1}^{p} n_i \chi_i^j \bar{\chi}_i^k = g\, \delta_{jk}. \qquad (6{:}54b)$$

If the complete group multiplication table is known, or rather when the order of the group is not so large as to make the calculation impracticable, then the characters may be readily evaluated as follows: With the multiplication table we determine the class constants $c_{jk}^{\ l}$ from

$$C_j C_k = \sum_l c_{jk}^{\ l} C_l \qquad \text{[cf. (6:49)]}, \qquad (6{:}55)$$

and substitute in the relation

$$n_j n_k \chi_j \chi_k = \chi_1 \sum_l c_{jk}^{\ l} n_l \chi_l \qquad \text{[cf. (6:50}c\text{)]}. \qquad (6{:}56)$$

This last result plus the equation $\sum_{i=1}^{p} (\chi_1^{\ i})^2 = g$ [cf. (6:52a)], which for groups of low order can usually be satisfied in only one way, then determine the characters, e.g. for the symmetric group of order 3! [cf. (6:33)] we find

$$\left.\begin{aligned} C_2^{\,2} &= 3\,(C_1 + C_3), \quad \text{or} \quad c_{22}^{\ 1} = 3,\ c_{22}^{\ 2} = 0,\ c_{22}^{\ 3} = 3, \text{ etc.}, \\ C_3^{\,2} &= 2C_1 + C_3, \\ C_2 C_3 &= 2C_2; \end{aligned}\right\} \qquad (6{:}57)$$

and from (6:56),

$$\left.\begin{aligned} 9\,(\chi_2)^2 &= \chi_1\,(3\chi_1 + 6\chi_3), \\ 4\,(\chi_3)^2 &= \chi_1\,(2\chi_1 + 2\chi_3), \\ 6\chi_2\chi_3 &= 6\chi_1\chi_2. \end{aligned}\right\} \qquad (6{:}58)$$

[29] Cf. Appendix I, Theorem I.

Hence, knowing that the characters of the unit class are 1, 1, 2 [i.e. that there are three irreducible representations of these respective dimensions (6:52*a*)], we solve (6:58) for the other classes and obtain the character Table 6.2.

TABLE 6.2.—CHARACTER TABLE OF SYMMETRIC GROUP ON 3 LETTERS

Representation

Class	$\chi^{(1)}$	$\chi^{(2)}$	$\chi^{(3)}$	Order
$\{ 1^3 \}^+$	1	2	1	1
$\{ 1, 2 \}^-$	1	0	−1	3
$\{ 3 \}^+$	1	−1	1	2

In the table the irreducible representations are listed at the top, as indicated by the superscripts on the χ's; the classes at the left in partition notation with ($\pm$) affixed to indicate even-odd classes, and the order or number of elements in each class at the right.[30] If we proceed in the same fashion for the symmetric groups on 2 and 4 letters, we obtain Tables 6.3 and 6.4.

TABLE 6.3.—SYMMETRIC GROUP ON 2 LETTERS

Class	$\chi^{(1)}$	$\chi^{(2)}$	Order
$\{ 1^2 \}^+$	1	1	1
$\{ 2 \}^-$	1	−1	1

TABLE 6.4.—SYMMETRIC GROUP ON 4 LETTERS

Class	$\chi^{(1)}$	$\chi^{(2)}$	$\chi^{(3)}$	$\chi^{(4)}$	$\chi^{(5)}$	Order
$\{ 1^4 \}^+$	1	3	2	3	1	1
$\{ 1^2, 2 \}^-$	1	1	0	−1	−1	6
$\{ 1, 3 \}^+$	1	0	−1	0	1	8
$\{ 2^2 \}^+$	1	−1	2	−1	1	3
$\{ 4 \}^-$	1	−1	0	1	−1	6

[30] Character tables are found in a variety of forms in the group literature since there is obviously considerable choice in the labelling of the various representations and classes. To conform with the later quantal eigenvalue notation our group-character labelling is inverse to Murnaghan's.

§ 50. Permutations as Quantal Operators

Returning now to the study of systems composed of n identical units (particles), we take the $\{ \mathbf{q} \}$ representation with eigenvectors $| \,'q \rangle = | q_1'q_2' \ldots q_n' \rangle$ defined as before.[31] Then any permutation $\mathbf{P}$ may be defined operationally by the statement that for any $| \rangle$, if

$$| 1 \rangle = \mathbf{P} | \rangle, \qquad (6:59a)$$

then

$$\langle \,'q | 1 \rangle = \langle P'q | \rangle, \qquad (6:59b)$$

i.e. the operator $\mathbf{P}$ applied to a $| \rangle$ vector sends it into another vector whose representative $\langle P'q | \rangle$ is obtained by applying the permutation [32] to the representative $\langle \,'q | \rangle$ of $| \rangle$. We may write this explicitly as

$$\int \langle \,'q | \mathbf{P} | \,''q \rangle d''q \langle \,''q | \rangle = \langle P'q | \rangle, \qquad (6:60)$$

from which

$$\langle \,'q | \mathbf{P} | \,''q \rangle = \delta (P'q - \,''q) = \delta (\,'q - P^{-1}\,''q), \qquad (6:61)$$

the last form of the representative following from the properties of the δ function,[33] and the existence of the inverse permutation. The function $\delta (P'q - \,''q)$ in (6:61) obviously stands for the product of n factors $\delta\{(P'q)_1 - q_1''\} \ldots \delta\{(P'q)_n - q_n''\}$ where $(P'q)_n$ is the number into which q_n' is sent by P applied to the set $'q$, e.g. for the cyclic permutation $\mathbf{P}_{123}$,

$$\int \langle q_1'q_2'q_3' | \mathbf{P}_{123} | q_1''q_2''q_3'' \rangle d''q \langle q_1''q_2''q_3'' | \rangle = \langle P_{123}'q | \rangle = \langle q_2'q_3'q_1' | \rangle, \qquad (6:62a)$$

whence

$$\delta (P_{123}'q - \,''q) = \delta (q_2' - q_1'') \delta (q_3' - q_2'') \delta (q_1' - q_3''). \qquad (6:62b)$$

Here, as in the similar case for unitary transformations in § 18, the δ functions are meaningful because the variables are homologous and have the same spectral range. It follows from the definition that the permutations form a group of *unitary* operators, since

$$\langle \,'q | \mathbf{P}^* | \,''q \rangle = \langle \,''q | \mathbf{P} | \,'q \rangle^* = \delta (\,''q - P^{-1}\,'q) = \langle \,'q | \mathbf{P}^{-1} | \,''q \rangle, \qquad (6:63)$$

or symbolically,[34]

$$\mathbf{P}^* = \mathbf{P}^{-1}.$$

We have already noted that for systems whose component units are identical, the general observables are of necessity symmetrical in the coordinates of the

[31] The complete set $\mathbf{q}$ formed by taking the set $\mathbf{q}_1$ out of ξ_1 describing system [1], $\mathbf{q}_2$ out of ξ_2, etc., need not be coordinate-spin observables $\mathbf{X} = (\mathbf{x}, \mathbf{y}, \mathbf{z}, \boldsymbol{\sigma}_z)$, but if they are, as in most important cases, we can select the phases so that the correspondence $\mathbf{p}_x = -i\hbar d/d\mathbf{x}$, etc., holds for each particle.

[32] $P'q$ denotes the set of numbers obtained by applying P to the indices of $q_1', q_2', \ldots q_n'$.

[33] It should be clear that the representation can also be discrete or mixed, which simply leads to trivial change in notation.

[34] Since the $\mathbf{P}$'s (other than the interchanges) are not Hermitian we shall refer to them simply as operators rather than as dynamical variables, although the latter characterization is permissible.

components. Anything less than complete symmetry would contradict the principle of identity (i.e. indistinguishability), and lead to predictions which would be at variance with experimental fact. In terms of the complete $\mathbf{q}$-representation, the symmetry condition for the total Hamiltonian, for example, takes the simple form

$$\langle\, 'q \mid \mathbf{H} \mid ''q\,\rangle = \langle\, P'q \mid \mathbf{H} \mid P''q\,\rangle, \quad . \quad . \quad . \quad . \quad . \qquad (6{:}64a)$$

or equivalently,

$$[\,\mathbf{P}, \mathbf{H}\,]_- = 0, \quad . \quad . \quad . \quad . \quad . \quad . \quad . \quad . \quad . \quad . \quad . \qquad (6{:}64b)$$

i.e. every permutation commutes with the Hamiltonian. This readily follows from (6:63) and (6:64a), since

$$\langle\, 'q \mid \mathbf{PH} \mid ''q\,\rangle = \int \delta\,(P'q - '''q)\, d'''q\, \langle\, '''q \mid \mathbf{H} \mid ''q\,\rangle = \langle\, P'q \mid \mathbf{H} \mid ''q\,\rangle,$$

and

$$\langle\, 'q \mid \mathbf{HP} \mid ''q\,\rangle = \int \langle\, 'q \mid \mathbf{H} \mid '''q\,\rangle\, d'''q\, \delta\,('''q - P^{-1}''q) = \langle\, 'q \mid \mathbf{H} \mid P^{-1}''q\,\rangle. \quad (6{:}64c)$$

The result (6:64b) is in the form of the previously discussed supplementary conditions (6:10b), and shows that every permutation is a constant of the motion. Indeed, the permutation operators are the rare instance of perfect constants since they remain such under all symmetrical perturbations of the system; but we shall discuss this in more detail in a later section.

§ 51. Symmetrical and Antisymmetrical States

We have yet to prove that the permutation operators, as an example of the supplementary condition, are physically meaningful as regards the equation of motion of states (in the S picture). To this end we must first consider which subspaces, of the space of all possible states, are relevant to the physical scheme of *our world*. The answer to this question is perfectly definite and, as previously mentioned, is not an independent quantal postulate, but a direct consequence of the identity principle and the basic interpretation of states and probability amplitudes. Thus, if we consider a normalized state $\mid\,\rangle$, whose representative is

$$\langle\, q_1'q_2' \ldots q_n' \mid \,\rangle = \langle\, 'q \mid \,\rangle,$$

then the squared modulus $|\langle 'q \mid \,\rangle|^2$ gives just the probability (per unit interval) that the set of $\mathbf{q}$'s will have values in the neighbourhood of $\{\, 'q \,\}$. If now we apply any permutation $\mathbf{P}$ to $\mid\,\rangle$, obtaining the representative $\langle\, P'q \mid \,\rangle$, we have again the same set of values $\{\, 'q \,\}$ though they are in general differently labelled. Hence, with the identity principle, the physical situation described by $\langle\, P'q \mid \,\rangle$ is the same as that for $\langle\, 'q \mid \,\rangle$, so that $|\langle\, P'q \mid \,\rangle|^2 = |\langle\, 'q \mid \,\rangle|^2$, or $\langle\, P'q \mid \,\rangle$ differs from $\langle\, 'q \mid \,\rangle$ by at most a constant factor[35] of unit modulus:

$$\langle\, P'q \mid \,\rangle = c_P\, \langle\, 'q \mid \,\rangle, \qquad |\, c_P\,|^2 = 1. \quad . \quad . \quad . \quad . \quad . \quad . \qquad (6{:}65)$$

[35] If we transform (6:65) to another representation we find that c_P must be independent of the variables defining the representation.

If we repeat the process by applying sequentially a second permutation **Q**, it follows that

$$\langle QP'q \mid \rangle = c_P \langle Q'q \mid \rangle = c_P c_Q \langle 'q \mid \rangle = c_{PQ} \langle 'q \mid \rangle. \qquad (6:66)$$

In other words, the application of the **P**'s generates a one-dimensional representation of the symmetry group, and we know that there are two such representations, namely,

$$\left.\begin{matrix} c_P = 1 \\ c_P = \delta_P \end{matrix}\right\} \text{for every } \mathbf{P}, \qquad (6:67)$$

where δ_P is the signature of **P** and is $(\pm)$ according as **P** is odd or even. We thus have obtained the important result that physical states of our world are either symmetrical or antisymmetrical in the variables of the identical component units.[36] Now we see that the permutations are meaningful as operators provided that the symmetry type of a state is maintained in time. This is readily shown to be the case, since from

$$i\hbar \frac{d}{dt} \mid \rangle = \mathbf{H} \mid \rangle, \qquad (6:68a)$$

or

$$i\hbar \frac{d}{dt} \langle 'q \mid \rangle = \int \langle 'q \mid \mathbf{H} \mid ''q \rangle \, d''q \langle ''q \mid \rangle,$$

and

$$i\hbar \frac{d}{dt} \mathbf{P} \mid \rangle = \mathbf{HP} \mid \rangle, \qquad (6:68b)$$

or

$$i\hbar \frac{d}{dt} \langle P'q \mid \rangle = \int \langle 'q \mid \mathbf{H} \mid ''q \rangle \, d''q \rangle \, d''q \langle P''q \mid \rangle,$$

it follows that $\langle P'q \mid \rangle$ is a solution of the S equation, and that if $\langle 'q \mid \rangle$ is initially symmetric or antisymmetric, i.e. $\langle P'q \mid \rangle = \langle 'q \mid \rangle$ or $\langle P'q \mid \rangle = \delta_P \langle 'q \mid \rangle$, the symmetry type is unchanged in time. Furthermore, since all interactions between identical systems must be symmetrical in the variables of the component systems, it follows that symmetric and antisymmetric states are mutually exclusive; there can be no transition from one type to the other. Within the framework of the present non-relativistic theory, this is the only possible theoretical correlate to the experimentally known division of the elementary (?) particles into symmetrical and antisymmetrical types. With regard to the latter type, which is of most interest to us here, the above derivation constitutes essentially the Dirac antisymmetry principle, which as we shall see is the generalized statement of Pauli's exclusion principle.[37]

[36] However, we have yet to specify the nature and number of variables required to make this result physically meaningful.

[37] It may be noted that both Fermi and Dirac arrived at the general principle at essentially the same time.

§ 52. Electron Spin

Since we shall be primarily interested in many-electron systems, we shall give a brief résumé of the electron-spin properties, leading to the discussion of the exclusion principle; and for our present purposes we may consider these properties to be entirely empirical.[38] The spin of the electron is the simplest non-trivial quantal angular-momentum vector, being such that the component of angular momentum about any direction has only the two possible values $\pm\frac{1}{2}\hbar$. The mathematical description of the spin is given directly by the specification of the components $\mathbf{s}_x$, $\mathbf{s}_y$, $\mathbf{s}_z$, which must satisfy the usual commutator relations

$$[\,\mathbf{s}_x, \mathbf{s}_y\,]_- = i\hbar\mathbf{s}_z \qquad \text{(cyclically)}, \qquad (6:69a)$$

but with the additional condition

$$\mathbf{s}_x^{\,2} = \mathbf{s}_y^{\,2} = \mathbf{s}_z^{\,2} = \tfrac{1}{4}\hbar^2, \qquad (6:69b)$$

since the eigenvalues of each component are required to be $\pm\frac{1}{2}\hbar$. It follows that the quantities $\mathbf{s}_x^2$, $\mathbf{s}_y^2$, $\mathbf{s}_z^2$ are simply numbers since they have but one eigenvalue. It is often more convenient to deal with variables $\boldsymbol{\sigma}_x$, $\boldsymbol{\sigma}_y$, $\boldsymbol{\sigma}_z$, defined by $\underline{\boldsymbol{\sigma}} = 2\underline{\mathbf{s}}/\hbar$, which then satisfy the relations

$$[\,\boldsymbol{\sigma}_x, \boldsymbol{\sigma}_y\,]_- = 2i\boldsymbol{\sigma}_z, \qquad (6:70a)\,^{39}$$

$$\boldsymbol{\sigma}_x^{\,2} = 1, \qquad (6:70b)$$

etc.

It is a matter of simple algebra to deduce the relations

$$\boldsymbol{\sigma}_x\boldsymbol{\sigma}_y = -\boldsymbol{\sigma}_y\boldsymbol{\sigma}_x = i\boldsymbol{\sigma}_z, \qquad (6:71)$$

and

$$\boldsymbol{\sigma}_x\boldsymbol{\sigma}_y\boldsymbol{\sigma}_z = i,$$

showing that the components of $\underline{\boldsymbol{\sigma}}$ anticommute; and if we take a $\boldsymbol{\sigma}_z$-diagonal representation, the representatives of $\boldsymbol{\sigma}_x$, $\boldsymbol{\sigma}_y$, $\boldsymbol{\sigma}_z$, respectively, are readily found to be [cf. (3:64)]

$$\begin{Vmatrix} 0 & 1 \\ 1 & 0 \end{Vmatrix}, \quad \begin{Vmatrix} 0 & -i \\ i & 0 \end{Vmatrix}, \quad \begin{Vmatrix} 1 & 0 \\ 0 & -1 \end{Vmatrix}, \qquad (6:72)$$

[38] We shall not discuss the Dirac Electron Theory wherein the spin is found to be related to relativistic invariance. It cannot be said, however, to be merely a simple consequence of this invariance, since an additional operator *ansatz* is essential to the derivation.

[39] Note that the conditions (6:69*a*, *b*), or equivalently (6:70*a*, *b*), guarantee that there is no preferred direction; or, conversely, the condition of rotational invariance of (6:70*b*), for example, leads to the conditions (6:70*a*). Thus, denoting components of $\underline{\boldsymbol{\sigma}}$ by the indices 1, 2, 3, an orthogonal transformation to a new coordinate system is given by

$$\boldsymbol{\sigma}_{\tau i} = \sum_j c_{ij}\boldsymbol{\sigma}_j, \qquad \text{with} \qquad \sum_j c_{ij}c_{kj} = \delta_{ik}, \qquad \sum_k c_{ki}c_{kj} = \delta_{ij};$$

and the condition

$$\boldsymbol{\sigma}_{\tau i}^{\,2} = 1 = \sum_{j,k} c_{ij}c_{ik}\left(\frac{\boldsymbol{\sigma}_j\boldsymbol{\sigma}_k + \boldsymbol{\sigma}_k\boldsymbol{\sigma}_j}{2}\right)$$

leads to (6:71). The commutation rules for particles of higher spin also obtain from similar considerations.

where the rows and columns are labelled by the eigenvalues of $\boldsymbol{\sigma}_z$, e.g.

$$\langle \sigma_z' | \boldsymbol{\sigma}_x | \sigma_z'' \rangle \sim \begin{array}{c} \\ 1 \\ -1 \end{array} \begin{array}{c} \begin{array}{cc} 1 & -1 \end{array} \\ \left\| \begin{array}{cc} 0 & 1 \\ 1 & 0 \end{array} \right\| \end{array}.$$

For future reference we shall also list the addition properties of spin vectors, confining our considerations for the moment to the fundamental case of two electrons. The relations in this case are an especially simple form of the general laws of combining angular momenta as given in Chapter III. Thus, we introduce the dynamical variable $\mathbf{S}$ which defines the magnitude of the total spin $\frac{1}{2}(\underline{\boldsymbol{\sigma}}_1 + \underline{\boldsymbol{\sigma}}_2)$ (in units of $\hbar$) through the relation

$$\mathbf{S}(\mathbf{S}+1) = \tfrac{1}{4}\underline{\boldsymbol{\sigma}}^2 = \tfrac{1}{4}[(\boldsymbol{\sigma}_{1x} + \boldsymbol{\sigma}_{2x})^2 + (\boldsymbol{\sigma}_{1y} + \boldsymbol{\sigma}_{2y})^2 + (\boldsymbol{\sigma}_{1z} + \boldsymbol{\sigma}_{2z})^2]. \quad (6:73)$$

From the properties of the $\boldsymbol{\sigma}$'s, this takes the form

$$\mathbf{S}(\mathbf{S}+1) = \tfrac{3}{2} + \tfrac{1}{2}(\underline{\boldsymbol{\sigma}}_1 \cdot \underline{\boldsymbol{\sigma}}_2), \quad (6:74)$$

where $(\underline{\boldsymbol{\sigma}}_1 \cdot \underline{\boldsymbol{\sigma}}_2)$ denotes the scalar product of $\underline{\boldsymbol{\sigma}}_1$ and $\underline{\boldsymbol{\sigma}}_2$. Furthermore, one may easily verify the relation

$$(\underline{\boldsymbol{\sigma}}_1 \cdot \underline{\boldsymbol{\sigma}}_2)^2 = 3 - 2(\underline{\boldsymbol{\sigma}}_1 \cdot \underline{\boldsymbol{\sigma}}_2), \quad (6:75)$$

from which the eigenvalues of $(\boldsymbol{\sigma}_1 \cdot \boldsymbol{\sigma}_2)$ are seen to be 1 and -3, and correspondingly the eigenvalues of $\mathbf{S}$ are 1 and 0. This latter result is the same as would be obtained from the old vector picture which preceded quantum mechanics, and in which one would speak of parallel and antiparallel spins with these respective resultants. We may note that in the general case of n electrons, the relation (6:74) becomes

$$\mathbf{S}(\mathbf{S}+1) = \tfrac{1}{4}(\sum_j \underline{\boldsymbol{\sigma}}_j \cdot \sum_k \underline{\boldsymbol{\sigma}}_k) = \tfrac{1}{4}[\sum_j (\underline{\boldsymbol{\sigma}}_j \cdot \underline{\boldsymbol{\sigma}}_j) + 2\sum_{j<k}(\underline{\boldsymbol{\sigma}}_j \cdot {}_k\underline{\boldsymbol{\sigma}})]$$

$$= \frac{3n}{4} + \tfrac{1}{2}\sum_{j<k}(\boldsymbol{\sigma}_j \cdot \boldsymbol{\sigma}_k). \quad (6:76)$$

§ 53. Spin Rotations

According to the results obtained in Chapter III (cf. §§ 16, 18, 19), a rotation through an infinitesimal angle ϵ about the z-axis is produced by the unitary operator $\mathbf{U}_l = e^{-i\epsilon \mathbf{l}_z/\hbar} \approx 1 - i\epsilon \mathbf{l}_z/\hbar$, where $-\mathbf{l}_z$ is the generator; the transformed coordinates $\mathbf{x}_\tau$, $\mathbf{y}_\tau$ of a particle being given by

$$\left.\begin{aligned} \mathbf{x}_\tau &= \mathbf{x} + \epsilon\mathbf{y}, \\ \mathbf{y}_\tau &= -\epsilon\mathbf{x} + \mathbf{y}. \end{aligned}\right\} \quad (6:77)$$

Clearly, $\mathbf{U}_l$ has no effect on the spin, but we can readily see that the corresponding rotation of spin coordinates will be generated by $\mathbf{U}_s = e^{-i\epsilon \mathbf{s}_z/\hbar} = e^{-i\epsilon \boldsymbol{\sigma}_z/2}$, and hence a simultaneous rotation of space and spin coordinates by

$$\mathbf{U}_j = \mathbf{U}_l\mathbf{U}_s = 1 - i\epsilon(\mathbf{l}_z + \mathbf{s}_z)/\hbar = 1 - i\epsilon\mathbf{j}_z/\hbar.$$

Indeed, we find

$$\left.\begin{aligned}\boldsymbol{\sigma}_{x\tau} &= \mathbf{U}_s\boldsymbol{\sigma}_x\mathbf{U}_s^{-1} = \boldsymbol{\sigma}_x + \epsilon\boldsymbol{\sigma}_y,\\ \boldsymbol{\sigma}_{y\tau} &= -\epsilon\boldsymbol{\sigma}_x + \boldsymbol{\sigma}_y,\\ \boldsymbol{\sigma}_{z\tau} &= \boldsymbol{\sigma}_z,\end{aligned}\right\} \quad . \; . \; . \; . \; . \; . \quad (6{:}78)$$

as expected. If $|\,1\,\rangle$ and $|\,-1\,\rangle$ denote the eigenvectors of $\boldsymbol{\sigma}_z$, the transformed eigenvectors $|\,\sigma_{z\tau}'\,\rangle$ are given by

$$|\,1_\tau\,\rangle = \mathbf{U}_s\,|\,1\,\rangle = \left(1-\frac{i\epsilon}{2}\right)|\,1\,\rangle, \quad . \; . \; . \; . \; . \quad (6{:}79a)$$

and

$$|-1_\tau\,\rangle = \left(1+\frac{i\epsilon}{2}\right)|-1\,\rangle, \quad . \; . \; . \; . \; . \; . \quad (6{:}79b)$$

so that, contrary to what one might expect, the spin eigenvectors (or eigenfunctions) are affected, though only to the extent of a phase factor. However, this change is essential, as is seen from the fact that

$$\left.\begin{aligned}\boldsymbol{\sigma}_\tau^+ &= \boldsymbol{\sigma}_{x\tau} + i\boldsymbol{\sigma}_{y\tau} = (\,1 - i\epsilon\,)\,\boldsymbol{\sigma}^+,\\ \boldsymbol{\sigma}_\tau^- &= \boldsymbol{\sigma}_{x\tau} - i\boldsymbol{\sigma}_{y\tau} = (\,1 + i\epsilon\,)\,\boldsymbol{\sigma}^-,\end{aligned}\right\} \quad . \; . \; . \; . \; . \quad (6{:}80)$$

so that the above modification in the eigenvectors guarantees the invariance of the necessary relations [cf. (3:64)]

$$\left.\begin{aligned}\boldsymbol{\sigma}^+\,|-1\,\rangle &= 2\,|\,1\,\rangle,\\ \boldsymbol{\sigma}^-\,|\,1\,\rangle &= 2\,|-1\,\rangle.\end{aligned}\right\} \quad . \; . \; . \; . \; . \; . \; . \quad (6{:}81)$$ [40]

For a finite rotation ϕ about the z-axis we have, noting that

$$e^{-\frac{1}{2}i\sigma_z\phi} = \cos(\phi/2) - i\boldsymbol{\sigma}_z \sin(\phi/2),$$

$$\left.\begin{aligned}\boldsymbol{\sigma}_{x\tau} &= \boldsymbol{\sigma}_x \cos\phi + \boldsymbol{\sigma}_y \sin\phi,\\ \boldsymbol{\sigma}_{y\tau} &= -\boldsymbol{\sigma}_x \sin\phi + \boldsymbol{\sigma}_y \cos\phi,\end{aligned}\right\} \quad . \; . \; . \; . \; . \quad (6{:}82a)$$

and for a finite rotation θ about the y-axis ($\mathbf{U} = e^{-\frac{1}{2}i\sigma_y\theta}$),

$$\left.\begin{aligned}\boldsymbol{\sigma}_{x\tau} &= \boldsymbol{\sigma}_x \cos\theta - \boldsymbol{\sigma}_z \sin\theta,\\ \boldsymbol{\sigma}_{z\tau} &= \boldsymbol{\sigma}_x \sin\theta + \boldsymbol{\sigma}_z \cos\theta.\end{aligned}\right\} \quad . \; . \; . \; . \; . \; . \quad (6{:}82b)$$

If now we apply a rotation θ about the y-axis followed by a rotation ϕ about the z-axis, $\boldsymbol{\sigma}_z$ will be rotated into the direction specified by the unit vector $\underline{n} = (\sin\theta\cos\phi, \sin\theta\sin\phi, \cos\theta)$ since

$$\begin{aligned}\boldsymbol{\sigma}_{z\tau} &= e^{-\frac{1}{2}i\sigma_z\varphi}\, e^{-\frac{1}{2}i\sigma_y\theta}\, \boldsymbol{\sigma}_z e^{\frac{1}{2}i\sigma_y\theta}\, e^{\frac{1}{2}i\sigma_z\varphi}\\ &= e^{-\frac{1}{2}i\sigma_z\varphi}\,(\,\boldsymbol{\sigma}_x \sin\theta + \boldsymbol{\sigma}_z \cos\theta\,)\, e^{\frac{1}{2}i\sigma_z\varphi}\\ &= \boldsymbol{\sigma}_x \sin\theta\cos\phi + \boldsymbol{\sigma}_y \sin\theta\sin\phi + \boldsymbol{\sigma}_z \cos\theta = (\,\underline{\boldsymbol{\sigma}}\cdot\underline{n}\,)\,; \quad . \quad (6{:}83)\end{aligned}$$

and

$$|\,\sigma_{z\tau}'\,\rangle = e^{-\frac{1}{2}i\sigma_z\varphi}\, e^{-\frac{1}{2}i\sigma_y\theta}\,|\,\sigma_z'\,\rangle, \quad . \; . \; . \; . \; . \quad (6{:}84a)$$

[40] Alternatively, this condition with (6:80) prescribes the form of $\mathbf{U}_s$.

i.e.

$$\left.\begin{aligned} |\,1_\tau\,\rangle &= \cos\left(\frac{\theta}{2}\right)e^{-\frac{1}{2}i\varphi}\,|\,1\,\rangle + \sin\left(\frac{\theta}{2}\right)e^{\frac{1}{2}i\varphi}\,|\,-1\,\rangle, \\ |\,-1_\tau\,\rangle &= -\sin\left(\frac{\theta}{2}\right)e^{-\frac{1}{2}i\varphi}\,|\,1\,\rangle + \cos\left(\frac{\theta}{2}\right)e^{\frac{1}{2}i\varphi}\,|\,-1\,\rangle. \end{aligned}\right\} \quad . \quad (6{:}84b)$$

Thus, if the system is known to have spin $\frac{1}{2}$ in the direction $\underline{n}$, the probabilities are $\cos^2(\theta/2)$ and $\sin^2(\theta/2)$ that the spin in the z-direction is $+\frac{1}{2}, -\frac{1}{2}$ respectively. The expectation value for $\boldsymbol{\sigma}_z$ in this state is

$$\langle\, 1_\tau \,|\, \boldsymbol{\sigma}_z \,|\, 1_\tau \,\rangle = \cos^2(\theta/2) - \sin^2(\theta/2) = \cos\theta. \quad . \quad . \quad (6{:}85)$$

The binary unimodular unitary transformation matrix $||\, W(\theta,\ \phi)\, ||$ in (6:84b) is not single-valued since $||\, W(\theta,\ \phi + 2\pi)\, || = -\, ||\, W(\theta,\ \phi)\, ||$, so that the correspondence between transformations in coordinate space and those in spin space is (2, 1) rather than (1, 1), as mentioned in Footnote 13, p. 94. For a given 3-dimensional rotation one can use either $\pm\, ||\, W\, ||$ to specify the associated transformation in spin space.[41] Pairs of quantities transforming under elements of the binary unimodular unitary group [such as (6:84b)] are just the components of a first-rank two-spinor.

Finally, we note the important fact that for any number of spin vectors $\boldsymbol{\sigma}_1$, $\underline{\boldsymbol{\sigma}}_2, \ldots$, the scalar products $(\underline{\boldsymbol{\sigma}}_j \cdot \underline{\boldsymbol{\sigma}}_k)$ are invariant under all rotations of spin axes, e.g. with $\mathbf{U} = \prod_j^n \mathbf{U}_j\ (\mathbf{U}_j = e^{-\frac{1}{2}i\sigma_{jz}\varphi})$

$$\begin{aligned} (\underline{\boldsymbol{\sigma}}_{j\tau} \cdot \underline{\boldsymbol{\sigma}}_{k\tau}) &= \mathbf{U}\,(\underline{\boldsymbol{\sigma}}_j \cdot \underline{\boldsymbol{\sigma}}_k)\,\mathbf{U}^{-1} \\ &= (\boldsymbol{\sigma}_{jx}\cos\phi + \boldsymbol{\sigma}_{jy}\sin\phi)(\boldsymbol{\sigma}_{kx}\cos\phi + \boldsymbol{\sigma}_{ky}\sin\phi) \\ &\quad + (\boldsymbol{\sigma}_{jy}\cos\phi - \boldsymbol{\sigma}_{jx}\sin\phi)(\boldsymbol{\sigma}_{ky}\cos\phi - \boldsymbol{\sigma}_{kx}\sin\phi) + \boldsymbol{\sigma}_{jz}\boldsymbol{\sigma}_{kz} \\ &= (\underline{\boldsymbol{\sigma}}_j \cdot \underline{\boldsymbol{\sigma}}_k). \quad . \quad . \quad . \quad . \quad (6{:}86) \end{aligned}$$

[41] For the general formulation in terms of Eulerian angles, see WIGNER, E. P., *op cit.*, and especially HILL, E. L., and LANDSHOFF, R., *R.M.P.*, **10**, 87 (1938). The latter also give the detailed results for the relativistic theory of spin. Cf. also MURNAGHAN, F. D., *op. cit.*

CHAPTER VII

The Antisymmetry Principle

§ 54. The Antisymmetry Principle

The antisymmetry principle may now be stated in the form: The wave-function $\langle \,'q \mid \rangle$ representing a state of identical elementary particles (of half-odd spin) must be antisymmetric in the $4n$ variables $\{ \,'q \} = q_1', q_2', \ldots q_n'$, where the individual q' sets consist of any four commuting functions of the coordinates, momenta, *and* spin variables. Note the two additional assumptions; namely, the special choice of the $\{ \mathfrak{q} \}$ representation (particularly including spin), and the correlation of antisymmetry with particles of half-odd spin. Correspondingly, particles of integral spin appear to be correlated with symmetric wave-functions. Both cases are contained in the statement that the density operator commutes with the permutations,

$$[\boldsymbol{\rho}, \mathbf{P}]_- = 0, \quad \text{or} \quad \langle \,'q \mid \boldsymbol{\rho} \mid {}''q \rangle = \langle P'q \mid \boldsymbol{\rho} \mid P''q \rangle;$$

the antisymmetric and symmetric cases are further differentiated by the conditions

$$\langle P'q \mid \boldsymbol{\rho} \mid {}''q \rangle = \langle \,'q \mid \boldsymbol{\rho} \mid P''q \rangle = \delta_P \langle \,'q \mid \boldsymbol{\rho} \mid {}''q \rangle,$$

$$\langle P'q \mid \boldsymbol{\rho} \mid {}''q \rangle = \langle \,'q \mid \boldsymbol{\rho} \mid P''q \rangle = \langle \,'q \mid \boldsymbol{\rho} \mid {}''q \rangle.$$

In general, the most useful quartet of variables $\mathfrak{q}$ is that consisting of the space-spin variables [1] $\mathbf{x} = (\mathbf{x}, \mathbf{y}, \mathbf{z}, \boldsymbol{\sigma}_z)$ which was historically the primary set considered, and from which the possibility of the more general choice follows by the transformation theory. Furthermore, one may readily show that the symmetry type of the wave-function is preserved under canonical transformations (cf. Dirac, *Q.M.*), so that it is entirely proper to speak of symmetric and antisymmetric *states*, which are symmetric or antisymmetric in any representation.

§ 55. The Exclusion Principle

The historical development of the preceding symmetry concepts was, in fact, inverse to that of our present mode of presentation. The Pauli exclusion principle was developed as the first conceptual expression of the experimentally observed regularities in atomic systems, and the antisymmetry principle later found as the general underlying principle. However, at least retrospectively, it appears more

[1] We shall generally use the symbol $\mathbf{x}$ to denote this particular coordinate-spin tetrad; correspondingly, $\mathbf{x}$ will be used to denote the space-coordinate triad $\mathbf{x}, \mathbf{y}, \mathbf{z}$.

logical to consider the exclusion concept as a particular approximate form of the more general discipline; particularly since the antisymmetry principle applies to nucleons (neutrons and protons) in nuclei, with the simple consequence that the compound system itself is symmetric or antisymmetric according as the number of nucleons is even or odd respectively; whereas the approximation (see below) involved in the Pauli principle in its original form is questionable in this case.[2]

In this sense the relation between the two principles is as follows: The Pauli principle states, essentially, that we can consider as an approximation that each electron in an atomic system has its own state (orbit), such that no two electrons can co-exist in the same state. The term *state* must here be interpreted in the Schroedinger sense of a wave-function expressed in the variables (including spin) of the single particle, and *orbit* as a convenient descriptive term without the literal connotation of the Bohr theory. If the ith orbit be represented by the wave-function[3] $\langle \chi' \mid E^i \rangle$ where the symbol E^i labelling or defining the ith orbit denotes the eigenvalues of a complete commuting set of observables $\mathbf{E}$, the same for each electron,[4] then an n-electron system can be represented by the product function

$$\prod_{i=1}^{n} \langle \chi_i' \mid E^i \rangle. \quad (7:1)$$

There is no correspondence of χ' subscripts and E superscripts intended and, in general, one would have $\langle \chi_1' \mid E^j \rangle \langle \chi_2' \mid E^k \rangle \ldots \langle \chi_n' \mid E^t \rangle$ where the orbits involved are not necessarily the first n possible; but in any case the orbits can always be labelled from 1 to n as in (7:1) without the implication of first, second, etc., orbit in any absolute sense. It is clear that the same distribution of electrons among orbits is obtained by applying any permutation P to the χ's or the inverse permutation P^{-1} to the E's in (7:1). However, it should be observed that while a permutation of the χ's is always a meaningful operation and can be applied to an arbitrary function of them, the permutations of the E's (i.e. of orbits among electrons) are dynamical variables in a very limited sense, having meaning only for functions of the preceding special type wherein a definite assignment of position is possible.

Thus, the same physical situation is described by each of the $n!$ possible functions[5] $\prod_i \langle \chi_i' \mid P^E E^i \rangle$, and more generally by the linear combinations

$$\sum_P \prod_i \langle \chi_i' \mid P^E E^i \rangle, \quad (7:2a)$$

$$\sum_P \delta_P \prod_i \langle \chi_i' \mid P^E E^i \rangle, \quad (7:2b)$$

which are symmetric and antisymmetric, respectively, in the χ's, and hence are, as we have shown, the only linear combinations we need consider.[6]

[2] However, this does not in any sense detract from the importance of the exclusion principle to the whole development of quantum theory.

[3] We shall at times write this simply as $\langle \chi' \mid i \rangle$ for brevity.

[4] Cf. § 56 *et seq.*

[5] We denote permutations of the E's by P^E.

[6] We could equally well have written these as $\sum_P \prod_i \langle P\chi_i' \mid E^i \rangle$ and $\sum_P \delta_P \prod_i \langle P\chi_i' \mid E^i \rangle$.

The antisymmetric function (7:2*b*) may be exhibited in the more familiar determinantal form

$$\Phi = \begin{vmatrix} \langle x_1' \mid E' \rangle & \langle x_2' \mid E' \rangle & \ldots & \langle x_n' \mid E' \rangle \\ \langle x_1' \mid E'' \rangle & \langle x_2' \mid E'' \rangle & \ldots & \langle x_n' \mid E'' \rangle \\ \cdot & \cdot & & \cdot \\ \cdot & \cdot & & \cdot \\ \cdot & \cdot & & \cdot \end{vmatrix}, \quad . \quad . \quad . \quad (7{:}3)$$ [7]

which obviously vanishes if two of the E's are equal. Hence, the antisymmetry principle leads to Pauli's exclusion principle, *and*, moreover, guarantees its permanence in time.

§ 56. The Nature of the Approximate Orbitals

It is not entirely trivial to indicate explicitly the significance of the preceding approximations as regards the interpretation of the wave-functions in general; and, in particular, the effect on the structure of the approximate orbitals owing to the introduction of spin. The ordinary Schroedinger function $\langle x'y'z' \mid H''k''l_z'' \rangle$ for a single electron [8] in a central field correlates the space coordinate observables with the usual elementary commuting constants of the motion. Though we neglect spin-dependent terms in the Hamiltonian, the exclusion principle requires that the above description be augmented by the introduction of the spin variable [9] $\boldsymbol{\sigma}$, so that the wave-function becomes $\langle x' \mid E'' \rangle = \langle x'y'z'\sigma' \mid H''k''l_z''\sigma'' \rangle$, i.e. the spin enters as a dynamical variable on both sides of the transformation function. Current literature sometimes implies a distinction between spin as coordinate variable and as quantum number, e.g. $\langle x'y'z's_z' \mid nlm_lm_s \rangle$ corresponding in one-to-one fashion with our notation above. However, from the point of view of transformation theory there is no distinction except as $\boldsymbol{\sigma}$ is considered as a member of the tetrad of commuting space-spin coordinates or the tetrad of commuting constants of the motion; the variable $\boldsymbol{\sigma}$ in both sets $\mathbf{x}$, $\mathbf{y}$, $\mathbf{z}$, $\boldsymbol{\sigma}$ and $\mathbf{H}$, $\mathbf{k}$, $\mathbf{l}_z$, $\boldsymbol{\sigma}$ taking on the eigenvalues ± 1. This is merely a convenient way (Pauli method) of imposing the spin duplication, and in general for exact wave-functions $\langle \text{`}x \mid \rangle$ no such artifice is possible, or meaningful.

For most problems dealing with atomic and molecular structure and ordinary chemical reactions it is usually sufficiently accurate to consider only Coulombic forces between the various electrons and nuclei, neglecting spin forces in the for-

[7] It should be noted that only the state of maximum spin of any number of electrons or the state of minimum (zero) spin for an even number of electrons can be approximated by a single determinantal wave-function. In the general case spin degeneracy leads to a linear combination of such determinants (cf. §§ 83, 88).

[8] Corresponding to the introduction of functions of the constants of the motion, we obtain the alternative form $\langle x'y'z' \mid nlm_l \rangle$ in the usual quantum number notation of hydrogenic systems.

[9] We usually use $\boldsymbol{\sigma}$ instead of $\boldsymbol{\sigma}_z$ as spin argument of the wave-function, but no confusion should arise since the vector operator $\underline{\boldsymbol{\sigma}}$ is always underlined.

mulation of the Hamiltonian. In this approximation the preceding wave-function splits up into a product of space and spin eigenfunctions, e.g.

$$\langle x' \mid E'' \rangle = \langle x' \mid \alpha'' \rangle \langle \sigma' \mid \sigma'' \rangle = \langle x' \mid \alpha \rangle \delta(\sigma', \sigma''). \quad . \quad . \quad (7{:}4)$$

Assigning the values ± 1 to σ'', we see that the essential effect of spin is a doubling of the number of orbits (states); the simple Schroedinger function assuming the two-fold form

$$\langle x' \mid \alpha'' \rangle \begin{Bmatrix} \delta(\sigma', 1) \\ \delta(\sigma', -1) \end{Bmatrix}, \quad . \quad . \quad . \quad . \quad . \quad . \quad (7{:}5)$$ [10]

where the spin eigenfunctions $\delta(\sigma', 1)$, $\delta(\sigma', -1)$ are obviously orthogonal and normalized to unity, e.g. $\sum_{\sigma'} \delta(\sigma', 1)\, \delta(\sigma', -1) = 0$, etc. We have thus far considered the functions $\langle x' \mid E^i \rangle$ in terms of hydrogenic orbitals because the argument then corresponds quite closely to the ideas behind the original exclusion concept, and the properties of these simple orbitals are comparatively well known. The complete neglect of electronic interactions implicit in the use of these orbitals means that determinantal eigenfunctions of the type (7:3) formed from them would, in general, be a rather poor starting-point for a perturbation calculation,[11] since the ordinary Coulomb interactions could hardly be considered as a small perturbation. Actually, we must in general determine some *effective* field which *ab initio* takes some account of these interactions. However, the preceding illustrative case shows most clearly that we deal with many electrons—but only one field problem. As remarked before, the **E** set is the same for all electrons, even though in the more general cases the eigenvalue set H'', k'', l_z'', σ'' will not stand in simple one-to-one correspondence to the quantum numbers n, l, m_l, m_s, since the energy in other central, but non-Coulombic, fields [12] depends on both n and l.

The perturbation methods for determining more accurate functions $\langle x' \mid i \rangle$ in (7:2) and related quantities in many-particle systems will be the main subject of our further study, but the result (7:2) has an immediate simple application of a general theoretic nature which does not depend on the explicit knowledge of the functions forming Φ—namely, the antisymmetric function constitutes the basis for the generalization of the density matrix which was mentioned (§ 37) as being necessary if we are to be able to express correlations between systems in terms of $\boldsymbol{\rho}$.

[10] For a general state $|\,\rangle$, $\quad |\,\rangle = \sum_{\sigma''} \int | x''\sigma'' \rangle\, dx'' \langle x''\sigma'' \,|\,\rangle$

and $\quad \langle x'\sigma' \,|\,\rangle = \langle x', + \,|\,\rangle\, \delta(\sigma', 1) + \langle x', - \,|\,\rangle\, \delta(\sigma', -1).$

When there is no spin-orbit coupling $\langle x', \pm \,|\,\rangle = c_\pm \langle x' \,|\,\rangle$ where $|c_+|^2$, for example, is the probability of positive spin orientation.

[11] One has in this case the additional inconvenience of the Coulomb degeneracy, which complicates the calculation.

[12] The Coulomb degeneracy is characteristic of the two-particle approximation.

§ 57. The Density Matrix in Many-Electron Systems *

In the abbreviated notation Φ may equivalently be written as

$$\Phi = \begin{vmatrix} \langle x_1' \mid 1 \rangle \langle x_1' \mid 2 \rangle \ldots \langle x_1' \mid n \rangle \\ \langle x_2' \mid 1 \rangle \langle x_2' \mid 2 \rangle \ldots \langle x_2' \mid n \rangle \\ \cdot \quad \cdot \quad \cdot \\ \cdot \quad \cdot \quad \cdot \\ \cdot \quad \cdot \quad \cdot \\ \langle x_n' \mid 1 \rangle \langle x_n' \mid 2 \rangle \ldots \langle x_n' \mid n \rangle \end{vmatrix}, \quad . \quad . \quad . \quad . \quad (7{:}6)$$

and we may without loss of generality require that the component wave-functions be orthonormal,[13] i.e.

$$\int \langle i \mid x_r' \rangle \, dx_r' \, \langle x_r' \mid j \rangle = \delta\,(i, j) \qquad \text{(for all } r\text{)}, \quad . \quad . \quad . \quad (7{:}7)$$

where we must also sum over both spin states,[14] e.g.

$$\int = \sum_{\sigma_r'} \int \langle \ldots \sigma^i \mid x_r'\sigma_r' \rangle \, dx_r' \, \langle x_r'\sigma_r' \mid \ldots \sigma^j \rangle,$$

and the spin summation splits off in the expression $\sum_{\sigma_r'} \delta\,(\sigma^i, \sigma_r')\,\delta\,(\sigma_r', \sigma^j)$. The determinant Φ has the simple property that it retains its value (up to a constant factor) when we transform to any set of independent linear functions of the original component wave-functions. In particular, if the above orthonormality condition is imposed on both old and new functions, then Φ has the *same* value in terms of the transformed functions

$$\langle x_r' \mid i\,;\tau \rangle = \sum_j c_{ij} \langle x_r' \mid j \rangle, \quad . \quad . \quad . \quad . \quad . \quad . \quad (7{:}8)$$

with the transformation obviously restricted to be unitary, viz.

$$\int \langle i\,;\tau \mid x' \rangle \, dx' \, \langle x' \mid j\,;\tau \rangle = \sum_{k,\,l} \bar{c}_{ik} c_{jl} \int \langle k \mid x' \rangle \, dx' \, \langle x' \mid l \rangle$$

$$= \sum_k \bar{c}_{ik} c_{jk} = \delta\,(i, j). \quad . \quad . \quad . \quad . \quad . \quad (7{:}9)$$

The invariance of Φ is readily seen in the following geometrical way: Corresponding to a definite assignment of x''s, say $x', x'', \ldots x^{(n)}$ [i.e. a (any) particle having its $\mathbf{x}$ in the neighbourhood of x', another in the neighbourhood of x'', etc.], Φ takes the form

$$\Phi = \begin{vmatrix} \langle x' \mid 1 \rangle \langle x' \mid 2 \rangle \ldots \langle x' \mid n \rangle \\ \langle x'' \mid 1 \rangle \langle x'' \mid 2 \rangle \ldots \langle x'' \mid n \rangle \\ \cdot \quad \cdot \quad \cdot \\ \cdot \quad \cdot \quad \cdot \\ \cdot \quad \cdot \quad \cdot \\ \langle x^{(n)} \mid 1 \rangle \langle x^{(n)} \mid 2 \rangle \ldots \langle x^{(n)} \mid n \rangle \end{vmatrix}, \quad . \quad . \quad . \quad . \quad (7{:}10)$$

* DIRAC, P. A. M.: *Proc. Camb. Phil. Soc.*, **26**, 376 (1930), and **27**, 240 (1930); also Princeton Lectures.

13 As solutions of the *same* central field problem they are automatically orthonormal.

14 The summation will be implicit in the use of the symbol x in our further work.

and is simply proportional to the volume of the hyper-pyramid formed by the origin and the n vectors represented by the $\langle x^{(i)} \mid j \rangle$ in an n-dimensional space, the coordinates of the ith vector being $\langle x^{(i)} \mid 1 \rangle, \ldots, \langle x^{(i)} \mid n \rangle$. Since the transformation (7:8) corresponds to a rotation of coordinates, it follows that Φ must be invariant, but by the same token the determinant Φ *does not* determine a unique set of wave-functions. We are interested only in those quantities which remain invariant under the transformation (7:8), and it is readily seen that all such quantities are expressible in terms of the scalar products $\sum_j \langle x' \mid j \rangle \langle j \mid x'' \rangle$, since

$$\sum_i \langle x' \mid i\,;\tau \rangle \langle i\,;\tau \mid x'' \rangle = \sum_{i,j,k} c_{ij}\bar{c}_{ik} \langle x' \mid j \rangle \langle k \mid x'' \rangle$$
$$= \sum \langle x' \mid j \rangle \langle j \mid x'' \rangle. \quad . \quad . \quad . \quad . \quad (7{:}11)$$

Thus the invariants are simply the elements of the density matrix

$$\langle x' \mid \rho \mid x'' \rangle = \sum_j \langle x' \mid j \rangle \langle j \mid x'' \rangle, \quad . \quad . \quad . \quad . \quad . \quad (7{:}12)$$

from which it follows that ρ is determined if we know Φ, and conversely; or, that ρ conveys all the information contained in Φ. In particular we note that the Pauli exclusion principle is most succinctly expressed in terms of ρ, since we have

$$\langle x' \mid \rho^2 \mid x'' \rangle = \int \sum_{j,k} \langle x' \mid j \rangle \langle j \mid x''' \rangle \, dx''' \langle x''' \mid k \rangle \langle k \mid x'' \rangle$$
$$= \langle x' \mid \rho \mid x'' \rangle; \quad . \quad . \quad . \quad . \quad . \quad . \quad . \quad . \quad . \quad . \quad (7{:}13)$$

or symbolically,

$$\rho^2 = \rho, \quad . \quad . \quad . \quad . \quad . \quad . \quad . \quad . \quad . \quad . \quad (7{:}14)$$

showing that the eigenvalues of ρ are all either zero or one, which corresponds physically to the fact that, at most, there can be but one particle in a given state.

The formulation of the equations of motion of many-electron systems in terms of ρ will be given detailed consideration in the next chapter in connection with the associated problem of determining the component functions in Φ. We shall here consider only the physical interpretation of ρ for the present case and, in particular, show that the density matrix actually contains all the obtainable information about the electrons in atomic systems. In the simplest one-electron case the interpretation of the density matrix is well known, namely, that a diagonal element $\langle \xi' \mid \rho \mid \xi' \rangle$ gives the probability per unit range (or probability) of there being an electron, each of whose variables ξ have values in the neighbourhood of (or equal to) the specified values ξ'. The alternative meanings depend, of course, on whether the variables ξ have continuous or discrete eigenvalue spectra.

According to the transformation theory the ξ's may be any set of commuting variables, and it should therefore be possible to answer any meaningful question as to the probability of there being an electron with specified numerical values for certain of its variables. In the present case under consideration the $\mathbf{x}$'s are the position and spin variables of the electrons, and the diagonal elements give just the effective charge density due to all electrons corresponding to a definite spin state.

It should now be possible to calculate, for example, the probability of finding simultaneously any two electrons, one of which has $\mathbf{x}$ equal to x', and the other with $\mathbf{x}$ equal to x''. We must first calculate the probability of the n particles having $\mathbf{x}$'s equal to $x', x'', \ldots$, which is the primary datum essentially contained in (7:10). Summing or integrating this probability over all $x^{(n)}$ then gives the probability of $n-1$ particles having $\mathbf{x}$'s equal to $x', x'', \ldots x^{(n-1)}$, and by repetition of this process we finally obtain the probability in question. According to the usual interpretation the probability of finding n electrons having $\mathbf{x}$'s equal to $x', x'', \ldots$ is given by

$$\Psi^*\Psi = \frac{1}{n!}\begin{vmatrix} \langle 1 \mid x' \rangle \langle 1 \mid x'' \rangle \ldots \langle 1 \mid x^{(n)} \rangle \\ \langle 2 \mid x' \rangle \langle 2 \mid x'' \rangle \ldots \langle 2 \mid x^{(n)} \rangle \\ \cdot \quad \cdot \quad \cdot \\ \cdot \quad \cdot \quad \cdot \\ \cdot \quad \cdot \quad \cdot \\ \langle n \mid x' \rangle \langle n \mid x'' \rangle \ldots \langle n \mid x^{(n)} \rangle \end{vmatrix} \begin{vmatrix} \langle x' \mid 1 \rangle \langle x' \mid 2 \rangle \ldots \langle x' \mid n \rangle \\ \langle x'' \mid 1 \rangle \langle x'' \mid 2 \rangle \ldots \langle x'' \mid n \rangle \\ \cdot \quad \cdot \quad \cdot \\ \cdot \quad \cdot \quad \cdot \\ \cdot \quad \cdot \quad \cdot \\ \langle x^{(n)} \mid 1 \rangle \langle x^{(n)} \mid 2 \rangle \ldots \langle x^{(n)} \mid n \rangle \end{vmatrix}, \quad (7:15)$$

where the factor $1/n!$ arises from the normalization of Φ.

Calculations involving determinantal functions are so frequently met that it is convenient to have available the useful concepts of the operators $\mathbf{S}$ and $\mathbf{A}$ which are known as the symmetrizer and antisymmetrizer respectively. The results which we shall obtain will be seen to apply to any symmetric or antisymmetric function of the variables $x_1', x_2', \ldots x_n'$, but for our present purpose we shall consider only arbitrary n-particle wave-functions, denoting the two symmetry types by $\langle\, `x \mid s \,\rangle$ and $\langle\, `x \mid a \,\rangle$ for brevity. These are characterized by the conditions that for any permutation

$$\left.\begin{aligned} \langle\, P`x \mid s \,\rangle &= \langle\, `x \mid s \,\rangle, \\ \langle\, P`x \mid a \,\rangle &= \delta_P \langle\, `x \mid a \,\rangle, \end{aligned}\right\} \quad \ldots \ldots \ldots \quad (7:16)$$

and, in principle, the symmetry type of the particles is ascertained by considering the effect of all possible permutations on their wave-functions. However, it is readily shown that we can avoid considering all permutations individually by introducing the operators

$$\left.\begin{aligned} \mathbf{S} &= \frac{1}{\sqrt{n!}} \sum_P \mathbf{P}, \\ \mathbf{A} &= \frac{1}{\sqrt{n!}} \sum_P \delta_P \mathbf{P}. \end{aligned}\right\} \quad \ldots \ldots \ldots \quad (7:17)$$

From (7:16) and (7:17) we see that a necessary condition that $\langle\, `x \mid \rangle$ be symmetric *or* antisymmetric is that

$$\langle\, `x \mid \mathbf{S} \mid \rangle = \frac{1}{\sqrt{n!}} \sum_P \langle\, P`x \mid \rangle = \sqrt{n!}\,\langle\, `x \mid \rangle, \quad \ldots \quad (7:18a)$$

or

$$\langle\, `x \mid \mathbf{A} \mid \rangle = \frac{1}{\sqrt{n!}} \sum_P \delta_P \langle\, P`x \mid \rangle = \sqrt{n!}\,\langle\, `x \mid \rangle. \quad \ldots \quad (7:18b)$$

To show the sufficiency of these conditions and also determine the properties of **S** and **A**, it is convenient to introduce an operator $\mathbf{\Lambda}$ defined by

$$\mathbf{\Lambda} = \frac{1}{\sqrt{n!}} \sum_P \lambda_P \mathbf{P}, \qquad (7:19)$$

where $\lambda_P = 1$ or δ_P for symmetric or antisymmetric particles respectively; and in either case

$$\lambda_P \lambda_Q = \lambda_{PQ}, \quad \lambda_P{}^2 = 1. \qquad (7:20)$$

From (7:20) we have $\lambda_P = \lambda_{PQ}\lambda_Q$, so that for a fixed **Q**,

$$\mathbf{\Lambda Q} = \frac{1}{\sqrt{n!}} \sum_P \lambda_P \mathbf{PQ} = \lambda_Q \mathbf{\Lambda}, \qquad (7:21)$$

since as previously observed $\sum_P \lambda_{PQ}\mathbf{PQ} = \sum_P \lambda_P \mathbf{P}$, the two summations being over the same quantities but in different order. Thus,

$$\mathbf{\Lambda Q} = \mathbf{Q\Lambda}, \qquad (7:22)$$

and the sufficiency of the conditions (7:18) follows immediately; since if

$$\langle \text{'x} \mid \mathbf{S} \mid \rangle = \sqrt{n!}\, \langle \text{'x} \mid \rangle, \qquad (7:23)$$

then $\langle \text{'x} \mid \mathbf{PS} \mid \rangle = \sqrt{n!}\, \langle P\text{'x} \mid \rangle$ for any permutation **P**, and from $\mathbf{PS} = \mathbf{S}$ $(\lambda_P = 1)$ [equations (7:19, 21, 22)] we have

$$\langle P\text{'x} \mid \rangle = \langle \text{'x} \mid \rangle. \qquad (7:24)$$

Similarly, if

$$\langle \text{'x} \mid \mathbf{A} \mid \rangle = \sqrt{n!}\, \langle \text{'x} \mid \rangle, \qquad (7:25)$$

then $\langle \text{'x} \mid \mathbf{PA} \mid \rangle = \sqrt{n!}\, \langle P\text{'x} \mid \rangle$, and since $\mathbf{PA} = \delta_P \mathbf{A}$ (here $\lambda_P = \delta_P$),

$$\langle P\text{'x} \mid \rangle = \delta_P \langle \text{'x} \mid \rangle. \qquad (7:26)$$

The properties of $\mathbf{\Lambda}$ (and hence of **S** and **A**) are very simple, namely, that $\mathbf{\Lambda}$ is Hermitian and has the eigenvalues 0 and $\sqrt{n!}$.

$$\mathbf{\Lambda}^* = \frac{1}{\sqrt{n!}} \sum_P \lambda_P \mathbf{P}^* = \frac{1}{\sqrt{n!}} \sum_P \lambda_{P^{-1}} \mathbf{P}^{-1} = \mathbf{\Lambda}. \qquad (7:27)$$

$$\mathbf{\Lambda}^2 = \frac{1}{\sqrt{n!}} \sum_P \lambda_P \mathbf{\Lambda P} = \frac{1}{\sqrt{n!}} \sum_P \lambda_P{}^2 \mathbf{\Lambda} = \sqrt{n!}\,\mathbf{\Lambda}. \qquad (7:28)$$

Finally, if we consider the equation

$$\mathbf{PAS} = \mathbf{APS} \quad \text{(cf. 7:22)}, \qquad (7:29)$$

then, with the conditions $\mathbf{PS} = \mathbf{S}$, $\mathbf{PA} = \delta_P \mathbf{A}$, this reduces to

$$\delta_P \mathbf{AS} = \mathbf{AS}, \qquad (7:30)$$

and choosing a $\mathbf{P}$ such that $\delta_P = -1$, we have the important result

$$\mathbf{AS} = \mathbf{SA} = 0. \qquad (7:31)$$

From equation (7:27) we see that we can always symmetrize or antisymmetrize any arbitrary function. Thus, if $\langle\, `\mathsf{x} \mid \rangle$ is a function with no special symmetry properties, $\langle\, `\mathsf{x} \mid \mathbf{S} \mid \rangle$ is symmetric and $\langle\, `\mathsf{x} \mid \mathbf{A} \mid \rangle$ is antisymmetric, since from (7:27),

$$\langle\, `\mathsf{x} \mid \mathbf{\Lambda}^2 \mid \rangle = \sqrt{n!}\,\langle\, `\mathsf{x} \mid \mathbf{\Lambda} \mid \rangle. \qquad (7:32)$$

Because of (7:28) and (7:31) any symmetric function $\langle\, `\mathsf{x} \mid s \,\rangle$ is always orthogonal to any antisymmetric function $\langle\, `\mathsf{x} \mid a \,\rangle$, since

$$\int \langle\, a \mid `\mathsf{x} \,\rangle\, d`\mathsf{x}\, \langle\, `\mathsf{x} \mid s \,\rangle = \frac{1}{n!}\int \langle\, a \mid \mathbf{A} \mid `\mathsf{x} \,\rangle\, d`\mathsf{x}\, \langle\, `\mathsf{x} \mid \mathbf{S} \mid s \,\rangle$$

$$= \frac{1}{n!}\int \langle\, a \mid `\mathsf{x} \,\rangle\, d`\mathsf{x}\, \langle\, `\mathsf{x} \mid \mathbf{A}^*\mathbf{S} \mid s \,\rangle = 0. \qquad (7:33)$$

The proof of normalization (7:15) becomes especially simple when Ψ is expressed in the form $\Psi = A \prod\limits_r \langle\, \mathsf{x}_r' \mid r \,\rangle$, since we have

$$\int \Psi^* d`\mathsf{x} \Psi = \int A \prod_r \langle\, r \mid \mathsf{x}_r' \,\rangle \cdot d`\mathsf{x} A \prod \langle\, \mathsf{x}_r' \mid r \,\rangle$$

$$= \sqrt{n!} \int \prod_r \langle\, r \mid \mathsf{x}_r' \,\rangle\, d`\mathsf{x} A \prod_r \langle\, \mathsf{x}_r' \mid r \,\rangle = 1, \qquad (7:34)$$

the identity permutation contributing the only non-zero term.

We may also note that Φ in the form (7:6) or (7:10) is normalized as it stands, without the factor $1/\sqrt{n!}$, if we adopt the convention that the points $\{\, \mathsf{x}_1'\mathsf{x}_2' \ldots \mathsf{x}_n' \,\}$ and $P\{\, \mathsf{x}_1'\mathsf{x}_2' \ldots \mathsf{x}_n' \,\}$ be considered as the same point in configuration space for all permutations P; e.g. in the simplest case of $n = 2$, we agree to count the points $\{\, \mathsf{x}_1'\mathsf{x}_2' \,\} = \{\, \mathsf{x}'\mathsf{x}'' \,\}$ and $\{\, \mathsf{x}_1'\mathsf{x}_2' \,\} = \{\, \mathsf{x}''\mathsf{x}' \,\}$ as the same, so that *only one* of them appears in any summation or integration over all values of x_1', x_2'.

Returning to the problem at hand, this convention can be used to advantage inasmuch as the normalized probability density can be written simply as

$$\Delta^{(n)} = \begin{vmatrix} \langle\, \mathsf{x}' \mid \rho \mid \mathsf{x}' \,\rangle & \langle\, \mathsf{x}' \mid \rho \mid \mathsf{x}'' \,\rangle & \ldots & \langle\, \mathsf{x}' \mid \rho \mid \mathsf{x}^{(n)} \,\rangle \\ \langle\, \mathsf{x}'' \mid \rho \mid \mathsf{x}' \,\rangle & \langle\, \mathsf{x}'' \mid \rho \mid \mathsf{x}'' \,\rangle & \ldots & \langle\, \mathsf{x}'' \mid \rho \mid \mathsf{x}^{(n)} \,\rangle \\ \cdot & \cdot & & \cdot \\ \cdot & \cdot & & \cdot \\ \cdot & \cdot & & \cdot \\ \langle\, \mathsf{x}^{(n)} \mid \rho \mid \mathsf{x}' \,\rangle & \langle\, \mathsf{x}^{(n)} \mid \rho \mid \mathsf{x}'' \,\rangle & \ldots & \langle\, \mathsf{x}^{(n)} \mid \rho \mid \mathsf{x}^{(n)} \,\rangle \end{vmatrix}, \qquad (7:35)$$

from which it follows that all probabilities will be expressible in terms of the matrix elements of ρ alone. Corresponding to the above notation we shall denote by $\Delta^{(j)}$ the determinant formed by the first j rows and columns of $\Delta^{(n)}$. To find the probability of $n - 1$ electrons having $\mathbf{x}$'s equal to x', x'', ... $\mathsf{x}^{(n-1)}$, $\Delta^{(n)}$ must be integrated (in the present case) over all values of $x^{(n)}$. This procedure is easily carried out by expanding according to the last row and column to separate out terms referring to $x^{(n)}$, and also invoking the condition $\rho^2 = \rho$, e.g.

$$\Delta^{(n)} = \{ \langle x^{(n)} \mid \rho \mid x^{(n)} \rangle \Delta^{n-1} - \sum_{i,j}^{n-1} \langle x^{(n)} \mid \rho \mid x^{(i)} \rangle \langle x^{(j)} \mid \rho \mid x^{(n)} \rangle C_{j,i}^{(n-1)} \}, \quad (7:36)$$

where $C_{j,i}^{(n-1)}$ denotes the cofactor of $\langle x^{(j)} \mid \rho \mid x^{(i)} \rangle$ in $\Delta^{(n-1)}$. Further,

$$\int \langle x^{(n)} \mid \rho \mid x^{(n)} \rangle \, dx^{(n)} = \int \sum_r \langle x^{(n)} \mid r \rangle \langle r \mid x^{(n)} \rangle \, dx^{(n)} = n, \quad . \quad (7:37)$$

and

$$\int \langle x^{(n)} \mid \rho \mid x^{(i)} \rangle \, dx^{(n)} \langle x^{(j)} \mid \rho \mid x^{(n)} \rangle = \langle x^{(j)} \mid \rho \mid x^{(i)} \rangle. \quad . \quad . \quad . \quad (7:38)$$

Therefore,

$$\int \Delta^{(n)} \, dx^{(n)} = n\Delta^{(n-1)} - \sum_{i,j}^{n-1} \langle x^{(j)} \mid \rho \mid x^{(i)} \rangle C_{j,i}^{(n-1)}$$

$$= n\Delta^{(n-1)} - (n-1)\,\Delta^{(n-1)} = \Delta^{(n-1)}, \quad . \quad . \quad . \quad (7:39)$$

so that $\Delta^{(n-1)}$ is the probability for $n-1$ electrons simultaneously to have their $\mathbf{x}$'s equal to $x', x'', \ldots x^{(n-1)}$.

It follows by induction that the corresponding probability of $m < n$ electrons having $\mathbf{x}$'s equal to $x', x'', \ldots x^{(m)}$ is $\Delta^{(m)}$, since

$$\Delta^{(m+1)} = \langle x^{(m+1)} \mid \rho \mid x^{(m+1)} \rangle \Delta^{(m)} - \sum_{i,j}^{m} \langle x^{(m+1)} \mid \rho \mid x^{(i)} \rangle \langle x^{(j)} \mid \rho \mid x^{(m+1)} \rangle C_{j,i}^{(m)}, \quad (7:40)$$

from which

$$\int \Delta^{(m+1)} \, dx^{(m+1)} = n\Delta^{(m)} - m\Delta^{(m)} = (n-m)\,\Delta^{(m)}, \quad . \quad . \quad (7:41)$$

the factor $(n-m)$ corresponding physically to the fact that there are $(n-m)$ electrons to choose from as regards assignment of the eigenvalues $x^{(m+1)}$.

We have thus far approached the interpretation of the density matrix from above, so to speak; starting from the general matrix (7:35) and working down to the originally posed question as to the probability of finding simultaneously (any) two electrons such that the numerical values of the $\mathbf{x}$'s are x' for one and x'' for the other. However, we can also approach this question in more primitive and direct fashion, and thus gain insight into the physical meaning of the preceding results. In general, if there are two electrons occupying the orbits i, j, the normalized wave-function for the system (with the preceding normalization convention) is given by

$$\begin{vmatrix} \langle x_1' \mid i \rangle & \langle x_1' \mid j \rangle \\ \langle x_2' \mid i \rangle & \langle x_2' \mid j \rangle \end{vmatrix}, \quad . \quad . \quad . \quad . \quad . \quad . \quad . \quad . \quad (7:42)$$

and the probability (density) for the stated values is given by the squared modulus of (7:42) with x', x'' substituted for x_1', x_2', namely,

$$\begin{vmatrix} \langle i \mid x' \rangle & \langle i \mid x'' \rangle \\ \langle j \mid x' \rangle & \langle j \mid x'' \rangle \end{vmatrix} \begin{vmatrix} \langle x' \mid i \rangle & \langle x' \mid j \rangle \\ \langle x'' \mid i \rangle & \langle x'' \mid j \rangle \end{vmatrix}. \quad . \quad . \quad . \quad . \quad (7:43)$$

However, when all n orbits are occupied, the *total* probability for any two electrons to have the eigenvalues x', x'', respectively, will be (7:43) summed over all pairs i, j; i, j being counted the same as j, i, corresponding to the physically required condition that all electrons be considered on equal footing without possibility of distinction. This sum is readily seen to be the determinant of the matrix product

$$\left\| \begin{matrix} \langle x' \mid 1 \rangle \langle x' \mid 2 \rangle \ldots \langle x' \mid n \rangle \\ \langle x'' \mid 1 \rangle \langle x'' \mid 2 \rangle \ldots \langle x'' \mid n \rangle \end{matrix} \right\| \left\| \begin{matrix} \langle 1 \mid x' \rangle \langle 1 \mid x'' \rangle \\ \langle 2 \mid x' \rangle \langle 2 \mid x'' \rangle \\ \cdot \quad \cdot \\ \cdot \quad \cdot \\ \cdot \quad \cdot \\ \langle n \mid x' \rangle \langle n \mid x'' \rangle \end{matrix} \right\|, \qquad (7:44)$$

or

$$\Delta^{(2)} = \begin{vmatrix} \langle x' \mid \rho \mid x' \rangle & \langle x' \mid \rho \mid x'' \rangle \\ \langle x'' \mid \rho \mid x' \rangle & \langle x'' \mid \rho \mid x'' \rangle \end{vmatrix}. \qquad (7:45)$$

Integrating over x'' we find

$$\int \Delta^{(2)}\, dx'' = (n-1)\, \Delta^{(1)}, \qquad (7:46)$$

in accord with (7:41) and the usual interpretation of $\Delta^{(1)} = \langle x' \mid \rho \mid x' \rangle$ as the probability of there being an electron whose $\mathbf{x}$'s have the values x'.

§ 58. Application to Free Electrons

The interelectronic correlations described by the determinant $\Delta^{(2)}$ can be readily evaluated in explicit form for the special case of a system of free electrons enclosed in a cubical box;[15] and despite its simplicity, this illustrative case has the advantage that there are no extraneous effects to consider. Thus, from (7:45) we have the probability density

$$\Delta^{(2)}(x', x'') = \frac{1}{n(n-1)} \sum_{i,j} \{ |\langle x' \mid i \rangle|^2 |\langle x'' \mid j \rangle|^2 - \langle i \mid x' \rangle \langle x' \mid j \rangle \langle j \mid x'' \rangle \langle x'' \mid i \rangle \}; \qquad (7:47)$$

the normalization corresponding to the usual convention rather than that adopted in the preceding discussion. Assuming periodic boundary conditions, the wave-functions are of the form

$$\langle x' \mid i \rangle = \langle x' \mid p_i \rangle\, \delta(\sigma', \sigma^i) = \frac{\delta(\sigma', \sigma^i)}{\sqrt{V}}\, e^{(i/\hbar)\underline{x}' \cdot \underline{p}_i}, \qquad (7:48)$$

[15] The present calculation corresponds to the state of zero total spin, i.e. an *even* number of electrons with two assigned to each spinless orbit. Cf. Wigner, E. P., and Seitz, F.: *Phys. Rev.*, **43**, 804 (1933).

where the components of the vector $\underline{p}$ are $p_x = n_x h/L$, etc. Then $\Delta^{(2)}(x', x'')$ becomes

$$\Delta^{(2)} = \frac{1}{n(n-1)} \sum_{i,j} \{1 - e^{-i(\underline{x}'-\underline{x}'')\cdot(\underline{p}_i - \underline{p}_j)} \delta(\sigma^i, \sigma') \delta(\sigma^i, \sigma'') \delta(\sigma^j, \sigma') \delta(\sigma^j, \sigma'')\}; \quad (7{:}49)$$

where the summation extends over all $\underline{p}_i$ such that

$$|\underline{p}| \leqslant p_0 = \left(\frac{3nh^3}{8\pi}\right)^{\frac{1}{3}}.$$

For electrons with antiparallel spin components the second term above vanishes so that there is *no* statistical correlation;[16] hence, we confine our attention to electrons with parallel spins. The probability will not depend on direction, so that we may first simplify the above expression by averaging over all directions of $\underline{x}' - \underline{x}'''$, and then integrate, since the assumption of a very large number of electrons implies a sufficiently dense distribution of energy levels. The final expression, in terms of the maximum wave-number vector k_0 and separation $r = |\underline{x}' - \underline{x}''|$, is

$$\Delta^{(2)}(r) = \frac{1}{V^2}\left\{1 - 9\left(\frac{\sin 2\pi k_0 r - 2\pi k_0 r \cos 2\pi k_0 r}{(2\pi k_0 r)^3}\right)^2\right\}, \quad . \quad . \quad (7{:}50)$$

which differs from the classical value only through the bracketed expression, describing what may be termed a *repulsion* of statistical origin. Perhaps the most significant conclusion we can reach is that these effects (deviation from classical value) become operative only at very small distances, and this is quite generally true (cf. Footnote 8, p. 144).

§ 59. The Spinless Density Operator

We may also introduce a quantum density $\boldsymbol{\rho}_1$, defined over spinless states, i.e. the diagonal sum of $\boldsymbol{\rho}$ over spin

$$\boldsymbol{\rho}_1 = \mathscr{S}_{p\sigma}\, \boldsymbol{\rho}, \quad . \quad . \quad . \quad . \quad . \quad . \quad . \quad . \quad (7{:}51)$$

and it is readily shown that $\boldsymbol{\rho}_1$ must have one or other of the eigenvalues 0, 1, 2. To this end, we first express the typical wave-function $\langle x' | r \rangle$ explicitly in terms of its coordinate-spin eigenfunctions as

$$\langle x' | r \rangle = \langle x' | \alpha^r \rangle \, \delta(\sigma', \sigma^r), \quad . \quad . \quad . \quad . \quad . \quad (7{:}52)$$

where, in general, α^r denotes the quantities in addition to σ^r which are required to specify the rth orbit. We then consider the case of $n = 2\nu + 1$ electrons, with ν pairs assigned the same coordinate eigenfunction—the unpaired electron, of course, being assigned a distinct function. Let us further require that the $\nu + 1$

[16] To a large extent the absence of statistical correlation in the positions of electrons with antiparallel spin *components* is a matter of the approximation involved in the (Slater-Fock) determinantal form, rather than of basic principle. One may allow for this correlation by suitable modification of the determinantal function. Cf. WIGNER, E. P.: *Phys. Rev.*, **46**, 1002 (1934).

distinct orbitals be orthonormal, and label the unpaired function by α^0, the 2ν paired functions being ordered according to $\alpha^1 = \alpha^{\nu+1}, \ldots \alpha^\nu = \alpha^{2\nu}$. Then we have

$$\begin{aligned}\langle x' \mid \rho_1 \mid x'' \rangle &= \sum_{\sigma'} \langle x'\sigma' \mid \rho \mid x''\sigma' \rangle \\ &= \sum_{\sigma'} \Big\{ \langle x'\sigma' \mid \alpha^0\sigma^0 \rangle \langle \alpha^0\sigma^0 \mid x''\sigma' \rangle + \sum_r^{2\nu} \langle x'\sigma' \mid \alpha^r\sigma^r \rangle \langle \alpha^r\sigma^r \mid x''\sigma' \rangle \Big\} \\ &= \langle x' \mid \alpha^0 \rangle \langle \alpha^0 \mid x'' \rangle + 2 \sum_r^{\nu} \langle x' \mid \alpha^r \rangle \langle \alpha^r \mid x'' \rangle, \quad . \quad . \quad . \quad (7{:}53a)\end{aligned}$$

$$\begin{aligned}\langle x' \mid \rho_1^2 \mid x'' \rangle &= \int \langle x' \mid \rho_1 \mid x''' \rangle \, dx''' \, \langle x''' \mid \rho_1 \mid x'' \rangle \\ &= \langle x' \mid \alpha^0 \rangle \langle \alpha^0 \mid x'' \rangle + 4 \sum_r^{\nu} \langle x' \mid \alpha^r \rangle \langle \alpha^r \mid x'' \rangle, \quad . \quad . \quad . \quad (7{:}53b)\end{aligned}$$

and

$$\langle x' \mid \rho_1^3 \mid x'' \rangle = \langle x' \mid \alpha^0 \rangle \langle \alpha^0 \mid x'' \rangle + 8 \sum_r^{\nu} \langle x' \mid \alpha^r \rangle \langle \alpha^r \mid x'' \rangle. \quad . \quad . \quad . \quad (7{:}53c)$$

Combining these expressions, we see that

$$\langle x' \mid \rho_1^3 \mid x'' \rangle = 3 \langle x' \mid \rho_1^2 \mid x'' \rangle - 2 \langle x' \mid \rho_1 \mid x'' \rangle, \quad . \quad . \quad (7{:}54)$$

or symbolically,

$$\rho_1 (\rho_1 - 1) (\rho_1 - 2) = 0, \quad . \quad . \quad . \quad . \quad . \quad . \quad (7{:}55)$$

from which the eigenvalues of ρ_1 are 0, 1, 2. Consideration of higher powers introduces no further conditions on ρ_1. In the particular case $n = 2\nu$, the electrons are paired exactly so that the odd term in (7:53) vanishes, and we obtain $\rho_1(\rho_1 - 2) = 0$, as required. For $\rho_1' = 2$, we speak of the assignment of two electrons per spinless state, and it is usually in this sense that the quantum density occurs in the purely statistical treatment of many-electron problems (cf. Chap. IX).

CHAPTER VIII

The Variation Principle

§ 60. Stationary States

Since we cannot in general determine exact eigen-$|\,\rangle$'s it is necessary to consider the possibility of assuming eigen-$|\,\rangle$'s of a certain definite form, and then determining which of these gives the best approximation to the solution of the wave-equation. The particular approximate form of $|\,\rangle$, or class of $|\,\rangle$'s, to be chosen can only be inferred from physical considerations, and this point will be treated in the next section. Here we consider the purely mathematical question of the determination of the arbitrary parameters, which may occur in a selected form, such that the best approximation (within this class of $|\,\rangle$'s) is obtained. This problem is of greatest practical importance in connection with stationary states, when they exist, and we shall therefore consider first the determination of the eigen-$|\,\rangle$'s of $\mathbf{H}$ before passing to the general theory. Essentially, all perturbation methods are derivable from the basic theorem. If $\langle\,|\,\rangle = 1$, $\langle\,|$ being the conjugate of $|\,\rangle$, then the necessary condition that $|\,\rangle$ be an eigen-$|\,\rangle$ of $\mathbf{H}$ is that $\langle\,|\,\mathbf{H}\,|\,\rangle$ be stationary for all variations which leave $|\,\rangle$ normalized. This is proved as follows: It is required that

$$\delta \langle\,|\,\mathbf{H}\,|\,\rangle = 0, \qquad (8:1)$$ [1]

with the accessory condition

$$\delta \langle\,|\,\rangle = 0; \qquad (8:2)$$

or equivalently (ϵ denotes a Lagrangian multiplier),

$$\delta \langle\,|\,\mathbf{H} - \epsilon\,|\,\rangle = 0, \qquad (8:3)$$

or

$$\delta \langle\,|\cdot(\,\mathbf{H} - \epsilon\,)\,|\,\rangle + \langle\,|\,(\,\mathbf{H} - \epsilon\,)\cdot\delta\,|\,\rangle = 0.$$

The variations $\delta\langle\,|$ and $\delta\,|\,\rangle$, being conjugate, are not independent, but we may nevertheless equate the two terms above separately to zero, since if we take a new $\delta\,|\,\rangle$ which is i times the original, then $\delta\langle\,|$ is $-i$ times the original, so that

$$-i\delta \langle\,|\cdot(\,\mathbf{H} - \epsilon\,)\,|\,\rangle + i\langle\,|\,(\,\mathbf{H} - \epsilon\,)\cdot\delta\,|\,\rangle = 0. \qquad (8:4)$$

Comparing (8:3) and (8:4), it follows that

$$\delta \langle\,|\cdot(\,\mathbf{H} - \epsilon\,)\,|\,\rangle = 0, \qquad (8:5a)$$ [2]

and

$$\langle\,|\,(\,\mathbf{H} - \epsilon\,)\cdot\delta\,|\,\rangle = 0. \qquad (8:5b)$$

[1] The symbolic form is equivalent to $\delta \int \langle\,|\,q'\,\rangle\,dq'\,\langle\,q'\,|\,\mathbf{H}\,|\,q''\,\rangle\,dq''\,\langle\,q''\,|\,\rangle$.

[2] These are equivalent to $\int \langle\,|\,q'\,\rangle\,dq'\,\langle\,q'\,|\,(\,\mathbf{H} - \epsilon\,)\,|\,q''\,\rangle\,dq''\,\delta\langle\,q''\,|\,\rangle$, etc.

Since $\delta \mid \rangle$ is arbitrary we have

$$(\mathbf{H} - \epsilon) \mid \rangle = 0, \qquad (8:6)$$

which states that $\mid \rangle$ is an eigenvector of **H** belonging to the eigenvalue ϵ. We may note that in further work involving variations we shall use the results expressed by (8:5), namely, that the correct result is obtained if $\delta \mid \rangle$ and its conjugate are treated as though independent, thus avoiding needless repetition.

Quite aside from the symbolic approach, which merely simplifies the treatment, it should be pointed out that this fundamental theorem must usually be accepted on faith in most physical applications. It is not possible, in general, to establish the sufficiency of the conditions, nor determine the nature of the extremal, although in most cases it is found to be a true minimum. If now, in lieu of the exact solution, we choose a particular form $\mid 1 \rangle$, which means that the approximate solution is limited to a definite subspace of the whole $\mid \rangle$-space, then in order that $\mid 1 \rangle$ be the best approximation, it is necessary that $\langle 1 \mid \mathbf{H} \mid 1 \rangle$ be stationary for all variations of $\mid 1 \rangle$ that preserve its special form, i.e.

$$\delta \langle 1 \mid (\mathbf{H} - \epsilon) \mid 1 \rangle = \delta \int \langle 1 \mid q' \rangle dq' \langle q' \mid \mathbf{H} - \epsilon \mid q'' \rangle dq'' \langle q'' \mid 1 \rangle = 0, \quad (8:7)$$

where the approximate eigenvalue is given by $\langle 1 \mid \mathbf{H} \mid 1 \rangle$ when $\mid 1 \rangle$ is suitable normalized.[3]

§ 61. Non-stationary States

Before considering the applications of the preceding theory, let us examine the necessary generalization to include non-stationary states. Here the exact equation of motion is

$$i\hbar \frac{d}{dt} \mid ; t \rangle = \mathbf{H} \mid ; t \rangle, \qquad (8:8)$$

so that, if $\mid ; t \rangle$ is specified at some particular time t_0, it is determined for all other times. If now we assume the initial $\mid \rangle$ at the time t_0 to be of the special approximate form $\mid 1 ; t_0 \rangle$, then the equation of motion of $\mid 1 ; t \rangle$ will be of the form

$$i\hbar \frac{d}{dt} \mid 1 ; t \rangle = \mathbf{H} \mid 1 ; t \rangle + \mid 2 ; t \rangle, \qquad (8:9)$$

where the correction term $\mid 2 ; t \rangle$ must be small if $\mid 1 ; t \rangle$ is to be a good approximation ($\mid 2 ; t \rangle \to 0$ as $\mid 1 ; t \rangle \to \mid ; t \rangle$). Equation (8:9) may be written in the form

$$i\hbar \mid 1 ; t_0 + dt \rangle = i\hbar \mid 1 ; t_0 \rangle + \{ \mathbf{H} \mid 1 ; t_0 \rangle + \mid 2 ; t_0 \rangle \} dt, \quad (8:10)$$

and it is required that $\mid 1 ; t_0 + dt \rangle$ be such that $\mid 2 ; t_0 \rangle$ shall be the smallest possible vector corresponding to *fixed* $\mid 1 ; t_0 \rangle$. From (8:10) it follows that if $\mid 1 ; t_0 + dt \rangle$

[3] If we wish to approximate to the nth energy state, we must of course introduce the additional conditions specifying orthogonality to all the lower states previously obtained.

is altered by an amount $\delta \mid 1 ; t_0 + dt \rangle$ the corresponding variation in the correction term is given by

$$\delta \mid 2 ; t_0 \rangle \, dt = i\hbar \, \delta \mid 1 ; t_0 + dt \rangle. \quad . \quad . \quad . \quad . \quad . \qquad (8{:}11)$$

The condition that $\mid 2 ; t_0 \rangle$ be as small as possible is that $\langle 2 ; t_0 \mid 2 ; t_0 \rangle$ be a minimum, i.e.

$$\delta \langle 2 ; t_0 \mid 2 ; t_0 \rangle = 0, \quad . \quad . \quad . \quad . \quad . \quad . \quad . \qquad (8{:}12a)$$

or

$$\delta \langle 2 ; t_0 \mid \cdot \mid 2 ; t_0 \rangle = 0, \quad . \quad . \quad . \quad . \quad . \quad . \quad . \qquad (8{:}12b)$$

according to a previous remark. From (8:11) it follows that

$$\delta \langle 2 ; t_0 \mid = -i\hbar \, \delta \langle 1 ; t_0 + dt \mid, \quad . \quad . \quad . \quad . \quad . \quad . \qquad (8{:}13)$$

which, combined with (8:12b), gives

$$\delta \langle 1 ; t_0 + dt \mid \cdot \mid 2 ; t_0 \rangle = 0. \quad . \quad . \quad . \quad . \quad . \quad . \quad . \quad . \qquad (8{:}14)$$

Passing to the limit $dt = 0$, and dropping the zero subscript, since our criterion must obtain for all t, we find

$$\delta \langle 1 ; t \mid \cdot \mid 2 ; t \rangle = 0 \quad . \quad . \quad . \quad . \quad . \quad . \quad . \quad . \qquad (8{:}15)$$

as the criterion of *least correction*, i.e. the correction term $\mid 2 ; t \rangle$ must be orthogonal to any variation of the approximate solution $\mid 1 ; t \rangle$. If now equation (8:9) is premultiplied by $\delta \langle 1 ; t \mid$, the correction term is eliminated, and we obtain

$$i\hbar \, \delta \langle 1 ; t \mid \cdot \frac{d}{dt} \mid 1 ; t \rangle = \delta \langle 1 ; t \mid \cdot \mathbf{H} \mid 1 ; t \rangle \quad . \quad . \quad . \qquad (8{:}16)$$

as the condition that $\mid 1 ; t \rangle$ be the best approximate solution of the wave-equation.[4] It will be observed that equation (8:16), which is the criterion that the correction $\mid 2 ; t \rangle$ be permanently small, is simply the variational transcription of equation (8:8).

The preceding analysis may be given a very simple geometrical interpretation. According to the exact equation (8:8), the true state vector $\mid ; t \rangle$ traverses a path in the general $\mid \rangle$-space, which will not in general lie in the subspace corresponding to vectors of the assumed form $\mid 1 ; t \rangle$. Let us denote by $\widehat{\mathrm{AB}}$ and $\widehat{\mathrm{AB}}'$ typical segments of the true path and its orthogonal projection on to the $\mid 1 ; \rangle$-subspace; the vector $\mid 1 ; t \rangle$ joining the origin and the point A being indicated by $\underline{\mathrm{OA}}$. If the vector $\mid 1 ; t \rangle$ were exact, it would in time dt move along the path $\widehat{\mathrm{AB}}$ to a point B; the vector $\underline{\mathrm{AB}}$ then representing the increment $\mathbf{H} \mid 1 ; t \rangle \, dt/i\hbar$, and $\underline{\mathrm{OB}}$ the final vector $\mid 1 ; t + dt \rangle$ in accord with the equation

$$\mid 1 ; t + dt \rangle = \mid 1 ; t \rangle + \mathbf{H} \mid 1 ; t \rangle \, dt/i\hbar. \quad . \quad . \quad . \quad . \qquad (8{:}17)$$

[4] The whole argument can of course be carried through in representative form, leading to the condition

$$i\hbar \int \delta \langle 1 ; t \mid q' \rangle \, dq' \frac{d}{dt} \langle q' \mid 1 ; t \rangle = \iint \delta \langle 1 ; t \mid q' \rangle \, dq' \langle q' \mid \mathbf{H} \mid q'' \rangle \, dq'' \langle q'' \mid 1 ; t \rangle$$

as in (8:16) above.

Actually $|\,1\,;t\,\rangle$ is only approximate, which has the consequence that we go for a time dt along $\widehat{AB}$ to B in accord with (8:17), and then from B a perpendicular $\underline{BB'}$ is dropped on to the subspace of the $|\,1\,;\,\rangle$'s so that the actual approximate vector $|\,1\,;t+dt\,\rangle$ is represented by $\underline{OB'}$ in accord with the equation

$$|\,1\,;t+dt\,\rangle = |\,1\,;t\,\rangle + \mathbf{H}\,|\,1\,;t\,\rangle\,dt/i\hbar + |\,2\,;t\,\rangle\,dt/i\hbar. \quad . \quad (8{:}18)$$

The vector indicated by $\underline{BB'}$ is just $|\,2\,;t\,\rangle\,dt/i\hbar$, and the orthogonality of $\underline{BB'}$ to the $|\,1\,;\,\rangle$-subspace is the geometrical correlate of the condition

$$\delta\,\langle\,1\,;t+dt\,|\cdot|\,2\,;t\,\rangle = 0. \quad . \quad . \quad . \quad . \quad . \quad . \quad . \quad (8{:}19)$$

We may readily verify that if $|\,1\,;t\,\rangle$ is initially taken to be normalized according to $\langle\,1\,|\,1\,\rangle = 1$, for example, then it will remain normalized when its motion is determined according to (8:16), provided the special form of $|\,1\,;t\,\rangle$ involves no restriction on the normalization. In other words, if $|\,1\,;t\,\rangle$ is of the special form, $\kappa\,|\,1\,;t\,\rangle$ is of the special form for any arbitrary number κ. A possible variation will be $\delta\,|\,1\,;t\,\rangle = \mu\,|\,1\,;t\,\rangle$ where μ is a small number, and substituting into (8:16) and its adjoint, it follows that

$$\langle\,1\,;t\,|\cdot\frac{d}{dt}\,|\,1\,;t\,\rangle + \frac{d}{dt}\,\langle\,1\,;t\,|\cdot|\,1\,;t\,\rangle = 0 \quad . \quad . \quad . \quad . \quad (8{:}20)$$

as required. If $|\,1\,;t\,\rangle$ be taken such that

$$i\hbar\,\frac{d}{dt}\,|\,1\,;t\,\rangle = \epsilon\,|\,1\,;t\,\rangle,$$

then (8:16) becomes

$$\epsilon\,\delta\,\langle\,1\,|\cdot|\,1\,\rangle = \delta\,\langle\,1\,|\cdot\mathbf{H}\,|\,1\,\rangle, \quad . \quad . \quad . \quad . \quad . \quad . \quad (8{:}21)$$

so that the general analysis includes that for stationary states as a special case.

§ 62. Applications of the Variational Method—Hartree Equations

The variational method finds its most important and powerful application in the approximate solution of the problem of several interacting systems which are described by n sets of commuting observables, and are not necessarily similar. Hence, in general these sets of observables will be neither homologous nor, by the same token, will they necessarily consist of particle space-spin variables as we shall here assume to be the case, i.e. for an n-electron system. For our present purpose we do not require a definite explicit form for the total Hamiltonian $\mathbf{H}$, and we write the exact wave-function as $\langle\,'x\,|\,\rangle$. As a possible approximation to this function we may assume the special product form

$$\langle\,x_1'x_2'\ldots x_n'\,|\,1\,\rangle = \prod_r \langle\,x_r'\,|\,r\,\rangle, \quad . \quad . \quad . \quad . \quad . \quad . \quad (8{:}22)$$

where the individual wave-functions refer to single-system variables only, and the ordinal label r need not at present be specialized. Considering first the case of stationary states, we have

$$\delta \langle 1 \mid {}'x \rangle = \delta \prod_r \langle r \mid x_r' \rangle$$

$$= \sum_s \delta \langle s \mid x_s' \rangle \prod_{r \neq s} \langle r \mid x_r' \rangle, \quad . \quad . \quad . \quad . \quad (8{:}23)$$

and

$$\delta \langle 1 \mid \cdot \mathbf{H} \mid 1 \rangle = \int \delta \langle 1 \mid {}'x \rangle d'x \langle {}'x \mid \mathbf{H} \mid {}''x \rangle d''x \langle {}''x \mid 1 \rangle$$

$$= \sum_s \int \delta \langle s \mid x_s' \rangle \prod_{r \neq s} \langle r \mid x_r' \rangle d'x \langle {}'x \mid \mathbf{H} \mid {}''x \rangle d''x \prod_t \langle x_t' \mid t \rangle, \quad (8{:}24)$$

or

$$\delta \langle 1 \mid \cdot \mathbf{H} \mid 1 \rangle = \sum_s \int \delta \langle s \mid x_s' \rangle dx_s' \langle x_s' \mid \mathbf{H}_s \mid x_s'' \rangle dx_s'' \langle x_s'' \mid s \rangle, \quad (8{:}25)$$

where

$$\langle x_s' \mid \mathbf{H}_s \mid x_s'' \rangle = \int \prod_{r \neq s} \langle r \mid x_r' \rangle dx_r' \langle {}'x \mid \mathbf{H} \mid {}''x \rangle \prod_{t \neq s} dx_t'' \langle x_t'' \mid t \rangle \quad (8{:}26)$$

is a function of the variables x_s', x_s'' only. We may, without loss of generality, assume the individual wave-functions to be normalized, thus

$$\int \langle r \mid x_r' \rangle dx_r' \langle x_r' \mid r \rangle = 1, \quad . \quad . \quad . \quad . \quad . \quad . \quad (8{:}27)$$

so that

$$\epsilon \delta \langle 1 \mid \cdot \mid 1 \rangle = \epsilon \sum_s \int \delta \langle s \mid x_s' \rangle \prod_{r \neq s} \langle r \mid x_r' \rangle d'x \prod \langle x_t' \mid t \rangle$$

$$= \epsilon \sum_s \int \delta \langle s \mid x_s' \rangle dx_s' \langle x_s' \mid s \rangle. \quad . \quad . \quad . \quad . \quad . \quad (8{:}28)$$

The variational condition thus becomes

$$\delta \langle 1 \mid \cdot (\epsilon - \mathbf{H}) \mid 1 \rangle$$

$$= \sum_s \iint \delta \langle s \mid x_s' \rangle dx_s' \{ \epsilon \langle x_s' \mid s \rangle - \langle x_s' \mid \mathbf{H}_s \mid x_s'' \rangle dx_s'' \langle x_s'' \mid s \rangle \} = 0, \quad (8{:}29)$$

from which it follows that the individual functions must satisfy the equations

$$\int \langle x_s' \mid \mathbf{H}_s \mid x_s'' \rangle dx_s'' \langle x_s'' \mid s \rangle = \epsilon \langle x_s' \mid s \rangle, \quad . \quad . \quad . \quad (8{:}30)$$

since the variations $\delta \langle s \mid x_s' \rangle$ are arbitrary and independent. Thus the function $\langle x_s' \mid s \rangle$ is required to be an eigenfunction of the corresponding operator $\mathbf{H}_s$ belonging to the eigenvalue ϵ, which is given by

$$\epsilon = \int \langle s \mid x_s' \rangle dx_s' \langle x_s' \mid \mathbf{H}_s \mid x_s'' \rangle dx_s'' \langle x_s'' \mid s \rangle. \quad . \quad . \quad (8{:}31)$$

The result (8:30) corresponds physically to defining an *effective* Hamiltonian for each system which is obtained, in effect, by averaging the total Hamiltonian over all systems except the one under consideration [cf. (8:26)].

The corresponding equations for the non-stationary states are

$$i\hbar\,\delta\,\langle\, 1\,;t\,|\cdot\frac{d}{dt}\,|\,1\,;t\,\rangle$$

$$=i\hbar\int\sum_s\delta\,\langle\, s\,|\,x_s'\,\rangle\prod_{r\neq s}\langle\, r\,|\,x_r'\,\rangle\, d'x\sum_u\frac{d}{dt}\langle\, x_u'\,|\,u\,\rangle\prod_{t\neq u}\langle\, x_t'\,|\,t\,\rangle$$

$$=i\hbar\sum_s\int\delta\,\langle\, s\,|\,x_s'\,\rangle\, dx_s'\,\frac{d}{dt}\langle\, x_s'\,|\,s\,\rangle+\sum_s\sum_{u\neq s}\lambda_u\int\delta\,\langle\, s\,|\,x_s'\,\rangle\, dx_s'\,\langle\, x_s'\,|\,s\,\rangle,\quad(8{:}32)$$

where

$$\lambda_u=i\hbar\int\langle\, u\,|\,x_u'\,\rangle\, dx_u'\,\frac{d}{dt}\langle\, x_u'\,|\,u\,\rangle.\quad .\quad .\quad .\quad .\quad(8{:}32a)$$

Combining the above with the previous result (8:25) to form the variational equation (8:16), and equating coefficients of $\delta\,\langle\, s\,|\,x_s'\,\rangle$, we find

$$i\hbar\,\frac{d}{dt}\langle\, x_s'\,|\,s\,\rangle+\sum_{u\neq s}\lambda_u\,\langle\, x_s'\,|\,s\,\rangle=\int\langle\, x_s'\,|\,\mathbf{H}_s\,|\,x_s''\,\rangle\, dx_s''\,\langle\, x_s''\,|\,s\,\rangle,\quad(8{:}33)$$

which is the generalized equation corresponding to (8:31). If we multiply equation (8:33) by $\langle\, s\,|\,x_s'\,\rangle$ and integrate, we find a simple symmetrical expression for the sum of *all* the numbers λ_u, namely

$$\sum_u\lambda_u=\iint\langle\, s\,|\,x_s'\,\rangle\, dx_s'\,\langle\, x_s'\,|\,\mathbf{H}_s\,|\,x_s''\,\rangle\, dx_s''\,\langle\, x_s''\,|\,s\,\rangle.\quad .\quad(8{:}34)$$

However, in general we can obtain little further information about the λ's, so that the equations are to a certain extent arbitrary in that if we know the functions $\langle\, x_s'\,|\,s\,\rangle$, etc., at one particular time, their values at a later time are undefined. This arbitrariness arises simply because the individual wave-functions can be multiplied by arbitrary numerical factors of unit modulus (either individually or collectively) without affecting the total wave-function. The λ's can be further defined only to the extent that they will be real if the individual wave-functions are required to be normalized at all times, viz.

$$\int\frac{d}{dt}\langle\, r\,|\,x_r'\,\rangle\, dx_r'\,\langle\, x_r'\,|\,r\,\rangle+\int\langle\, r\,|\,x_r'\,\rangle\, dx_r'\,\frac{d}{dt}\langle\, x_r'\,|\,r\,\rangle=0,\quad(8{:}35a)$$

which according to (8:32*a*) simply states that

$$-\lambda_r^*+\lambda_r=0.\quad .\quad .\quad .\quad .\quad .\quad .\quad .\quad .\quad .\quad(8{:}35b)$$

In all physical problems the Hamiltonian is of the form

$$\mathbf{H}=\sum_k\mathbf{u}_k+\sum\sum_{k<l}\mathbf{v}_{kl}=\mathbf{U}+\mathbf{V};\quad .\quad .\quad .\quad .\quad .\quad(8{:}36)$$

the two groups of terms referring respectively to the systems individually and to their interactions taken in pairs. We may enter the preceding equations of motion with the above form of Hamiltonian, but for the sake of greater generality we shall proceed in more direct fashion. Noting that

$$\langle \text{'}x \mid \mathbf{u}_k \mid \text{''}x \rangle = \langle x_k' \mid \mathbf{u}_k \mid x_k'' \rangle \prod_{m \neq k} \delta(x_m' - x_m''), \qquad (8{:}37a)$$

and

$$\langle \text{'}x \mid \mathbf{v}_{kl} \mid \text{''}x \rangle = \langle x_k' x_l' \mid \mathbf{v}_{kl} \mid x_k'' x_l'' \rangle \prod_{m \neq k, l} \delta(x_m' - x_m''), \qquad (8{:}37b)$$

we have

$$\begin{aligned}\delta \langle 1 \mid \mathbf{H} \mid 1 \rangle &= \delta \int \langle 1 \mid \text{'}x \rangle d\text{'}x \langle \text{'}x \mid \mathbf{H} \mid \text{''}x \rangle d\text{''}x \langle \text{''}x \mid 1 \rangle \\ &= \sum_i \int \delta \langle i \mid x_i' \rangle \prod_{j \neq i} \langle j \mid x_j' \rangle d\text{'}x \Big(\sum_k \langle x_k' \mid \mathbf{u}_k \mid x_k'' \rangle \prod_{m \neq k} \delta(x_m' - x_m'') \\ &\qquad + \sum_{k<l}\sum \langle x_k' x_l' \mid \mathbf{v}_{kl} \mid x_k'' x_l'' \rangle \prod_{m \neq kl,} \delta(x_m' - x_m'') \Big) d\text{''}x \prod_j \langle x_j' \mid j \rangle \\ &\qquad + (\text{symmetrical term in } \delta \langle x_i' \mid i \rangle) \\ &= 0, \end{aligned} \qquad (8{:}38)$$

where as previously observed we need only consider one term, i.e. the equivalent of $\delta \langle 1 \mid \cdot \mathbf{H} \mid 1 \rangle$. Developing this term, we obtain

$$\begin{aligned}&\sum_i \int \delta \langle i \mid x_i' \rangle dx_i' \Big\{ \langle x_i' \mid \mathbf{u}_i \mid x_i'' \rangle + \delta(x_i' - x_i'') \sum_{k \neq i} \int \langle k \mid x_k' \rangle dx_k' \langle x_k' \mid \mathbf{u}_k \mid x_k'' \rangle \\ &dx_k'' \langle x_k'' \mid k \rangle + \sum_{l \neq i}{}' \iint \langle l \mid x_l' \rangle dx_l' \langle x_i' x_l' \mid \mathbf{v}_{il} \mid x_i'' x_l'' \rangle dx_l'' \langle x_l'' \mid l \rangle \\ &+ \delta(x_i' - x_i'') \sum{}' \sum_{k<l}{}' \int \ldots \int \langle k \mid x_k' \rangle \langle l \mid x_l' \rangle dx_k' \, dx_l' \langle x_k' x_l' \mid \mathbf{v}_{kl} \mid x_k'' x_l'' \rangle \\ &dx_k'' dx_l'' \langle x_k'' \mid k \rangle \langle x_l'' \mid l \rangle \Big\} dx_i'' \langle x_i'' \mid i \rangle = 0, \end{aligned} \qquad (8{:}39)$$

which may be conveniently written in the self-explanatory form

$$\begin{aligned}&\sum_i \int \delta \langle i \mid x_i' \rangle dx_i' \Big\{ \langle x_i' \mid \mathbf{u}_i \mid x_i'' \rangle + \delta(x_i' - x_i'') \sum_{k \neq i}{}' \langle k \mid \mathbf{u}_k \mid k \rangle + \sum_{l \neq i}{}' \langle x_i' \mid \boldsymbol{\beta}_{il} \mid x_i'' \rangle \\ &\qquad + \delta(x_i' - x_i'') \sum{}' \sum_{k<l}{}' \langle kl \mid \mathbf{v}_{kl} \mid kl \rangle \Big\} dx_i'' \langle x_i'' \mid i \rangle = 0. \end{aligned} \qquad (8{:}40)$$

This variational equation is to hold for normalized functions $\langle x_i' \mid i \rangle$, i.e. for variations satisfying

$$\int \delta \langle i \mid x_i' \rangle dx_i' \langle x_i' \mid i \rangle = 0, \qquad (8{:}41)$$ [5]

which means that the coefficients of $\delta \langle i \mid x_i' \rangle$ in (8:40) must be a linear combination (in the present case simply a constant factor λ_i; cf. below) of the coefficients of $\delta \langle i \mid x_i' \rangle$ in the accessory conditions. Hence,

$$\begin{aligned}&\int \langle x_i' \mid \mathbf{u}_i + \sum_{l \neq i}{}' \boldsymbol{\beta}_{il} \mid x_i'' \rangle dx_i'' \langle x_i'' \mid i \rangle \\ &\qquad + \Big(\sum_{k \neq i}{}' \langle k \mid \mathbf{u}_k \mid k \rangle + \sum_{k<l}{}'' \langle kl \mid \mathbf{v}_{kl} \mid kl \rangle - \lambda_i \Big) \langle x_i' \mid i \rangle = 0. \end{aligned} \qquad (8{:}42)$$

[5] Here again we refer to the remark below (8:6) *et seq.*

If we generalize the accessory normalization condition so as to require orthogonality, then instead of (8:41) we have

$$\int \delta \langle i \mid x_i' \rangle \, dx_i' \langle x_i' \mid j \rangle = 0, \quad \quad (8{:}43)$$

so that there are in this case n accessory conditions, and $\lambda_i \langle x_i' \mid i \rangle$ in (8:42) is replaced by the linear combination $\sum_j \lambda_{ij} \langle x_j' \mid j \rangle$. If we introduce an *individual system* energy ϵ_i, defined by

$$\epsilon_i = -\Big(\sum_{k \neq i} \langle k \mid \mathbf{u}_k \mid k \rangle + \sum_{k<l} \langle kl \mid \mathbf{v}_{kl} \mid kl \rangle - \lambda_i\Big), \quad \quad (8{:}44)$$

then (8:42) becomes

$$\int \langle x_i' \mid \mathbf{u}_i + \sum_{l \neq i}{}' \boldsymbol{\beta}_{il} \mid x_i'' \rangle \, dx_i'' \langle x_i'' \mid i \rangle = \epsilon_i \langle x_i' \mid i \rangle, \quad \quad (8{:}45)$$

which for n-electron systems is known as Hartree's equation. It was originally obtained on the basis of the plausible assumption that each single-electron function should satisfy a Schroedinger equation which takes into account the averaged interaction with all other electrons. This is exactly the result obtained here, since $\boldsymbol{\beta}_{il}$ corresponds to an effective potential for the ith particle due to the lth defined by [cf. (8:39, 40)]

$$\langle x_i' \mid \boldsymbol{\beta}_{il} \mid x_i'' \rangle = \iint \langle l \mid x_l' \rangle \, dx_l' \langle x_i' x_l' \mid \mathbf{v}_{il} \mid x_i'' x_l'' \rangle \, dx_l'' \langle x_l'' \mid l \rangle, \quad (8{:}46)$$

i.e. the interaction energy $\mathbf{v}_{il}$ for the pair (i, l), averaged over the orbit (state) of the lth which is assumed to be $\langle l \mid x_l' \rangle$. The mean value of the total Hamiltonian $\mathbf{H}$ is readily found to be

$$\epsilon = \sum_k \langle k \mid \mathbf{u}_k \mid k \rangle + \sum_{k<l} \langle kl \mid \mathbf{v}_{kl} \mid kl \rangle, \quad \quad (8{:}47)$$

which, it should be observed, is *not* the sum of the single-particle energies ϵ_i, since this procedure would count the interactions twice. The correct relation between ϵ and ϵ_i is obtained by multiplying (8:45) by $\langle i \mid x_i' \rangle$ and integrating, viz.

$$\langle i \mid \mathbf{u}_i \mid i \rangle + \sum_{l \neq i} \langle il \mid \mathbf{v}_{il} \mid il \rangle = \epsilon_i, \quad \quad (8{:}48)$$

from which

$$\sum_i \langle i \mid \mathbf{u}_i \mid i \rangle + \sum_i \sum_{l \neq i} \langle il \mid \mathbf{v}_{il} \mid il \rangle = \sum_i \epsilon_i, \quad \quad (8{:}49)$$

or

$$\epsilon = \sum_i \epsilon_i - \sum_{i<l} \langle il \mid \mathbf{v}_{il} \mid il \rangle. \quad \quad (8{:}50)$$

From (8:44) and (8:48) we find $\lambda_i = \epsilon$, in agreement with our previous result (8:30); again showing that in the present case the whole analysis is obtained by substituting the effective Hamiltonian $\langle x_s' \mid \mathbf{H}_s \mid x_s'' \rangle$, defined by (8:36), into (8:30). If, in particular, the single-electron operators are taken to be

$$\mathbf{u}_i = \frac{1}{2m}\,\underline{\mathbf{p}}_i^2 + \boldsymbol{\varphi}_i \quad \text{and} \quad \mathbf{v}_{ij} = \frac{e^2}{\mid \underline{\mathbf{x}}_i - \underline{\mathbf{x}}_j \mid}, \quad . \quad . \quad . \quad (8:51)\,[6]$$

then equations (8:45) and (8:50) become, respectively,

$$\left\{ -\frac{\hbar^2}{2m}\Delta_i + \phi_i + \sum_{l \neq i} e^2 \int \frac{\mid \langle x_l' \mid l \rangle \mid^2}{\mid \underline{x}_i' - \underline{x}_l' \mid} dx_l' \right\} \langle x_i' \mid i \rangle = \epsilon_i \langle x_i' \mid i \rangle, \quad (8:52)$$

and

$$\epsilon = \sum_i \epsilon_i - \sum_{i<l}\sum e^2 \int \frac{\mid \langle x_i' \mid i \rangle \mid^2 \mid \langle x_l' \mid l \rangle \mid^2}{\mid \underline{x}_i' - \underline{x}_l' \mid} dx_i'\,dx_l'. \quad . \quad (8:53)$$

We shall not be interested in the analysis of non-stationary states in this simple product-function approximation, but for completeness we note that the corresponding equations for this case are

$$\int \langle x_i' \mid \mathbf{u}_i + \sum_{l \neq i} \boldsymbol{\beta}_{il} \mid x_i'' \rangle \, dx_i'' \langle x_i'' \mid i \rangle$$
$$= i\hbar \frac{d}{dt} \langle x_i' \mid i \rangle + \left\{ \langle i \mid \mathbf{u}_i \mid i \rangle + \sum_{l \neq i} \langle il \mid \mathbf{v}_{il} \mid il \rangle - \lambda_i \right\} \langle x_i' \mid i \rangle. \quad (8:45')$$

§ 63. Physical Aspects of the Hartree Method—Matrix Elements

We can obtain a qualitative picture of the degree of approximation involved in the Hartree field equations by considering more closely the matrix elements of the total Hamiltonian. In general, an arbitrary system of n constituents will be describable by the sets of variables

$$\left. \begin{matrix} \mathbf{E}_1, \mathbf{E}_2, \ldots \mathbf{E}_n, \\ \mathbf{x}_1, \mathbf{x}_2, \ldots \mathbf{x}_n, \end{matrix} \right\} \quad . \quad . \quad . \quad . \quad . \quad . \quad . \quad . \quad (8:54)$$

where the various **E**'s represent complete commuting sets of observables which will be different if the systems (particles) are different or if the fields they move in are different,[7] but will be homologous, as will be the **x**'s, if the particles are identical and move in the same field. In this latter case we have in effect just the *mathematical* problem of one particle in a given field (which, however, may depend on the other particles), and the ordinal subscripts of the variables (**x**'s or **E**'s) merely tell us that there are n particles present in the *physical* problem. Any consistent labelling con-

[6] $\langle x_i' x_j' \mid \mathbf{v} \mid x_i'' x_j'' \rangle = \dfrac{e^2\,\delta(x_i' - x_i'')\,\delta(x_j' - x_j'')}{\mid \underline{x}_i' - \underline{x}_j' \mid}$.

[7] This latter condition is exactly the case for the foregoing Hartree equations, as is evident since orthogonality has to be introduced through accessory conditions, this being automatically fulfilled for systems moving in the same field represented by a Hermitian operator.

vention would be acceptable and, as we have seen, the homology of the variables permits us to drop indices in the final results. Writing the approximate eigenvector of **H** as $|\,1\,\rangle$, we have explicitly

$$\langle\,'\mathsf{x}\,|\,1\,\rangle = \prod_j \langle\,\mathsf{x}_j'\,|\,E_j'\,\rangle, \qquad (8{:}55)$$

with the assumption $\int\langle\,E_i'\,|\,\mathsf{x}'\,\rangle\,d\mathsf{x}'\,\langle\,\mathsf{x}'\,|\,E_j'\,\rangle = \delta\,(E_i', E_j')$. A general matrix element of **H** computed for two approximate states $\langle\,'\mathsf{x}\,|\,'E\,\rangle$ and $\langle\,'\mathsf{x}\,|\,''E\,\rangle$ appears as

$$\langle\,E_1'\ldots E_n'\,|\,\mathbf{H}\,|\,E_1''\ldots E_n''\,\rangle$$
$$= \int\ldots\int\prod_i\langle\,E_i'\,|\,\mathsf{x}_i'\,\rangle\,d\mathsf{x}_i'\,\langle\,'\mathsf{x}\,|\,\mathbf{H}\,|\,''\mathsf{x}\,\rangle\prod_i d\mathsf{x}_i''\,\langle\,\mathsf{x}_i''\,|\,E_i''\,\rangle, \qquad (8{:}56)$$

where $\langle\,\mathsf{x}_i'\,|\,E_i'\,\rangle$ represents the ith electron probability amplitude from the diagonal set $\mathbf{x}$ to the set **E**.

With the obvious notation

$$\langle\,E_i'\,|\,\mathbf{u}_i\,|\,E_i''\,\rangle = \iint\langle\,E_i'\,|\,\mathsf{x}_i'\,\rangle\,d\mathsf{x}_i'\,\langle\,\mathsf{x}_i'\,|\,\mathbf{u}_i\,|\,\mathsf{x}_i''\,\rangle\,d\mathsf{x}_i''\,\langle\,\mathsf{x}_i''\,|\,E_i''\,\rangle, \qquad (8{:}56a)$$

$$\langle\,E_i'E_k'\,|\,\mathbf{v}_{ik}\,|\,E_i''E_k''\,\rangle = \int\ldots\int\langle E_i'\,|\,\mathsf{x}_i'\,\rangle\langle\,E_k'\,|\,\mathsf{x}_k'\,\rangle\,d\mathsf{x}_i'\,d\mathsf{x}_k'\,\langle\,\mathsf{x}_i'\mathsf{x}_k'\,|\,\mathbf{v}_{ik}\,|\,\mathsf{x}_i''\mathsf{x}_k''\,\rangle$$
$$d\mathsf{x}_i''\,d\mathsf{x}_k''\,\langle\mathsf{x}_i''\,|\,E_i''\,\rangle\langle\,\mathsf{x}_k''\,|\,E_k''\,\rangle, \qquad (8{:}56b)$$

the diagonal elements of (8:56) take the form

$$\langle\,E_1'\ldots E_n'\,|\,\mathbf{H}\,|\,E_1'\ldots E_n'\rangle = \sum_i\langle E_i'\,|\,\mathbf{u}_i|\,E_i'\,\rangle + \sum_{i<k}\langle E_i'E_k'\,|\,\mathbf{v}_{ik}\,|\,E_i'E_k'\rangle; \qquad (8{:}56c)$$

while the non-zero off-diagonal elements are

$$\langle E_1'\ldots E_i'\ldots|\,\mathbf{H}\,|\,E_1'\ldots E_i''\ldots\rangle = \langle E_i'\,|\mathbf{u}_i|E_i''\rangle + \sum_{k\neq i}{}'\langle E_i'E_k'|\mathbf{v}_{ik}|E_i''E_k'\rangle, \qquad (8{:}56d)$$

and

$$\langle E_1'\ldots E_i'\ldots E_k'\ldots|\,\mathbf{H}\,|E_1'\ldots E_i''\ldots E_k''\ldots\rangle = \langle E_i'E_k'|\,\mathbf{v}_{ik}\,|\,E_i''E_k''\rangle. \qquad (8{:}56e)$$

These matrix elements are quite general for n-particle systems whose total wave-function satisfies no particular symmetry conditions. The degree of approximation of this type of product solution will then be qualitatively described by the statement that the better the approximation, the fewer the remanent non-diagonal elements, and these are required to be as small as possible. Furthermore, the single product function must be unique, i.e. the foregoing approximation to each true energy level is acceptable only insofar as there is no degeneracy. In the contrary case there will of course be other functions corresponding to the same total energy (and spin if included), which will necessitate the usual extension in the treatment. However, we shall not consider this most important question at this point, but refer to Chapter X. The Hartree case was characterized by the individual wave-functions satisfying the equation [cf. (8:45)]

$$\int \langle x_i' \mid \mathbf{u}_i + \sum_{l \neq i} \boldsymbol{\beta}_{il} \mid x_i'' \rangle \, dx_i'' \langle x_i'' \mid E_i' \rangle = \epsilon_i \langle x_i' \mid E_i' \rangle, \quad . \quad (8:57)$$

from which it follows that the matrix elements (8:56*a*) become [cf. (8:46)]

$$\langle E_i' \mid \mathbf{u}_i \mid E_i'' \rangle = \epsilon_i \delta(E_i', E_i'') - \sum_{l \neq i} \langle E_i'E_l' \mid \mathbf{v}_{il} \mid E_i''E_l' \rangle, \qquad (8:58)$$

which, on comparison with (8:56), shows that the diagonal matrix elements reduce to

$$\langle E_1' \ldots E_n' \mid \mathbf{H} \mid E_1' \ldots E_n' \rangle = \sum_i \epsilon_i - \sum_{i<l} \langle E_i'E_l' \mid \mathbf{v}_{il} \mid E_i'E_l' \rangle, \quad (8:58a)$$

in accord with our previous findings, while the elements (8:56*d*) are all zero. Thus, in the Hartree approximation all non-diagonal elements connecting different configurations vanish except those (8:56*e*) involving double electron transitions.

§ 64. The Extended Hartree Equations

As previously noted, the Hartree field solutions are not automatically orthonormal since each particle moves in a different field; and, furthermore, the *a priori* inclusion of accessory orthonormality conditions as in our previous treatment is quite complicated in practice. Hence, it is usually necessary to orthogonalize the solutions *a posteriori* by essentially *hammer-and-tongs* methods; or one might solve for an extended Hartree-type field in which all electrons move in the same effective field defined by $\mathbf{V}_i = \sum_l \boldsymbol{\beta}_{il}$, which differs from the preceding case in that the summation extends over all electrons, including the ith. In this case the orthogonality of the partial wave-functions is automatically secured, and the matrix elements corresponding to (8:56*a*, *b*, *c*, *d*) are readily seen to be

$$\langle E_i' \mid \mathbf{u}_i \mid E_i'' \rangle = \epsilon_i \delta(E_i', E_i'') - \sum_l \langle E_i'E_l' \mid \mathbf{v}_{il} \mid E_i''E_l' \rangle, \quad . \quad (8:59a)$$

$$\langle E_1' \ldots E_n' \mid \mathbf{H} \mid E_1' \ldots E_n' \rangle$$
$$= \sum_i \epsilon_i - \langle E_i'E_i' \mid \mathbf{v} \mid E_i'E_i' \rangle - \sum_{i<l} \langle E_i'E_l' \mid \mathbf{v}_{il} \mid E_i'E_l' \rangle, \quad (8:59b)$$

$$\langle E_1' \ldots E_i' \ldots \mid \mathbf{H} \mid E_1' \ldots E_i'' \ldots \rangle = -\langle E_i'E_i' \mid \mathbf{v} \mid E_i''E_i' \rangle, \quad (8:59c)$$

$$\langle E_1' \ldots E_i' \ldots E_l' \ldots \mid \mathbf{H} \mid E_1' \ldots E_i'' \ldots E_l'' \ldots \rangle = \langle E_i'E_l' \mid \mathbf{v} \mid E_i''E_l'' \rangle. \quad (8:59d)$$

Here, as is to be expected, the approximation is less accurate and leads to additional non-zero elements (8:59*c*) which, like the additional terms in (8:59*b*), correspond to the spurious self-interaction.

§ 65. Antisymmetric Functions

The foregoing analysis takes no account of symmetry restrictions, so that, aside from the inaccuracies inherent in the single-system approximation (separation into individual wave-functions), it involves the further error due to neglect of statistical correlations when the systems involved are identical. In particular, for a system of n electrons we know that the wave-functions must be antisymmetric, so that in the same approximation we must take the approximate wave-functions as

$$\langle \,'\mathbf{x} \mid 1 \rangle = A \prod_j \langle \mathbf{x}_j' \mid j \rangle, \quad \dots \dots \dots \quad (8{:}60)$$

where $\mathbf{x}_j' = x_j', \sigma_j'$, so that $\langle \mathbf{x}_j' \mid j \rangle = \langle x_j' \mid j \rangle \, \delta(\sigma_j', \sigma^j)$, and

$$\int \langle i \mid \mathbf{x}_j' \rangle \, d\mathbf{x}_j' \, \langle \mathbf{x}' \mid k \rangle = \delta(i, k). \quad \dots \dots \quad (8{:}61)$$

The analysis now becomes somewhat more complex, so that instead of considering an arbitrary general Hamiltonian it is convenient to take the explicit form

$$\mathbf{H} = \sum_k \mathbf{u}_k + \sum_{k<l} \mathbf{v}_{kl}, \quad \dots \dots \dots \quad (8{:}62)$$

which permits an easy evaluation of the effect on the average total energy due to the use of the determinantal function. Thus, from (8:60) and (8:62), we have

$$\begin{aligned} \langle 1 \mid \mathbf{H} \mid 1 \rangle &= \int \dots \int A \prod_j \langle j \mid \mathbf{x}_j' \rangle \, d'\mathbf{x} \, \langle \,'\mathbf{x} \mid \mathbf{H} \mid {}''\mathbf{x} \rangle \, d''\mathbf{x} \, A \prod_j \langle \mathbf{x}_j'' \mid j \rangle \quad (8{:}63) \\ &= \sqrt{n!} \int \dots \int \prod_j \langle j \mid \mathbf{x}_j' \rangle \, d'\mathbf{x} \, \langle \,'\mathbf{x} \mid \sum_k \mathbf{u}_k + \sum_{k<l} \mathbf{v}_{kl} \mid {}''\mathbf{x} \rangle \, d''\mathbf{x} \, A \prod_j \langle \mathbf{x}_j'' \mid j \rangle, \end{aligned}$$

which reduces to

$$\begin{aligned} &\sum_k \iint \langle k \mid \mathbf{x}_k' \rangle \, d\mathbf{x}_k' \, \langle \mathbf{x}_k' \mid \mathbf{u}_k \mid \mathbf{x}_k'' \rangle \, d\mathbf{x}_k'' \, \langle \mathbf{x}_k'' \mid k \rangle \\ &\quad + \sum_{k<l} \int \dots \int \langle k \mid \mathbf{x}_k' \rangle \langle l \mid \mathbf{x}_l' \rangle \, d\mathbf{x}_k' \, d\mathbf{x}_l' \, \langle \mathbf{x}_k' \mathbf{x}_l' \mid \mathbf{v}_{kl} \mid \mathbf{x}_k'' \mathbf{x}_l'' \rangle \, d\mathbf{x}_k'' \, d\mathbf{x}_l'' \\ &\qquad \times \{ \langle \mathbf{x}_k'' \mid k \rangle \langle \mathbf{x}_l'' \mid l \rangle - \langle \mathbf{x}_k'' \mid l \rangle \langle \mathbf{x}_l'' \mid k \rangle \}, \quad (8{:}64) \end{aligned}$$

since in the first term of (8:63) only the identity permutation gives a non-zero integral, while in the second a non-zero result is obtained for each pair (k, l) both from the identity and the simple interchange of $\mathbf{x}_k'$, $\mathbf{x}_l'$ (or alternatively, of the orbits specified by k, l). However, with the use of the function (8:60), all electrons are placed on equal footing [i.e. no implication of distinct identity as in (8:22)], and, since the variables are homologous, the representatives $\langle \mathbf{x}_k' \mid \mathbf{u}_k \mid \mathbf{x}_k'' \rangle$ and $\langle \mathbf{x}_k' \mathbf{x}_l' \mid \mathbf{v}_{kl} \mid \mathbf{x}_k'' \mathbf{x}_l'' \rangle$ may be written as

$$\left. \begin{aligned} &\langle \mathbf{x}' \mid \mathbf{u} \mid \mathbf{x}'' \rangle, \\ &\langle \mathbf{x}' \mathbf{x}'' \mid \mathbf{v} \mid \mathbf{x}''' \mathbf{x}^{\mathrm{IV}} \rangle, \end{aligned} \right\} \quad \dots \dots \dots \quad (8{:}65)$$

i.e. we no longer need specify which sets of **x**'s are involved. Then (8:64) takes the form

$$\sum_k \iint \langle k \mid \mathsf{x}' \rangle \, d\mathsf{x}' \, \langle \mathsf{x}' \mid \mathbf{u} \mid \mathsf{x}'' \rangle \, d\mathsf{x}'' \, \langle \mathsf{x}'' \mid k \rangle$$

$$+ \sum_{k<l} \int \cdots \int \langle k \mid \mathsf{x}' \rangle \langle l \mid \mathsf{x}'' \rangle \, d\mathsf{x}' \, d\mathsf{x}'' \, \langle \mathsf{x}'\mathsf{x}'' \mid \mathbf{v} \mid \mathsf{x}'''\mathsf{x}^{\mathrm{IV}} \rangle \, d\mathsf{x}''' \, d\mathsf{x}^{\mathrm{IV}}$$

$$\times \{ \langle \mathsf{x}''' \mid k \rangle \langle \mathsf{x}^{\mathrm{IV}} \mid l \rangle - \langle \mathsf{x}''' \mid l \rangle \langle \mathsf{x}^{\mathrm{IV}} \mid k \rangle \}. \quad (8{:}66)$$

For definiteness we take **v** as the Coulomb interaction so that

$$\langle \mathsf{x}'\mathsf{x}'' \mid \mathbf{v} \mid \mathsf{x}'''\mathsf{x}^{\mathrm{IV}} \rangle = \frac{e^2}{\mid \underline{x}' - \underline{x}'' \mid} \, \delta(\mathsf{x}' - \mathsf{x}''') \, \delta(\mathsf{x}'' - \mathsf{x}^{\mathrm{IV}}), \quad (8{:}67)$$

and performing the summation over spin, we find

$$\epsilon = \sum_k \int \mid \langle x' \mid k \rangle \mid^2 u(x') \, dx' + \sum_{k<l} e^2 \iint \frac{\mid \langle x' \mid k \rangle \mid^2 \mid \langle x'' \mid l \rangle \mid^2}{\mid \underline{x}' - \underline{x}'' \mid} \, dx' \, dx''$$

$$- \sum_{\substack{k<l \\ \parallel \text{ spins}}} e^2 \iint \frac{\langle k \mid x' \rangle \, dx' \, \langle x' \mid l \rangle \langle l \mid x'' \rangle \, dx'' \, \langle x'' \mid k \rangle}{\mid \underline{x}' - \underline{x}'' \mid}, \quad (8{:}68)$$

or, in general,

$$\epsilon = \sum_k \langle k \mid \mathbf{u} \mid k \rangle + \sum_{k<l} \langle kl \mid \mathbf{v} \mid kl \rangle - \sum_{\substack{k<l \\ \parallel \text{ spins}}} \langle kl \mid \mathbf{v} \mid lk \rangle, \quad (8{:}69)$$

which differ from (8:53) and (8:47) respectively, through the appearance of the new terms representing the exchange energy.[8] To avoid possible misunderstanding it should be noted that we have used the standard relation in the spins, from which it follows that only parallel spin (component) terms ($\sigma^k = \sigma^l$) give non-zero exchange integrals.[9]

In atoms the exchange integral is positive, which is to say that the energy is lowest when the spins are parallel,[10] and this conclusion results for this case only because it is possible to employ orthogonal functions in the perturbation calculation, as above. In molecular problems, by contrast, non-orthogonality is the rule, and this leads to *additional* (non-orthogonality) correction terms in the exchange in-

[8] An informative view on the nature of exchange is provided by the application of this result to the very simple system of two electrons represented by isotropic wave packets; the one centred about the origin and the other about some point $x = \rho$, say, with assumed (common) uncertainty in position σ. The *interaction* energy is found to be

$$\frac{e^2}{\rho} \operatorname{erf}(\rho/\sigma\sqrt{2}) - \left(\frac{e^2}{\sigma}\sqrt{\frac{2}{\pi}}\right) \exp(-\rho^2/2\sigma^2),$$

which is seen to deviate appreciably from the classical Coulomb energy only when the uncertainty is of the order of the distance between electrons, since the exchange term tends rapidly to zero with increasing separation or decreasing uncertainty. See also TOLMAN, R. C.: *The Principles of Statistical Mechanics* (Oxford, 1938).

[9] An incidental consequence of this latter is that the energies of the Fock-Dirac (8:68) and Hartree (8:53) approximations are identical for the normal state of helium.

[10] This corresponds to Hund's well-known rule that the deepest state for a given configuration is that of highest multiplicity consistent with the Pauli principle (cf. Chap. X).

tegral such that it may be negative (positive exchange energy). Usually one finds that the energy is lowest when the spins are antiparallel in so far as possible [11] (cf. Chap. X). For the general case, in particular that of metallic problems, the sign of the exchange *energy* cannot be predicted on any general grounds and must be investigated for each specific case. If it is negative, the charge distribution corresponding to the determinantal function has a lower self-potential than that corresponding to the product-type function. This may be interpreted as due to an added effective repulsion between electrons, although it is in fact simply a consequence of the use of one-electron functions coupled with the antisymmetry condition. The contrary case of an increased self-energy (resultant positive sign) then corresponds to an effective attraction, and for general purposes it is often convenient to refer to these effects simply as *statistical* or *correlation* forces. In this connection it should be pointed out that confusion sometimes arises because the term *correlation* energy has two meanings. One of these meanings corresponds to the above, and the second corresponds to the previously noted fact that ordinary determinantal functions cannot lead to a statistical correlation between positions of electrons with antiparallel spins. To correct for this the determinantal-type function can be generalized so as to introduce a correlation between electrons of antiparallel spin,[12] e.g. by introducing the coordinates of the electrons of a given spin as parameters in the wave-functions of the electrons of opposite spin. In principle this should lead to better individual wave-functions as determined by a variational analysis, and a lowering of the total energy. It is this energy gain which is also termed *correlation* energy.

§ 66. Fock-Dirac Equations

The derivation of the equations for the present case, corresponding to the stationary states (8:45) and non-stationary (8:45′), is somewhat more involved, although, as will be seen, the results are eventually simpler in form, as they possess several symmetry elements not found in the Hartree approximation. It is therefore desirable to make as many simplifying assumptions as possible in so far as these involve no loss of generality. To this end we assume as before that the individual functions are orthonormal, and in addition that the varied wave-functions are also orthonormal, viz.

$$\int \langle k \mid x' \rangle dx' \langle x' \mid l \rangle = \delta(k, l), \quad \ldots \ldots \quad (8{:}70)$$

and

$$\int \delta \langle k \mid x' \rangle dx' \langle x' \mid l \rangle = \delta(k, l). \quad \ldots \ldots \quad (8{:}71)$$

With the above conditions it is permissible to calculate the mean energy $\langle 1 \mid \mathbf{H} \mid 1 \rangle$, reduce it as in (8:66), and then take the variation to obtain the desired quantity

[11] This corresponds to the fact that most diatomic molecules are diamagnetic, hence indicating a singlet state as normal.

[12] Cf. WIGNER, E. P.: *Phys. Rev.*, **46**, 1002 (1934); SEITZ, F.: *Modern Theory of Solids* (McGraw-Hill, 1940).

$\delta \langle 1 | \cdot \mathbf{H} | 1 \rangle$. However, for clarity we shall start with the general form (8:63), from which it readily follows that

$$\delta \langle 1 | \cdot \mathbf{H} | 1 \rangle = \sum_k \iint \delta \langle k | x_k' \rangle dx_k' \langle x_k' | \mathbf{u}_k | x_k'' \rangle dx_k'' \langle x_k'' | k \rangle$$
$$+ 2 \sum_{k<l} \int \ldots \int \delta \langle k | x_k' \rangle \langle l | x_l' \rangle dx_k' dx_l' \langle x_k' x_l' | \mathbf{v}_{kl} | x_k'' x_l'' \rangle$$
$$\times dx_k'' dx_l'' \{ \langle x_k'' | k \rangle \langle x_l'' | l \rangle - \langle x_k'' | l \rangle \langle x_l'' | k \rangle \}, \quad (8:72)$$

or

$$\sum_k \int \delta \langle k | x' \rangle dx' \Big(\int \langle x' | \mathbf{u} | x'' \rangle dx'' \langle x'' | k \rangle$$
$$+ \sum_l \int \ldots \int \langle l | x'' \rangle dx'' \langle x'x'' | \mathbf{v} | x''' x^{\mathrm{IV}} \rangle dx''' dx^{\mathrm{IV}}$$
$$\times \{ \langle x''' | k \rangle \langle x^{\mathrm{IV}} | l \rangle - \langle x''' | l \rangle \langle x^{\mathrm{IV}} | k \rangle \} \Big). \quad (8:73)$$

This may be written as

$$\delta \langle 1 | \cdot \mathbf{H} | 1 \rangle = \sum_k \int \delta \langle k | x' \rangle dx' \int \langle x' | \mathbf{u} + \mathbf{B} - \mathbf{A} | x'' \rangle dx'' \langle x'' | k \rangle, \quad (8:74)$$

where the operators $\mathbf{B}$ and $\mathbf{A}$ are defined by

$$\langle x' | \mathbf{B} | x'' \rangle = \sum_l \iint \langle l | x''' \rangle dx''' \langle x'x''' | \mathbf{v} | x'' x^{\mathrm{IV}} \rangle dx^{\mathrm{IV}} \langle x^{\mathrm{IV}} | l \rangle$$
$$= \iint \langle x^{\mathrm{IV}} | \boldsymbol{\rho} | x''' \rangle dx''' \langle x'x''' | \mathbf{v} | x'' x^{\mathrm{IV}} \rangle dx^{\mathrm{IV}}. \quad (8:75a)$$

$$\langle x' | \mathbf{A} | x'' \rangle = \sum_l \iint \langle l | x^{\mathrm{IV}} \rangle dx^{\mathrm{IV}} \langle x'x^{\mathrm{IV}} | \mathbf{v} | x''' x'' \rangle dx''' \langle x''' | l \rangle$$
$$= \iint \langle x''' | \boldsymbol{\rho} | x^{\mathrm{IV}} \rangle dx^{\mathrm{IV}} \langle x'x^{\mathrm{IV}} | \mathbf{v} | x''' x'' \rangle dx'''$$
$$= \iint \langle x^{\mathrm{IV}} | \boldsymbol{\rho} | x''' \rangle dx''' \langle x''' x' | \mathbf{v} | x'' x^{\mathrm{IV}} \rangle dx^{\mathrm{IV}}. \quad (8:75b)$$ [13]

It is readily seen that the operators so defined are Hermitian, e.g. for $\mathbf{A}$ we have

$$\langle x' | \mathbf{A}^* | x'' \rangle = \langle x'' | \mathbf{A} | x' \rangle^* = \Big(\iint \langle x^{\mathrm{IV}} | \boldsymbol{\rho} | x''' \rangle dx''' \langle x''' x'' | \mathbf{v} | x' x^{\mathrm{IV}} \rangle dx^{\mathrm{IV}} \Big)^*$$
$$= \iint \langle x' x^{\mathrm{IV}} | \mathbf{v} | x''' x'' \rangle dx''' \langle x''' | \boldsymbol{\rho} | x^{\mathrm{IV}} \rangle dx^{\mathrm{IV}}$$
$$= \langle x' | \mathbf{A} | x'' \rangle. \quad (8:76)$$

The operator $\mathbf{B}$ corresponds to the operator $\sum_{l \neq i} \boldsymbol{\beta}_{il}$ in the Hartree case; the effect of $\mathbf{B}$ on a wave-function being essentially to multiply it by the interaction potential averaged over *all* electrons, e.g. since

$$\langle x'x''' | \mathbf{v} | x'' x^{\mathrm{IV}} \rangle = v(x', x''') \delta(x' - x'') \delta(x''' - x^{\mathrm{IV}}),$$

[13] This alternative form uses the relation $\langle x' x^{\mathrm{IV}} | \mathbf{v} | x''' x'' \rangle = \langle x^{\mathrm{IV}} x' | \mathbf{v} | x'' x''' \rangle$.

we find

$$\int \langle x' \mid \mathbf{B} \mid x'' \rangle \, dx'' \langle x'' \mid k \rangle = \langle x' \mid k \rangle \int \langle x''' \mid \rho \mid x''' \rangle \, v(x', x''') \, dx'''. \qquad (8:77)$$

Correspondingly,

$$\int \langle x' \mid \mathbf{A} \mid x'' \rangle \, dx'' \langle x'' \mid k \rangle = \int \langle x' \mid \rho \mid x''' \rangle \, dx''' v(x', x''') \langle x''' \mid k \rangle, \qquad (8:78)$$

so that the effect of **A** is to multiply the wave-function by $\langle x' \mid \rho \mid x''' \rangle \, v(x', x''')$, change the variable of the wave-function from x'' to x''', and integrate. The action of **B** means that it represents the contribution to the Hamiltonian of the kth electron due to interaction with all electrons, including that of the kth with itself. This self-interaction is of course physically meaningless and merely arises as a consequence of the symmetrical definition of **B**; but by the same token this is taken into account in the definition of **A**, which makes a corresponding allowance such that **B** — **A** contains no self-interaction term. Furthermore, **A** introduces exchange terms which, like the exchange energy terms in (8:69), are a consequence of the introduction of the determinantal function rather than of physical argument. Since $\delta \langle 1 \mid \cdot \mathbf{H} \mid 1 \rangle$ is to be zero for variations satisfying (8:71), it follows that the coefficient of $\delta \langle k \mid x' \rangle$ in (8:74) must be a linear combination of the coefficients of $\delta \langle k \mid x' \rangle$ in (8:71), viz.

$$\int \langle x' \mid \mathbf{u} + \mathbf{B} - \mathbf{A} \mid x'' \rangle \, dx'' \langle x'' \mid k \rangle = \sum_l \lambda_{kl} \langle x' \mid l \rangle, \qquad (8:79)$$

the Lagrangian multipliers λ_{kl} being chosen so as to guarantee orthogonality. For the non-degenerate case, at least, these may be chosen as $\lambda_{kl} = \lambda_k \, \delta(k, l)$, since the Hamiltonian $\mathcal{H} = \mathbf{u} + \mathbf{B} - \mathbf{A}$ is the same for all electrons and, being Hermitian, its eigenfunctions are orthonormal by definition. It is important to note that, as previously remarked, these special properties do not obtain in the Hartree case. We may compare the Fock-Dirac (8:79) and Hartree equations by choosing the same form for **u** and **v** as in the latter, with which (8:79) becomes

$$\left\{ -\frac{\hbar^2}{2m} \Delta + \phi + \sum_l e^2 \int \frac{|\langle x''' \mid l \rangle|^2}{|\underline{x}' - \underline{x}'''|} dx''' \right\} \langle x' \mid k \rangle$$

$$- \sum_l e^2 \langle x' \mid l \rangle \int \frac{\langle l \mid x''' \rangle \, dx''' \langle x''' \mid k \rangle}{|\underline{x}' - \underline{x}'''|} = \lambda_k \langle x' \mid k \rangle + \sum_{l \neq k}' \lambda_{kl} \langle x' \mid l \rangle. \qquad (8:80)$$

§ 67. General Comments

As we have seen [cf. (8:69)], the matrix elements of **H** computed for antisymmetrized product functions (including spin) take the form

$$\langle E_1' \ldots E_n' \mid \mathbf{H} \mid E_1' \ldots E_n' \rangle$$

$$= \sum_k \langle E_k' \mid \mathbf{u} \mid E_k' \rangle + \sum_{k<l} \langle E_k' E_l' \mid \mathbf{v} \mid E_k' E_l' \rangle - \sum_{\substack{k<l \\ \parallel \text{ spin}}} \langle E_k' E_l' \mid \mathbf{v} \mid E_l' E_k' \rangle. \qquad (8:81a)$$

Correspondingly, the general non-diagonal elements are given by

$$\langle \ldots E_k' \ldots | \mathbf{H} | \ldots E_k'' \ldots \rangle$$
$$= \langle E_k' | \mathbf{u} | E_k'' \rangle + \sum_{l \neq k} \langle E_k' E_l' | \mathbf{v} | E_k'' E_l' \rangle - \sum_{l \neq k} \langle E_k' E_l' | \mathbf{v} | E_l' E_k'' \rangle, \quad (8{:}81b)$$

$$\langle \ldots E_k' \ldots E_l' \ldots | \mathbf{H} | \ldots E_k'' \ldots E_l'' \ldots \rangle$$
$$= \langle E_k' E_l' | \mathbf{v} | E_k'' E_l'' \rangle - \langle E_k' E_l' | \mathbf{v} | E_l'' E_k'' \rangle, \quad (8{:}81c)$$

and it is readily seen that the Fock-Dirac approximation is characterized by the vanishing of all elements of the type (8:81*b*).

The Hartree or extended Hartree equations do not *a priori* take account of exchange; but there is no inconsistency involved if we form determinantal functions from their solutions, and then calculate the total energy, as this retrospective antisymmetrization leads to the same general equations as above,[14] and thus introduces some exchange correction, although admittedly in a cruder sense than in the Fock-Dirac approximation. A further important consequence of this retrospective antisymmetrization is that the initially non-orthogonal Hartree solutions can easily be orthogonalized by taking suitable linear combinations of rows or columns of the initially formed determinant. As is well known, this process gives a new determinant which is at most a simple multiple of the original, and the complete identity of the original and final determinants can be secured by first normalizing the new wave-functions obtained by the above composition process. It should be further added that this orthogonalization procedure is absolutely essential if the ordinary Hartree solutions are to be used in the analysis of degenerate problems as in the method of Slater, which will be briefly considered in Chapter X.

§ 68. Equations of Motion—Density Matrix

Returning to the analysis of non-stationary states, we require the quantity $\delta \langle 1 | \cdot \frac{d}{dt} | 1 \rangle$, and for this we first reduce $\langle 1 | \frac{d}{dt} | 1 \rangle$ to its simplest form and then take the variation, i.e.

$$\langle 1 | \frac{d}{dt} | 1 \rangle = \int \ldots \int A \prod_j \langle j | x_j' \rangle d'x\, A \sum_k \frac{d}{dt} \langle x_k' | k \rangle \prod_{j \neq k} \langle x_j' | j \rangle$$
$$= \sqrt{n!} \int \ldots \int A \prod_j \langle j | x_j' \rangle d'x \sum_k \frac{d}{dt} \langle x_k' | k \rangle \prod_{j \neq k} \langle x_j' | j \rangle$$
$$= \sum_k \int \langle k | x' \rangle dx' \frac{d}{dt} \langle x' | k \rangle, \quad \ldots \ldots \ldots \quad (8{:}82)$$

and

$$\delta \langle 1 | \cdot \frac{d}{dt} | 1 \rangle = \sum_k \int \delta \langle k | x' \rangle dx' \frac{d}{dt} \langle x' | k \rangle. \quad \ldots \quad (8{:}83)$$

[14] However, it must be borne in mind that the above elements reduce differently in these two cases though they retain many points of similarity; in particular for such antisymmetrized Hartree solutions the elements (8:81*b*) do not cancel.

With the help of (8:70) and (8:74), the equation $i\hbar\,\delta\langle 1 \mid \cdot \frac{d}{dt} \mid 1\rangle = \delta\langle 1 \mid \cdot \mathbf{H} \mid 1\rangle$ becomes

$$\int \langle x' \mid \mathbf{u} + \mathbf{B} - \mathbf{A} \mid x'' \rangle \, dx'' \langle x'' \mid k \rangle = i\hbar \frac{d}{dt} \langle x' \mid k \rangle + \Sigma \mu_{lk} \langle x' \mid l \rangle. \quad (8:84)$$

The Lagrangian multipliers μ_{lk} can, in the present case [cf. (8:35)], be shown to form a Hermitian matrix if the functions $\langle x' \mid k \rangle$ are required to be orthonormal for all time. Thus,

$$\frac{d}{dt}\int \langle k \mid x' \rangle \, dx' \langle x' \mid l \rangle$$
$$= \int \frac{d}{dt} \langle k \mid x' \rangle \, dx' \langle x' \mid l \rangle + \int \langle k \mid x' \rangle \, dx' \frac{d}{dt} \langle x' \mid l \rangle = 0, \quad (8:85)$$

which means that the matrix whose elements are $\left[i\hbar \int \langle k \mid x' \rangle \, dx' \frac{d}{dt} \langle x' \mid l \rangle\right]$ is Hermitian, and multiplying (8:84) by $\langle l \mid x' \rangle$ and integrating, we find

$$i\hbar \int \langle l \mid x' \rangle \, dx' \frac{d}{dt} \langle x' \mid k \rangle + \mu_{lk}$$
$$= \int\int \langle l \mid x' \rangle \, dx' \langle x' \mid \mathbf{u} + \mathbf{B} - \mathbf{A} \mid x'' \rangle \, dx'' \langle x'' \mid k \rangle, \quad (8:86)$$

from which the Hermiticity of the Lagrangian multipliers follows, since the extreme left and right terms are Hermitian.

Our previous considerations on the density operator (§ 57) only took account of the antisymmetry condition. We can now really extend that work so as to include interactions, thus showing that all the information pertaining to a system of electrons can be expressed in terms of the density matrix. With suitable modification the results obtained will, of course, be applicable to any ensemble of identical antisymmetric systems. Thus, the derivative $d\rho/dt$ is given by

$$i\hbar \frac{d}{dt} \langle x' \mid \rho \mid x'' \rangle = \sum_k \left(i\hbar \frac{d}{dt} \langle x' \mid k \rangle \langle k \mid x'' \rangle + i\hbar \langle x' \mid k \rangle \frac{d}{dt} \langle k \mid x'' \rangle \right), \quad (8:87)$$

and with (8:84) the right-hand side becomes

$$\sum_k \Big(\Big\{ \int \langle x' \mid \mathcal{H} \mid x''' \rangle \, dx''' \langle x''' \mid k \rangle - \sum_l \mu_{lk} \langle x' \mid l \rangle \Big\} \langle k \mid x'' \rangle$$
$$- \langle x' \mid k \rangle \Big\{ \int \langle k \mid x''' \rangle \, dx''' \langle x''' \mid \mathcal{H} \mid x'' \rangle - \sum_l \bar{\mu}_{kl} \langle l \mid x'' \rangle \Big\} \Big), \quad (8:88)$$

with the effective Hamiltonian $\mathcal{H} = \mathbf{u} + \mathbf{B} - \mathbf{A}$. Owing to their Hermiticity, the terms involving the Lagrangian multipliers cancel out; this of course is to be expected, since these multipliers express the arbitrariness in the individual wave-functions (non-invariance under rotations, cf. § 57), whereas the density involves no such arbitrariness. Thus, (8:88) reduces to

$$i\hbar \frac{d}{dt} \langle x' \mid \rho \mid x'' \rangle = \langle x' \mid \rho\mathcal{H} - \mathcal{H}\rho \mid x'' \rangle, \quad . \quad . \quad . \quad . \quad (8:89)$$

or symbolically,

$$i\hbar \frac{d}{dt}\boldsymbol{\rho} = -[\boldsymbol{\rho}, \mathcal{H}]_{-}. \qquad (8:90)$$

$\boldsymbol{\rho}$ satisfies the usual equation of motion for a density operator; but it should be noted that the Hamiltonian here is not a given quantity but depends linearly on $\boldsymbol{\rho}$, as follows from the definitions (8:75*a*, *b*) of **B** and **A**. When the single-particle operator **u** does not explicitly depend on the time, we can, with the help of equation (8:90), obtain a constant of the motion of the form

$$\mathscr{S}p\,[\boldsymbol{\rho}(\mathbf{u} + \tfrac{1}{2}\mathbf{B} - \tfrac{1}{2}\mathbf{A})], \qquad (8:91)$$

which on comparison with equation (8:69) is seen to be the energy integral, $\mathscr{S}p(\boldsymbol{\rho}\mathbf{u})$ representing the proper energy of the electrons (kinetic and potential—other than interelectronic), $\frac{1}{2}\mathscr{S}p(\boldsymbol{\rho}\mathbf{B})$ and $-\frac{1}{2}\mathscr{S}p(\boldsymbol{\rho}\mathbf{A})$ representing the ordinary and exchange interaction energies respectively. The proof of the constancy of this quantity follows readily from the definitions of **B**, **A** and equation (8:90), viz.

$$\begin{aligned}
\mathscr{S}p(\boldsymbol{\rho}\dot{\mathbf{B}}) &= \iint \langle x'' \mid \boldsymbol{\rho} \mid x' \rangle\, dx' \langle x' \mid \dot{\mathbf{B}} \mid x'' \rangle\, dx'' \\
&= \iint \langle x'' \mid \boldsymbol{\rho} \mid x' \rangle \langle x'x''' \mid \mathbf{v} \mid x''x^{\mathrm{IV}} \rangle \langle x^{\mathrm{IV}} \mid \dot{\boldsymbol{\rho}} \mid x''' \rangle\, dx'\, dx''\, dx'''\, dx^{\mathrm{IV}} \\
&= \int \cdots \int \langle x^{\mathrm{IV}} \mid \dot{\boldsymbol{\rho}} \mid x''' \rangle \langle x'''x' \mid \mathbf{v} \mid x^{\mathrm{IV}}x'' \rangle \langle x'' \mid \boldsymbol{\rho} \mid x' \rangle\, dx'\, dx''\, dx'''\, dx^{\mathrm{IV}} \\
&= \mathscr{S}p(\dot{\boldsymbol{\rho}}\mathbf{B}), \qquad (8:92)
\end{aligned}$$

and similarly,

$$\mathscr{S}p(\boldsymbol{\rho}\dot{\mathbf{A}}) = \mathscr{S}p(\dot{\boldsymbol{\rho}}\mathbf{A}). \qquad (8:93)$$

With these relations, and (8:90), we find

$$\begin{aligned}
\frac{d}{dt}\mathscr{S}p[\boldsymbol{\rho}(\mathbf{u} + \tfrac{1}{2}\mathbf{B} - \tfrac{1}{2}\mathbf{A})] &= \mathscr{S}p[\dot{\boldsymbol{\rho}}(\mathbf{u} + \tfrac{1}{2}\mathbf{B} - \tfrac{1}{2}\mathbf{A}) + \tfrac{1}{2}\boldsymbol{\rho}\dot{\mathbf{B}} - \tfrac{1}{2}\boldsymbol{\rho}\dot{\mathbf{A}}] \\
&= \mathscr{S}p(\dot{\boldsymbol{\rho}}\mathcal{H}), \qquad (8:94)
\end{aligned}$$

and finally,

$$i\hbar \frac{d}{dt}\mathscr{S}p[\boldsymbol{\rho}(\mathbf{u} + \tfrac{1}{2}\mathbf{B} - \tfrac{1}{2}\mathbf{A})] = \mathscr{S}p[(\mathcal{H}\boldsymbol{\rho} - \boldsymbol{\rho}\mathcal{H})\mathcal{H}] = 0. \qquad (8:95)$$

§ 69. Critique of the Fock-Dirac Equations *

In application, the solution of the Hartree and Fock-Dirac integro-differential equations involves an iterative process known as the method of the *self-consistent field*, which we shall sketch later. Here we need only note that a solution of the Fock-Dirac equations which determines a specified set of one-electron wave-functions (specified by a chosen set of central-field quantum numbers) also defines the density

* The present section follows the development given by MØLLER, C., and PLESSET, M.: *Phys. Rev.*, **46**, 618 (1934).

$\boldsymbol{\rho}$, and hence the operators **A** and **B** over this particular set. Thus, the effective Fock-Dirac Hamiltonian must be labelled as $\mathcal{H}_\mu$, for example, indicating that its form is determined by a stationary state μ of the whole system;[15] the latter being described by the antisymmetric wave-function

$$\langle \text{`}\mathsf{x} \mid {}^{(0)}_{\mu} \rangle = \frac{1}{\sqrt{n!}} \begin{vmatrix} \langle \mathsf{x}_1' \mid 1^\mu \rangle \langle \mathsf{x}_2' \mid 1^\mu \rangle \ldots \langle \mathsf{x}_n' \mid 1^\mu \rangle \\ \langle \mathsf{x}_1' \mid 1^\mu \rangle \langle \mathsf{x}_2' \mid 2^\mu \rangle \ldots \langle \mathsf{x}_n' \mid 2^\mu \rangle \\ \cdot \qquad \cdot \qquad \cdot \\ \cdot \qquad \cdot \qquad \cdot \\ \cdot \qquad \cdot \qquad \cdot \\ \langle \mathsf{x}_1' \mid n^\mu \rangle \langle \mathsf{x}_2' \mid n^\mu \rangle \ldots \langle \mathsf{x}_n' \mid n^\mu \rangle \end{vmatrix} \quad . \quad . \quad (8{:}96)$$

Corresponding to the stationary state under consideration, our general equations (8:79, 90, 91) become, respectively,

$$\int \langle \mathsf{x}' \mid \mathbf{u} + \mathbf{B}_\mu - \mathbf{A}_\mu \mid \mathsf{x}'' \rangle \, d\mathsf{x}'' \langle \mathsf{x}'' \mid r^\mu \rangle = \lambda_r^\mu \langle \mathsf{x}' \mid r^\mu \rangle, \quad . \quad (8{:}97)$$

or

$$\left. \begin{aligned} \mathcal{H}_\mu \mid r^\mu \rangle &= \lambda_r^\mu \mid r^\mu \rangle, \\ \boldsymbol{\rho}_\mu \mathcal{H}_\mu - \mathcal{H}_\mu \boldsymbol{\rho}_\mu &= 0, \end{aligned} \right\} \quad . \quad . \quad . \quad . \quad . \quad . \quad . \quad (8{:}98)$$

and

$$\epsilon_\mu^{(0)} = \mathscr{S}\!p \{ \boldsymbol{\rho}_\mu (\mathbf{u} + \tfrac{1}{2}\mathbf{B}_\mu - \tfrac{1}{2}\mathbf{A}_\mu) \}. \quad . \quad . \quad . \quad . \quad . \quad (8{:}99)$$

The *system* wave-function (8:96) satisfies the equation

$$\int \ldots \int \langle \text{`}\mathsf{x} \mid \mathbf{G}_\mu \mid \text{``}\mathsf{x} \rangle \, d\text{``}\mathsf{x} \langle \text{``}\mathsf{x} \mid {}^{(0)}_{\mu} \rangle = \Lambda_\mu \langle \text{`}\mathsf{x} \mid {}^{(0)}_{\mu} \rangle, \quad . \quad (8{:}100)$$ [16]

or

$$\mathbf{G}_\mu \mid {}^{(0)}_{\mu} \rangle = \Lambda_\mu \mid {}^{(0)}_{\mu} \rangle,$$

with

$$\mathbf{G}_\mu = \sum_i \mathcal{H}_\mu^i; \quad . \quad . \quad . \quad . \quad . \quad . \quad . \quad . \quad (8{:}101)$$

$\mathcal{H}_\mu^i$ being understood to operate only on functions of the variables x_i', so that

$$\langle \text{`}\mathsf{x} \mid \mathbf{G}_\mu \mid \text{``}\mathsf{x} \rangle = \sum_i \langle \mathsf{x}_i' \mid \mathcal{H}_\mu^i \mid \mathsf{x}_i'' \rangle \prod_{j \neq i} \delta(\mathsf{x}_j' - \mathsf{x}_j''), \quad . \quad . \quad (8{:}102)$$

$$\Lambda_\mu = \sum_r \lambda_r^\mu.$$

If now we wish to consider the Fock-Dirac equations as the zero-order approximation to the exact solution in a perturbation analysis, we require equation (8:100) in the standard form with the zero-order energy $\epsilon_\mu^{(0)}$ on the right. This is readily done by introducing a suitably defined related operator $\mathbf{H}_\mu$, such that $\langle \text{`}\mathsf{x} \mid {}^{(0)}_{\mu} \rangle$ is an exact

[15] A similar condition obtains in the Hartree case for the operator $\sum_{l \neq i} \boldsymbol{\beta}_{il}$, which corresponds to **B** here.

[16] This corresponds to taking the representative of the *antisymmetric* (approximate) $\mid \rangle$,

$$\frac{1}{\sqrt{n!}} \sum_P \delta_P \mathbf{P} \mid r^\mu \rangle,$$

in a *symmetrical* **x**-*representation.*

eigenfunction of this operator belonging to the eigenvalue $\epsilon_\mu^{(0)}$. From (8:97) and (8:102) we have

$$\Lambda_\mu = \sum_r \langle r^\mu \mid \mathcal{H}_\mu \mid r^\mu \rangle = \sum_r \iint \langle r^\mu \mid x' \rangle \, dx' \, \langle x' \mid \mathcal{H}_\mu \mid x'' \rangle \, dx'' \, \langle x'' \mid r^\mu \rangle$$

$$= \mathscr{S}p\,(\boldsymbol{\rho}_\mu \mathcal{H}_\mu), \quad \ldots \quad (8{:}103)$$ [17]

and from (8:99),

$$\Lambda_\mu = \epsilon_\mu^{(0)} + \tfrac{1}{2}\mathscr{S}p\,[\,\boldsymbol{\rho}_\mu(\mathbf{B}_\mu - \mathbf{A}_\mu)\,], \quad \ldots \quad (8{:}104)$$

so that an operator $\mathbf{H}_\mu$, defined by

$$\mathbf{H}_\mu = \mathbf{G}_\mu - \tfrac{1}{2}\mathscr{S}p\,[\,\boldsymbol{\rho}_\mu(\mathbf{B}_\mu - \mathbf{A}_\mu)\,], \quad \ldots \quad (8{:}105)$$

will satisfy the equation $\mathbf{H}_\mu \mid {}^{(0)}_{\mu} \rangle = \epsilon_\mu^{(0)} \mid {}^{(0)}_{\mu} \rangle$, i.e.

$$\int \cdots \int \langle\, 'x \mid \mathbf{H}_\mu \mid ''x \,\rangle \, d''x \, \langle\, ''x \mid {}^{(0)}_{\mu} \rangle = \epsilon_\mu^{(0)} \langle\, 'x \mid {}^{(0)}_{\mu} \rangle. \quad \ldots \quad (8{:}106)$$

The corresponding exact equation for the system may be written as

$$\mathbf{K} \mid \rangle = [\,\sum_i \mathbf{u}_i + \tfrac{1}{2}\sum_{i \neq j} \mathbf{v}_{ij}\,] \mid \rangle = \epsilon \mid \rangle, \quad \ldots \quad (8{:}107)$$

or

$$\int \cdots \int \langle\, 'x \mid \mathbf{K} \mid ''x \,\rangle \, d''x \, \langle\, ''x \mid \rangle = \epsilon \, \langle\, 'x \mid \rangle;$$

and for the perturbation analysis we consider a particular exact eigenvector $\mid {}_\mu \rangle$ (eigenfunction $\langle\, 'x \mid {}_\mu \rangle$) and energy ϵ_μ which, as indicated by the subscripts, are assumed to differ but little from the correspondingly labelled approximate eigenvector $\mid {}^{(0)}_{\mu} \rangle$ and energy level $\epsilon_\mu^{(0)}$. The corresponding perturbing potential then takes the form

$$\mathbf{S}_\mu = \mathbf{K} - \mathbf{H}_\mu = \tfrac{1}{2}\sum_{i \neq j} \mathbf{v}_{ij} - \sum_i (\,\mathbf{B}^i_\mu - \mathbf{A}^i_\mu\,) + \tfrac{1}{2}\mathscr{S}p\,[\,\boldsymbol{\rho}_\mu(\mathbf{B}_\mu - \mathbf{A}_\mu)\,], \quad (8{:}108)$$

so that we have the rather unusual circumstance wherein the perturbation depends on the particular stationary state involved. The exact vector and associated energy may now be developed in the usual series

$$\left.\begin{aligned} \mid {}_\mu \rangle &= \mid {}^{(0)}_{\mu} \rangle + \mid {}^{(1)}_{\mu} \rangle + \mid {}^{(2)}_{\mu} \rangle + \cdots, \\ \epsilon_\mu &= \epsilon_\mu^{(0)} + \epsilon_\mu^{(1)} + \epsilon_\mu^{(2)} + \cdots, \end{aligned}\right\} \quad \ldots \quad (8{:}109)$$

which, when substituted into the exact equation (8:107), and separated into terms of the same order, give the usual equations:

zero-order $\quad (\,\mathbf{H}_\mu - \epsilon_\mu^{(0)}\,) \mid {}^{(0)}_{\mu} \rangle = 0; \quad \ldots \quad (8{:}110a)$

first-order $\quad (\,\mathbf{H}_\mu - \epsilon_\mu^{(0)}\,) \mid {}^{(1)}_{\mu} \rangle = (\,\epsilon_\mu^{(1)} - \mathbf{S}_\mu\,) \mid {}^{(0)}_{\mu} \rangle; \quad \ldots \quad (8{:}110b)$

second-order $\quad (\,\mathbf{H}_\mu - \epsilon_\mu^{(0)}\,) \mid {}^{(2)}_{\mu} \rangle = (\,\epsilon_\mu^{(1)} - \mathbf{S}_\mu\,) \mid {}^{(1)}_{\mu} \rangle + \epsilon_\mu^{(2)} \mid {}^{(0)}_{\mu} \rangle. \quad (8{:}110c)$

[17] We note that the last form, $\mathscr{S}p\,(\boldsymbol{\rho}_\mu \mathcal{H}_\mu)$, follows directly from the first, so that it is often convenient to omit the intermediate steps.

Alternatively, on multiplying the symbolic form by $\langle\, 'x \mid$, these may be written as

$$\int\cdots\int\langle\, 'x \mid \mathbf{H}_\mu - \epsilon_\mu^{(0)} \mid ''x \,\rangle\, d''x\, \langle\, ''x \mid {}^{(1)}_{\mu} \,\rangle$$

$$= \int\cdots\int\langle\, 'x \mid \epsilon_\mu^{(1)} - \mathbf{S}_\mu \mid ''x \,\rangle\, d''x\, \langle\, ''x \mid {}^{(0)}_{\mu} \,\rangle, \text{ etc.,}$$

the particular way of writing these equations depending on convenience and preference.

In addition to the n selected eigenfunctions of $\mathcal{H}_\mu$ which enter the definition of $\langle\, 'x \mid {}^{(0)}_{\mu} \,\rangle$, and by the same token define $\mathcal{H}_\mu$, there is an infinite set of eigenfunctions $\langle\, x' \mid R^\mu \,\rangle$ of $\mathcal{H}_\mu$ satisfying the equation

$$\mathcal{H}_\mu \mid R^\mu \,\rangle = \lambda^\mu_R \mid R^\mu \,\rangle. \quad . \quad . \quad . \quad . \quad . \quad . \quad . \quad . \qquad (8{:}111)$$

These are distinguished from the selected set by the use of capital letters, but they are also associated with the given stationary state μ since they belong to the associated one-electron operator $\mathcal{H}_\mu$. The two groups of functions $\langle\, x' \mid r^\mu \,\rangle$ and $\langle\, x' \mid R^\mu \,\rangle$ constitute a complete set belonging to $\mathcal{H}_\mu$, and correspondingly generate a complete set of antisymmetric eigenfunctions of the operator $\mathbf{H}_\mu$, satisfying

$$\mathbf{H}_\mu \mid {}^{(0)}_{\mu,\nu} \,\rangle = \epsilon^{(0)}_{\mu,\nu} \mid {}^{(0)}_{\mu,\nu} \,\rangle, \quad . \quad . \quad . \quad . \quad . \quad . \quad . \qquad (8{:}112)$$

i.e.

$$\int\cdots\int\langle\, 'x \mid \mathbf{H}_\mu \mid ''x \,\rangle\, d''x\, \langle\, ''x \mid {}^{(0)}_{\mu,\nu} \,\rangle = \epsilon^{(0)}_{\mu,\nu} \langle\, 'x \mid {}^{(0)}_{\mu,\nu} \,\rangle,$$

of which set the function (8:96) $\langle\, 'x \mid {}^{(0)}_{\mu} \,\rangle = \langle\, 'x \mid {}^{(0)}_{\mu,0} \,\rangle$ is the prototype, here arbitrarily chosen as the zero-th member of the set. All other $\langle\, 'x \mid {}^{(0)}_{\mu,\nu} \,\rangle$ are obtained from this one by replacing one or more of the functions $\langle\, x' \mid r^\mu \,\rangle$, $\langle\, x' \mid t^\mu \,\rangle$ by $\langle\, x' \mid R^\mu \,\rangle$, $\langle\, x' \mid T^\mu \,\rangle$, etc., and we shall indicate by $\langle\, 'x \mid {}^{(0)}_{\mu,\, rt\ldots;\, RT\ldots} \,\rangle$ the particular $\langle\, 'x \mid {}^{(0)}_{\mu,\nu} \,\rangle$ obtained by this substitution. With this observation it follows that the vectors $\mid {}^{(1)}_{\mu} \,\rangle$, $\mid {}^{(2)}_{\mu} \,\rangle, \ldots$ may be developed in terms of the complete set of all $\mid {}^{(0)}_{\mu,\nu} \,\rangle$ as

$$\mid {}^{(1)}_{\mu} \,\rangle = \sum_\nu a^{(1)}_{\mu\nu} \mid {}^{(0)}_{\mu,\nu} \,\rangle, \quad . \quad . \quad . \quad . \quad . \quad . \quad . \quad . \qquad (8{:}113)$$

$$\mid {}^{(2)}_{\mu} \,\rangle = \sum_\nu a^{(2)}_{\mu\nu} \mid {}^{(0)}_{\mu,\nu} \,\rangle. \quad . \quad . \quad . \quad . \quad . \quad . \quad . \quad . \qquad (8{:}114)$$

Substituting (8:113) into (8:110*b*), we find

$$\sum_\nu a^{(1)}_{\mu\nu} \left(\epsilon^{(0)}_{\mu,\nu} - \epsilon^{(0)}_{\mu,0} \right) \mid {}^{(0)}_{\mu,\nu} \,\rangle = \left(\epsilon^{(1)}_\mu - \mathbf{S}_\mu \right) \mid {}^{(0)}_{\mu,0} \,\rangle, \quad . \quad . \qquad (8{:}115)$$

and on pre-multiplying by $\langle\, {}^{(0)}_{\mu,\nu} \mid$, it follows that

$$a^{(1)}_{\mu\nu} \left(\epsilon^{(0)}_{\mu,\nu} - \epsilon^{(0)}_{\mu,0} \right) = \langle\, {}^{(0)}_{\mu,\nu} \mid \epsilon^{(1)}_\mu - \mathbf{S}_\mu \mid {}^{(0)}_{\mu,0} \,\rangle. \quad . \quad . \quad . \qquad (8{:}116)$$

For simplicity we shall assume $\epsilon^{(0)}_{\mu,\nu} \neq \epsilon^{(0)}_{\mu,0}$ for $\nu \neq 0$, since the generalization for the degenerate case is not essential to the argument and can be included in the usual way if necessary. Then from (8:116) we obtain

$$\epsilon_\mu^{(1)} = \langle \,{}^{(0)}_{\mu,0} \mid \mathbf{S}_\mu \mid {}^{(0)}_{\mu,0} \rangle, \quad . \; . \; . \; . \; . \; . \; . \; . \; . \tag{8:117}$$

and

$$a_{\mu\nu}^{(1)} = \frac{\langle \,{}^{(0)}_{\mu,\nu} \mid \mathbf{S}_\mu \mid {}^{(0)}_{\mu,0} \rangle}{\epsilon^{(0)}_{\mu,0} - \epsilon^{(0)}_{\mu,\nu}} \qquad (\nu \neq 0); \quad . \; . \; . \tag{8:118}$$

the undetermined coefficient $a_{\mu 0}^{(1)}$ being zero, as usual, from the normalization condition on $|\,{}_\mu\rangle$ [cf. (8:109)]. Similarly, from (8:114) and (8:110*c*), the second-order correction is found to be

$$\epsilon_\mu^{(2)} = \sum_{\nu \neq 0} \frac{\langle \,{}^{(0)}_{\mu,0} \mid \mathbf{S}_\mu \mid {}^{(0)}_{\mu,\nu} \rangle \langle \,{}^{(0)}_{\mu,\nu} \mid \mathbf{S}_\mu \mid {}^{(0)}_{\mu,0} \rangle}{\epsilon^{(0)}_{\mu,0} - \epsilon^{(0)}_{\mu,\nu}}. \quad . \; . \; . \; . \; . \tag{8:119}$$

Then from (8:117) and (8:108), we find

$$\epsilon_\mu^{(1)} = \int \ldots \int A \prod_r \langle r \mid x_r' \rangle \, d'x \, \langle 'x \mid \tfrac{1}{2} \sum_{i \neq j} \mathbf{v}_{ij} - \sum_i (\mathbf{B}^i_\mu - \mathbf{A}^i_\mu) \mid ''x \rangle \, d''x A \prod_s \langle x_s'' \mid s \rangle$$
$$+ \tfrac{1}{2} \mathscr{S}p [\, \boldsymbol{\rho}_\mu (\mathbf{B}_\mu - \mathbf{A}_\mu)\,]. \quad . \; . \; . \tag{8:120}$$

This expression is readily reduced in the usual way, e.g. for the first term we have

$$\frac{\sqrt{n!}}{2} \sum_{i \neq j} \int \ldots \int A \prod_r \langle r | x_r' \rangle \, d'x \, \langle x_i' x_j' | \mathbf{v} | x_i'' x_j'' \rangle dx_i'' dx_j'' \langle x_i'' | i \rangle \langle x_j'' | j \rangle \prod_{s \neq i,j} \langle x_s' | s \rangle$$
$$= \tfrac{1}{2} \sum_{i \neq j} \int \ldots \int \langle x_i' x_j' \mid \mathbf{v} \mid x_i'' x_j'' \rangle \, dx_i' \, dx_j' \, dx_i'' \, dx_j''$$
$$\times \{ \langle i \mid x_i' \rangle \langle j \mid x_j' \rangle - \langle i \mid x_j' \rangle \langle j \mid x_i' \rangle \} \langle x_i'' \mid i \rangle \langle x_j'' \mid j \rangle, \tag{8:121}$$

where as usual the terms in curly brackets arise from the identity permutation and the simple interchange, and this reduces to

$$\tfrac{1}{2} \int \ldots \int \langle x' x'' \mid \mathbf{v} \mid x''' x^{\mathrm{IV}} \rangle \, dx' \, dx'' \, dx''' \, dx^{\mathrm{IV}}$$
$$\times \{ \langle x''' \mid \boldsymbol{\rho}_\mu \mid x' \rangle \langle x^{\mathrm{IV}} \mid \boldsymbol{\rho}_\mu \mid x'' \rangle - \langle x''' \mid \boldsymbol{\rho}_\mu \mid x'' \rangle \langle x^{\mathrm{IV}} \mid \boldsymbol{\rho}_\mu \mid x' \rangle \}$$
$$= \tfrac{1}{2} \mathscr{S}p [\, \boldsymbol{\rho}_\mu (\mathbf{B}_\mu - \mathbf{A}_\mu)\,]. \quad . \; . \; . \; . \; . \; . \; . \tag{8:122}$$

Similarly, it is seen that the second term reduces to

$$-\mathscr{S}p [\, \boldsymbol{\rho}_\mu (\mathbf{B}_\mu - \mathbf{A}_\mu)\,], \quad . \; . \; . \; . \; . \; . \tag{8:123}$$

and combining these results, we find

$$\epsilon_\mu^{(1)} = 0; \quad . \; . \; . \; . \; . \; . \; . \; . \; . \tag{8:124}$$

or in other words, the Fock-Dirac approximation is accurate to the second order in the energy.

The determination of the coefficients $a_{\mu\nu}^{(1)}$ (8:118), of the first-order correction in the wave-function, is only slightly more complex, since those terms $\langle {}^{(0)}_{\mu,\nu} \mid \mathbf{S}_\mu \mid {}^{(0)}_{\mu,0} \rangle$, wherein $\langle {}^{(0)}_{\mu,\nu} \mid$ is obtained by replacing more than two of the functions $\langle r^\mu \mid x' \rangle$ by functions of the set $\langle R^\mu \mid x' \rangle$, vanish identically because of the complete orthogonality of these two sets of functions. Thus, the non-zero integrals are, at most, of the type

$$\int\cdots\int \langle {}^{(0)}_{\mu,r;\,R} \mid {}'x \rangle\, d'x \,\langle {}'x \mid \mathbf{S}_\mu \mid {}''x \rangle\, d''x \,\langle {}''x \mid {}^{(0)}_{\mu,0} \rangle \quad . \quad (8{:}125a)$$

and

$$\int\cdots\int \langle {}^{(0)}_{\mu,rt;\,RT} \mid {}'x \rangle\, d'x \,\langle {}'x \mid \mathbf{S}_\mu \mid {}''x \rangle\, d''x \,\langle {}''x \mid {}^{(0)}_{\mu,0} \rangle . \quad . \quad (8{:}125b)$$

However, it is readily shown that all integrals of the first type are in fact zero. Thus, on expanding (8:125a), we obtain

$$\frac{\sqrt{n!}}{2}\sum_{i\neq j}\int\cdots\int A \prod_{k\neq r}\langle k \mid x_k' \rangle \langle R \mid x_r' \rangle\, d'x \,\langle x_i' x_j' \mid \mathbf{v} \mid x_i'' x_j'' \rangle\, dx_i''\, dx_j'' \times \prod_{l\neq i,j}\langle x_l' \mid l \rangle \langle x_i'' \mid i \rangle \langle x_j'' \mid j \rangle$$

$$-\sqrt{n!}\sum_i \int\cdots\int A \prod_{k\neq r}\langle k \mid x_k' \rangle \langle R \mid x_r' \rangle\, d'x \,\langle x_i' \mid \mathbf{B}_\mu - \mathbf{A}_\mu \mid x_i'' \rangle\, dx_i'' \times \prod_{l\neq i}\langle x_l' \mid l \rangle \langle x_i'' \mid i \rangle \quad (8{:}126)$$

(the integral over the term $\frac{1}{2}\mathscr{S}p\,[\boldsymbol{\rho}_\mu(\mathbf{B}_\mu - \mathbf{A}_\mu)]$ in $\mathbf{S}_\mu$ being identically zero), in which the first term gives non-zero contributions only for terms of the type $i = r$, $j \neq r$, and $j = r$, $i \neq r$, while the second vanishes except for $i = r$. Therefore, the first reduces to

$$\begin{aligned}
\tfrac{1}{2}\Big\{ &\sum_{j\neq r}\int\cdots\int [\langle R \mid x_r' \rangle \langle j \mid x_j' \rangle - \langle j \mid x_r' \rangle \langle R \mid x_j' \rangle] \\
&\quad \times dx_r'\, dx_j' \,\langle x_r' x_j' \mid \mathbf{v} \mid x_r'' x_j'' \rangle\, dx_r''\, dx_j'' \,\langle x_r'' \mid r \rangle \langle x_j'' \mid j \rangle \\
&+ \sum_{i\neq r}\int\cdots\int [\langle i \mid x_i' \rangle \langle R \mid x_r' \rangle - \langle R \mid x_i' \rangle \langle i \mid x_r' \rangle] \\
&\quad \times dx_i'\, dx_r' \,\langle x_i' x_r' \mid \mathbf{v} \mid x_i'' x_r'' \rangle\, dx_i''\, dx_r'' \,\langle x_i'' \mid i \rangle \langle x_r'' \mid r \rangle \Big\} \\
= \tfrac{1}{2}\int\cdots\int \Big\{ &\langle R \mid x' \rangle \langle x''' \mid r \rangle \big(\langle x^{\mathrm{IV}} \mid \boldsymbol{\rho}_\mu \mid x'' \rangle - \langle x^{\mathrm{IV}} \mid r \rangle \langle r \mid x'' \rangle \big) \\
&- \langle R \mid x'' \rangle \langle x''' \mid r \rangle \big(\langle x^{\mathrm{IV}} \mid \boldsymbol{\rho}_\mu \mid x' \rangle - \langle x^{\mathrm{IV}} \mid r \rangle \langle r \mid x' \rangle \big) \\
&+ \langle R \mid x'' \rangle \langle x^{\mathrm{IV}} \mid r \rangle \big(\langle x''' \mid \boldsymbol{\rho}_\mu \mid x' \rangle - \langle x''' \mid r \rangle \langle r \mid x' \rangle \big) \\
&- \langle R \mid x' \rangle \langle x^{\mathrm{IV}} \mid r \rangle \big(\langle x''' \mid \boldsymbol{\rho}_\mu \mid x'' \rangle - \langle x''' \mid r \rangle \langle r \mid x'' \rangle \big) \Big\} \\
&\times \langle x' x'' \mid \mathbf{v} \mid x''' x^{\mathrm{IV}} \rangle\, dx' \ldots dx^{\mathrm{IV}}, \quad . \quad . \quad (8{:}127)
\end{aligned}$$

which is just

$$\iint \langle R \mid x' \rangle\, dx' \,\langle x' \mid \mathbf{B}_\mu - \mathbf{A}_\mu \mid x'' \rangle\, dx'' \,\langle x'' \mid r \rangle ; \quad . \quad . \quad (8{:}128)$$

and it follows immediately from (8:126) that the second reduces to

$$-\iint \langle R \mid x' \rangle\, dx' \,\langle x' \mid \mathbf{B}_\mu - \mathbf{A}_\mu \mid x'' \rangle\, dx'' \,\langle x'' \mid r \rangle . \quad . \quad (8{:}129)$$

Thus, from (8:118),

$$a^{(1)}_{\mu,r;R} = \frac{\langle {}^{(0)}_{\mu,r;R} \mid \mathbf{S}_\mu \mid {}^{(0)}_{\mu,0} \rangle}{\epsilon^{(0)}_{\mu,0} - \epsilon^{(0)}_{\mu,r;R}} = 0. \quad . \quad . \quad . \quad . \quad . \quad . \quad (8:130)$$

Similarly, the corresponding first term for the integrals of the type (8:125*b*) vanishes except for $i = r,\ j = t$ and $i = t,\ j = r$, while the second vanishes identically, so that we find

$$\langle {}^{(0)}_{\mu,rt;RT} \mid \mathbf{S}_\mu \mid {}^{(0)}_{\mu,0} \rangle = \int \ldots \int \langle R \mid x' \rangle \langle T \mid x'' \rangle \, dx' \, dx'' \, \langle x'x'' \mid \mathbf{v} \mid x'''x^{\mathrm{IV}} \rangle$$
$$\Big(\langle x''' \mid r \rangle \langle x^{\mathrm{IV}} \mid t \rangle - \langle x^{\mathrm{IV}} \mid r \rangle \langle x''' \mid t \rangle \Big) \, dx''' \, dx^{\mathrm{IV}}, \quad (8:131)$$

which determines the first-order correction [cf. (8:109, 115, 118)] to the wave-function:

$$\langle `x \mid {}_\mu \rangle = \langle `x \mid {}^{(0)}_{\mu,0} \rangle + \sum_{rt;RT} a^{(1)}_{\mu,rt;RT} \langle `x \mid {}^{(0)}_{\mu,rt;RT} \rangle + \ldots \quad . \quad (8:132)$$

Recalling the relations [cf. (8:97, 111, 112)]

$$\left.\begin{aligned} \epsilon^{(0)}_{\mu,0} &= \sum_j \lambda^\mu_j - \tfrac{1}{2}\mathscr{S}p\,[\,\boldsymbol{\rho}_\mu\,(\,\mathbf{B}_\mu - \mathbf{A}_\mu\,)\,], \\ \epsilon^{(0)}_{\mu,rt;RT} &= \lambda^\mu_R + \lambda^\mu_T + \sum_{j \neq r,t} \lambda^\mu_j - \tfrac{1}{2}\mathscr{S}p\,[\,\boldsymbol{\rho}_\mu\,(\,\mathbf{B}_\mu - \mathbf{A}_\mu\,)\,], \end{aligned}\right\} \quad . \quad (8:133)$$

the second-order energy correction (8:119) becomes

$$\epsilon^{(2)}_\mu = \sum_{rt;RT} \left| \int \ldots \int \frac{\langle R \mid x' \rangle \langle T \mid x'' \rangle dx' dx'' \langle x'x'' \mid \mathbf{v} \mid x'''x^{\mathrm{IV}} \rangle dx''' dx^{\mathrm{IV}} \Big(\langle x''' \mid r \rangle \langle x^{\mathrm{IV}} \mid t \rangle - \langle x^{\mathrm{IV}} \mid r \rangle \langle x''' \mid t \rangle \Big)}{\lambda^\mu_r + \lambda^\mu_t - \lambda^\mu_R - \lambda^\mu_T} \right|^2 . \quad (8:134)$$

The electric density in the approximation (8:132) is given by

$$\begin{aligned} \langle x' \mid \boldsymbol{\rho} \mid x' \rangle &= n \int \ldots \int \mid \langle `x \mid {}^{(0)}_{\mu,0} \rangle + \sum_{rt;RT} a^{(1)}_{\mu,rt;RT} \langle `x \mid {}^{(0)}_{\mu,rt;RT} \rangle \mid^2 dx'' \ldots dx^{(n)} \\ &= n \int \ldots \int \Big(\mid \langle `x \mid {}^{(0)}_{\mu,0} \rangle \mid^2 + \mid \sum_{rt;RT} a^{(1)}_{\mu,rt;RT} \langle `x \mid {}^{(0)}_{\mu,rt;RT} \rangle \mid^2 \Big) dx'' \ldots dx^{(n)} \\ &= \langle x' \mid \boldsymbol{\rho}_\mu \mid x' \rangle + \ldots, \quad . \quad . \quad . \quad . \quad . \quad . \quad . \quad (8:135) \end{aligned}$$ [18]

from which it follows that the *effective* density given by the diagonal elements of the Fock-Dirac density operator $\boldsymbol{\rho}_\mu$ is correct to the second order.

[18] Cf. equations (7:35–41).

CHAPTER IX

The Statistical Method

§ 70. Introduction

The essence of the *self-consistent* field method is, as the name implies, an iterative process of solving the differential and integro-differential equations of the Hartree and Fock-Dirac approximations. Aside from the potential due to the nucleus (or nuclei and other external sources, depending on the type of physical problem), the true effective potential depends essentially on the total electronic density, and thus involves all the as yet unknown wave-functions. As a first approximation, this true potential is replaced by some reasonable form of effective potential V_1, and from the solutions obtained, a new electronic density and effective potential V_2 are computed for a second trial solution. Repeating the process, we ultimately converge on those solutions which determine a total density (kth effective potential) such that the solutions with this potential reproduce the potential V_k to within a stated accuracy.

From the point of view of computation, the above procedure simply involves very tedious numerical integrations, but of theoretical interest is the question of the determination or selection of a first approximate potential with which to initiate the calculations. There are a variety of ways possible, which usually involve considerable experience and judgment, and probably the most useful and least complicated is the statistical or semi-classical approximation which we shall now consider. It is also of interest to see what improvements can be made in this analysis and, in particular, to show its relation to the Fock-Dirac and extended Hartree (spin-included) theories. The limiting equations which we shall now derive follow from the Fock-Dirac and extended Hartree (spin-included) theories by essentially correspondence-principle arguments, so that it is reasonable to refer to them as the Fock-Dirac and Hartree correspondence equations. Following the mode of derivation, it will be seen that these differ only in that the former takes account of exchange and contains no self-energy terms.

§ 71. Elements of Physical Statistics

In §§ 27, 57, 68, certain of the mathematical properties of the density operator were described, and we consider now the application of this and other closely related operators to the statistical description and analysis of many-particle systems. The incomplete specification of a system as being distributed over a number of states according to a definite probability law constitutes, in one form or another, the starting-point of a statistical analysis in either the quantal or classical case.[1]

[1] A state, in the classical sense, being understood as a complete specification of all the coordinates and momenta at a given time.

The classical approach is, in brief, as follows: Any state of a system (of f degrees of freedom) can be represented as a point in a conceptual $2f$-dimensional space, the so-called phase space, whose orthogonal axes are all the coordinates and momenta, the representative point moving according to Hamilton's canonical equations of motion along a definite and, in principle, calculable trajectory in this space. This one-to-one correspondence between states and points in phase space is perfectly general, but it is obviously impossible to correlate a system with one definite point in phase (space) if, as above, the initial specification does not correspond to the assignment of a definite state. Rather, the system must be correlated with a sort of cloud in phase space whose mass in any region gives the probability of the system being in any state represented by a point in that region. In terms of unit volume of phase space, this defines the phase density at any point as the probability of the system being in the neighbourhood of the corresponding state. Each element of the representative cloud must, of course, move according to the canonical equations, and it is a simple matter to derive the equation of conservation of density in phase (space),

$$\frac{d\rho}{dt} = 0, \qquad (9{:}1)$$

or

$$\frac{\partial \rho}{\partial t} = -\sum_r \left\{ \frac{\partial}{\partial q_r}(\rho \dot{q}_r) + \frac{\partial}{\partial p_r}(\rho \dot{p}_r) \right\} = -[\rho, H], \qquad (9{:}2)$$

which is the mathematical statement of Liouville's Theorem; from this we can deduce the equivalent theorem of the conservation of volume or extension in phase. Thus, according to equation (9:1), if we follow a group of representative points of a system, it is found that their motion is such that they occupy equal volumes at successive instants in time, although at a fixed point the density varies according to equation (9:2). It is often convenient to consider the *cloud* as representing an ensemble of a large number, N, of identical independent systems executing their motions in the same place; in which case, the phase density at any point equals the probable number of systems in the neighbourhood of the associated state. In this sense, an equivalent interpretation of equation (9:1) is that if the representative points (states) of the ensemble fill a region of phase space with a certain density, then, at a later time, they fill the new region to which they have moved with the same density. Since the probability of a system being in some state is unity, ρ in these two interpretations is normalized according to

$$\int \cdots \int \rho \, dq_1 \ldots dp_f = 1, \qquad (9{:}3)$$

and

$$\int \cdots \int \rho \, dq_1 \ldots dp_f = N, \qquad (9{:}4)$$

and correspondingly for a function α of the dynamical variables, the integral

$$\int \cdots \int \alpha\rho \, dq_1 \ldots dp_f \qquad (9{:}5)$$

gives the average value of α for one system, and the ensemble.

The average of such a function over the phase space is *per se* of limited physical interest. It becomes important if the ensemble average is shown to be equivalent to the time average over the motion of the actual system of interest, which is the quantity of primary interest since it is correlated with observation. That such an equivalence holds cannot be proved, but is inferred from Liouville's Theorem and the quasi-ergodic hypothesis.[2] In the absence of more specific information about the state of a system, if all the equivalent regions of phase space are accessible and there is no inherent tendency for the phase points to crowd into one region in preference to any other (Liouville's Theorem), then it follows that equal volumes in phase space are equally probable. In other words, for a given volume or extension in phase, the representative point of a system is equally likely to be in any region of phase space which is consistent with the available information about the system. This conclusion may be taken independently and instead of the ergodic hypothesis as the basic postulate, and, as such, is known as the hypothesis of equal *a priori* probability of equal volumes in phase space. The quantal analogue is the hypothesis [3] of equal *a priori* probability of single (non-degenerate) quantum states, which in turn can be mathematically proved if we accept the ergodic hypothesis.[4] The converse is not true since the two postulates are not identical.

We have considered the classical statistical principles only in the briefest manner, sufficient for our present purposes. However, one additional simple fact will be of use to us; namely, that (aside from the obvious case) the phase density and, hence, the average value of properties of the systems in an ensemble will be independent of the time if the density is some function of a constant of the motion.[5] An ensemble of this type is described as being in statistical equilibrium, since the original distribution in phase is permanently maintained. An interesting and important result is obtained when we examine the quantal case of a system (of f degrees of freedom) which is specified as being in one or another of the simultaneous eigenstates of the f momenta, the probability for the $\mathfrak{p}$'s in the range $d`p$ at $`p$ being $P(`p)\,d`p$. In the $\mathfrak{q}$-diagonal representation, the general expression for $\boldsymbol{\rho}$ will now be

$$\langle `q \mid \boldsymbol{\rho} \mid ``q \rangle = \int \langle `q \mid `p \rangle P(`p)\, d`p \langle `p \mid ``q \rangle, \quad . \quad . \quad . \quad (9:6)$$

and hence, in view of (4:19), the diagonal element is

$$\langle `q \mid \boldsymbol{\rho} \mid `q \rangle = h^{-f} \int P(`p)\, d`p. \quad . \quad . \quad . \quad . \quad . \quad . \quad (9:7)$$

[2] In brief, that starting from a given phase point every phase value consistent with the specific energy value of the system is ultimately approached infinitely closely; or that every phase volume consistent with a given energy range is eventually reached.

The ergodic hypothesis in original form stated that each consistent phase value is attained; but it is easily shown that, in general, it would be impossible for the representative point of a system to pass through every phase point compatible with a given energy.

Cf. Tolman, R. C.: *Principles of Statistical Mechanics,* Oxford (1938).

[3] This hypothesis seems more in keeping with modern theory since it permits us to correlate the ensemble average with the average obtained from repeated identical experiments instead of a time average. Hence, in contrast to the ergodic hypothesis, it does not exclude the possibility that an individual system may deviate considerably from the average; nor is there any question as to what constitutes a sufficiently long time.

[4] Cf. Jordan, P.: *Statistical Mechanics,* Braunschweig (1933).

[5] Thus, if $\rho = \rho(\alpha)$, where α is a constant of the motion, then from $\dfrac{d\alpha}{dt} = \sum_r \left\{\dfrac{\partial\alpha}{\partial q_r}\dot{q}_r + \dfrac{\partial\alpha}{\partial p_r}\dot{p}_r\right\} = 0$, it follows that $\dfrac{\partial\rho}{\partial t} = -\dfrac{d\rho}{d\alpha}\sum_r\left\{\dfrac{\partial\alpha}{\partial q_r}\dot{q}_r + \dfrac{\partial\alpha}{\partial p_r}\dot{p}_r\right\} = 0.$

From this result it is obvious that the spur of $\boldsymbol{\rho}$ in the $\mathbf{q}$-representation is infinite, which can be given meaning only in the sense that $\boldsymbol{\rho}$ represents an ensemble of infinitely many systems—the diagonal element being the probability that a system of the ensemble chosen at random has its $\mathbf{q}$'s in the range $d'q$ at $'q$, or equivalently, the density of systems in coordinate space. This interpretation also suggests that in terms of the classical picture one may consider $h^{-f}P\,('p)$ as the phase density or probable number of systems per unit of phase space.

In dealing with problems involving continuous eigenspectra, it is possible [6] to reason in terms of a corresponding dense but discrete spectrum extending over the same range, and pass to the limit in the final analysis. If we apply this process to the present case, equation (9:6) is replaced by

$$\langle 'q \mid \boldsymbol{\rho} \mid ''q \rangle = \sum_{'p} \langle 'q \mid 'p \rangle_d P\,('p)\,{}_d\langle 'p \mid ''q \rangle, \quad . \quad . \quad . \quad (9{:}8)$$

in which $P\,('p)$ now gives the probable number of systems in the discrete momentum eigenstate $\mid 'p \rangle_d$ corresponding to $'p$. When the $'p$'s are densely distributed, we can replace this sum by the corresponding integral provided we know the density of eigenvalues in the range $d'p$. Comparing these two interpretations, we see that h^{-f} is the density of states in phase space and, hence, h^f is the phase volume of one state.[7] This result provides the justification for the common procedure of dividing the volume of phase space consistent with the specified energy interval, by h in the power of the total number of degrees of freedom, to obtain the corresponding number of quantum states.[8]

§ 72. Equations of Motion

The result that a cell [9] in phase space of volume h^f is equivalent to a discrete state, is practically all that is required for the statistical analysis of polyelectronic atoms. The method was first developed by Fermi and Thomas,[10] and the essential idea is remarkably simple; namely, that since the electrons in an atom occupy (effectively) a region of $\sim$1–2 Ångstroms in radius, the density of the electron distribution is of the order 10^{24}/cm.^{3}, which means that the system is a highly degenerate electron gas and should be amenable to treatment in terms of the Fermi-Dirac statistic. Hence, we can obtain a relation between the charge density and

[6] In fact, for certain general theoretical problems, as in parts of quantum field theory, this device is not only convenient, but necessary. Cf. DIRAC, *Q.M.*

[7]
$$\int \langle 'q \mid 'p \rangle_d P\,('p)\,\sigma('p)\,d'p\,{}_d\langle 'p \mid ''q \rangle = \int \langle 'q \mid 'p \rangle P\,('p)\,d'p \langle 'p \mid ''q \rangle$$
or
$$\frac{1}{V}\int e^{(i/\hbar)\,'\underline{p}\cdot('\underline{q}-''\underline{q})} P\,('p)\,\sigma('p)\,d'p = h^{-f}\int e^{(i/\hbar)\,'\underline{p}\cdot('\underline{q}-''\underline{q})} P\,('p)\,d'p,$$
so that the number of momentum eigenstates per unit range is Vh^{-f}. This result is sometimes obtained by the heuristic argument as to the minimum volume of phase space which must be assigned to a state in accord with the uncertainty relation $\delta_q\delta_p \sim h$; but there is no *a priori* reason for using this form leading to a volume h^f rather than $\hbar^f$.

[8] The number of states obtained by actual counting and by the above process will differ unless the discrete quantum states actually form a dense set as prescribed.

[9] The term " cell " is rather expressive and of fairly general usage in this connection.

[10] FERMI, E.: *Zeits. f. Phys.*, **48**, 73 (1928); **49**, 550 (1928). THOMAS, L.: *Proc. Camb. Phil. Soc.*, **23**, 542 (1927).

potential, which, combined with the Poisson equation of electrostatics, determines the potential itself. However, the full artillery of the Fermi-Dirac statistic is not required, since the exclusion principle sets a maximum phase density of electrons (particles of the antisymmetric type), and we can restrict our attention to the case of all the electrons occupying the lowest permissible energy levels. The fact that we are thus limiting our considerations to conditions at zero absolute temperature is not material, because the full-fledged statistical analysis merely adds a temperature-dependent term to our final result which, for all ordinary temperatures, is negligible, as would be expected on purely physical grounds.[11]

The broad principles involved in the transition to the statistical viewpoint are the same in both the Fock-Dirac and Hartree cases, namely, that the equations describing a given system can be entirely formulated in terms of the density matrix $\boldsymbol{\rho}$, which, as we know, is determined by the equations of motion:

$$i\hbar\dot{\boldsymbol{\rho}} = [\,\mathbf{H}, \boldsymbol{\rho}\,]_-, \qquad (9{:}9)$$

$$\mathbf{H} = \mathbf{U} + \mathbf{B} - \mathbf{A}. \quad \text{(Fock-Dirac, cf. § 68.)} \qquad (9{:}10)$$

$$\mathbf{H} = \mathbf{U} + \mathbf{B}. \quad \text{(Extended Hartree, cf. § 64.)} \qquad (9{:}11)$$ [12]

Formally, at least, we do not need to introduce the individual wave-functions defining the total electronic density, so that the number of electrons involved is immaterial, i.e. we can deal with any number of electrons by introducing the density operator, which thus establishes the first point of similarity with the classical concepts. In a semi-classical analysis of problems involving very many electrons, we may assume as an approximation that the non-commutativity of conjugate coordinates and momenta may be neglected, which corresponds to the assumption that the density, considered as a function of the coordinates *and* momenta, varies appreciably only over regions of phase space large relative to h^3. However, the equation $\boldsymbol{\rho}^2 = \boldsymbol{\rho}$ indicates that we must still require that for each point of phase space the classical phase density shall have one of the values 0, 1; or 0, 1, 2 when we take the diagonal sum over spin. Hence, the number of electrons per phase volume h^3 must not exceed 2; and if, in particular, we consider the normal (lowest) energy state of an atomic system, it follows that there will be a sharp boundary surface between the region of phase space occupied to the maximum density and the empty region. It is the equation of this boundary which we wish to determine, and it is evident that this surface will be one of constant $\mathbf{H}$, since $\boldsymbol{\rho}$ is constant for a stationary state, and the consequent commutation of $\boldsymbol{\rho}$ and $\mathbf{H}$ (9:9) simply means that $\boldsymbol{\rho}$ is a function of $\mathbf{H}$. The problem thus resolves itself finally into the determination of the correct classical transcription of the Hamiltonian. This transcription is readily obtainable by a number of essentially equivalent arguments based on: the W.J.B.K. phase integral method, which is probably least

[11] We may note in passing that the phase density can be expressed as the product of the constituent densities in coordinate space and momentum space, and, from the existence of maximum phase density, it follows that as the density in q-space increases, the density in p-space decreases, thus extending the occupied region of p-space (i.e. the boundary), which corresponds to raising the maximum of momentum and kinetic energy.

[12] This form for the extended Hartree method is self-evident from the discussion of §§ 64, 68.

elegant but also perhaps least heuristic; [13] the formal application of standard correspondence principle arguments; [14] the direct comparison of the physical interpretations of the quantal and classical densities. We shall here adopt the last-mentioned because it appears to be the simplest approach and is no less rigorous than the others.

From our discussion of the interpretation of the elements $\langle x' \mid \boldsymbol{\rho} \mid x' \rangle$ in the case of continuous eigenvalues, it follows that to make connection with the classical density in phase $\rho(x', p')$, we should expect to have the relation

$$\langle x' \mid \boldsymbol{\rho} \mid x' \rangle \doteqdot h^{-3} \int \rho\,(x', p')\,dp'; \qquad (9{:}12)$$

i.e. the diagonal representative of the density operator is approximated to by the integral over the p' variables of the probable number of electrons per unit volume of phase space. The consistency of this correspondence may be demonstrated as follows. We introduce a function defined by

$$\Psi\,(x', p') = h^{-3/2} \langle x' \mid \boldsymbol{\rho} \mid p' \rangle\, e^{-i\underline{x}' \cdot \underline{p}'/\hbar}, \qquad (9{:}13)$$

which is seen to have the properties of a simultaneous probability for coordinates and momenta since its integral over the momentum variables gives essentially the probability in coordinate space, and conversely, viz.

$$\int \Psi\,(x', p')\,dp' = \langle x' \mid \boldsymbol{\rho} \mid x' \rangle, \qquad (9{:}14a)$$

$$\int \Psi\,(x', p')\,dx' = \langle p' \mid \boldsymbol{\rho} \mid p' \rangle. \qquad (9{:}14b)$$

Such a function obviously has no physical meaning *per se* for quantal systems, but when we disregard the uncertainty principle (non-commutation) and make the transition to an almost classical system (assuming the density in phase varies appreciably only over regions large compared to h^3), we may interpret it naïvely in the literal sense, namely,

$$\Psi\,(x', p') \doteqdot h^{-3} \rho\,(x', p'), \qquad (9{:}15a)$$

which leads directly to the *ansatz* (9:12), thus lending plausibility to it although not constituting a proof. To be consistent, a similar relation must hold for every quantal operator $\boldsymbol{\beta}$ and its classical transcript $\beta(x', p')$, viz.

$$\beta\,(x', p') \doteqdot h^{3/2} \langle x' \mid \boldsymbol{\beta} \mid p' \rangle\, e^{-i\underline{x}' \cdot \underline{p}'/\hbar}. \qquad (9{:}15b)$$

If we now calculate the quantal average of $\boldsymbol{\beta}$, then with (9:15a, b) we find

$$\langle \boldsymbol{\beta} \rangle = \int \langle x' \mid \boldsymbol{\rho\beta} \mid x' \rangle\, dx' = \iint \langle x' \mid \boldsymbol{\rho} \mid p' \rangle\, dp' \langle p' \mid \boldsymbol{\beta} \mid x' \rangle\, dx'$$

$$\doteqdot h^{-3} \int \rho\beta\, dx'\, dp', \qquad (9{:}16a)$$

[13] Cf. BRILLOUIN, L.: *Actualities Scient. et Ind.*, **39**, Hermann & Cie (1932).

[14] Cf. DIRAC, P. A. M.: *Proc. Camb. Phil. Soc.*, **26**, 376 (1930); FRENKEL, J.: *Wave Mechanics—Advanced General Theory*, Oxford (1934).

which is, of course, the correct correspondence under the conditions assumed. Furthermore, we note that

$$\iint \Psi\,(x', p')\,dx'\,dp' = \int \langle x' \mid \boldsymbol{\rho} \mid x' \rangle\,dx' = n \quad \text{(number of particles);} \qquad (9{:}16b)$$

or with (9:15),

$$\iint \frac{\rho}{h^3}\,dx'\,dp' = n, \quad . \quad . \quad . \quad . \quad . \quad . \quad . \quad . \qquad (9{:}16c)$$

so that our normalization is correct, and the correspondence assumed is self-consistent. An equivalent way of expressing these results is that each representative $\langle x' \mid \boldsymbol{\beta} \mid x'' \rangle$ is related to a Fourier component in the p' variables of $\beta(x', p')$, considered as a function of commuting coordinates and momenta, according to

$$\langle x' \mid \boldsymbol{\beta} \mid x'' \rangle \doteq h^{-3} \int \beta\,(x', p')\,dp' e^{-i(\underline{x}'-\underline{x}'')\cdot \underline{p}'/\hbar}; \quad . \quad . \quad . \qquad (9{:}17a)$$

and, by inversion,

$$\beta\,(x', p') \doteq \int \langle x' \mid \boldsymbol{\beta} \mid x'' \rangle\,dx'' e^{-i(\underline{x}'-\underline{x}'')\cdot \underline{p}'/\hbar}. \quad . \quad . \quad . \qquad (9{:}17b)$$ [15]

Applied to $\underline{\mathbf{p}}^2$, for example, we find

$$\underline{p}^2\,(x', p') = \int \langle x' \mid \underline{\mathbf{p}}^2 \mid x'' \rangle\,dx'' e^{-i(\underline{x}'-\underline{x}'')\cdot \underline{p}'/\hbar}$$

$$= \hbar^2 \int \delta''\,(x' - x'')\,dx'' e^{-i(\underline{x}'-\underline{x}'')\cdot \underline{p}'/\hbar}$$

$$= \underline{p}'^2, \quad . \quad . \quad . \quad . \quad . \quad . \quad . \quad . \quad . \quad . \quad . \quad . \qquad (9{:}18a)$$

after a double integration. Similarly, for an operator $\boldsymbol{\varphi}(\mathbf{x})$, which is a function of the coordinates only,

$$\phi\,(x', p') = \phi\,(x') \int \delta\,(x' - x'')\,dx'' e^{-i(\underline{x}'-\underline{x}'')\cdot \underline{p}'/\hbar}$$

$$= \phi\,(x'). \quad . \quad . \quad . \quad . \quad . \quad . \quad . \quad . \quad . \quad . \quad . \quad . \quad . \qquad (9{:}18b)$$ [16]

[15] We note that the adjoint function $\Psi^* = h^{-3/2} \langle p' \mid \boldsymbol{\rho} \mid x' \rangle e^{i\underline{x}'\cdot \underline{p}'/\hbar}$ has the same properties and can be used in the same way. Moreover, there are other closely related functions of this type, which can be chosen to be real but, again, will not be everywhere positive. In the present problem we deal with the so-called μ-space of statistical mechanics, but it is more usual to work in the γ-space, in which case the definition (9:13) becomes $\Psi\,(\,'x,\,'p\,) = h^{-3n/2} \langle\,'x \mid \boldsymbol{\rho} \mid\,'p\,\rangle, e^{-i\,'\underline{x}\cdot\,'\underline{p}/\hbar}$ corresponding to $3n$ degrees of freedom ($'\underline{x} \to \underline{x}_1', \underline{x}_2', \ldots \underline{x}_n'$). This is just the function introduced by Wigner, *Phys. Rev.*, **40**, 749 (1932), and discussed by him and Kirkwood, *ibid.*, **44**, 31 (1933), in its relation to the evaluation of the sum of states.

As kindly pointed out to the writer by Prof. Wigner, one of the fundamental questions regarding such distribution functions is that it is difficult to see, if an arbitrary function of p and q is given, whether it corresponds to a physically possible situation. Moreover, there is the question as to the conditions which such a function must fulfil, as, for example, arise from the positive-definite nature of the statistical matrix.

The idempotency of $\boldsymbol{\rho}$ leads quite trivially, in the present case, to $\int \{ \mid \Psi \mid^2 - h^{-3}\Psi \}\,dp' = 0$, but the necessary and sufficient general conditions have yet to be obtained.

[16] In the following, as above, we proceed for the moment as though the spin variables were entirely absent.

Applying (9:17b) to **B**, we find

$$B(x', p') = \int \langle x' \mid \mathbf{B} \mid x'' \rangle \, dx'' e^{-i(\underline{x}'-\underline{x}'')\cdot \underline{p}'/\hbar}$$

$$= e^2 \int \frac{\langle x''' \mid \rho \mid x''' \rangle}{\mid \underline{x}' - \underline{x}''' \mid} dx''' = \frac{e^2}{h^3} \int \frac{dx'''}{\mid \underline{x}' - \underline{x}''' \mid} \int \rho(x''', p''') \, dp''', \quad (9{:}19a)$$

where we have used the relation [cf. (8:75a)]

$$\langle x' \mid \mathbf{B} \mid x'' \rangle = e^2 \delta(x' - x'') \int \frac{\langle x''' \mid \rho \mid x''' \rangle}{\mid \underline{x}' - \underline{x}''' \mid} dx'''. \quad . \quad (9{:}19b)$$

Thus, $B(x', p')$ is independent of p', as it should be, since $\langle x' \mid \mathbf{B} \mid x'' \rangle$ is diagonal, and it is seen to be simply the potential due to a distribution of electrons of density $\rho(x''', p''')$ per phase volume h^3, which is, of course, the physically reasonable transcription of the quantal **B**. Similarly, using the definition [cf. (8:75b)]

$$\langle x' \mid \mathbf{A} \mid x'' \rangle = e^2 \frac{\langle x' \mid \rho \mid x'' \rangle}{\mid \underline{x}' - \underline{x}'' \mid}, \quad . \quad . \quad . \quad . \quad . \quad (9{:}20a)$$

we obtain

$$A(x', p') = \frac{e^2}{h^3} \iint \frac{\rho(x', p'')}{\mid \underline{x}' - \underline{x}'' \mid} e^{-i(\underline{x}'-\underline{x}'')\cdot(\underline{p}'-\underline{p}'')/\hbar} \, dp'' \, dx''. \quad . \quad (9{:}20b)$$ [17]

The integral over the variables x'' represents the value at the point $\underline{x}'$ of the potential due to a charge distribution $e^{i\underline{x}''\cdot(\underline{p}'-\underline{p}'')/\hbar}$, so that this integral may be most easily evaluated by using Poisson's equation. By this simple device, the potential is found to be

$$\frac{h^2}{\pi \mid \underline{p}' - \underline{p}'' \mid^2} e^{i\underline{x}'\cdot(\underline{p}'-\underline{p}'')/\hbar}, \quad . \quad . \quad . \quad . \quad . \quad . \quad . \quad (9{:}21a)$$

and equation (9:20b) reduces to

$$A(x', p') = \frac{e^2}{\pi h} \int \frac{\rho(x', p'')}{\mid \underline{p}' - \underline{p}'' \mid} dp''. \quad . \quad . \quad . \quad . \quad . \quad (9{:}21b)$$

To proceed further we require the explicit form of $\rho(x', p')$, for which, following our previous discussion, we make the plausible assumption that for each $\underline{x}'$ the phase space is separated into the saturated and empty regions according as the magnitude of $\underline{p}'$ is less than, or greater than, a certain momentum P, which, of course, depends on $\underline{x}'$. The maximum value of ρ for the saturated region will be 1 or 2 electrons per volume h^3, depending on whether we transcribe from the spin-dependent or spinless (diagonal sum) quantal density operator. Our derivation corresponds to the latter, so that we have

$$\left.\begin{aligned} \rho(x', p') &= 2, \qquad \mid \underline{p}' \mid < P(\underline{x}'), \\ &= 0, \qquad \mid \underline{p}' \mid > P(\underline{x}'), \end{aligned}\right\} \quad . \quad . \quad . \quad . \quad . \quad (9{:}22)$$

[17] With regard to the many-particle problem, it is somewhat of a curiosum that the permutation operators **P** give rise to the correspondence

$$P(`q, `p) \doteqdot \exp - \frac{i}{\hbar}[\Sigma \underline{q}' . \underline{p}' - \Sigma (P\underline{q}') . \underline{p}'],$$

which gives a simple formal interpretation to the analogous factor (pair interchange) in (9:20b).

with which $B(x', p')$ and $A(x', p')$ reduce to

$$B(x') = \frac{8\pi e^2}{3h^3}\int P^3(x')\,dx', \quad \ldots\ldots\ldots \quad (9:23)$$

$$A(x', p') = \frac{2e^2}{h}\left[\frac{P^2 - |\underline{p}'|^2}{|\underline{p}'|}\, ln \left|\frac{P + |\underline{p}'|}{P - |\underline{p}'|}\right| + 2P\right], \quad \ldots \quad (9:24)$$

and the transcription of the individual particle operator **U** is simply

$$U(x', p') = \frac{p'^2}{2m} + \phi(x'). \quad \ldots\ldots\ldots \quad (9:25)$$

It might appear that the transcription is now complete, and that we can write the constant energy value at the boundary, namely $H(x', P)$, as

$$H(x', P) = U(x', P) + B(x') - A(x', P) = \text{constant}; \quad . \quad (9:26)$$

but this leads to an incorrect result, as is readily seen when we examine more closely the physical meaning of B and A. The term $B(x')$ represents the potential energy due to the interaction of one electron with all the electrons, and could just as well have been written down without bothering about transcribing the quantal operator **B**; but the term in A cannot be so obtained since exchange interaction has no physically derivable classical analogue. Now the assumption $\rho(x', p') = 2$ corresponds to complete pairing of electrons or, strictly speaking, to the distribution of n electrons among $n/2$ doubly occupied spinless orbits, so that the error in (9:26) arises because it gives an exchange energy between one electron and all electrons; whereas we know that the exchange can occur only for electrons of like spin. This incorrect double count of exchange is to be expected in our treatment, since the semi-classical theory (as indicated by the neglect of spin variables, which is here necessary in order to transcribe our equations) can take account of spin only to the extent of doubling the maximum value of $\rho(x', p')$; it cannot cope with the preferential spin dependence of exchange correlation $[\rho(x', p') = 1]$, and simultaneously allow for Coulomb interaction between all electrons $[\rho(x', p') = 2]$. To make the above conclusions more precise, we may calculate the correct exchange energy between one electron and all electrons of like spin in the plane wave approximation, which is readily seen to be the equivalent of our preceding transcription to classical form.

For two parallel spin electrons (i and j) in a cubical box, the interaction term in the total (antisymmetrized) energy [cf. § 65, equation (8:69)] is given by

$$\epsilon(i, j) = \langle ij \,|\, \mathbf{v} \,|\, ij \rangle - \langle ij \,|\, \mathbf{v} \,|\, ji \rangle, \quad \ldots\ldots \quad (9:27)$$

where the matrix elements are computed over the spinless wave-functions

$$\langle x' \,|\, i \rangle = \frac{1}{\sqrt{V}}\, e^{i\underline{k}_i \cdot \underline{x}'}, \quad \ldots\ldots\ldots \quad (9:28)$$

since the spin restriction is automatically satisfied. Taking $\mathbf{v}$ as the Coulomb potential, we have

$$\epsilon(i,j) = \int \frac{|\langle i\,|\,x'\rangle|^2\,|\langle j\,|\,x''\rangle|^2}{|\underline{x}' - \underline{x}''|}\,dx'\,dx'' - \int \frac{\langle i\,|\,x'\rangle\langle j\,|\,x''\rangle\langle x'\,|\,j\rangle\langle x''\,|\,i\rangle}{|\underline{x}' - \underline{x}''|}\,dx'\,dx''$$

$$= J(i,j) - K(i,j), \qquad (9{:}29)$$

where J, K indicate the Coulomb and exchange integrals respectively. With the wave-functions (9:28), $K(i,j)$ takes the form

$$K(i,j) = \frac{1}{V^2}\int \frac{e^2}{|\underline{x}' - \underline{x}''|}\,e^{i(\underline{k}_i - \underline{k}_j)\cdot(\underline{x}' - \underline{x}'')}\,dx'\,dx'', \qquad (9{:}30)$$

which, apart from the factor $1/V^2$, is simply the electrostatic interaction of two charge distributions

$$\left.\begin{aligned} c_1 &= e^{i(\underline{k}_i - \underline{k}_j)\cdot\underline{x}}, \\ c_2 &= e^{-i(\underline{k}_i - \underline{k}_j)\cdot\underline{x}''}, \end{aligned}\right\} \qquad (9{:}31)$$

and can be evaluated in the equivalent forms

$$-e\int V_2(x')\,c_1\,dx' = -e\int V_1(x'')\,c_2\,dx''. \qquad (9{:}32)$$

Taking the first of these with $V_2(x')$ given by [cf. (9:21a)]

$$V_2(x') = \frac{-4\pi e}{|\underline{k}_i - \underline{k}_j|^2}\,e^{-i(\underline{k}_i - \underline{k}_j)\cdot\underline{x}'} \qquad (9{:}33)$$

we obtain

$$K(i,j) = \frac{4\pi e^2}{V\,|\underline{k}_i - \underline{k}_j|^2} = \frac{h^2 e^2}{\pi V\,|\underline{p}_i - \underline{p}_j|^2}, \qquad (9{:}34)$$

and the total exchange energy $K(i)$ for the ith electron is then the integral of $K(i,j)$ over all j. Now the number of electrons of given spin with momenta in $d\underline{p}_j$ at $\underline{p}_j$ is simply

$$\frac{2\pi V}{h^3}\,p_j^2\,dp_j\,d\cos\theta, \qquad (9{:}35)$$

corresponding to the assignment of *one* electron of given spin per phase volume h^3 as required by the exclusion principle, so that

$$K(i) = \frac{2\pi V}{h^3}\int_0^P \int_{-1}^1 K(i,j)\,p_j^2\,dp_j\,d\cos\theta$$

$$= \frac{e^2}{h}\left[\frac{P^2 - |\underline{p}_i|^2}{|\underline{p}_i|}\,ln\left|\frac{P + |\underline{p}_i|}{P - |\underline{p}_i|}\right| + 2P\right], \qquad (9{:}36)$$

which is just half the result obtained before [(9:24)] for obvious reasons. Thus, dividing (9:24) by a factor[18] 2, the correct boundary equation is given by

$$H(x', P) = U(x', P) + B(x') - \frac{2e^2P}{h} = \text{const.} \qquad (9:37)$$

Applying the Laplacian operator, we have $\nabla^2 H = 0$, or

$$\nabla^2\left(\frac{P^2}{2m} - \frac{2e^2P}{h}\right) = \frac{32\pi^2e^2P^3}{3h^3}, \qquad (9:38)$$

which follows directly from the observation that the potential term in $U(x', P)$ satisfies Laplace's equation, while B satisfies Poisson's equation in the form

$$\nabla^2 B = -4\pi e^2 \rho(x); \qquad (9:39a)$$

where obviously

$$\rho(x) = \frac{1}{h^3}\int \rho(x, p)\, dp = \frac{8\pi P^3}{3h^3}. \qquad (9:39b)$$

Assuming spherical symmetry, we have

$$\frac{1}{r^2}\frac{\partial}{\partial r}\left\{r^2\frac{\partial}{\partial r}\left(\frac{P^2}{2m} - \frac{2e^2P}{h}\right)\right\} = \frac{32\pi^2e^2P^3}{3h^3}, \qquad (9:40)$$

determining P as function of r.

The Thomas-Fermi equation, which follows essentially from the extended Hartree theory, is seen to be just the above equation without the term linear in P. If we group together the ordinary potential energy terms in (9:37) in the form $-eV$, and express the constant $H(x', P)$ as $-eE$, then the maximum momentum is given by

$$\frac{P^2}{2m} - \frac{2e^2P}{h} + e(E - V) = 0, \qquad (9:41a)$$

or

$$P = \frac{2me^2}{h} \pm \left[\frac{4m^2e^4}{h^2} + 2me(V - E)\right]^{1/2}. \qquad (9:41b)$$

which may be used in equation (9:40) to obtain the differential equation governing the potential, namely,

$$\frac{1}{r^2}\frac{\partial}{\partial r}\left(r^2\frac{\partial V}{\partial r}\right) = \frac{32\pi^2 e}{3h^3}\left\{\frac{2me^2}{h^3} + \left[\frac{4m^2e^4}{h^2} + 2me(V - E)\right]^{1/2}\right\}^3, \qquad (9:42)$$

where the correct root of (9:41b) is determined by the requirement that, with neglect of exchange, (9:42) must agree with the Thomas-Fermi case. The above equation should, of course, be the more accurate, although the exchange correction

[18] This method of correction can be avoided if we write down $B(x')$ on purely physical grounds, and treat **A** as above, or separately transcribe **A** by introducing two equal spinless densities $\boldsymbol{\rho}_+$, $\boldsymbol{\rho}_-$, defined by $\langle x' | \boldsymbol{\rho}_\pm | x'' \rangle = \Sigma^{n/2} \langle x' | i \rangle \langle i | x'' \rangle$, corresponding to positive and negative spin respectively. Cf. Brillouin, *loc. cit.* However, this device treats **A** and **B** on separate footing too, and is hardly more satisfactory from the theoretical standpoint.

can be expected to be quantitatively small since the ratio of the coefficients of the linear and quadratic terms in P is the very small quantity $4me^2/h$. However, it should be noted that (9:42) does not possess physically acceptable solutions for arbitrarily large r, since the linear term causes P and hence ρ to become negative and oscillatory in character.[19] Moreover, the fact that this does not occur in the Thomas-Fermi (Hartree) form appears to be merely fortuitous, since the approximation which considers the phase density in terms of commuting coordinates and momenta is certainly a particularly poor one for the outer regions of an atomic system.

§ 73. Variational Aspect *

In order to round off our picture of the theoretical basis of this method, it would seem worth while to consider the variational formulation which brings the physical concepts to the foreground, and hence has been, perhaps, of the greatest value in further development of the statistical method and its applications. The general concept is again quite simple. We seek an approximate semi-classical expression for the total energy of a system in the form

$$H = \int \epsilon(\rho)\, dx, \quad . \quad . \quad . \quad . \quad . \quad . \quad . \quad . \quad . \qquad (9:43)$$

where $\epsilon(\rho)$ is the energy density, and the best density function $\rho(x)$ is determined as that one for which this integral is stationary, subject to the normalization condition

$$\int \rho\, dx = n \qquad \text{(number of electrons)}. \quad . \quad . \quad . \quad . \qquad (9:44)$$

The essential question is that of determining the energy density $\epsilon(\rho)$ which, of course, depends on the system under study, and the accuracy of the approximations used. For our present illustrative purposes it will suffice to consider the simple problem of the preceding section. In the plane wave approximation, it is well known that the kinetic energy density is given by

$$\epsilon_K = \frac{3h^2}{40m}\left(\frac{3}{\pi}\right)^{2/3} \rho^{5/3} = \lambda_K \rho^{5/3}, \quad . \quad . \quad . \quad . \quad . \qquad (9:45)$$ [20]

while the density of ordinary potential energy is simply

$$\epsilon_P = -eV'\rho = -e\left(V_N + \tfrac{1}{2}V_C\right)\rho, \quad . \quad . \quad . \quad . \quad . \qquad (9:46)$$

where V_N and V_C denote the potential due to the nucleus, etc., and the self-potential of the charge distribution, with the usual correction of the latter for the double counting of charge elements.[21]

[19] Cf. (9:40); and (9:69), § 75 (*b*).

* Cf. FRENKEL, J.: *Zeits. f. Phys.*, **49**, 30 (1928); JENSEN, H.: *ibid.*, **89**, 713 (1934).

[20] This is seen to be just the Fermi energy density.

[21] The self-energy is given by $\frac{1}{2}\iint \frac{e^2}{|\underline{x}_1 - \underline{x}_2|}\rho_1\rho_2\, dx_1\, dx_2 = -\frac{e}{2}\int V_C\rho\, dx$, where $\nabla^2 V_C = 4\pi\rho e$.

The total exchange energy is readily obtained from equation (9:36), namely,

$$K = \tfrac{1}{2}\int_0^P \frac{V}{h^3} K\,(\,i\,)\, 4\pi p_i^2\, dp_i$$

$$= \frac{2\pi e^2 V P^4}{h^4}, \quad \dots\dots\dots\dots \quad (9:47)$$

which, combined with the previous relation $\rho = 8\pi P^3/3h^3$, gives the exchange density

$$\epsilon_A = -2K/V = -\frac{3}{4}\left(\frac{3}{\pi}\right)^{1/3} e^2 \rho^{4/3}$$

$$= -\lambda_A \rho^{4/3}. \quad \dots\dots\dots\dots \quad (9:48)$$

Hence, we require

$$\delta H = \delta \int (\,\lambda_K \rho^{5/3} - \lambda_A \rho^{4/3} - eV'\rho\,)\, dx = 0, \quad \dots \quad (9:49)$$

subject to

$$\delta n = \delta \int \rho\, dx = 0. \quad \dots\dots\dots \quad (9:50)$$

Introducing the Langrangian multiplier $-eE$, this becomes

$$\delta \int [\,\lambda_K \rho^{5/3} - \lambda_A \rho^{4/3} - e\,(\,V' - E\,)\,\rho\,]\, dx = 0, \quad \dots \quad (9:51)$$

or

$$\tfrac{5}{3}\lambda_K \rho^{2/3} - \tfrac{4}{3}\lambda_A \rho^{1/3} - e\,(\,V - E\,) = 0, \quad \dots \quad (9:52)$$

where V now indicates [22] $V_N + V_C$.

This equation is readily shown to be just the previous result (9:41*a*) expressed in terms of ρ, and it is seen from the root

$$\frac{h}{2}\left(\frac{3\rho}{\pi}\right)^{1/3} = \left\{\frac{2me^2}{h^2} + \left[\frac{4m^2e^4}{h^2} + 2me\,(\,V - E\,)\right]^{1/2}\right\}, \quad \dots \quad (9:53)$$

that the presence of the constant term prevents fulfilment of the normalization condition, if the latter is taken over all space.

§ 74. General Remarks

The apparent simplicity of the statistical method has stimulated many investigations dealing with its application to various atomic problems, and further theoretical development. However, the hope that it might be developed into a fairly accurate independent means of analysing atomic systems seems to be largely unrealized, since the results obtained are in general disappointing. This is perhaps not unexpected in view of the assumptions on which the statistical method is based, and the *a priori* limitation which these assumptions place on the type of physical variable to which we can logically expect to approximate with any accuracy.

22 $-\frac{e}{2}\delta \int V_C \rho\, dx = -\frac{e^2}{2}\iint \frac{\rho_1\,\delta\rho_2 + \rho_2\,\delta\rho_1}{|\,x_1 - x_2\,|}\, dx_1\, dx_2 = -e^2 \iint \frac{\rho_1\,\delta\rho_2}{|\,x_1 - x_2\,|}\, dx_1\, dx_2 = -e\int V_C\,\delta\rho\, dx.$

The evident criterion is that this method cannot be expected to account for the periodic properties of the elements, which means that the relative success or failure in different applications is largely determined by the type of physical quantity considered. Hence, although the charge distributions calculated from these semi-classical equations lack the shell structure found in better approximations, they still constitute, within limits, a reasonable averaged or *smeared* approximation.[23] This results since the equations are designed to deal with any large number of electrons, and hence the solutions differ only in scale. On the other hand, it is known that the gross variation in charge distribution with increasing atomic number is a fairly uniform contraction in scale. Similarly, the agreement with total atomic binding energies is better than just *order of magnitude*,[24] whereas calculated ionization energies, for example, are in general not worth mentioning.

The failure of the usual normalization condition for the statistical atom with exchange illustrates clearly the problem of appropriate boundary conditions. Nor is it evident, as we shall see, that there exist adequate physical criteria which can, in general, determine a unique set of boundary conditions universally equivalent to the basic assumptions of the theory.

§ 75. Boundary Conditions—Interpretation

(*a*) *Thomas-Fermi* (*Hartree*) *Approximation.*

With neglect of the exchange correction the equation to be solved is [cf. (9:42)]

$$\frac{1}{r}\frac{\partial^2}{\partial r^2}[\,r\,(\,V-E\,)\,] = \frac{32\pi^2 e}{3h^3}[\,2me\,(\,V-E\,)\,]^{3/2}, \qquad (9{:}54a)$$

subject to the boundary conditions

$$[\,rV\,]_{r=0} = Ze, \qquad \int_0 \rho\,d\tau = n. \qquad (9{:}54b)$$ [25]

We now introduce the change of variables

$$\left.\begin{aligned} r &= \mu x, \qquad \mu = \frac{\hbar^2}{me^2}\left(\frac{9\pi^2}{128Z}\right)^{1/3}, \\ V - E &= \frac{\gamma\phi}{x}, \qquad \gamma = Ze/\mu, \end{aligned}\right\} \qquad (9{:}55)$$

with which equations (9:54) reduce to the form

$$\frac{d^2\phi}{dx^2} = \frac{\phi^{3/2}}{x^{1/2}}; \qquad (9{:}56a)$$

$$\phi\,(\,0\,) = 1, \qquad \int \phi^{3/2} x^{1/2}\,dx = n/Z. \qquad (9{:}56b)$$ [26]

[23] The density as a function of distance diminishes too slowly at large distances, namely, as the inverse sixth power rather than exponentially. Cf. discussion of boundary conditions, § 75.

[24] Consistently in the neighbourhood of 25–30 per cent less (i.e. lower) than experimental or extrapolated experimental values (for the heavier atoms).

[25] It is clear that the upper limit will, in general, depend on the physical system under study, hence we purposely leave it unspecified.

[26] We note that $Ze\varphi$ is an effective *nuclear charge for potential*, i.e. the charge which divided by the distance from the nucleus gives the potential, so that as r approaches zero, φ approaches unity.

The discussion of these equations is considerably simplified by the introduction of two auxiliary quantities, namely, the number $n(X)$ of electrons between 0 and some as yet arbitrary distance X, which quantity is readily found to be

$$n(X) = Z\left[\left(x\frac{d\phi}{dx}\right)_X - \phi(X) + 1\right], \quad \ldots \quad (9{:}57a)$$

or

$$\phi(X) - \left[x\frac{d\phi}{dx}\right]_X = 1 - \frac{n(X)}{Z} \quad \ldots \quad (9{:}57b)$$

(where $x = X$ corresponds to some $r = R$), and a comparison plot in terms of ϕ and x of the Coulomb potential due to an arbitrary charge σe. These are sketched in the self-explanatory figure below.

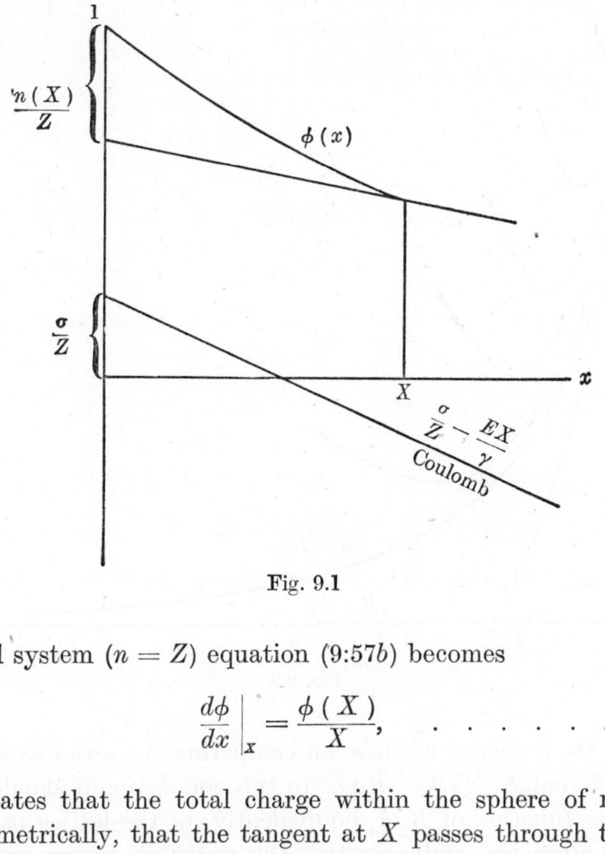

Fig. 9.1

For a neutral system ($n = Z$) equation (9:57b) becomes

$$\left.\frac{d\phi}{dx}\right|_X = \frac{\phi(X)}{X}, \quad \ldots \quad (9{:}58)$$

which simply states that the total charge within the sphere of radius $X(r = R)$ is zero,[27] or geometrically, that the tangent at X passes through the origin. It is clear that ϕ must not be negative, since negative values of ρ are meaningless; and from (9:56) we see that all solutions will be convex toward the axis of abscissa. The solution of (9:56) can be developed in the series

$$\phi(x) = 1 - Bx + \tfrac{4}{3}x^{3/2} - \tfrac{2}{5}Bx^{5/2} + \tfrac{1}{3}x^3 + \ldots \quad (9{:}59)$$

in the neighbourhood of the origin and continued by numerical integration. The

[27] Equation (9:58) is just the transformation of $\left.\frac{\partial V}{\partial r}\right|_R = 0$, i.e. the field vanishes at $r = R$.

appearance of the solutions for various initial slopes $-B$ is sketched in the figure below.[28]

The integral curve with initial slope $-B_0 = -1.58808$ is asymptotic to the axis of abscissæ which, according to fig. 9.1, corresponds to the auxiliary condition $E = 0$, i.e. maximum energy[29] $-eE = 0$. The solutions for various $B < B_0$, corresponding to maximum energies $-eE > 0$ (cf. fig. 9.1—Coulomb plot), can be formally correlated with the study of metals of appropriate lattice, but in this case the auxiliary condition is less obvious. For most purposes, a simple and physically reasonable condition is the requirement that the potential for the free atom and corresponding

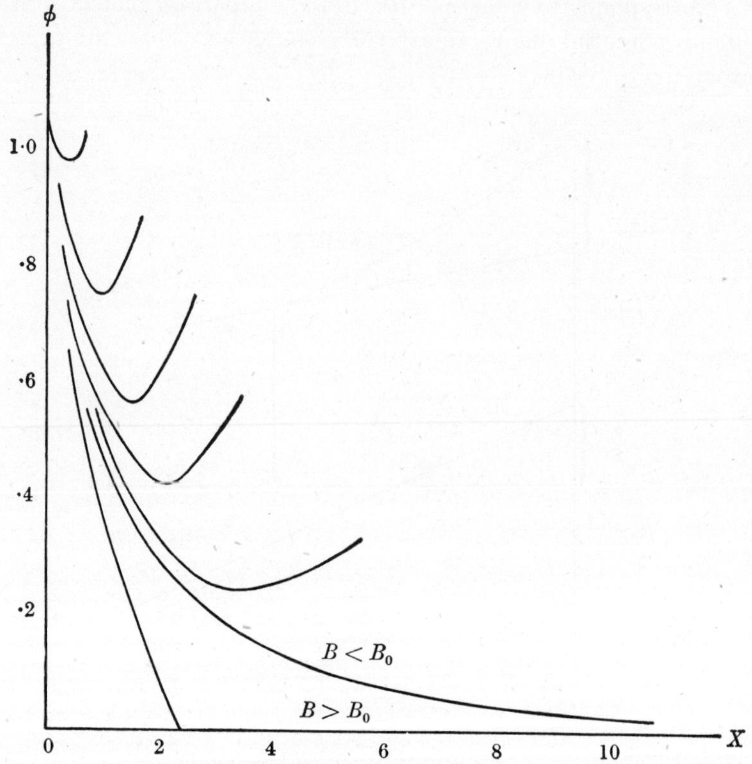

Fig. 9.2

metal agree near the nucleus; whence, on comparing the series expansions near the origin, it follows[30] that $E = (B - B_0)\gamma$. In this connection it should be emphasized that the energy as function of B or, equivalently, of the lattice parameter X, *does not* show a minimum, which indicates that the statistical theory cannot account for metallic cohesion.[31]

From fig. 9.1 and equation (9:57*b*) it follows that integral curves for which

[28] The precise numerical data and figures can be found, for example, in the detailed article by *SLATER, J. C., and KRUTTER, H. M., *Phys. Rev.*, **47**, 559 (1935). See also *BRILLOUIN, L.: *Act. Scient. et Ind.*, **60**, Hermann, Paris (1934).

[29] This solution for the neutral atom is usually mentioned with the auxiliary condition included *a priori* on obvious physical grounds.

[30] Cf. * SLATER, J. C., and KRUTTER, H. M., *loc cit.*

[31] This is, of course, rather to be expected in a theory which endows all atoms with rare-gas properties.

$B \gtrless B_0$ are formally related to ionic systems for which $n \lessgtr Z$, respectively; but the existence of negative ions is precluded [32] because the energy maximum is greater than zero, as indicated in the preceding discussion. Furthermore, as contrasted with the analysis for metals there is now no criterion for choosing one of the whole family of curves with $B < B_0$, so that the problem for the negative ion is entirely arbitrary. The integral curves for $B > B_0$ are evidently associated with positive ions;

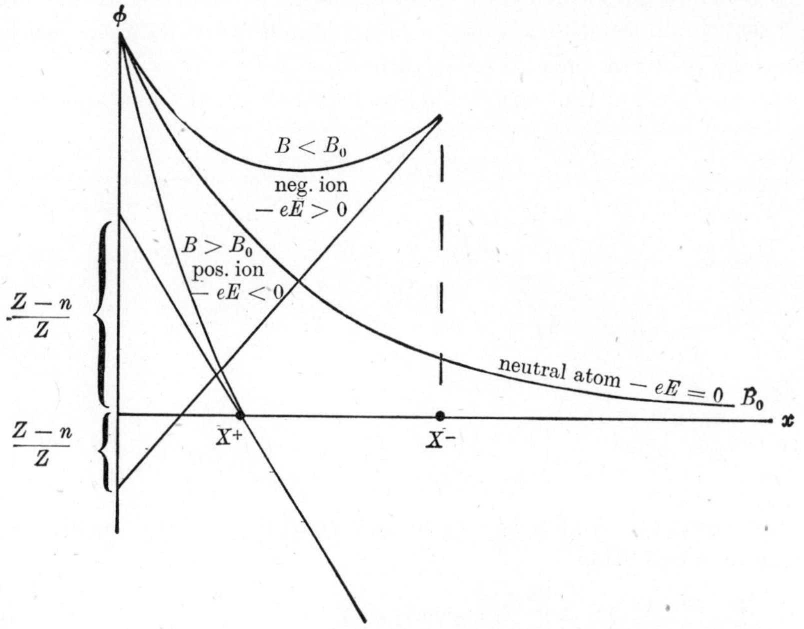

Fig. 9.3

the radius X_+ being defined by the equation $\phi(X_+) = 0$, and the extended tangent to this point representing the Coulomb field beyond. The auxiliary condition is here given by

$$\phi(X_+) = 0 = \frac{\sigma}{Z} - \frac{EX_+}{\gamma}, \quad . \quad . \quad . \quad . \quad . \quad . \quad (9{:}60)$$

or $E = \dfrac{\sigma e}{\mu X_+}$, where $\sigma = Z - n$ [cf. figs. 9.1, 9.3, equation (9:57*b*)].

(*b*) *Fock-Dirac Approximation.*

The failure of normalization in the ordinary sense (infinite domain) for the neutral atom with exchange correction can be interpreted in several different ways, none of which can be said to be wholly satisfactory. One viewpoint is essentially that the normalization difficulty and the concommitant anomalous behaviour of the integral curve simply indicate that the analysis is not applicable to the atomic case without further modification. Since the difficulty occurs at relatively large distances

[32] In view of the neglect of *exchange* it would be surprising were this not the case. Cf. Brillouin, *loc. cit.*

it might appear to be attributable to the poorness of the commutative approximation for the outer regions; but if this were actually the case it would be impossible to explain the absence of this phenomenon in the Thomas-Fermi theory, except as fortuitous. Hence, it would seem at first glance that to accept this viewpoint is to cast considerable doubt on the significance of the whole theory. An alternative approach to the problem is to consider only such density functions as vanish at some definite distance R, which itself is an unknown to be determined.[33] However, as we shall see, this normalization over a finite domain provides a *hammer-and-tongs* escape from one problem, only to create others.

With this assumption the variational equations (9:49–51) now take the form:

$$\delta\int_0^R [\,\lambda_K\rho^{5/3} - \lambda_A\rho^{4/3} - eV'\rho\,]\,dx = 0, \qquad (9{:}61)$$

$$\delta\int_0^R \rho\,dx = 0, \qquad (9{:}62)$$

$$\delta\int_0^R [\,\epsilon(\rho) + eE\rho\,]\,dx = 0, \qquad (9{:}63)$$

or

$$\int_0^R \frac{\partial}{\partial\rho}[\,\epsilon(\rho) + eE\rho\,]\,\delta\rho\,dx + \left\{ [\,4\pi r^2(\epsilon + eE\rho)\,]_{r=R} + \int_0^R \frac{\partial\epsilon}{\partial R}\,dx \right\}\delta R = 0. \qquad (9{:}64)$$

However, we know that (9:52) is a necessary condition in any event, so that we now have the two conditions

$$\tfrac{5}{3}\lambda_K\rho^{2/3} - \tfrac{4}{3}\lambda_A\rho^{1/3} - e(V - E) = 0, \qquad (9{:}65a)$$

$$4\pi R^2[\,\lambda_K\rho^{5/3} - \lambda_A\rho^{4/3} - e(V' - E)\rho\,]_{r=R} - \frac{e}{2}\int_0^R \frac{\partial V_c}{\partial R}\rho\,dx = 0. \qquad (9{:}65b)$$

The quantity $\partial V_c/\partial R$ is readily evaluated since the increment in the potential V_c due to the change in radius is just $\partial V_c = -4\pi R^2 e\rho(R)\partial R/R$, i.e. the added potential due to the incremental spherical shell. Hence,

$$-\frac{e}{2}\int_0^R \frac{\partial V_c}{\partial R}\rho\,dx = \frac{e^2}{2}\cdot\frac{4\pi R^2}{R}\rho(R)\int_0^R \rho\,dx = -[\,2\pi r^2 eV\rho\,]_R, \qquad (9{:}66)$$

which with (9:65b) gives

$$[\,\lambda_K\rho^{5/3} - \lambda_A\rho^{4/3} - e(V - E)\rho\,]_{r=R} = 0. \qquad (9{:}67)$$

Subtracting this equation (after factoring) from (9:65b), we find

$$[\,\tfrac{2}{3}\lambda_K\rho^{2/3} - \tfrac{1}{3}\lambda_A\rho^{1/3}\,]_R = 0, \qquad (9{:}68a)$$

or

$$\rho(R) = \frac{\pi}{3}\left(\frac{5me^2}{h^2}\right)^3, \qquad (9{:}68b)$$

[33] Cf. FRENKEL, J.: *Zeits f. Phys.*, **49**, 30 (1928); JENSEN, H.: *ibid.*, **89**, 713 (1934).

which is a universal boundary value for the density, from which the values of R appropriate to different systems are to be obtained.

Hence with (9:53) we have the equation [cf. (9:42)]

$$\frac{1}{r}\frac{\partial^2}{\partial r^2}[\,r\,(\,V - E\,)\,] = \frac{32\pi^2 e}{3h^3}\left\{\frac{2me^2}{h} + \left[\frac{4m^2e^4}{h^2} + 2me\,(\,V - E\,)\right]^{\frac{1}{2}}\right\}^3, \quad (9{:}69)$$

subject to the boundary conditions

$$\left[\frac{1}{r}\frac{\partial^2}{\partial r^2}(\,rV\,)\right]_R = \frac{4\pi^2 e}{3}\left(\frac{5me^2}{h^2}\right)^3 \quad \text{[cf. (9:68}b\text{)]}, \quad . \quad . \quad (9{:}69a)$$

$$[\,rV\,]_0 = Ze, \quad . \quad . \quad . \quad . \quad . \quad . \quad . \quad . \quad . \quad . \quad . \quad (9{:}69b)$$

$$[\,V\,]_R = (\,Z - n\,)\,e/R, \quad . \quad . \quad . \quad . \quad . \quad . \quad . \quad . \quad (9{:}69c)$$

$$\left[\frac{\partial V}{\partial r}\right]_R = -\,(\,Z - n\,)\,e/R^2; \quad . \quad . \quad . \quad . \quad . \quad . \quad (9{:}69d)$$

or, with the change of variables (9:55),

$$\frac{d^2\phi}{dx^2} = x\{\,\beta + [\,\beta^2 + \phi/x\,]^{\frac{1}{2}}\,\}^3, \qquad \beta = \left(\frac{2me^3}{\gamma h^2}\right)^{\frac{1}{2}}, \quad . \quad . \quad (9{:}70)$$ [34]

$$\left[\frac{1}{x}\frac{d^2\phi}{dx^2}\right]_X = \frac{4\pi^2\mu^2 e}{3\gamma}\left(\frac{5me^2}{h^2}\right), \quad . \quad . \quad . \quad . \quad . \quad . \quad (9{:}70a)$$

$$\phi\,(\,0\,) = 1, \quad . \quad . \quad . \quad . \quad . \quad . \quad . \quad . \quad . \quad . \quad . \quad (9{:}70b)$$

$$\phi\,(\,X\,) = \frac{Z - n}{Z} - \frac{EX}{\gamma}, \quad . \quad . \quad . \quad . \quad . \quad . \quad (9{:}70c)$$

$$\left[x\frac{d\phi}{dx} - \phi\right]_X = -\frac{(\,Z - n\,)}{Z}. \quad . \quad . \quad . \quad . \quad . \quad . \quad (9{:}70d)$$

Here, as in the previous analysis, we must determine the particular curve for given (n, Z) whose continuation beyond the radius X is the tangent with intercept $(Z - n)/Z$; the slope of this line determines E, and hence the maximum energy. From the boundary conditions (9:70) and the equation [cf. (9:53)]

$$\left(\frac{3\rho}{\pi}\right)^{\frac{1}{3}} = \frac{4me^2}{h^3} + \left[\frac{8me}{h^2}\left(\frac{2me^3}{h^2} + V - E\right)\right]^{\frac{1}{2}}, \quad . \quad . \quad . \quad (9{:}71)$$

[34] We see from (9:70) that the line $\phi = -\beta^2 x$ constitutes a lower bound for permissible values of ϕ. In general, the radical (9:70) must be taken with positive sign, but the particular integral curve which is tangent to the critical line must be continued with change of sign before the radical. With this sign, the expansion of the right-hand side of (9:70) for small (ϕ/x) gives $d^2\phi/dx^2 = -\phi^3/8\beta^3x^2$ with neglect of higher-order terms, and it is seen that beyond the point of tangency the integral curve oscillates about the axis of abscissa.

the energy values are readily found to be:

System	$E - \frac{15}{16}\gamma\beta^2$	*Radius*	
neutral	0	X_0	
positive	$(Z - n)\,e/\mu X_+$	X_+	. . (9:72) [35]
negative	$(Z - n)\,e/\mu X_-$	X_-	

Aside from the fact that all atoms as well as ions are assigned finite radii in this approximation, the essentially new feature is the recognition of the existence of stable negative ions. However, detailed investigation has shown that the maximum possible excess charge (determined by the intercept of the horizontal line $\phi = -\sigma/Z$) is only a fraction of one electron, so that the accord with the exchange correction is only qualitative. Although the restriction to solutions in a finite domain appears to be more in keeping with the limitations of the basic theory, still, the corollary condition that all systems have the same boundary density is not particularly plausible from the physical standpoint. By the same token, it is an unsatisfactory feature that the density suffers an abrupt discontinuity at the boundary of the system. As in the Thomas-Fermi case, equation (9:70) with the boundary conditions (9:70*b*, *d*) can be solved without special assumptions when formally applied to the metallic problem, but in view of the difficulties for the elementary systems this interpretation seems rather optimistic.[36]

[35] An alternative boundary density $\rho(R) = \frac{\pi}{3}\left(\frac{4me^2}{h^2}\right)^3$ may be defined by setting the radical in (9:71) equal to zero for the neutral atom. When this value is used it is seen that the line $\phi = -\frac{15}{16}\beta^2 x$ is replaced by $\phi = -\beta^2 x$; the changes in maximum energies and radii are, of course, negligible.

[36] Here again no evidence of cohesion is found, although the total crystal energy is lowered considerably.

CHAPTER X

The Dirac Vector Model *

§ 76. The Dirac Character Operators

The existence of constants of the motion, $\boldsymbol{\alpha}_1$, $\boldsymbol{\alpha}_2$, . . . affords, in general, a significant classification of the energy levels according to simultaneous eigenvalues of the $\boldsymbol{\alpha}$'s, if they commute. In the contrary case, which indicates the presence of degeneracy, we know that the characterization of the various levels can only be achieved by finding a function $\boldsymbol{\beta}$ of the $\boldsymbol{\alpha}$'s which will have a single eigenvalue β' for all those states belonging to the degenerate level H'; or as we may say, $\boldsymbol{\beta}$ must be a function of **H**.[1] In the general case we may find several such $\boldsymbol{\beta}$'s which must then commute among themselves.

Such is the case for the permutation operators (cf. § 50), and it is clear that the functions of the **P**'s of the required type must be defined over classes, so that their number is equal to that of the classes. For the symbolic treatment it is convenient to define these commuting class functions, which are termed the Dirac character operators, as the average of the permutations in the class, e.g. for the jth class

$$\boldsymbol{\chi}_j = \frac{1}{n_{c_j}} \Sigma \, \mathbf{P}_{c_j}.$$

It is clear from our previous discussion of the symmetric group that the set of $\boldsymbol{\chi}$'s, $\boldsymbol{\chi}_1, \boldsymbol{\chi}_2, \ldots \boldsymbol{\chi}_p$ (one for each class) will have p sets of eigenvalues corresponding to the p irreducible representations. Each such set of eigenvalues then corresponds to a set of states which will be exclusive, since the $\boldsymbol{\chi}$'s are perfect constants of the motion, and there cannot be transitions from a state in one set, characterized by $\chi_1', \chi_2', \ldots \chi_p'$, say, to a state in another, characterized by $\chi_1'', \chi_2'', \ldots \chi_p''$.

Dirac has shown how these conclusions may be easily established by algebraic reasoning, but the analysis will be seen to correspond almost exactly to the orthogonality relations satisfied by the primitive group characters (cf. Chap. VI). Thus, Dirac notes that the permissible eigenvalue sets $\chi_1', \chi_2', \ldots \chi_p'$, etc., are limited by the algebraic relations that the $\boldsymbol{\chi}$'s must satisfy, namely, that the product of any two $\boldsymbol{\chi}$'s is expressible as a linear function of the **P**'s (and, moreover, as a linear

* Dirac, P. A. M.: *Proc. Roy. Soc.* A., **123**, 714 (1929); cf. also *Q.M.*

[1] A typical case is the characterization according to eigenvalues of the angular-momentum magnitude variable **K** [cf. § 20 (*a*)], the other constants of the motion (e.g. $\mathbf{L}_z$) merely describing the degeneracy.

function of the $\boldsymbol{\chi}$'s) since $\boldsymbol{\chi}_j\boldsymbol{\chi}_k$, for example, commutes with all the **P**'s. Therefore we may write

$$\boldsymbol{\chi}_j\boldsymbol{\chi}_k = \sum_l^p e_{jk}{}^l \boldsymbol{\chi}_l, \quad . \quad . \quad . \quad . \quad . \quad . \quad . \quad . \quad (10:1)$$

or

$$\chi_j'\chi_k' = \sum_l^p e_{jk}{}^l \chi_l', \quad . \quad . \quad . \quad . \quad . \quad . \quad . \quad . \quad (10:2)$$

since the permissible χ' values must satisfy the same algebraic equations. Equation (10:1) is the operator analogue of equation (6:50*b*), § 49, since Dirac's $\boldsymbol{\chi}_j = \mathbf{C}_j/n_j$; and setting

$$e_{jk}{}^l = \frac{n_l}{n_j n_k} c_{jk}{}^l,$$

equation (10:1) above reads as

$$\mathbf{C}_j\mathbf{C}_k = \sum_l^p c_{jk}{}^l \mathbf{C}_l. \quad . \quad . \quad . \quad . \quad . \quad . \quad . \quad . \quad (10:1')$$

Furthermore, since the $\boldsymbol{\chi}$'s commute with all permutations, it follows that in an irreducible representation of the symmetric group their matrices are scalar,[2] so that the eigenvalues of the $\boldsymbol{\chi}$'s are simply the corresponding primitive group characters divided by the dimension of the representation.[3] If the prime be considered as indicating the *h*th irreducible representation, then from this relation between the Dirac character eigenvalues and the primitive group characters, equation (10:2) reads as

$$n_j n_k \chi_j{}^h \chi_k{}^h = d_h \sum_l^p c_{jk}{}^l n_l \chi_l{}^h. \quad . \quad . \quad . \quad . \quad . \quad . \quad (10:2')\ ^4$$

Two solutions of the above equation (10:2) are of course immediately available, namely, that for which $\chi_j' = 1$ for every j (all classes), and that for which $\chi_j' = \pm 1$ depending on the parity of the permutations in the class. These correspond to the symmetric and antisymmetric set of states respectively. The other sets of states are characterized by intermediate types of symmetry, and the associated solutions of (10:2) may be obtained by algebraic reasoning similar to that considered in the section on groups. In this process we need to know the number of possible solutions of (10:2), i.e. the number of irreducible representations. Here again Dirac has very simply determined, from the observation that the $\boldsymbol{\chi}$'s are linearly independent,[5] that this number is just the number of classes.

The connection between the present considerations on the permutation operators and our study of the representations of the symmetric group is now very simple, viz. if we obtain a matrix representation of the **P**'s consistent with the $\boldsymbol{\chi}$'s having a set of values $\chi_1', \chi_2', \ldots \chi_p'$ (i.e. a specified irreducible representation), then the degree of the matrices representing the **P**'s is also the number of independent states belonging to each energy level, i.e. the degeneracy of the states in the exclusive set characterized by the particular $\{\chi'\}$ values. This is a rather important point

[2] By Schur's lemma. [3] Cf. (10:3) *et seq.* [4] I.e. (6:50*c*), § 49. [5] Cf. DIRAC, *Q.M.*

in the connection between quantum mechanics and group theory, and we may therefore consider it in more detail.

Let us consider *any group* of operators **R**, **S**, **T** (not necessarily the permutations) *which commute with the Hamiltonian.* If we consider a stationary state $| k\kappa \rangle$ which is one of d_k independent states belonging to the kth energy level, then $\mathbf{R} \, | k\kappa \rangle$, for example, will also be an eigenstate belonging to this same level in virtue of the commutation of **R** and **H**. Hence $\mathbf{R} \, | k\kappa \rangle$ is expressible as a linear combination of the states $| k1 \rangle, \ldots | kd_k \rangle$, or

$$\mathbf{R} \, | k\kappa \rangle = \sum_{\mu}^{d_k} | k\mu \rangle \langle k\mu \, | \, \mathbf{R} \, | \, k\kappa \rangle. \quad \ldots \ldots \quad (10{:}3a)$$

Similarly,

$$\mathbf{S} \, | k\mu \rangle = \sum_{\lambda}^{d_k} | k\lambda \rangle \langle k\lambda \, | \, \mathbf{S} \, | \, k\mu \rangle, \quad \ldots \ldots \quad (10{:}3b)$$

and

$$\mathbf{SR} \, | k\kappa \rangle = \sum_{\lambda, \mu} | k\lambda \rangle \langle k\lambda \, | \, \mathbf{S} \, | \, k\mu \rangle \langle k\mu \, | \, \mathbf{R} \, | \, k\kappa \rangle, \quad \ldots \quad (10{:}3c)$$

from which the matrix of **SR**, which is also a group element, is given by

$$\langle k\lambda \, | \, \mathbf{SR} \, | \, k\kappa \rangle = \sum_{\mu} \langle k\lambda \, | \, \mathbf{S} \, | \, k\mu \rangle \langle k\mu \, | \, \mathbf{R} \, | \, k\kappa \rangle. \quad \ldots \quad (10{:}3d)$$

The matrices obtained by the above process constitute a representation of the group of operators under which the Hamiltonian is invariant, i.e. the so-called *group of the Hamiltonian,* and as previously noted the dimension or degree of the representation is the degeneracy of the level. Moreover, the group representations obtained in this way are, in general, irreducible,[6] since in the contrary case one could construct new eigen-$| \, \rangle$'s as linear combinations of the original set which would form subsets —such that the application of any operation of the group would send a member of a subset into a linear combination of members of the same subset only.[7] This is, in general, impossible, since it would imply that the eigenvalues belonging to the various subsets of $| \, \rangle$'s are different, in contradiction to the original assumption of degeneracy. A further fact to be noted is that in quantum theory we are almost exclusively concerned with unitary representations (i.e. by unitary matrices), as follows from the orthogonality conditions on transformation amplitudes, e.g. from (10:3*a*),

$$\begin{aligned} \sum_{\mu, \lambda} \langle k\lambda \, | \, \mathbf{R} \, | \, k\nu \rangle^* \langle k\lambda \, | \, k\mu \rangle \langle k\mu \, | \, \mathbf{R} \, | \, k\kappa \rangle &= \delta(\nu, \kappa) \\ = \sum_{\lambda} \langle k\lambda \, | \, \mathbf{R} \, | \, k\nu \rangle^* \langle k\lambda \, | \, \mathbf{R} \, | \, k\kappa \rangle &= \sum_{\lambda} \langle k\nu \, | \, \mathbf{R}^* \, | \, k\lambda \rangle \langle k\lambda \, | \, \mathbf{R} \, | \, k\kappa \rangle. \quad (10{:}4) \end{aligned}$$

[6] We note that this result is essentially a converse statement of Schur's lemma, since the matrix of **H** for each eigenvalue is a scalar multiple of the unit matrix, of dimension equal to the degeneracy.

[7] I.e. the matrices obtained for a *single* energy level would be of the form

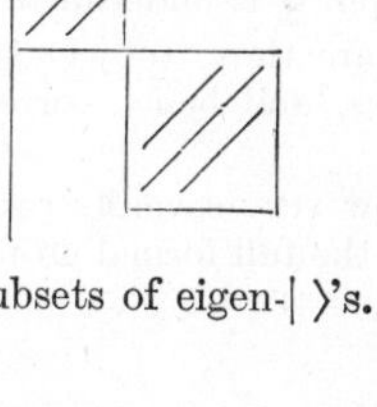

each block corresponding to one of the subsets of eigen-$| \, \rangle$'s.

Thus, from the knowledge of the group of the Hamiltonian and the irreducible representations, we obtain the possible degeneracies, and also information as to the transformation properties of the eigen-$| \rangle$'s (or eigenfunctions) which support the various representations. We shall have occasion to determine explicitly certain of the representations of the symmetric group, and this will also serve to illustrate the working of the process in general.

§ 77. The Dirac Exchange-Spin Identity

With the introduction of the spin variables *and* the requirement of the antisymmetry principle, the question of types of symmetry of states heretofore considered drops out, and we need only deal with the case for which

$$\langle P`\chi \mid \rangle = \langle P`xP^{\sigma}`\sigma_z \mid \rangle = \pm \langle `x`\sigma_z \mid \rangle, \quad . \quad . \quad . \quad . \quad (10{:}5)$$ [8]

according to the parity of the permutation. In the important approximation which omits spin-dependent terms in the Hamiltonian, the spin variables must still be retained in the wave-function in order to satisfy the antisymmetry requirement, and the preceding considerations which led to the notion of exclusive sets of states can, with modification, still be applied. This comes about by considering the permutations not as applied to both space and spin variables, which now leads to trivial results, but as applied to the spatial coordinates alone. Such permutations are still constants of the motion in the spin-free Hamiltonian approximation, and the $\boldsymbol{\chi}$'s, etc., are now expressed in terms of these more limited dynamical variables. There will again be exclusive sets of states even within the restriction to antisymmetry (10:5), but the exclusiveness is now only conditional, since the $\boldsymbol{\chi}$'s are now only conditionally constant. Hence, there will actually be a small probability of transitions between physical states [9] in sets characterized by different $`\chi$ values.[10]

The antisymmetry condition (10:5) may obviously be expressed as

$$\mathbf{P} = \pm \mathbf{P}^{\sigma} \quad . \quad . \quad . \quad . \quad . \quad . \quad . \quad . \quad . \quad (10{:}6)$$

for each of the $n!$ permutations, and this circumstance considerably simplifies the study of the n-electron problem, since it follows from (10:6) that we can obtain essentially all the required information as to character eigenvalues, etc., by studying the simpler variables $\mathbf{P}^{\sigma}$, the variables on which the latter act having each only a domain of the two points ± 1. The application of the group methods is in *some* cases considerably simplified because Dirac has shown that instead of studying the $\mathbf{P}^{\sigma}$'s themselves, we may reason in terms of an algebra whose elements are the

[8] $\mathbf{P}^{\sigma}$ indicates the permutation $\mathbf{P}$ applied to the spin variables, and as usual $`x = x_1', y_1', z_1', \ldots z_n'$; $`\sigma_z = \sigma_{1z}', \ldots \sigma_{nz}'$. When there is no danger of confusion we may drop the subscript z and write this as $`\sigma$ in wave-functions, since the vector spin $\underline{\boldsymbol{\sigma}}$ is underlined.

[9] The physical states here referred to are those subject to (10:5) which correspond to a particular selection from all possible symmetry types, and hence corresponding to the universe of our physical experience.

[10] The possible sets of $`\chi$ values are now very severely restricted by the condition of antisymmetry, and it is this restriction which here makes the full formal group method more powerful and general than actually necessary.

spin vectors. In other words, Dirac has obtained a spin-algebraic synthesis of the symmetric group *within the antisymmetry requirement.* The fundamental relation here is that the simple interchange of spin variables $\mathbf{P}_{ij}{}^{\sigma}$ is given by

$$\mathbf{P}_{ij}{}^{\sigma} = \tfrac{1}{2}\{1 + (\underline{\boldsymbol{\sigma}}_i \cdot \underline{\boldsymbol{\sigma}}_j)\}, \quad \ldots \ldots \quad (10:7)$$

which relation may be readily proved as follows:

We note that the quantity

$$\boldsymbol{\tau}_{ij} = \tfrac{1}{2}\{1 + (\underline{\boldsymbol{\sigma}}_i \cdot \underline{\boldsymbol{\sigma}}_j)\} \quad \ldots \ldots \quad (10:8)$$

satisfies the relation

$$\boldsymbol{\tau}_{ij}{}^2 = \tfrac{1}{4}\{1 + 2(\underline{\boldsymbol{\sigma}}_i \cdot \underline{\boldsymbol{\sigma}}_j) + (\underline{\boldsymbol{\sigma}}_i \cdot \underline{\boldsymbol{\sigma}}_j)^2\} = 1, \quad \ldots \quad (10:9)$$

which follows from the simple form

$$(\underline{\boldsymbol{\sigma}}_i \cdot \underline{\boldsymbol{\sigma}}_j)^2 = 3 - 2(\underline{\boldsymbol{\sigma}}_i \cdot \underline{\boldsymbol{\sigma}}_j), \quad \ldots \ldots \quad (10:10)$$

and

$$\boldsymbol{\tau}_{ij}\underline{\boldsymbol{\sigma}}_i = \underline{\boldsymbol{\sigma}}_j\boldsymbol{\tau}_{ij}, \quad \ldots \ldots \quad (10:11)$$

which is obtained by direct calculation of $\boldsymbol{\tau}_{ij}\boldsymbol{\sigma}_{ix}$, etc. From (10:11) and (10:9) we find

$$\boldsymbol{\tau}_{ij}\underline{\boldsymbol{\sigma}}_j = \underline{\boldsymbol{\sigma}}_i\boldsymbol{\tau}_{ij}, \quad \ldots \ldots \quad (10:11')$$

which is identical with the obvious relation

$$\mathbf{P}_{ij}{}^{\sigma}\underline{\boldsymbol{\sigma}}_j = \underline{\boldsymbol{\sigma}}_i\mathbf{P}_{ij}{}^{\sigma}. \quad \ldots \ldots \quad (10:12)$$

It follows that $\mathbf{P}_{ij}{}^{\sigma} = \pm\boldsymbol{\tau}_{ij}$, since the square of both sides is unity, and the plus sign is seen to be the correct one since the mean of the eigenvalues [11] of $\mathbf{P}_{ij}{}^{\sigma}$ is $\frac{1}{2}$, which is also the mean of the eigenvalues [12] of $\boldsymbol{\tau}_{ij}$.

Schroedinger [13] has given an alternative and rather simpler proof of (10:7) which runs essentially as follows:

The relation (10:7) combined with the relation

$$\mathbf{S}(\mathbf{S}+1) = \tfrac{1}{4}(\underline{\boldsymbol{\sigma}}_i + \underline{\boldsymbol{\sigma}}_j)^2 \quad \ldots \ldots \quad (10:13)$$

for the square of the resultant spin compounded of $\underline{\boldsymbol{\sigma}}_i$, $\underline{\boldsymbol{\sigma}}_j$ gives us

$$\mathbf{S}(\mathbf{S}+1) = 1 + \mathbf{P}_{ij}{}^{\sigma}; \quad \ldots \ldots \quad (10:13')$$

which is to say that the square of the resultant spin is the same as the symmetrizing operation which doubles any symmetric function of the two spin variables, and annihilates an antisymmetric one. That this is so follows from the fact that $\mathbf{S}(\mathbf{S}+1)$ has just the required eigenvalues, viz. the threefold degenerate value 2 and the simple value 0, corresponding respectively to the three independent sym-

[11] The eigenvalues of $\mathbf{P}_{ij}{}^{\sigma}$ are $-1, 1, 1, 1$, corresponding to the one antisymmetric and three symmetric independent functions of the two spin variables σ_{iz}, σ_{jz}.

[12] The eigenvalues of $(\underline{\boldsymbol{\sigma}}_i \cdot \boldsymbol{\sigma}_j)$ are correspondingly $-3, 1, 1, 1$, so that their mean is 0.

[13] *Proc. Roy. Irish Acad.*, **47**, A3, 4 (1941).

metric functions of two spin variables and the one antisymmetric. Schroedinger also develops an interesting generalization of the Dirac identity to arbitrary spin, of which the preceding case for spin $\frac{1}{2}$ is a first special case. We shall not stop to investigate this generalization here, but simply note that it leads to a more concise form of (10:7) and has interesting implications in the theory of nuclear bonding.

Since any permutation $\mathbf{P}^\sigma$ can be expressed as a product of interchanges, it follows that it may be expressed as a function of the $\underline{\boldsymbol{\sigma}}$'s. The same applies to the $\mathbf{P}$'s, since from (10:6–7) we get

$$\mathbf{P}_{ij} = -\tfrac{1}{2}\{1 + (\underline{\boldsymbol{\sigma}}_i \cdot \underline{\boldsymbol{\sigma}}_j)\}. \quad . \quad . \quad . \quad . \quad . \quad (10:14)$$

§ 78. Dirac Character Eigenvalues—Antisymmetric States

The character eigenvalues distinguishing the *almost* exclusive sets of physical states may be readily obtained from their definitions and the above result. Thus, for example, the class of simple interchanges (partition $\{1^{n-2}\,2\}$) contains $n(n-1)/2$ elements, and if we denote the character operator as $\chi[2]$ (omitting the unary cycles as usual), then

$$\chi[2] = \frac{2}{n(n-1)} \sum_{i<j} \mathbf{P}_{ij} = -\frac{2}{2n(n-1)} \sum_{i<j} (1 + \underline{\boldsymbol{\sigma}}_i \cdot \underline{\boldsymbol{\sigma}}_j)$$

$$= -\frac{2}{2n(n-1)} \left\{ \frac{n(n-1)}{2} + \boldsymbol{\mu} \right\}, \quad . \quad . \quad . \quad . \quad . \quad (10:15)$$

with

$$\boldsymbol{\mu} = \sum_{i<j} (\underline{\boldsymbol{\sigma}}_i \cdot \underline{\boldsymbol{\sigma}}_j) = \tfrac{1}{2}[4\mathbf{S}(\mathbf{S}+1) - 3n] \quad . \quad . \quad . \quad (10:16)$$

defining the total spin magnitude variable $\mathbf{S}$.

All of the χ's may be evaluated along similar lines in any given case and will also be functions of $\mathbf{S}$ and n only, although the evaluation becomes more difficult for higher orders. A general expression for χ corresponding to an arbitrary cycle structure $\{1^{\alpha_1}2^{\alpha_2} \ldots n^{\alpha_n}\}$ is difficult to obtain by the present method, but as further illustration we shall obtain the expressions for the character operators $\chi[3]$, $\chi[2^2]$, $\chi[4]$, and $\chi[5]$, which will also be useful for comparison with later group-theoretical results. For this purpose we require the easily verified relations

$$(\underline{\boldsymbol{\sigma}}_i \cdot \underline{\boldsymbol{\sigma}}_j)(\underline{\boldsymbol{\sigma}}_i \cdot \underline{\boldsymbol{\sigma}}_k) = (\underline{\boldsymbol{\sigma}}_j \cdot \underline{\boldsymbol{\sigma}}_k) + i(\underline{\boldsymbol{\sigma}}_i \cdot \underline{\boldsymbol{\sigma}}_j \times \underline{\boldsymbol{\sigma}}_k) \qquad (i \neq j, k). \quad (10:17a)$$ [14]

$$(\underline{\boldsymbol{\sigma}}_i \cdot \underline{\boldsymbol{\sigma}}_j)(\underline{\boldsymbol{\sigma}}_i \cdot \underline{\boldsymbol{\sigma}}_k) + (\underline{\boldsymbol{\sigma}}_j \cdot \underline{\boldsymbol{\sigma}}_i)(\underline{\boldsymbol{\sigma}}_j \cdot \underline{\boldsymbol{\sigma}}_k) = (\underline{\boldsymbol{\sigma}}_j \cdot \underline{\boldsymbol{\sigma}}_k) + (\underline{\boldsymbol{\sigma}}_i \cdot \underline{\boldsymbol{\sigma}}_k). \quad (10:17b)$$

$$(\underline{\boldsymbol{\sigma}}_i \cdot \underline{\boldsymbol{\sigma}}_j)(\underline{\boldsymbol{\sigma}}_i \cdot \underline{\boldsymbol{\sigma}}_k) + (\underline{\boldsymbol{\sigma}}_k \cdot \underline{\boldsymbol{\sigma}}_j)(\underline{\boldsymbol{\sigma}}_k \cdot \underline{\boldsymbol{\sigma}}_i) = (\underline{\boldsymbol{\sigma}}_j \cdot \underline{\boldsymbol{\sigma}}_k) + (\underline{\boldsymbol{\sigma}}_i \cdot \underline{\boldsymbol{\sigma}}_j). \quad (10:17c)$$

Thus the class $\{1^{n-3}\,3\}$ contains $n(n-1)(n-2)/3$ elements, and we find

$$\chi[3] = \frac{3}{4n(n-1)(n-2)} \sum_{i=1}^{n-2} \sum_{j>i} \sum_{\substack{k>i \\ \neq j}} \{(1 + \underline{\boldsymbol{\sigma}}_i \cdot \underline{\boldsymbol{\sigma}}_j)(1 + \underline{\boldsymbol{\sigma}}_j \cdot \underline{\boldsymbol{\sigma}}_k)\}$$

$$= \frac{3}{4n(n-1)(n-2)} \left\{ \frac{n(n-1)(n-2)}{3} + 2(n-2)\boldsymbol{\mu} \right\}, \quad (10:18)$$

[14] Cf. DIRAC, *Q.M.* In general, $(\underline{\boldsymbol{\sigma}} \cdot \underline{\mathbf{B}})(\underline{\boldsymbol{\sigma}} \cdot \underline{\mathbf{C}}) = (\underline{\mathbf{B}} \cdot \underline{\mathbf{C}}) + i(\underline{\boldsymbol{\sigma}} \cdot \underline{\mathbf{B}} \times \underline{\mathbf{C}})$ for vectors that commute with $\underline{\boldsymbol{\sigma}}$. Equation (10:10) is of course a special case for which $j = k$.

where we leave the result in unsimplified form (as in later cases) to show more clearly the origin of the various terms in the final expression. Similarly,

$$\chi[2^2] = \frac{8}{4n(n-1)(n-2)(n-3)} \sum_{i=1}^{n-3} \sum_{j>i} \sum_{\substack{k>i \\ \neq j}} \sum_{\substack{l>k \\ \neq j}} \{(1+\boldsymbol{\sigma}_i\cdot\boldsymbol{\sigma}_j)(1+\boldsymbol{\sigma}_k\cdot\boldsymbol{\sigma}_l)\}$$

$$= \frac{8}{4n(n-1)(n-2)(n-3)} \left\{ \frac{n(n-1)(n-2)(n-3)}{8} + \frac{\mu^2}{2} + \frac{(n-3)(n-4)}{2}\mu - \frac{3n(n-1)}{4} \right\}. \tag{10:19}$$

$$\chi[4] = \frac{-4}{8n(n-1)(n-2)(n-3)} \sum_{i=1}^{n-3} \sum_{j>i} \sum_{\substack{k>i \\ \neq j}} \sum_{\substack{l>i \\ \neq j,k}} \{(1+\boldsymbol{\sigma}_i\cdot\boldsymbol{\sigma}_j)(1+\boldsymbol{\sigma}_i\cdot\boldsymbol{\sigma}_k)(1+\boldsymbol{\sigma}_i\cdot\boldsymbol{\sigma}_l)\}$$

$$= \frac{-4}{8n(n-1)(n-2)(n-3)} \left\{ \frac{n(n-1)(n-2)(n-3)}{4} + \mu^2 + (n-3)(3n-8)\mu - \frac{3n(n-1)}{2} \right\}. \tag{10:20}$$

$$\chi[5] = \frac{5}{16n(n-1)(n-2)(n-3)(n-4)}$$

$$\sum_{i=1}^{n-4} \sum_{j>i} \sum_{\substack{k>i \\ \neq j}} \sum_{\substack{l>i \\ \neq j,k}} \sum_{\substack{m>i \\ \neq j,k,l}} \{(1+\boldsymbol{\sigma}_i\cdot\boldsymbol{\sigma}_j)(1+\boldsymbol{\sigma}_i\cdot\boldsymbol{\sigma}_k)(1+\boldsymbol{\sigma}_i\cdot\boldsymbol{\sigma}_l)(1+\boldsymbol{\sigma}_i\cdot\boldsymbol{\sigma}_m)\}$$

$$= \frac{5}{16n(n-1)(n-2)(n-3)(n-4)}$$

$$\left\{ \frac{n(n-1)(n-2)(n-3)(n-4)}{5} + 4(n-4)\mu^2 + 4(n-3)(n-4)^2\mu - 6n(n-1)(n-4) \right\} \tag{10:21}$$

Here we have obtained the important result that the exclusive sets of states (equivalently different sets of permissible χ values) are defined by the eigenvalues[15] S' of $\mathbf{S}$, which we know to be

$$\frac{n}{2}, \ \frac{n}{2} - 1, \ldots \tfrac{1}{2} \ \text{or} \ 0, \qquad \ldots \ldots \tag{10:22}$$

according as n is odd or even. Moreover, it is clear that the degeneracy of the states characterized by S' is $2S' + 1$, i.e. the corresponding number of associated eigenvalues of the projection of total spin $\frac{1}{2} \sum_i \boldsymbol{\sigma}_{iz}$.

§ 79. Application to n-Particle Systems

We now consider a problem in n similar particles, which need not be electrons, and restrict our study to the product approximation which distributes the particles among n spinless (i.e. without spin function) single-particle orbits, assumed for

[15] I.e. the eigenvalues of $\mathbf{S}$ determine the particular irreducible representation (cf. §§ 86, 87).

the present to be all distinct. Then a typical wave-function of the unperturbed system may be written as

$$\langle \text{`}x \mid \alpha \rangle = \prod_j \langle x_j' \mid \alpha_j \rangle, \quad \ldots\ldots\ldots \quad (10{:}23)$$

with the α's indicating such variables as are required to label the different orbits; and we know that by applying an arbitrary permutation **P** to the α's we obtain another wave-function

$$\langle \text{`}x \mid P\alpha \rangle = \prod_j \langle x_j' \mid P\alpha_j \rangle, \quad \ldots\ldots\ldots \quad (10{:}24)$$

representing another unperturbed state of the same energy, so that the given level is $n!$-fold degenerate—in the absence of other sources of degeneracy.

According to the perturbation theory for degenerate systems, we must consider those elements of the matrix representing the perturbation energy **V** that refer to pairs of these states with the same energy, i.e. those of the type $\langle P_a\alpha \mid \mathbf{V} \mid P_b\alpha \rangle$, which taken together form a matrix of degree $n!$ whose eigenvalues are the first-order corrections in the energy levels. The representatives $\langle P_a\alpha \mid \mathbf{V} \mid P_b\alpha \rangle$ are obtained from the representatives $\langle \text{`}x \mid \mathbf{V} \mid \text{``}x \rangle$ by the usual canonical transformation, viz.

$$\langle P_a\alpha \mid \mathbf{V} \mid P_b\alpha \rangle = \int \ldots \int \langle P_a\alpha \mid \text{`}x \rangle\, d\text{`}x\, \langle \text{`}x \mid \mathbf{V} \mid \text{``}x \rangle\, d\text{``}x\, \langle \text{``}x \mid P_b\alpha \rangle, \quad (10{:}25)$$

assuming the transformation amplitudes $\langle \text{``}x \mid P_b\alpha \rangle$ and $\langle P_a\alpha \mid \text{`}x \rangle$ are suitably normalized. Similarly, for an arbitrary **P**,

$$\begin{aligned}\langle P_aP\alpha \mid \mathbf{V} \mid P_bP\alpha \rangle \\ &= \int \ldots \int \langle P_aP\alpha \mid \text{`}x \rangle\, d\text{`}x\, \langle \text{`}x \mid \mathbf{V} \mid \text{``}x \rangle\, d\text{``}x\, \langle \text{``}x \mid P_bP\alpha \rangle \\ &= \int \ldots \int \langle P_aP\alpha \mid P\text{`}x \rangle\, d\text{`}x\, \langle P\text{`}x \mid \mathbf{V} \mid P\text{``}x \rangle\, d\text{``}x\, \langle P\text{``}x \mid P_bP\alpha \rangle, \quad (10{:}26)\end{aligned}$$

where the latter step follows because the integral is unaffected by permutation of the variables of integration. Furthermore, as previously noted, the correspondence established by (10:23) is such that the permutations of x's and α's are reciprocal in effect,[16] so that

$$\langle \text{`}x \mid \alpha \rangle = \langle P\text{`}x \mid P\alpha \rangle, \quad \ldots\ldots \quad (10{:}27a)$$

$$\langle \text{`}x \mid P_a\alpha \rangle = \langle P\text{`}x \mid P_aP\alpha \rangle. \quad \ldots\ldots \quad (10{:}27b)$$

Comparing (10:25 and 26), we obtain

$$\langle P_a\alpha \mid \mathbf{V} \mid P_b\alpha \rangle = \langle P_aP\alpha \mid \mathbf{V} \mid P_bP\alpha \rangle. \quad \ldots \quad (10{:}28)$$ [17]

[16] It is ordinarily unnecessary to indicate by labels such as $\mathbf{P}^\alpha$, $\mathbf{P}^x$ the permutation **P** applied to the α's or x's unless the meaning is not obvious from the equation or context.

[17] $\langle \text{`}x \mid \mathbf{V} \mid \text{``}x \rangle = \langle P\text{`}x \mid \mathbf{V} \mid P\text{``}x \rangle$, since **V** must be symmetric in all particles.

Taking $\mathbf{P} = \mathbf{P}_b^{-1}$ in (10:28), we obtain

$$\langle P_a\alpha \mid \mathbf{V} \mid P_b\alpha \rangle = \langle P_aP_b^{-1}\alpha \mid \mathbf{V} \mid \alpha \rangle, \quad . \quad . \quad . \quad . \quad (10:29)$$

which may be alternatively written as

$$V_{P_a, P_b} = V_{P_aP_b^{-1}, I} = V_{P_aP_b^{-1}}, \quad . \quad . \quad . \quad . \quad . \quad . \quad (10:30)$$

showing that the general element $\langle P_a\alpha \mid \mathbf{V} \mid P_b\alpha \rangle = V_{P_a, P_b}$ depends only on the ratio $\mathbf{P}_a\mathbf{P}_b^{-1}$, so that of the $(n!)^2$ elements there are at most $n!$ different ones. In other words, the coefficient of any one of these *distinct* elements, e.g. $\langle P\alpha \mid \mathbf{V} \mid \alpha \rangle = V_P$, will itself be a matrix each of whose elements is zero or one, the latter occurring when $\langle P_a\alpha \mid \mathbf{V} \mid P_b\alpha \rangle = \langle P\alpha \mid \mathbf{V} \mid \alpha \rangle$, i.e. $\mathbf{P} = \mathbf{P}_a\mathbf{P}_b^{-1}$.

It is now readily seen that this coefficient matrix is simply the matrix representing the restricted dynamical variable $\mathbf{P}^\alpha$, since the elements of $\mathbf{P}^\alpha$ are given by $\langle P_a\alpha \mid \mathbf{P}^\alpha \mid P_b\alpha \rangle = \langle P_a\alpha \mid PP_b\alpha \rangle$, which are zero unless $\mathbf{P}_a = \mathbf{P}\mathbf{P}_b$, in which case they are unity. Thus, the whole matrix $\langle P_a\alpha \mid \mathbf{V} \mid P_b\alpha \rangle$ is equal to the matrix representing $\sum_P \langle P\alpha \mid \mathbf{V} \mid \alpha \rangle \mathbf{P}^\alpha$, where the summation is over all the permutations, viz.

$$\mathbf{V} = \sum_P \langle P\alpha \mid \mathbf{V} \mid \alpha \rangle \mathbf{P}^\alpha = \sum_P V_P\mathbf{P}. \quad . \quad . \quad . \quad . \quad . \quad (10:31)$$

Equation (10:31) must be understood as indicating the equivalence of the two sides (in particular as regards eigenvalues) relative to the preceding product-type eigenfunctions *only*—and with neglect of those matrix elements of $\mathbf{V}$ which refer to two *different* energy levels of the unperturbed systems—*not* as a general operator equality. To show this equivalence explicitly, we have from (10:31),

$$\begin{aligned}\langle P_a\alpha \mid \mathbf{V} \mid P_b\alpha \rangle &= \sum_P \langle P\alpha \mid \mathbf{V} \mid \alpha \rangle \langle P_a\alpha \mid \mathbf{P}^\alpha \mid P_b\alpha \rangle \\ &= \langle P_aP_b^{-1}\alpha \mid \mathbf{V} \mid \alpha \rangle, \quad . \quad . \quad . \quad . \quad . \quad . \quad (10:32)\end{aligned}$$

since the integral is zero unless $\mathbf{P}_a = \mathbf{P}\mathbf{P}_b$ by virtue of the orthonormality. If the orbits are orthonormal as assumed above, then

$$\begin{aligned}\langle P\alpha \mid \mathbf{V} \mid \alpha \rangle &= \int \cdots \int P\alpha \mid {}'x \rangle \, d'x \, \langle {}'x \mid \mathbf{V} \mid {}''x \rangle \, d''x \, \langle {}''x \mid \alpha \rangle \\ &= \langle \alpha_i\alpha_j \mid \mathbf{V} \mid \alpha_j\alpha_i \rangle = \langle ij \mid \mathbf{V} \mid ij \rangle \qquad (\text{if } \mathbf{P} = \mathbf{I}) \\ &= \langle \alpha_i\alpha_j \mid \mathbf{V} \mid \alpha_j\alpha_i \rangle = \langle ij \mid \mathbf{V} \mid ji \rangle \qquad (\text{if } \mathbf{P} = \mathbf{P}_{ij}); \quad (10:33)\end{aligned}$$

and with $\mathbf{V} = \sum_{i<j} \mathbf{v}_{ij}$, equation (10:31) becomes

$$\mathbf{V} = \sum_{i<j} \langle ij \mid \mathbf{v} \mid ij \rangle + \sum_{i<j} \langle ij \mid \mathbf{v} \mid ji \rangle \mathbf{P}_{ij}^\alpha. \quad . \quad . \quad . \quad (10:34)$$

If we carry through the calculation with the complete Hamiltonian $\mathbf{H} = \sum_i \mathbf{u}_i + \sum_{i<j} \mathbf{v}_{ij}$, we obtain

$$\mathbf{H} = \sum_i \langle i \mid \mathbf{u} \mid i \rangle + \sum_{i<j} \langle ij \mid \mathbf{v} \mid ij \rangle + \sum_{i<j} \langle ij \mid \mathbf{v} \mid ji \rangle \mathbf{P}_{ij}^\alpha. \quad . \quad (10:35)$$

Generally we shall write

$$\mathbf{V} = C + \sum_{i<j} \langle ij \mid \mathbf{v} \mid ji \rangle \mathbf{P}_{ij}, \quad . \quad . \quad . \quad . \quad . \quad . \quad (10:36)$$

where C denotes the Coulomb energy, and the $\mathbf{P}^{\alpha}$'s are replaced by the $\mathbf{P}$'s; since the latter have exactly the same properties, the substitution does not affect the eigenvalues of $\mathbf{V}$.

Restricting our further work to the case of n electrons, our previous result (10:14) combined with (10:36) gives

$$\mathbf{V} = C - \tfrac{1}{2} \sum_{i<j} \langle ij \mid \mathbf{v} \mid ji \rangle (1 + \underline{\sigma}_i \cdot \underline{\sigma}_j), \quad . \quad . \quad . \quad (10:37)$$ [18]

which shows that the exchange interaction arising from the equivalence of the electrons, although purely of electrostatic origin, appears as an apparent strong spin coupling owing to the requirement of the Pauli principle. Van Vleck [19] describes this situation most succinctly by the statement that the spin is only an *indicator*.

It is convenient to denote the exchange and Coulomb integrals as $K(i, j)$ and $J(i, j)$ respectively, in Slater's usual notation, and to introduce the spin vectors $\underline{\mathbf{s}}_i$, $\underline{\mathbf{s}}_j$ themselves (measured in units of $\hbar$) so that (10:37) becomes

$$\mathbf{V} = \sum_{i<j} J(i, j) - \tfrac{1}{2} \sum_{i<j} K(i, j) (1 + 4\underline{\mathbf{s}}_i \cdot \underline{\mathbf{s}}_j). \quad . \quad . \quad (10:37')$$

Hence, we see that except for additive terms there is a formal mathematical similarity between the permutation problem for a configuration of n free orbits, and the problem of n angular-momentum vectors, each of magnitude $\frac{1}{2}$, whose coupling energies depend on their scalar products. Before considering the applications of these results and the generalization required in the case of identical pairs of orbits and non-orthogonality, it is desirable to have available the expression for the mean energy of all those states arising from a given state of the unperturbed system, which have a total spin S, i.e. which belong to one exclusive set of multiplicity $2S + 1$. In other words, we require the mean eigenvalue of $\mathbf{V}$ corresponding to a specified set of χ''s. Considering first (10:31), we note that the mean eigenvalue of $\mathbf{P}^{\alpha}$ equals that of all similar permutations, e.g. $\mathbf{P}_a{}^{\alpha}\mathbf{P}^{\alpha}(\mathbf{P}_a{}^{\alpha})^{-1}$ for arbitrary $\mathbf{P}_a$, or equivalently, that of

$$\frac{1}{n!} \sum_{P_a} \mathbf{P}_a{}^{\alpha}\mathbf{P}^{\alpha}(\mathbf{P}_a{}^{\alpha})^{-1} = \chi [\mathbf{P}^{\alpha}], \quad . \quad . \quad . \quad . \quad . \quad (10:38)$$

which is $\chi'[P^{\alpha}] = \chi'[P]$. Thus, in the general case, the required average eigenvalue of $\mathbf{V}$ is

$$\langle V' \rangle = \sum_{P} \langle P\alpha \mid \mathbf{V} \mid \alpha \rangle \chi' [P], \quad . \quad . \quad . \quad . \quad (10:39a)$$ [20]

[18] It should be remembered that the Coulomb and exchange integrals here are computed over spinless orbital functions.

[19] Cf. VAN VLECK, J. H.: *Rev. Mod. Phys.*, **3**, 167 (1935).

[20] This averaging will be seen to correspond essentially to taking the spur of the energy matrix, which in the group-theoretical sense means that we replace each permutation by its primitive character (cf. § 85).

and for electrons,

$$\begin{aligned}\langle V' \rangle &= \sum_{i<j} \langle ij \mid \mathbf{v}\, ij \rangle + \sum_{i<j} \langle ij \mid \mathbf{v} \mid ji \rangle \chi' [P_{ij}] \\ &= \sum_{i<j} J(i, j) - \tfrac{1}{2}\left[1 + \frac{4S(S+1) - 3n}{n(n-1)}\right] \sum_{i<j} K(i, j), \qquad (10{:}39b)\end{aligned}$$

from (10:37′) and (10:15).

§ 80. Specification of Unperturbed States—Free and Filled Orbits

The preceding theory takes account only of the degeneracy due to exchange, and assumes the orbits to be all distinct; but in the calculation of atomic spectral terms we must also take account of the spatial degeneracy *and* allow for the occurrence of doubly occupied or *filled* (spinless) orbits as well as singly occupied or *free* orbits. The orbits may be labelled by the customary principle, azimuthal and axial (spatial) quantum numbers n, l, m_l; the various l values 0, 1, 2, . . . being conveniently indicated by the usual s, p, d, . . . , and the m_l values . . . -1, 0, 1, 2, . . . , for example, being indicated by Mulliken's Greek notation . . . π_-, σ, π, δ, . . . , etc. The unperturbed states of the preceding theory are in this case the *spatial* configurations such as $d\delta\, d\pi\, d\sigma$, $d\delta\, d\pi^2$, etc.,[21] which occur for three electrons, or $p\pi\, p\sigma$, $p\pi^2$, etc., which occur for two. These pairs of different spatial configurations represent in each case but *one* atomic or electronic configuration, viz. d^3 and p^2 respectively (omitting the principal quantum numbers). The term "configuration" here will, in general, indicate the totality of states arising with a given specification of the orbital quantum numbers of all the orbits, apart from permutation of electrons among orbits.

§ 81. Modification of the Vector Model for Filled Orbits *

As long as we restrict our considerations to the rather artificial assumption of n free orbits only, the total number of eigenvalues of the right side of (10:37) which must be considered is 2^n, a factor 2 occurring for the representation of the spin vector of each electron. However, these 2^n eigenvalues will not, in general, be distinct, since each must occur a number of times sufficient to give the correct multiplicity of the corresponding term. When a pair of filled orbits occurs, say orbits a and b are identical, then any wave-function (of the product type) is unaffected by $\mathbf{P}_{ab}$, so that the only non-vanishing states are those for which $\mathbf{P}_{ab} = 1$, or equivalently, $\mathbf{P}_{ab}{}^s = -1$. This of course means that the spins of the two electrons in the filled orbit must be antiparallel, and the only eigenvalues of the right side of (10:37′) which will be eigenvalues of $\mathbf{V}$ are those consistent with this condition. There is now no distinction between exchange and Coulomb energy for these two identical orbits,[22] so that $K(a, b) = 0$ as well as $K(a, r) = K(b, r)$, for r equal to all values

[21] $d\pi^2 = d\pi\, d\pi$, i.e. a filled orbit (cf. § 81).

* Van Vleck, J. H.: *Phys. Rev.*, **45**, 405 (1934).

[22] There is no question of exchange of orbits when the orbits are the same; the necessary energy is given by the Coulomb term.

except a, b, and the right-hand side of (10:37′) is symmetrical in $\underline{s}_a$, $\underline{s}_b$. Hence, any spin eigenfunction must be either symmetric or antisymmetric in s_{az}, s_{bz}, and the condition $\mathbf{P}_{ab}{}^s = -1$ selects the antisymmetric case going with antiparallel spins. Correspondingly, the number of eigenvalues of (10:37′) is evidently reduced by a factor 4. We shall consider these questions in greater detail when we examine the extension of the Dirac model to include interaction between configurations, and for the present restrict our attention to the secular problem for a single configuration.

From the result above, the following changes must be made in (10:37′), viz. if a, b are identical and hence differ from r, then a typical term in orbits a, b becomes

$$-\tfrac{1}{2}K(r,a)(1+4\underline{s}_r\cdot\underline{s}_a)-\tfrac{1}{2}K(r,b)(1+4\underline{s}_r\cdot\underline{s}_b)$$
$$=-K(r,a)(1+2(\underline{s}_a+\underline{s}_b)\cdot\underline{s}_r)=-K(r,a), \quad (10:40)$$

since $\underline{s}_a+\underline{s}_b=0$. If now we denote the free orbits *only* by Roman indices and the paired orbits by Greek indices, then with the preceding results (10:37′) takes the form

$$\mathbf{V}=\sum_{i<j}[J(i,j)-\tfrac{1}{2}(1+4\underline{s}_i\cdot\underline{s}_j)K(i,j)]+\sum_{j,\mu}[2J(j,\mu)-K(j,\mu)]$$
$$+\sum_{\mu<\nu}[4J(\mu,\nu)-2K(\mu,\nu)]+\sum_{\mu}J(\mu,\mu), \quad . \quad . \quad . \quad . \quad (10:41)$$

where obviously each pair of identical orbits (i.e. each filled orbit) contributes only one term in the Greek summations. Correspondingly, for the case of p paired orbits, (10:39b) for the average eigenvalues becomes

$$\langle V'\rangle=C-\tfrac{1}{2}\left[1+\frac{4S(S+1)-3(n-2p)}{(n-2p)(n-2p-1)}\right]\sum_{i<j}K(i,j), \quad (10:42a)$$

the additive constant C now denoting *all* the Coulomb energy terms, and those exchange terms involving one or more filled orbits, viz.

$$C=\sum_{i<j}J(i,j)+\sum_{j,\mu}[2J(j,\mu)-K(j,\mu)]$$
$$+\sum_{\mu<\nu}[4J(\mu,\nu)-2K(\mu,\nu)]+\sum_{\mu}J(\mu,\mu). \quad (10:42b)$$

It is of interest to note that the result (10:42a) follows quite simply from the general expression $\mathbf{V}=\sum_{i<j}J(i,j)+\sum_{i<j}K(i,j)\mathbf{P}_{ij}$ (i,j here include all orbits) with the observation that for paired orbits

$$\mathbf{P}_{ab}=1, \quad . \quad . \quad . \quad . \quad . \quad . \quad . \quad . \quad . \quad . \quad (10:43a)$$

$$\mathbf{P}_{ai}+\mathbf{P}_{bi}=-1; \quad . \quad . \quad . \quad . \quad . \quad . \quad . \quad . \quad . \quad (10:43b)$$

whence

$$\mathbf{P}_{bi}=\mathbf{P}_{ab}\mathbf{P}_{ai}\mathbf{P}_{ab}=\mathbf{P}_{ai}, \quad . \quad . \quad . \quad . \quad . \quad (10:44)$$

or

$$\mathbf{P}_{ai}=-\tfrac{1}{2}.$$

Thus, the interchanges of identical orbits drop out of the Hamiltonian and the interchanges involving at least one filled orbit may be regarded as the numerical factor $-\frac{1}{2}$. If the first $2p$ orbits (of n) be considered as paired, then in the averaging process, the character $\chi[2]$ is that appropriate to $(n - 2p)$ free orbits, which is just our result (10:42a). In other words, the sufficient condition for

$$\Sigma \mathbf{P}_{ij} = 2 \sum_{j,\,\mu} \mathbf{P}_{j\mu} + 4 \sum_{\mu<\nu} \mathbf{P}_{\mu\nu} + \sum_{i>j>n-2p}{}' \mathbf{P}_{ij}$$

to have a definite value is that the sum of non-commuting quantities $\Sigma' \mathbf{P}_{ij}$ has a definite value which clearly must be equal to the value for the permutations of the $(n - 2p)$ free orbits. The same can be said for any class of permutations in view of the composition in terms of interchanges, and we now see how the occurrence of filled orbits restricts the character eigenvalues, the resultant spin $\mathbf{S}$ being determined by composition of the unpaired spins.

§ 82. The Branching Rule

A single spatial configuration will, in general, have several possible values for its resultant spin $\mathbf{S}$, and a given value of $\mathbf{S}$ for the configuration will usually yield more than one energy level. In order to apply the preceding theory we need to know the number of states of a given spin S (i.e. of multiplicity $2S + 1$) arising from a configuration of n *free* orbits. In addition, any number of filled orbits may occur, but these obviously do not affect the multiplicity, since the resultant spin of electrons in identical orbits can only be zero in virtue of the exclusion principle. This number,

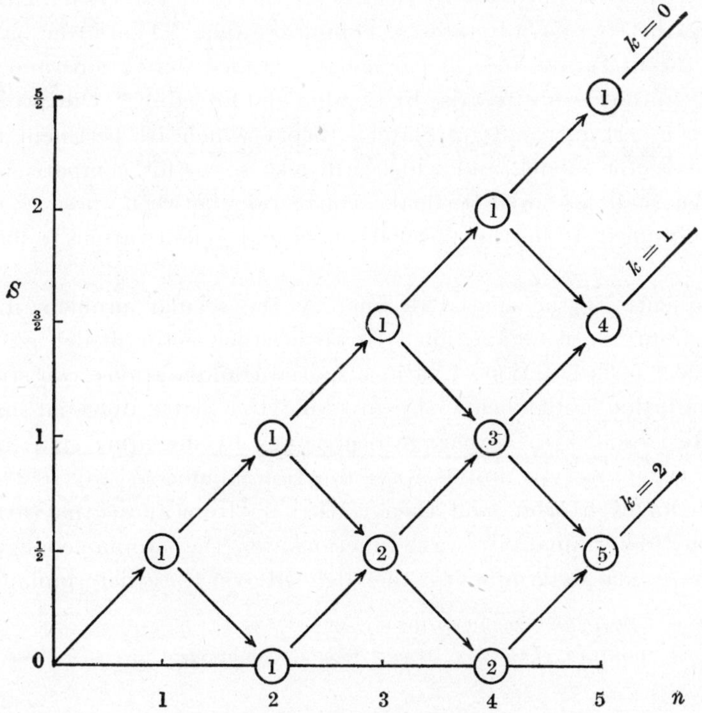

Fig. 10.1.—Branching diagram

which is the frequency of occurrence of any S, is readily obtained by compounding the spin values in the usual way so that, for example, with two electrons we get a resultant (magnitude eigenvalue) $S = 1, 0$ from $s_1 = s_2 = \frac{1}{2}$; adding a third spin gives $\frac{3}{2}, \frac{1}{2}, \frac{1}{2}$, etc., from which we obtain the so-called branching diagram (fig. 10.1).

The analytical expression for this number $N(S)$ may readily be obtained, since the number of states having a given S_z' $(=M_s)$ is

$$\nu(M_s) = \frac{n!}{(\frac{1}{2}n + M_s)!\,(\frac{1}{2}n - M_s)!}, \quad . \quad . \quad . \quad . \quad (10{:}45a)$$

since M_s corresponds to the division of the electrons into two groups, one of $\frac{1}{2}n + M_s$ electrons having $m_s = \frac{1}{2}$, and one of $\frac{1}{2}n - M_s$ electrons having $m_s = -\frac{1}{2}$. Then, since $\nu(M_s)$ contains all states with $S \geqslant |M_s|$, $N(S)$ is given by

$$N(S) = \nu(S) - \nu(S+1)$$
$$= \binom{n}{k} - \binom{n}{k-1} \quad . \quad . \quad . \quad . \quad . \quad . \quad (10{:}45b)$$

with $k = \frac{1}{2}n - S$. If there are just n electrons and p pairs of identical orbits included among them, then clearly the expression for N must be modified by replacing n by $n - 2p$.

§ 83. Spatial Degeneracy—Calculation of Spectral Term Values

Before considering the detailed application of the Dirac-Van Vleck vector model, we shall briefly review the salient features of the closely related Slater method [23] of calculating the energies of states of complex atoms. The latter has been often discussed in the literature and, in particular, detailed derivations and applications may be found in the elegant treatise by Condon and Shortley.[24] Our primary purpose here is to recall certain results of Slater's theory which are pertinent to the application of the vector model, and which will also serve for comparison of the two methods. We shall also wish to make connection between these results and the conclusions obtained from the method of second quantization to be considered later.

In consequence of the spatial degeneracy the secular problem in general involves more than one configuration. However, the vector model as developed so far, with neglect of interaction of various spatial configurations, can still be applied (with the limitation noted below) by invoking the Slater diagonal-sum method.[25] In brief, Slater resolves the exchange degeneracy by including spin from the outset, so that the prototype initial wave-function analogous to (10:23) includes a spin function for each orbit, and then constructs from these the various possible antisymmetric (determinantal) wave-functions for the atomic configuration [26] in question. The secular determinant is then defined over these determinantal functions

[23] SLATER, J. C.: *Phys. Rev.*, **34**, 1293 (1929).

[24] CONDON and SHORTLEY, *Theory of Atomic Spectra*, Cambridge University Press (referred to as *T.A.S.*).

[25] SLATER, *loc. cit.*

[26] E.g. one for the closed shell $2p^6$, twelve for $1s2p$, and fifteen for $2p^2$, etc.

in the usual way. In other words, Slater starts out with what may be briefly termed an $\mathbf{l}_{iz}$, $\mathbf{s}_{iz}$-diagonal, or m_{l_i}, m_{s_i}, representation, in which the electrons are individually space-quantized so that $M_L = \Sigma m_{l_i}$, $M_S = \Sigma m_{s_i}$, where M_L, M_S, as usual, denote the eigenvalues (in units of $\hbar$) of the projections $\mathbf{L}_z$, $\mathbf{S}_z$ of total orbital and spin angular momentum; the eigenvalues of total orbital and spin magnitude being denoted by L, S. Slater further notes that the spin-free Hamiltonian[27] is diagonal in $\underline{\mathbf{L}}^2$, $\underline{\mathbf{S}}^2$, $\mathbf{L}_z$, $\mathbf{S}_z$, and, moreover, that the energy values for given L, S are independent[28] of M_L, M_S. Ordinarily, two or more spatial configurations lead to the same M_L, M_S values, but, as Slater shows, consideration of interconfigurational interactions is unnecessary as far as the sum of the roots of the secular equation is concerned. By the Spur Theorem (§ 27) this quantity is invariant under any transformation,

† TABLE 10.1

p^2		M_S: 1	0	−1
M_L	2		(1^+1^-)	
	1	(1^+0^+)	(1^+0^-) (1^-0^+)	(1^-0^-)
	0	(1^+-1^+)	(1^+-1^-) (0^+0^-) (1^--1^+)	(1^--1^-)
	−1	(0^+-1^+)	(0^+-1^-) (0^--1^+)	(0^--1^-)
	−2		(-1^+-1^-)	

and by definition is independent of the interactions between various spatial configurations which are represented by *off-diagonal* matrix elements. A certain number of individual roots in the sum for given M_L, M_S are known if we have already solved the secular equations for larger M_L, M_S values, since (cf. above) a state of given L, S appears once in the secular equation for each pair of M_L, M_S values consistent with $M_L = L, L-1, \ldots -L$; $M_S = S, S-1, \ldots -S$.

We shall briefly sketch the workings of this method for the atomic configurations p^2, pp, which are among the simplest illustrations of the case of equivalent and non-equivalent electrons respectively. Taking first the case p^2, we compound the individual m_l, m_s values to obtain a table of resultant values (Table 10.1). The entries

[27] Since $\mathbf{H}$ commutes with $\underline{\mathbf{L}}^2$, $\underline{\mathbf{S}}^2$, $\mathbf{L}_z$, $\mathbf{S}_z$ (cf. Chap. III).

[28] This is proved as follows: with the stated condition we have, for example, $[\mathbf{H}, \mathbf{L}^\pm]_- = 0$, and

$$\mathbf{L}^\pm\mathbf{H}\,|\,\gamma LSM_LM_S\rangle = \hbar[(L\mp M_L)(L\pm M_L+1)]^{\frac12}\sum_{\gamma'}|\,\gamma' LSM_L\pm 1M_S\rangle\langle\gamma' LSM_LM_S\,|\,\mathbf{H}\,|\,\gamma LSM_LM_S\rangle,$$

$$\mathbf{H}\mathbf{L}^\pm\,|\,\gamma LSM_LM_S\rangle = \hbar[(L\mp M_L)(L\pm M_L+1)]^{\frac12}\sum_{\gamma'}|\,\gamma' LSM_L\pm 1M_S\rangle\langle\gamma' LSM_L\pm 1M_S\,|\,\mathbf{H}\,|\,\gamma LSM_L\pm 1M_S\rangle,$$

whence $$\langle\gamma' LSM_L\pm 1M_S\,|\,\mathbf{H}\,|\,\gamma LSM_L\pm 1M_S\rangle = \langle\gamma' LSM_LM_S\,|\,\mathbf{H}\,|\,\gamma LSM_LM_S\rangle$$

and similarly for $\mathbf{S}^\pm$.

† In this table the common l value 1 is omitted and only the m_l values are entered together with the superscripts $\pm$ denoting the associated spin values which are now taken into account *ab initio*.

of Table 10.1 denote the arguments (other than the common n and l) of the wave-functions on the principal diagonal of the corresponding determinantal (total system) wave-function, i.e. with the usual notation $\langle \chi \mid nlm_l m_s \rangle$ for a one-electron co-ordinate-spin function, the entry (1^+0^-) corresponds to the determinantal function

$$\frac{1}{\sqrt{2}}\begin{vmatrix} \langle \chi_1 \mid n11\tfrac{1}{2} \rangle & \langle \chi_2 \mid n11\tfrac{1}{2} \rangle \\ \langle \chi_1 \mid n10{-}\tfrac{1}{2} \rangle & \langle \chi_2 \mid n10{-}\tfrac{1}{2} \rangle \end{vmatrix}. \quad . \quad . \quad . \quad . \qquad (10{:}46)^{29}$$

Thus, we have the 15 states which by well-known principles constitute the terms ^3P, ^1D, ^1S, and over which the secular determinant is computed. It is a trivial consequence of the commutation of $\mathbf{H}$ with $\mathbf{L}_z$ and $\mathbf{S}_z$ that the perturbation energy has no non-vanishing elements between states of different M_L, M_S, so that starting with the state of highest M_L, M_S, and proceeding across the table, we find that the secular determinant assumes the simple form of fig. 10.2, i.e. it reduces to 1 cubic, 2 quadratic, and 8 linear factors.

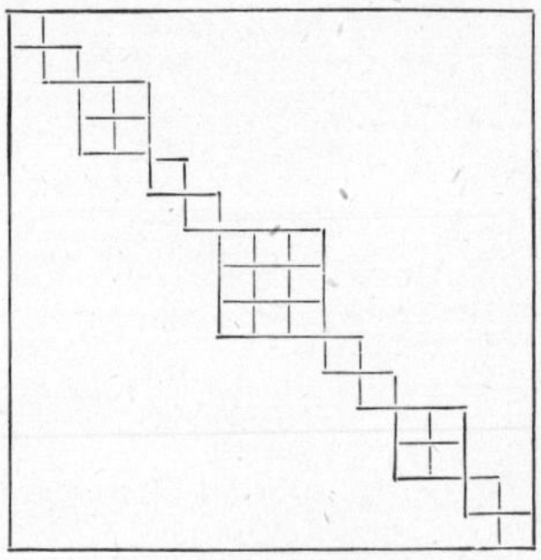

Fig. 10.2

The corresponding table for pp is Table 10.2, which is now seen to support 36 states, since the exclusion principle is satisfied *a priori* (non-equivalence), and hence

† TABLE 10.2

	pp	M_S = 1	M_S = 0
M_L	2	(1^+1^+)	(1^+1^-) (1^-1^+)
	1	(1^+0^+) (0^+1^+)	(1^+0^-) (0^+1^-) (1^-0^+) (0^-1^+)
	0	$(1^+{-}1^+)$ (0^+0^+) (-1^+1^+)	$(1^+{-}1^-)$ (0^+0^-) (-1^+1^-) $(1^-{-}1^+)$ (0^-0^+) (-1^-1^+)

[29] These determinantal functions will clearly be eigenstates of $\mathbf{L}_z$ and $\mathbf{S}_z$, but in general not of $\mathbf{L}^2$ and $\mathbf{S}^2$; however, they can be made so by the usual process of taking linear combinations of the determinantal functions, the correct combination being found by solving a secular equation. See, for example, EYRING, WALTER, KIMBALL, *Quantum Chemistry* (J. Wiley & Sons).

† We need only list half of the table since the symmetrically located parts differ by mere reversal of sign of m_l and/or m_s $(= \pm)$ values.

does not limit the permissible combinations of m_l, m_s values as before. As is well known, these states compose the terms $^3(D, P, S)$; $^1(D, P, S)$. The actual computation of the matrix elements over these determinantal functions is similar to our previous work (cf. Chap. VIII), from which it follows that the prototype matrix elements of $\mathbf{H} = \sum_k \mathbf{u}_k + \sum_{k<l} \mathbf{v}_{kl}$ over two such determinantal functions, say

$$\langle {}'\chi \mid {}'E \rangle = \frac{1}{\sqrt{n!}} \sum_P \delta_P \prod_j \langle P\chi_j' \mid E_j' \rangle, \text{ and } \langle {}'\chi \mid {}''E \rangle,$$

are

$$\langle E_1' \ldots E_n' \mid \mathbf{H} \mid E_1' \ldots E_n' \rangle = \sum_k \langle E_k' \mid \mathbf{u} \mid E_k' \rangle + \sum_{k<l} \langle E_k'E_l' \mid \mathbf{v} \mid E_k'E_l' \rangle - \sum_{\substack{k<l \\ \parallel \text{spin}}} \langle E_k'E_l' \mid \mathbf{v} \mid E_l'E_k' \rangle, \quad \ldots \quad (10{:}47a)$$

$$\langle \ldots E_k' \ldots \mid \mathbf{H} \mid \ldots E_k'' \ldots \rangle = \langle E_k' \mid \mathbf{u} \mid E_k'' \rangle + \sum_{l \neq k} \langle E_k'E_l' \mid \mathbf{v} \mid E_k''E_l' \rangle - \sum_{l \neq k} \langle E_k'E_l' \mid \mathbf{v} \mid E_l'E_k'' \rangle, \quad \ldots \quad (10{:}47b)$$

$$\langle \ldots E_k' \ldots E_l' \ldots \mid \mathbf{H} \mid \ldots E_k'' \ldots E_l'' \ldots \rangle = \langle E_k'E_l' \mid \mathbf{v} \mid E_k''E_l'' \rangle - \langle E_k'E_l' \mid \mathbf{v} \mid E_l''E_k'' \rangle, \quad (10{:}47c)$$

the three cases depending on the relation between the eigenvalue sets $\{ {}'E \}$ and $\{ {}''E \}$. The details may be found in *T.A.S.*; the final results are obtained in terms of the well-known undetermined integrals or Slater-Condon-Shortley (S.C.S.) F's and G's. Here we need only note that Slater proves that the exchange integrals in the diagonal sum are given the coefficient -1 if the electron spins are parallel, and 0 in the contrary case. We are already familiar with this effect, and we note here only that the choice of sign also follows directly from the vector model, i.e. by evaluating the diagonal elements of the factor $-\frac{1}{2}[1 + 4\underline{\mathbf{s}}_i \cdot \underline{\mathbf{s}}_j]$ in the m_l, m_s representation, which is seen to give $-\frac{1}{2}[1 + 4m_{s_i}m_{s_j}] = -1$ or 0 for parallel or antiparallel spins respectively.

The Spur Theorem is useful because all the levels corresponding to a given term have the same energy in the first approximation, so that we can write a set of linear equations, one for each M_L, M_S cell in Table 10.2, and equate the sum of the energies of the terms having states in that cell to the sum of the diagonal elements of the perturbation energy computed over the determinantal functions associated with the particular M_L, M_S pair. If for the moment we denote by $\{ a^+, b^+ \}$ the diagonal element of the perturbation computed over the determinantal function (a^+, b^+), and the term values by the term symbol, then for example we see from Table 10.1 that only the term ^1D can contribute to the cell $M_L = 2$, $M_S = 0$; only ^3P can contribute to $M_L = 1$, $M_S = 1$; while ^3P, ^1D, and ^1S all contribute to the cell $M_L = 0$, $M_S = 0$, etc. Thus we find

$$\left.\begin{aligned} ({}^1D) &= \{ 1^+, 1^- \}, \\ ({}^3P) &= \{ 1^+, 0^+ \}, \\ ({}^3P) + ({}^1D) + ({}^1S) &= \{ 1^+, -1^- \} + \{ 1^-, -1^+ \} + \{ 0^+, 0^- \}, \end{aligned}\right\} \quad (10{:}48)$$

which from (10:47) may be immediately expressed in terms of the Coulomb and exchange integrals as

$$\left.\begin{aligned}({}^1D) &= J(p\pi, p\pi),\\ ({}^3P) &= J(p\pi, p\sigma) - K(p\pi, p\sigma),\\ ({}^1S) &= 2J(p\pi, p\pi) + J(p\sigma, p\sigma) - J(p\pi, p\pi)\\ &\qquad - [J(p\pi, p\sigma) - K(p\pi, p\sigma)].\end{aligned}\right\} \quad (10:48')$$ [30]

Finally, from the table of Appendix II, these are expressed in terms of S.C.S. F's and G's as

$$\left.\begin{aligned}({}^1D) &= F_0 + F_2,\\ ({}^3P) &= F_0 - 5F_2,\\ ({}^1S) &= F_0 + 10F_2.\end{aligned}\right\} \quad . \; . \; . \; . \; . \; . \; . \quad (10:48'')$$ [31]

Similarly, from Table 10.2 for pp we find

$$\left.\begin{aligned}({}^3D) &= \{1^+, 1^+\} = J(p\pi, p\pi) - K(p\pi, p\pi),\\ ({}^3D)+({}^3P) &= \{1^+, 0^+\} + \{0^+, 1^+\} = 2[J(p\pi, p\sigma) - K(p\pi, p\sigma)],\\ ({}^3D)+({}^3P)+({}^3S) &= \{1^+, -1^+\} + \{-1^+, 1^+\} + \{0^+, 0^+\}\\ &= 2[J(p\pi, p\pi_-) - K(p\pi, p\pi_-)] + J(p\sigma, p\sigma) - K(p\sigma, p\sigma),\\ ({}^3D)+({}^1D) &= \{1^+, 1^-\} + \{1^-, 1^+\} = 2J(p\pi, p\pi),\end{aligned}\right\} \quad (10:49)$$

etc., and from the table of Appendix II these may be expressed as

$$\left.\begin{aligned}({}^3D) &= F_0 + F_2 - G_0 - G_2,\\ ({}^3P) &= F_0 - 5F_2 + G_0 - 5G_2,\\ ({}^3S) &= F_0 + 10F_2 - G_0 - 10G_2,\\ ({}^1D) &= F_0 + F_2 + G_0 + G_2,\end{aligned}\right\} \quad . \; . \; . \quad (10:49')$$

etc.

If an atomic configuration leads to more than one term of the same type, only the sum of their energies can be obtained from the above procedure, and to resolve them we must solve the secular equation including non-diagonal terms in either the Slater [32] or Dirac method. We shall consider the latter in some detail, but we must first examine the application of the Dirac model in the approximation corresponding to the preceding simple Slater method. The procedure here is very similar to the above, with only the difference that with the help of (10:39*b*–42*a*) it is now possible to obtain the term values for any given multiplicity without first determining those of the higher multiplicities, i.e. the secular determinant factors

[30] We omit here, as elsewhere, the constant part arising from the first term on the right of (10:47*a*) which is common to all terms above, and only affects the energy scale.

[31] The F's and G's are related to the so-called radial integrals, i.e. the integrals of the perturbation over the radial part of the wave-functions, which of course is undefined in the absence of an exact specification of the wave-functions, as by the Hartree or Fock-Dirac method, for example.

[32] Cf. *T.A.S.*, §§ 5^8–7^8.

according to characteristic values of **S** in the vector model.[33] However, this is only a nominal advantage since usually all term values are desired. The two methods are of course equivalent, so that it is largely a matter of taste and training in choosing one or the other, although the vector model is rather more elegant and affords a simple kinematical visualization of problems. We shall illustrate the method of the vector model by considering the evaluation of term values for the electronic configurations:

$$ps\,(\,{}^3P,\,{}^1P\,);\quad p^2\,(\,{}^3P\,{}^1D\,{}^1S\,);\quad pd\,(\,{}^3F\,{}^3D\,{}^3P\,{}^1F\,{}^1D\,{}^1P\,);\quad d^2\,(\,{}^3F\,{}^3P\,{}^1G\,{}^1D\,{}^1S\,);$$
$$p^3\,(\,{}^4S\,{}^2D\,{}^2P\,);\quad d^3\,(\,{}^4F\,{}^4P\,{}^2H\,{}^2G\,{}^2F\,{}^2D_+\,{}^2D_-\,{}^2P\,);$$

the configuration p^2 being included for comparison with the preceding Slater method, and d^3 because it leads to the analysis of interconfigurational elements.

For ps we have two free orbits, and $M_L = 1$ arises from the spatial configuration $p\pi s\sigma$. Noting the important fact that for $n = 2$ the factor $-\frac{1}{2}(1 + 4\underline{\mathbf{s}}_i \cdot \underline{\mathbf{s}}_j)$ equals $+1, -1$ for $S = 0,\ 1$ (singlet, triplet) respectively,[34] we find from (10:41) and Appendix II,

$$ps\,(\,{}^3P,\,{}^1P\,). \qquad (10{:}50)$$

$$(\,{}^1P\,) = J\,(\,p\pi,\,s\sigma\,) + K\,(\,p\pi,\,s\sigma\,) = F_0 + G_1, \qquad (10{:}50a)$$

$$(\,{}^3P\,) = J\,(\,p\pi,\,s\sigma\,) - K\,(\,p\pi,\,s\sigma\,) = F_0 - G_1. \qquad (10{:}50b)$$ [35]

$$pd\,(\,{}^{1,3}F\,{}^{1,3}D\,{}^{1,3}P\,). \qquad (10{:}51)$$

The only configuration compatible with $M_L = 3$ is $p\pi d\delta$, whence from (10:41)[36] and Appendix II,

$$(\,{}^3F\,) = J\,(\,np\pi,\,n'd\delta\,) - K\,(\,np\pi,\,n'd\delta\,) = F_0 + 2F_2 - (\,6G_1 + 3G^3\,), \qquad (10{:}51a)$$ [37]

$$(\,{}^1F\,) = J\,(\,p\pi,\,d\delta\,) + K\,(\,p\pi,\,d\delta\,) = F_0 + 2F_2 + (\,6G_1 + 3G_3\,). \qquad (10{:}51b)$$

For $M_L = 2$ we have $p\pi\ d\pi$ and $p\sigma\ d\delta$, so that from (10:41) and the invariance of the spur,

$$(\,{}^3F\,) + (\,{}^3D\,) = J\,(\,p\pi,\,d\pi\,) - K\,(\,p\pi,\,d\pi\,) + J\,(\,p\sigma,\,d\delta\,) - K\,(\,p\sigma,\,d\delta\,)$$
$$= 2F_0 - 5F_2 - 3G_1 - 24G_3;$$

and from (10:51a),

$$(\,{}^3D\,) = F_0 - 7F_2 + (\,3G_1 - 21G_3\,). \qquad (10{:}51c)$$

[33] This results because in the Dirac model we work essentially with an m_l, S rather than m_l, m_s representation.

[34] For $n = 2$, the same holds for $-\frac{1}{2}\left[1 + \dfrac{4S^2 + 4S - 3n}{n(n-1)}\right]$.

[35] It should be noted that this sign difference in the G's is characteristic of the case $n = 2$, arising as it does from the above-mentioned sign factor (indicator).

[36] Alternatively from (10:42a) with $S = 1,\ 0$.

[37] We include the principal quantum numbers in this first illustration to draw attention to the *non-equivalent arguments* of the F's and G's.

Similarly,

$$({}^1F) + ({}^1D) = J(p\pi, d\pi) + K(p\pi, d\pi) + J(p\sigma, d\delta) + K(p\sigma, d\delta),$$

whence

$$({}^1D) = F_0 - 7F_2 - (3G_1 - 21G_3), \qquad (10{:}51d)$$

or more simply by reversal of exchange sign in (10:51*c*). Finally, for $M_L = 1$ we have $p\sigma\, d\pi$, $p\pi\, d\sigma$, and $p\pi_-\, d\delta$, so that from (10:41),

$$({}^3F) + ({}^3D) + ({}^3P) = J(p\sigma, d\pi) - K(p\sigma, d\pi) + \ldots - K(p\pi_-, d\delta)$$
$$= 3F_0 + 2F_2 - 4G_1 - 87G^3,$$

therefore

$$({}^3P) = F_0 + 7F_2 - (G_1 + 63G_3), \qquad (10{:}51e)$$

and obviously

$$({}^1P) = F_0 + 7F_2 + (G_1 + 63G_3) \qquad (10{:}51f)$$

by mere reversal of the sign, as previously remarked.

$$p^2\,({}^3P\,{}^1D\,{}^1S). \qquad (10{:}52)$$

Here for $M_L = 2$ we have $p\pi^2$ which admits a singlet, viz.

$$({}^1D) = J(p\pi, p\pi) = F_0 + F_2. \qquad (10{:}52a)$$ [38]

For $M_L = 0$, singlets arise from $p\pi\, p\pi_-$ and $p\sigma^2$, whence

$$({}^1D) + ({}^1S) = J(p\sigma, p\sigma) + J(p\pi, p\pi_-) + K(p\pi, p\pi_-)$$
$$= 2F_0 + 11F_2,$$

and

$$({}^1S) = F_0 + 10F_2. \qquad (10{:}52b)$$

Taking $M_L = 1$, we have a triplet (and singlet) from $p\pi\, p\sigma$, viz.

$$({}^3P) = J(p\pi, p\sigma) - K(p\pi, p\sigma) = F_0 - 5F_2. \qquad (10{:}52c)$$ [39]

$$d^2\,({}^3F\,{}^3P\,{}^1G\,{}^1D\,{}^1S). \qquad (10{:}53)$$

The procedure here is similar to the above, and we find

$M_L = 3$: $d\delta\, d\pi$ (singlet and triplet).

$$({}^3F) = J(d\delta, d\pi) - K(d\delta, d\pi) = F_0 - 8F_2 - 9F_4. \qquad (10{:}53a)$$

$M_L = 1$: $d\delta\, d\pi_-$, $d\pi\, d\sigma$.

$$({}^3F) + ({}^3P) = J(d\delta, d\pi_-) - K(d\delta, d\pi_-) + J(d\pi, d\sigma) - K(d\pi, d\sigma)$$
$$= 2F_0 - F_2 - 93F_4,$$

therefore

$$({}^3P) = F_0 + 7F_2 - 84F_4. \qquad (10{:}53b)$$

[38] This arises from the one filled orbit $[J(\mu, \mu)]$ term of (10:41).

[39] This, of course. also obtains from the terms involving free orbits in (10:42*a*)—as do the previous results.

Proceeding to the singlets we have

$M_L = 4$: $d\delta^2$ (filled orbit, hence singlet).

$$({}^1G) = J(d\delta, d\delta) = F_0 + 4F_2 + F_4. \quad . \quad . \quad . \quad (10{:}53c)$$

$M_L = 2$: $d\delta\, d\sigma$, $d\pi^2$.

$$({}^1G) + ({}^1D) = J(d\pi, d\pi) + J(d\delta, d\sigma) + K(d\delta, d\sigma)$$
$$= 2F_0 + F_2 + 37F_4,$$

therefore

$$({}^1D) = F_0 - 3F_2 + 36F_4. \quad . \quad . \quad . \quad . \quad . \quad . \quad . \quad . \quad (10{:}53d)$$

$M_L = 0$: $d\delta\, d\delta_-$, $d\pi\, d\pi_-$, $d\sigma^2$.

$$({}^1G) + ({}^1D) + ({}^1S) = J(d\sigma, d\sigma) + J(d\delta, d\delta_-)$$
$$+ K(d\delta, d\delta_-) + J(d\pi, d\pi_-) + K(d\pi, d\pi_-)$$
$$= 3F_0 + 15F_2 + 163F_4,$$

therefore

$$({}^1S) = F_0 + 14F_2 + 126F_4. \quad . \quad . \quad . \quad . \quad . \quad . \quad . \quad . \quad (10{:}53e)$$

$$p^3\,({}^4S\,{}^2D\,{}^2P). \quad . \quad . \quad . \quad . \quad . \quad . \quad . \quad . \quad . \quad (10{:}54)$$

$M_L = 2$: $p\pi^2\, p\sigma$ [applying the procedure in (10:41) once with $j \to p\sigma$, $\mu \to p\pi$].

$$({}^2D) = 2J(p\pi, p\sigma) - K(p\pi, p\sigma) + J(p\pi, p\pi) = 3F_0 - 6F_2. \quad (10{:}54a)$$

$M_L = 1$: $p\pi\, p\sigma^2$, $p\pi^2\, p\pi_-$ (the above procedure twice).

$$({}^2D) + ({}^2P) = 2J(p\pi, p\sigma) - K(p\pi, p\sigma) + J(p\sigma, p\sigma)$$
$$+ 2J(p\pi, p\pi_-) - K(p\pi, p\pi_-) + J(p\pi, p\pi)$$
$$= 6F_0 - 6F_2,$$

therefore

$$({}^2P) = 3F_0. \quad . \quad . \quad . \quad . \quad . \quad . \quad . \quad . \quad . \quad . \quad . \quad . \quad . \quad . \quad (10{:}54b)$$

$M_L = 0$: $p\sigma\, p\pi_-\, p\pi$ [(10:41) with free orbits only].

$$({}^4S) = J(p\sigma, p\pi_-) - K(p\sigma, p\pi_-) + J(p\sigma, p\pi)$$
$$- K(p\sigma, p\pi) + J(p\pi, p\pi_-) - K(p\pi, p\pi_-)$$
$$= 3F_0 - 15F_2. \quad . \quad . \quad . \quad . \quad . \quad . \quad . \quad . \quad . \quad . \quad . \quad . \quad . \quad . \quad (10{:}54c)$$

$$d^3\,({}^4F\,{}^4P\,{}^2H\,{}^2G\,{}^2F\,{}^2D_+\,{}^2D_-\,{}^2P). \quad . \quad . \quad . \quad . \quad . \quad (10{:}55)$$

$M_L = 5$: $d\pi\, d\delta^2$ [applying the procedure in (10:41) once].

$$({}^2H) = 2J(d\pi, d\delta) - K(d\pi, d\delta) + J(d\delta, d\delta) = 3F_0 - 6F_2 - 12F_4. \quad (10{:}55a)$$

$\underline{M_L = 4}$: $d\delta\, d\pi^2,\ d\delta^2\, d\sigma$.

$$({}^2H) + ({}^2G) = 2J\,(d\delta, d\pi) - K\,(d\delta, d\pi) + J\,(d\pi, d\pi) + 2J\,(d\delta, d\sigma) - K\,(d\delta, d\sigma) + J\,(d\delta, d\delta)$$
$$= 6F_0 - 17F_2 + F_4,$$

therefore

$$({}^2G) = 3F_0 - 11F_2 + 13F_4. \qquad (10{:}55b)$$

$\underline{M_L = 3}$: $d\delta\, d\pi\, d\sigma,\ d\delta^2\, d\pi_-$.

$$({}^2H) + ({}^2G) + ({}^2F) = 2\,[\,J\,(d\delta, d\pi) + J\,(d\delta, d\sigma) + J\,(d\pi, d\sigma)\,] + 2J\,(d\delta, d\pi_-) - K\,(d\delta, d\pi_-) + J\,(d\delta, d\delta)$$
$$= 9F_0 - 8F_2 - 86F_4,$$

therefore

$$({}^2F) = 3F_0 + 9F_2 - 87F_4. \qquad (10{:}55c)$$ [40]

$\underline{M_L = 2}$: $d\delta\, d\pi\, d\pi_-$ (two doublets, one quartet). $d\delta\, d\sigma^2,\ d\delta^2\, d\delta_-,\ d\pi^2\, d\sigma$ (one doublet each).

$$({}^2H) + ({}^2G) + ({}^2F) + 2\,\overline{({}^2D_\pm)} = 2J\,(d\delta, d\sigma) - K\,(d\delta, d\sigma) + J\,(d\sigma, d\sigma) + 2J\,(d\delta, d\delta_-) - K\,(d\delta, d\delta_-) + J\,(d\delta, d\delta) + 2J\,(d\pi, d\sigma) - K\,(d\pi, d\sigma) + J\,(d\pi, d\pi) + 2\,[\,J\,(d\delta, d\pi) + J\,(d\delta, d\pi_-) + J\,(d\pi, d\pi_-)\,]$$
$$= 15F_0 + 2F_2 - 80F_4,$$

therefore

$$\overline{({}^2D_\pm)} = 3F_0 + 5F_2 + 3F_4. \qquad (10{:}55d)$$ [41]

$\underline{M_L = 1}$: $d\pi\, d\sigma^2,\ d\pi^2\, d\pi_-$ (one doublet each). $d\delta\, d\delta_-\, d\pi,\ d\delta\, d\pi_-\, d\sigma$ (two doublets each).

Applying (10:41) twice for the former, and (10:42*a*) twice for the latter, we find

$$({}^2H) + ({}^2G) + ({}^2F) + 2\,\overline{({}^2D_\pm)} + ({}^2P) = 18F_0 - 4F_2 - 92F_4,$$

whence

$$({}^2P) = 3F_0 - 6F^2 - 12F_4. \qquad (10{:}55e)$$

Returning now to the case $\underline{M_L = 3}$, we have one quartet from $d\sigma\, d\pi\, d\delta$; hence

$$({}^4F) = J\,(d\sigma, d\pi) - K\,(d\sigma, d\pi) + J\,(d\sigma, d\delta) - K\,(d\sigma, d\delta) + J\,(d\pi, d\delta) - K\,(d\pi, d\delta)$$
$$= 3F_0 - 15F_2 - 72F_4. \qquad (10{:}55f)$$ [42]

[40] Here the spatial configuration $d\delta\, d\pi\, d\sigma$ comprises only free orbits, and from the branching rule admits two doublets and a quartet. The first factor above gives the energy spur for these two doublets, and is twice the average energy of these doublets, computed from (10:42*a*) with $p = 0$, $S = \frac{1}{2}$.

[41] We find here only the average energy of the two terms [indicated as $\overline{({}^2D_\pm)}$] which we shall separate by the extended Dirac method in §88.

[42] Note that in using (10:41) or (10:42*a*) with $n = 3$, $S = \frac{3}{2}$, we have only free orbits and parallel spin electrons.

Finally, from $\underline{M_L = 1}$: $d\pi\, d\delta_-\, d\delta,\ d\sigma\, d\pi_-\, d\delta$, we have for the quartets,

$$\begin{aligned}({}^4F) + ({}^4P) &= J(d\pi, d\delta_-) - K(d\pi, d\delta_-) + J(d\pi, d\delta) - K(d\pi, d\delta)\\ &\quad + J(d\delta, d\delta_-) - K(d\delta, d\delta_-) + J(d\sigma, d\pi_-) - K(d\sigma, d\pi_-)\\ &\quad + J(d\sigma, d\delta) - K(d\sigma, d\delta) + J(d\pi_-, d\delta) - K(d\pi_-, d\delta)\\ &= 6F_0 - 15F_2 - 219F_4,\end{aligned}$$

therefore

$$({}^4P) = 3F_0 - 147F_4. \qquad (10{:}55g)$$ [43]

§ 84. Supplementary Notes on the Simple Vector Model

There are a number of special problems wherein the simple vector model (as developed so far) permits a remarkably neat and simple solution. We shall consider several of these to illustrate both the power of the method and the kinematical insight obtained therefrom.

In the problems previously considered we worked in the so-called Russell-Saunders (L, S) coupling scheme, wherein the total spin $\underline{\mathbf{S}}$ commuted with the Hamiltonian so that its magnitude was a constant of the motion. It may happen that the resultant spins of certain groups of orbits constituting only a portion of the system also commute with $\mathbf{H}$, so that their magnitudes are also constants of the motion,[44] and in such cases a great simplification can be made in our previous analysis and the final result (10:41). Let us suppose, for example, that

$$K(i, j) \text{ is independent of } i \text{ for } i \leqslant k, \text{ and } j > k; \qquad (10{:}56)$$

and we shall term orbits $1, 2, \ldots k$, and $k + 1, \ldots n$, as groups I and II respectively. Then (10:41) becomes

$$\mathbf{V} = C - \tfrac{1}{2}\Big[\sum_{\substack{1\\ i<j}}^{k} + \sum_{\substack{k+1\\ i<j}}^{n}\Big]\{(1 + 4\underline{\mathbf{s}}_i \cdot \underline{\mathbf{s}}_j)K(i,j)\} - \tfrac{1}{2}\sum_{j=k+1}^{n}(k + 4\underline{\mathbf{S}}_k \cdot \underline{\mathbf{s}}_j)K(i,j), \qquad (10{:}57)$$

where the important point is that the last term is a function of $\underline{\mathbf{S}}_k = \sum_1^k \underline{\mathbf{s}}_i$ instead of $\underline{\mathbf{s}}_1, \underline{\mathbf{s}}_2, \ldots \underline{\mathbf{s}}_k$. It readily follows that $\underline{\mathbf{S}}_k^2$ commutes with $(\underline{\mathbf{s}}_i \cdot \underline{\mathbf{s}}_j)$, for i, j both in group I or II, and obviously also commutes with $\underline{\mathbf{S}}_k$ and $\underline{\mathbf{s}}_j$ $(j > k)$. Hence, $\underline{\mathbf{S}}_k^2$ commutes with the whole Hamiltonian *and* $\underline{\mathbf{S}}^2$, and we have simultaneously

$$\left.\begin{aligned}\underline{S}^{2\prime} &= S(S+1),\\ \underline{S}_k^{2\prime} &= S_k(S_k+1).\end{aligned}\right\} \qquad (10{:}58)$$ [45]

[43] Note that all the preceding results can be obtained by proper application of (10:42*a*) *alone.*

[44] We exclude here the trivial case for which these groups consist exclusively of "filled" or paired orbits, and hence by the exclusion principle have zero resultant spin.

[45] The restriction (10:56) is essential, since if this does not obtain, $\underline{\mathbf{S}}_k^2$ does not commute with $(\underline{\mathbf{s}}_i \cdot \underline{\mathbf{s}}_j)$ for i, j in different groups.

If in addition $K(i, j)$ is independent of j as well as of i in (10:56), the magnitude of the total spin of group II, viz. $\underline{\mathbf{S}}_{>k} = \sum_{j=k+1}^{n} \underline{\mathbf{s}}_j$ is a constant of the motion and

$$\underline{S}^2_{>k}{}' = S_{>k}(S_{>k}+1). \qquad (10:59)$$

Then the last term of (10:57) reduces to

$$-\tfrac{1}{2}[k(n-k) + 4\underline{\mathbf{S}}_k \cdot \underline{\mathbf{S}}_{>k}]K(1, n)$$
$$= -\tfrac{1}{2}[k(n-k) + 2(\underline{\mathbf{S}}^2 - \underline{\mathbf{S}}_k{}^2 - \underline{\mathbf{S}}^2{}_{>k})]K(1, n), \qquad (10:60a)$$

with the allowed values

$$-\tfrac{1}{2}\{k(n-k)+2[S(S+1)-S_k(S_k+1)-S_{>k}(S_{>k}+1)]\}K(1,n); \qquad (10:60b)$$

and the n-electron problem factors into the k and $(n - k)$ electron problems, plus this simple additive term.

A rather remarkable application of this result is to the determination of the term values of configurations of the type $l^k s$ ($l = p, d, \ldots$, etc.; $0 < k < 4l + 2$), i.e. an s electron outside an incomplete shell of equivalent electrons. The above applies here because the spherical symmetry of the s electron wave-function results in the exchange and Coulomb integrals $K(l, s)$ and $J(l, s)$, between the s electron and any one of the l^k group, being independent of the spatial quantum number of the latter.[46] Then from (10:57) and (10:60b) with $S_{>k} = \frac{1}{2}$ and $n = k + 1$, we obtain the result that the term values of $l^k s$ are related to those of l^k by

$$({}^{2S+1}L\,;l^k s) = ({}^{2S_k+1}L\,;l^k)-\tfrac{1}{2}\{k+2[S(S+1)-S_k(S_k+1)-\tfrac{3}{4}]\}K(l,s)+kJ(l,s). \qquad (10:61)$$

We may illustrate an application of this result by computing the term of $p^3 s$ from those of p^3 which we have already found [cf. (10:54a, b, c)]. Thus, with $k = 3$ and $S_{>k} = \frac{1}{2}$, we find

$$({}^5S\,;p^3s) = ({}^4S\,;p^3) - 3K(np, n's) + 3J(np, n's)$$
$$= 3F_0 - 15F_2 - 3G_p + 3F_{0p}. \qquad (10:62a)$$ [47]

Similarly,

$$({}^3S\,;p^3s) = 3F_0 - 15F_2 + G_p + 3F_{0p}, \qquad (10:62b)$$

$$({}^3D\,;\quad) = 3F_0 - 6F_2 - 2G_p + 3F_{0p}, \qquad (10:62c)$$

$$({}^1D\,;\quad) = 3F_0 - 6F_2 + 3F_{0p}, \qquad (10:62d)$$

$$({}^3P\,;\quad) = 3F_0 - 2G_p + 3F_{0p}, \qquad (10:62e)$$

$$({}^1P\,;\quad) = 3F_0 + 3F_{0p}. \qquad (10:62f)$$

[46] This is not true if the s and l electrons are not on the same atom as in molecular problems, since then the two wave-functions are not concentric.

[47] Here $G_p = G_1(np, n's)$, $F_{0p} = F_0(np, n's)$, the subscripts distinguishing these factors from $F_0 = F_0(np, np)$ and $F_2 = F_2(np, np)$ which occur in $({}^{2S_k+1}L\,;p^3)$.

Another interesting special calculation [48] is that of the term system for the configurations of non-equivalent electrons of the type $nln'l'n''s(ll's)$, which is one of the simplest instances of the occurrence of more than one term of the same type. Clearly there will be a set of quartet terms occurring once and a set of doublets each occurring twice; and for definiteness we may consider the configuration $pds(^4F\,^4D\,^4P\,^2F_\pm\,^2D_\pm\,^2P_\pm)$, although the calculations can be readily made without such explicit specification. The interaction energy between the p and s electrons is [cf. (10:50)]

$$({}^{3,1}P\,;ps) = F_{0p} \mp G_p, \qquad (10:63a)$$ [49]

and, as is readily found for d and s by a similar calculation,

$$({}^{3,1}D\,;ds) = F_{0d} \mp G_d, \qquad (10:63b)$$ [50]

where in both cases the upper and lower signs correspond to parallel and antiparallel spins respectively. The configuration pd gives [cf. (10:51)]

$$({}^{3,1}F\,;pd) = F_0 + 2F_2 \mp (6G_1 + 3G_3), \qquad (10:64a)$$ [51]

$$({}^{3,1}D\,;pd) = F_0 - 7F_2 \mp (-3G_1 + 21G_3), \qquad (10:64b)$$

$$({}^{3,1}P\,;pd) = F_0 + 7F_2 \mp (G_1 + 63G_3). \qquad (10:64c)$$

In the general case we would have

$$({}^{3,1}l\,;ls) = F_{0l} \mp G_l, \qquad (10:65)$$

$$({}^{3,1}l'\,;l's) = F_{0l'} \mp G_{l'}, \qquad (10:66)$$

$$({}^{3,1}L\,;ll') = \mathscr{F}_L \mp \mathscr{G}_L, \qquad (10:67)$$

where $\mathscr{F}_L$, $\mathscr{G}_L$ indicate linear combinations of the S.C.S. F's and G's; the coefficients of these linear combinations depending on l, l' and L. Here, as in the preceding explicit example, the $\mp$ signs going with parallel and antiparallel spins, respectively, can be replaced by the indicator [52] $-\frac{1}{2}[1 + \boldsymbol{\sigma}_a \cdot \boldsymbol{\sigma}_b] = \mathbf{P}_{ab}$ from the vector model, so that the ls terms, for example, are the eigenvalues of the operator

$$\mathbf{V}_{ls} = F_{0l} + \mathbf{P}_{ls}G_l. \qquad (10:68)$$

Returning to the configuration pds, it is trivially evident that the electrostatic energies (term values, except for common constant as usual) are the eigenvalues of the operator [cf. (10:34)]

$$\mathbf{V} = F_{0p} + F_{0d} + \mathscr{F}_L + [\mathbf{P}_{sp}G_p + \mathbf{P}_{sd}G_d + \mathbf{P}_{pd}\mathscr{G}_L], \qquad (10:69)$$

where $\mathscr{F}_L$, $\mathscr{G}_L$ now refer to the linear combinations in (10:64) for our example pd.

[48] Cf. * Racah, G.: *Phys. Rev.*, **62**, 523 (1942).

[49] $F_{0p} = F_0(np, n''s)$; $G_p = G_1(np, n''s)$.

[50] $F_{0d} = F_0(n'd, n''s)$; $G_d = G_2(n'd, n''s)$.

[51] Throughout this example the arguments of F_k, G_k are $(np, n'd)$.

[52] To avoid confusion it is here convenient to use this first form in the $\boldsymbol{\sigma}$'s rather than the spin vectors. $\mathbf{P}_{ab}$ indicates exchange of the a and b orbits, e.g. p and s or p and d, etc.

The quartet terms are especially simple since every $\mathbf{P}_{ab}$ equals -1, i.e. all spins are parallel. Therefore

$$({}^4L\,;pds) = F_{0p} + F_{0d} + \mathscr{F}_L - G_p - G_d - \mathscr{G}_L, \quad . \quad . \quad (10{:}70)$$

and we need only substitute the appropriate $\mathscr{F}_L$ and $\mathscr{G}_L$ from (10:64) for the corresponding terms ${}^4F$, ${}^4D$, ${}^4P$, of *pds*.

With the relations (10:16, 17*a*, *b*, *c*), and since here $S(S+1) = \frac{3}{4}$, the eigenvalues for the doublet terms can be obtained simply by squaring the operator in (10:69), which, after simple reduction, becomes

$$[\,\mathbf{P}_{sp}G_p + \mathbf{P}_{sd}G_d + \mathbf{P}_{pd}\mathscr{G}_L\,]^2 = G_p^2 + G_d^2 + \mathscr{G}_L^2 - G_pG_d - (\,G_p + G_d\,)\,\mathscr{G}_L. \quad (10{:}71)$$

Hence

$$({}^2L_\pm\,;pds) = F_{0p} + F_{0d} + \mathscr{F}_L \pm [\,G_p^2 + G_d^2 + \mathscr{G}_L^2 - G_pG_d - (G_p + G_d)\mathscr{G}_L]^{\frac{1}{2}}. \quad (10{:}72)$$ [53]

We thus obtain, for example,

$$({}^4F\,;pds) = F_{0p} + F_{0d} + F_0 + 2F_2 - G_p - G_d - 6G_1 - 3G_3, \quad . \quad (10{:}73)$$

$$({}^2F_\pm\,;pds) = F_{0p} + F_{0d} + F_0 + 2F_2 \pm [\,G_p^2 + G_d^2 + (\,6G_1 + 3G_3\,)^2 - G_pG_d - (\,G_p + G_d\,)\,(\,6G_1 + 3G_3\,)\,]^{\frac{1}{2}}, \text{ etc.}$$

§ 85. Matrix Viewpoint—Formal Group Characters

The analysis of permutation degeneracy led us to the result that the whole matrix $\langle\, P_a\alpha \mid \mathbf{V} \mid P_b\alpha\,\rangle$ is equal to the matrix representing $\sum\limits_P \langle\, P\alpha \mid \mathbf{V} \mid \alpha\,\rangle\,\mathbf{P}$; and with the restriction to a single spatial configuration, this permitted the use of Dirac's symbolic form $\mathbf{V} = \sum\limits_P \mathrm{V}_P\mathbf{P}$. However, since this analysis gives only the mean energy for similar terms, we can ordinarily resolve [53a] them only by setting up the complete energy matrix including interconfigurational elements, i.e. we need to solve the full secular equation. To this end we may first note that the preceding theory does not in fact require that the Hamiltonian be separable into a perturbation term $\mathbf{V}$ and a Hamiltonian $\mathbf{H}_0$ for the unperturbed system, over whose solutions the matrix of $\mathbf{V}$ is defined. Indeed, as previously indicated [cf. (10:35)], we can take the initial one-electron functions $\langle\, x_i' \mid \alpha_i\,\rangle$, etc., to be any set of functions giving a good approximation to the distribution of electrons in the system (e.g. such as found by the Hartree or Fock theory); so that $\mathbf{V}$ no longer exists and is replaced by the whole Hamiltonian $\mathbf{H}$.

With this proviso we shall continue to use the original form, since we usually deal with a perturbation rather than the whole Hamiltonian,[54] but we now write (10:31) as

$$\mathscr{V} = \sum_{\mathscr{P}} \mathscr{V}_{\mathscr{P}}\mathscr{P}, \quad . \quad . \quad . \quad . \quad . \quad . \quad . \quad . \quad (10{:}74)$$

[53] The notation ${}^2L_\pm$ here indicates the occurrence of two terms of the same type as in $({}^2D_\pm\,;\,d^3)$ of a previous example.

[53a] However, cf. § 88*c*.

[54] Unless otherwise indicated.

where the script symbols will now indicate the entire matrix quantities as distinct from operators or single elements (except $\mathscr{V}_{\mathscr{P}}$, of course), since our further work is more conveniently developed in the more conventional matrix form. The matrices $\mathscr{P}$ are irreducible representations of the symmetric group whose determination corresponding to an assigned S value we shall presently consider. We shall not, however, develop (10:74) anew from the pure group-theoretical viewpoint, since it should be sufficiently evident from our previous work and the further development here.[55] Then the matrical analogue of the determination of the average eigenvalue $\langle V' \rangle$ [cf. (10:39*a*)] is the process of taking the spur of $\mathscr{V}$, viz.

$$\mathscr{S}p\,\mathscr{V} = \sum_{\mathscr{P}} \mathscr{V}_{\mathscr{P}} [\mathscr{P}], \quad \ldots \ldots \quad (10:75)$$

where $[\mathscr{P}]$ indicates the primitive group character of the class to which $\mathscr{P}$ belongs,[56] as distinct from the Dirac character eigenvalues. From the stated relation between these, it is seen how the (matrix) group-theoretical method gives the sum of energies of similar terms, while Dirac's symbolic theory gives the average. Dirac's original theory concerns itself only with the character eigenvalues; but to set up the complete energy matrix we also need the matrix representations of the permutations in (10:74), and must have recourse to group theory proper.

The primitive group characters to be used in the matrix method (10:74, 75) are given by Wigner's formula, viz. that the primitive character of the class of permutations of ρ cycles with cycle *lengths* $\lambda_1, \lambda_2, \ldots \lambda_\rho$, is the coefficient of x^k $(k = \frac{1}{2}n - S)$ in

$$(-)^{n-\rho}(1-x)(1+x^{\lambda_1})(1+x^{\lambda_2})\ldots(1+x^{\lambda_\rho}). \quad . \quad (10:76)$$ [57]

The group characters corresponding to the Dirac character eigenvalues (10:15–21), for example, are then

$$[2] = -\binom{n-2}{k} + \binom{n-2}{k-1} - \binom{n-2}{k-2} + \binom{n-2}{k-3}. \quad \ldots \quad (10:77a)$$

$$[3] = \binom{n-3}{k} - \binom{n-3}{k-1} + \binom{n-3}{k-3} - \binom{n-3}{k-4}. \quad \ldots \quad (10:77b)$$

$$[2^2] = \binom{n-4}{k} - \binom{n-4}{k-1} + 2\binom{n-4}{k-2} - 2\binom{n-4}{k-3} + \binom{n-4}{k-4} - \binom{n-4}{k-5}. \quad (10:77c)$$

$$[4] = -\binom{n-4}{k} + \binom{n-4}{k-1} - \binom{n-4}{k-4} + \binom{n-4}{k-5}. \quad \ldots \quad (10:77d)$$

$$[5] = \binom{n-5}{k} - \binom{n-5}{k-1} + \binom{n-5}{k-5} - \binom{n-5}{k-6}. \quad \ldots \quad (10:77e)$$

[55] Further details may be found in WIGNER, *op. cit.*, or HEITLER: *Zeits. f. Phys.*, **47**, 835 (1928); **46**, 47 (1927).

[56] For convenience we sometimes use the same symbol for the permutations and the permutation matrices.

[57] We need not derive this result here, since it is rather more lengthy than difficult, and may be found in WIGNER, *Gruppentheorie*, pp. 149, 196. From the connection between group and Dirac characters, and the discussion of the number of states of spin S [cf. (10:45)], we can readily infer that the characters given by (10:76) are simply the corresponding Dirac character eigenvalues multiplied by $N(S)$.

The character of the unit class, which is just the dimension of the representation, is given by

$$[I] = \binom{n}{k} - \binom{n}{k-1}, \quad . \quad . \quad . \quad . \quad . \quad (10:77f)$$

i.e. the number of states of multiplicity $2S + 1$ arising from a configuration of n free orbits—as previously found from the branching rule. With the stated relation

$$\chi'[2^{\alpha_2} \ldots n^{\alpha_n}] = [2^{\alpha_2} \ldots n^{\alpha_n}]/[I], \quad . \quad . \quad . \quad . \quad (10:78)$$ [58]

one may readily check the expressions (10:15–21).

§ 86. Matrix Representations of the Permutations

Before we can generalize equation (10:74) to set up the complete energy matrix, we need to determine the matrices of the irreducible representations allowed by the exclusion principle.[59] This can be done in a variety of ways, requiring more or less of formal group methods; and probably the simplest proceeds along lines similar in principle to those used in establishing the general expression (10:76). We use the fact that for an n-electron system there exist 2^n linearly independent functions of the spins, so that by using these 2^n functions as a basis,[60] we can construct the irreducible matrices representing the operators $\mathbf{P}^s$ which permute the spins; and from the relation [61] $\mathbf{P} = \pm \mathbf{P}^s$ between the $\mathbf{P}$'s and $\mathbf{P}^s$'s, obtain in turn the irreducible representations of the $\mathbf{P}$'s allowed by the exclusion principle. To this end we first need to express the spin eigenvectors (or eigenfunctions) corresponding to a given S and M_s of an n-electron system in terms of one-electron spin functions. These are obtained by repeated application of the formula (3:74) for the composition of angular momentum vectors, which in the present case ($\underline{\mathbf{s}}_1$, $\underline{\mathbf{s}}_2$ to a resultant $\underline{\mathbf{S}}$) takes the form

$$| s_1 s_2 S M_s \rangle = \sum_{m_{s_1}} | s_1 m_{s_1} \rangle | s_2 M_s - m_{s_1} \rangle \langle s_1 s_2 m_{s_1} M_s - m_{s_1} | s_1 s_2 S M_s \rangle; \quad (10:79)$$

or by pre-multiplying symbolically by $\langle s_1 s_{1z} | \langle s_2 s_{2z} | = \langle s_{1z} s_{2z} |$, the more conventional form,

$$\langle s_{1z} s_{2z} | S M_s \rangle = \sum_{m_{s_1}} \langle s_{1z} | m_{s_1} \rangle \langle s_{2z} | M_s - m_{s_1} \rangle \langle m_{s_1} M_s - m_{s_1} | S M_s \rangle, \quad (10:80)$$

where we suppress the indices [62] s_1, s_2. The construction of the matrices $\mathscr{P}^s$ can be carried out in a number of ways, depending on the purpose for which they are to be

[58] $2^{\alpha_2} \ldots n^{\alpha_n}$ is the usual group-theoretical notation (omitting unary cycle) for the cycle structure.

[59] Cf. * SERBER, R.: *Phys. Rev.*, **45**, 461 (1934). These are a very special type and do not include all irreducible representations of the symmetric group, cf. WIGNER, E. P., *op. cit.*, and MURNAGHAN, F. D., *op. cit.*

[60] The functions are linearly independent; hence, if properly chosen, they lead to an irreducible representation.

[61] Cf. also, WIGNER, E. P., *op. cit.*

[62] Correspondingly, the one-electron spin functions are indicated by $\langle s_1 s_{1z} | s_1 m_{s_1} \rangle = \langle s_{1z} | m_{s_1} \rangle$ instead of the usual $\delta(s_{1z}, m_{s_1})$.

used. For a reason to appear shortly, we wish to have $\mathscr{P}_{12}, \mathscr{P}_{34} \ldots (\mathbf{P}_{12}, \mathbf{P}_{34}, \ldots)$, etc., diagonal. This is accomplished if we compound $\underline{s}_1$ and $\underline{s}_2$ to a resultant $\underline{s}_{12}$, $\underline{s}_3$ and $\underline{s}_4$ to a resultant $\underline{s}_{34}$, etc.,[63] and then proceed to compound $\underline{s}_{12}$ and $\underline{s}_{34}$ to $\underline{\mathbf{S}}_{12,\,34}$, etc., until the total spin $\underline{\mathbf{S}}$ is diagonal. Only one value of M_s need be considered,[64] and it is simplest to take $M_s = S$.

For the simple case of all electrons parallel, we know that there is but a single state, and from the vector model it follows that every permutation is represented by $\pm I$, according to its parity. We shall here consider the case $n = 4$, which is sufficiently general to illustrate the method. Using Table 3.1 (p. 58) of transformation amplitudes, we find the well-known result that the two-electron spin functions are given by:

$$\langle s_{1z}s_{2z} \mid 1\,1 \rangle = \langle s_{1z} \mid \tfrac{1}{2} \rangle \langle s_{2z} \mid \tfrac{1}{2} \rangle. \qquad (10{:}81a)\ [65]$$

$$\langle s_{1z}s_{2z} \mid 1\,0 \rangle = \frac{1}{\sqrt{2}} \{ \langle s_{1z} \mid \tfrac{1}{2} \rangle \langle s_{2z} \mid -\tfrac{1}{2} \rangle + \langle s_{1z} \mid -\tfrac{1}{2} \rangle \langle s_{2z} \rangle \langle s_{2z} \mid \tfrac{1}{2} \rangle \}. \qquad (10{:}81b)$$

$$\langle s_{1z}s_{2z} \mid 1\,-1 \rangle = \langle s_{1z} \mid -\tfrac{1}{2} \rangle \langle s_{2z} \mid -\tfrac{1}{2} \rangle. \qquad (10{:}81c)$$

$$\langle s_{1z}s_{2z} \mid 0\,0 \rangle = \frac{1}{\sqrt{2}} \{ \langle s_{1z} \mid \tfrac{1}{2} \rangle \langle s_{2z} \mid -\tfrac{1}{2} \rangle - \langle s_{1z} \mid -\tfrac{1}{2} \rangle \langle s_{2z} \mid \tfrac{1}{2} \rangle \}. \qquad (10{:}81d)$$

Four electrons give one quintet, three triplet, and two singlet states (branching rule), and the wave-functions

$$\langle s_{1z}s_{2z}s_{3z}s_{4z} \mid s_{12}s_{34}SM_s \rangle = \langle :_{1234} \mid s_{12}s_{34}SM_s \rangle$$

of the triplet states are found in terms of the above two-electron functions as:

$$\langle :_{1234} \mid 1\,1\,1\,1 \rangle = \frac{1}{\sqrt{2}} \{ \langle :_{12} \mid 1\,1 \rangle \langle :_{34} \mid 1\,0 \rangle - \langle :_{12} \mid 1\,0 \rangle \langle :_{34} \mid 1\,1 \rangle \}. \qquad (10{:}82a)$$

$$\langle :_{1234} \mid 1\,0\,1\,1 \rangle = \langle :_{12} \mid 1\,1 \rangle \langle :_{34} \mid 0\,0 \rangle. \qquad (10{:}82b)$$

$$\langle :_{1234} \mid 0\,1\,1\,1 \rangle = \langle :_{12} \mid 0\,0 \rangle \langle :_{34} \mid 1\,1 \rangle. \qquad (10{:}82c)$$

In (10:82a, b) the spins of electrons 1, 2 are parallel, so that $P_{12}' = -P_{12}^{s\prime} = -1$, while for (10:82$c$) they are antiparallel, so that $P_{12}' = 1$. Similarly, the eigenvalues of $\mathbf{P}_{34}$ for these same states are -1, 1, -1, so that $\mathbf{P}_{12}$, $\mathbf{P}_{34}$ are diagonal as required. The determination of the other $\mathscr{P}$'s follows from (10:81–82),[66] e.g.

$$\langle P_{13}^{s} : s_{1z}s_{2z}s_{3z}s_{4z} \mid 0\,1\,1\,1 \rangle = -\frac{1}{\sqrt{2}} \langle :_{1234} \mid 1\,1\,1\,1 \rangle + \tfrac{1}{2} \langle :_{1234} \mid 1\,0\,1\,1 \rangle + \tfrac{1}{2} \langle :_{1234} \mid 0\,1\,1\,1 \rangle, \qquad (10{:}83)$$

[63] This is evident from the vector model. Cf. also fig. 10.1, p. 189.

[64] The $\mathbf{P}$'s and the energy, which is a function of them, have no matrix elements between states of different S or M_S, and for each value S we obtain a representation of the $\mathbf{P}$'s which is independent of M_S. This follows from the invariance of the $\mathbf{P}$'s under rotations of spin axes. Cf. § 53, and also Footnote 28, p. 191.

[65] Note $\langle s_{1z}s_{2z} \mid SM_S \rangle = \langle s_1s_2s_{1z}s_{2z} \mid s_1s_2SM_S \rangle$.

[66] For computational purposes it may be more convenient to replace $\langle s_{iz} \mid \frac{1}{2} \rangle$ and $\langle s_{iz} \mid -\frac{1}{2} \rangle$ by α_i, β_i, or some similar brief notation.

which determines the last column of the matrix $\mathscr{P}_{13}{}^s$ representing $\mathbf{P}_{13}{}^s$. The labour of computing these $\mathscr{P}$'s can be greatly reduced by taking advantage of the relations between the $\mathbf{P}$'s, symmetry properties of the wave-functions, and the fact that simple interchanges are both unitary and Hermitian. For example, if we apply $\mathbf{P}^s$ to (10:83), the left side becomes

$$\langle P^sP_{13}{}^s : {}_{1234} \,|\, 0\,1\,1\,1 \rangle = \langle P_a{}^sP_{13}{}^s : {}_{1234} \,|\, 0\,1\,1\,1 \rangle, \text{ with } \mathbf{P}_a{}^s = \mathbf{P}^s\mathbf{P}_{13}{}^s\mathbf{P}^{s-1}.$$

Taking $\mathbf{P}^s = \mathbf{P}^s_{12,34}$ gives $\mathbf{P}_a{}^s = \mathbf{P}_{13}{}^s$, and from (10:82) we find by inspection that

$$\left.\begin{aligned} \langle P^s_{13,24} : {}_{1234} \,|\, 1\,1\,1\,1 \rangle &= -\langle :{}_{1234} \,|\, 1\,1\,1\,1 \rangle, \\ \langle P^s_{13,24} : {}_{1234} \,|\, 1\,0\,1\,1 \rangle &= \langle :{}_{1234} \,|\, 0\,1\,1\,1 \rangle, \\ \langle P^s_{13,24} : {}_{1234} \,|\, 0\,1\,1\,1 \rangle &= \langle :{}_{1234} \,|\, 1\,0\,1\,1 \rangle, \end{aligned}\right\} \quad . \quad . \quad . \quad (10:84)$$

from which

$$\langle P_{13}{}^s : {}_{1234} \,|\, 1\,0\,1\,1 \rangle = \frac{1}{\sqrt{2}} \langle :{}_{1234} \,|\, 1\,1\,1\,1 \rangle + \tfrac{1}{2} \langle :{}_{1234} \,|\, 1\,0\,1\,1 \rangle$$
$$+ \tfrac{1}{2} \langle :{}_{1234} \,|\, 0\,1\,1\,1 \rangle, \quad . \quad . \quad . \quad . \quad . \quad (10:85)$$

which determines the second column. The remaining column is then simply determined from the above-mentioned property of the interchanges. Similarly, the matrix representing $\mathbf{P}_{23}{}^s$ can be simply obtained by means of the relation $\mathbf{P}_{23}{}^s = \mathbf{P}_{12}{}^s\,\mathbf{P}_{13}{}^s\,\mathbf{P}_{12}{}^s$, that of $\mathbf{P}_{14}{}^s$ from $\mathbf{P}_{14}{}^s = \mathbf{P}_{34}{}^s\,\mathbf{P}_{13}{}^s\,\mathbf{P}_{34}{}^s$, etc. With the matrices of the interchanges determined, the higher-order permutations, if required, can obviously be computed in a variety of ways. Thus, we find for $n = 4$, $S = 1$:

(*a*)

$$\mathscr{P}_{12} = \left\| \begin{array}{c|c|c} -1 & 0 & 0 \\ \hline 0 & -1 & 0 \\ \hline 0 & 0 & 1 \end{array} \right\|, \quad \mathscr{P}_{13} = \left\| \begin{array}{c|c|c} 0 & -\sqrt{\frac{1}{2}} & \sqrt{\frac{1}{2}} \\ \hline -\sqrt{\frac{1}{2}} & -\frac{1}{2} & -\frac{1}{2} \\ \hline \sqrt{\frac{1}{2}} & -\frac{1}{2} & -\frac{1}{2} \end{array} \right\|, \quad \mathscr{P}_{14} = \left\| \begin{array}{c|c|c} 0 & \sqrt{\frac{1}{2}} & \sqrt{\frac{1}{2}} \\ \hline \sqrt{\frac{1}{2}} & -\frac{1}{2} & \frac{1}{2} \\ \hline \sqrt{\frac{1}{2}} & \frac{1}{2} & -\frac{1}{2} \end{array} \right\|,$$

$$\mathscr{P}_{23} = \left\| \begin{array}{c|c|c} 0 & -\sqrt{\frac{1}{2}} & -\sqrt{\frac{1}{2}} \\ \hline -\sqrt{\frac{1}{2}} & -\frac{1}{2} & \frac{1}{2} \\ \hline -\sqrt{\frac{1}{2}} & \frac{1}{2} & -\frac{1}{2} \end{array} \right\|, \quad \mathscr{P}_{24} = \left\| \begin{array}{c|c|c} 0 & \sqrt{\frac{1}{2}} & -\sqrt{\frac{1}{2}} \\ \hline \sqrt{\frac{1}{2}} & -\frac{1}{2} & -\frac{1}{2} \\ \hline -\sqrt{\frac{1}{2}} & -\frac{1}{2} & -\frac{1}{2} \end{array} \right\|, \quad \mathscr{P}_{34} = \left\| \begin{array}{c|c|c} -1 & 0 & 0 \\ \hline 0 & 1 & 0 \\ \hline 0 & 0 & -1 \end{array} \right\|,$$

and for $n = 4$, $S = 0$:

(*b*)

$$\mathscr{P}_{12} = \mathscr{P}_{34} = \left\| \begin{array}{c|c} -1 & 0 \\ \hline 0 & 1 \end{array} \right\|, \quad \mathscr{P}_{13} = \mathscr{P}_{24} = \left\| \begin{array}{c|c} \frac{1}{2} & \sqrt{\frac{3}{4}} \\ \hline \sqrt{\frac{3}{4}} & -\frac{1}{2} \end{array} \right\|, \quad \mathscr{P}_{14} = \mathscr{P}_{23} = \left\| \begin{array}{c|c} \frac{1}{2} & -\sqrt{\frac{3}{4}} \\ \hline -\sqrt{\frac{3}{4}} & -\frac{1}{2} \end{array} \right\|.$$

We may note that the representations of $\mathbf{P}_{12}$, $\mathbf{P}_{13}$ and $\mathbf{P}_{23}$ for $n = 3$, $S = \frac{1}{2}$ are just the above representations of these permutations for $n = 4$, $S = 0$, since on removing the fourth electron, a state $S = 0$ for the four-electron problem goes over into a state $S = \frac{1}{2}$ of the three-electron problem. This is a particular example of the general relation between the representations of the interchanges for n, $S = 0$, and $n - 1$, $S = \frac{1}{2}$.

§ 87. Symbolic Determination of the Irreducible Representations of the Symmetric Group

The preceding is essentially a standard method for obtaining the irreducible representations of the symmetric group which are of importance in physical problems.[67] Needless to say, any calculation of the group representations is laborious, and the above procedure becomes particularly involved for many-electron problems in the successive applications of the expression for transformation coefficients leading to the appropriate spin functions. Moreover, it offers no special insight into the structure and relation of the various representations for varying numbers of electrons and multiplicities. Primarily for this latter reason, it is informative to consider an alternative inductive procedure [68] which gives all the required irreducible representations for successive n values, and permits a simple check on the calculations at every step. This method is in some respects also more direct, since it reduces the problem to elementary algebra and matrix multiplication.

We wish to find the irreducible representations of the symmetric group Π_n, assuming that we know all the irreducible representations for the subgroup Π_{n-1}. More precisely, we assume the as yet unknown representations of Π_n chosen in reduced form for the elements contained in Π_{n-1}, and since these reduced parts are previously known by hypothesis, we need only find the matrices representing the interchanges $\mathbf{P}_{in}$—those of the other permutations of higher cycle structure being obtainable from these. A convenient visualization of the problem, as well as the key to its solution, is afforded by the following physical picture.

We imagine an atom core of $n - 1$ electrons, add one electron, and consider the problem of determining the energies of the multiplets that arise from a given multiplet state of the core. That is, we require the eigenvalues of $\mathscr{V} = \sum_{\mathscr{P}} \mathscr{V}_{\mathscr{P}} \mathscr{P}$ for the *n-electron state* characterized by the *Dirac* character eigenvalues $\chi_c, \ldots$, such that the matrices of the n_c' elements $\mathbf{P}_c$ of the class C belonging to the *subgroup* Π_{n-1} (involving orbits 1, 2, . . . $n - 1$) are the irreducible representations of Π_{n-1} of dimension g' characterized by the eigenvalues $\chi_c', \ldots$. The class sums can be expressed in the form $\overset{(\Pi_n)}{\sum_c} \mathbf{P}_c = \overset{(\Pi_{n-1})}{\sum_c} \mathbf{P}_c + \sum_c \mathbf{P}_c$, where $\sum_c \mathbf{P}_c$ is the sum of the $n_c - n_c'$ elements of the class C *not* belonging to Π_{n-1}; the matrices for these elements being the g'-dimensional parts of the irreducible representations belonging to χ_c. Then

[67] It is clear that this method does not give *all* possible representations, only those falling within the antisymmetry condition. Cf. WIGNER, *op. cit.*

[68] Cf. * YAMANOUCHI, T.: *Proc. Phys. Math. Soc. Japan*, **18**, 623 (1936).

the semi-character operators $\boldsymbol{\zeta}_c$ defined as the average

$$\boldsymbol{\zeta}_c = \frac{1}{n_c - n_{c'}} \sum_c \mathbf{P}_c \quad . \quad . \quad . \quad . \quad . \quad . \quad . \quad . \qquad (10{:}86a)$$

also have constant values *for such a state*, given by

$$\zeta_c = \frac{1}{n_c - n_{c'}} (n_c \chi_c - n_c' \chi_c'). \quad . \quad . \quad . \quad . \quad . \quad . \qquad (10{:}86b)$$

As noted, we shall require only the interchanges in the following, and for these $\boldsymbol{\zeta}[2]$ is given by

$$(n-1)\boldsymbol{\zeta} = \sum_{i=1}^{n-1} \mathbf{P}_{in} = -\tfrac{1}{2}(n-1) - 2\sum_{i=1}^{n-1} \underline{\mathbf{s}}_i \cdot \underline{\mathbf{s}}_n$$

$$= \underline{\mathbf{S}}_{n-1}^2 + \underline{\mathbf{s}}_n{}^2 - \underline{\mathbf{S}}_n{}^2 - \tfrac{1}{2}(n-1), \quad . \quad . \quad . \quad . \qquad (10{:}86c)$$

where $\underline{\mathbf{S}}_n = \sum_{i=1}^{n} \underline{\mathbf{s}}_i$. If the n-electron state has resultant spin S, then the core or $(n-1)$-electron problem has resultant spin $S' = S + \frac{1}{2}$, or $S' = S - \frac{1}{2}$. Hence, the eigenvalues of $\boldsymbol{\zeta}$ are given by

$$\zeta = \frac{1}{n-1} \left\{ \begin{matrix} S + 2 - \frac{1}{2}n \\ -S + 1 - \frac{1}{2}n \end{matrix} \right\}, \quad . \quad . \quad . \quad . \quad . \quad . \qquad (10{:}86d)$$

or in terms of $k = \frac{1}{2}n - S$,

$$\zeta = \frac{1}{n-1} \left\{ \begin{matrix} 2 - k \\ -n + k + 1 \end{matrix} \right\}, \quad . \quad . \quad . \quad . \quad . \qquad (10{:}86e)$$

for the states arising from the $\left\{ \begin{matrix} \text{higher} \\ \text{lower} \end{matrix} \right\}$ multiplets of the core.

From the branching diagram (fig. 10.1) for a general set of (n, S) values we have the relation

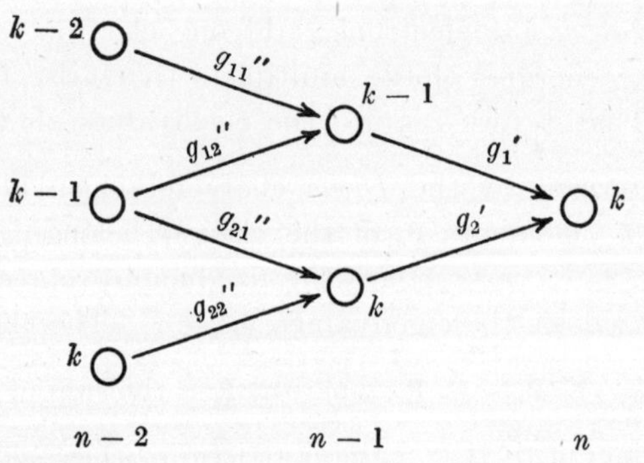

$(g_{12}'' = g_{21}'')$ (10:86f)

showing how the dimensions of representations for multiplets of lower n values add up to the dimensions of representations of higher successive n values, and we see that the reduced matrices for $\mathbf{P}_{i,\,n-1}$ $(i < n - 1)$ for (n, k) will have the form

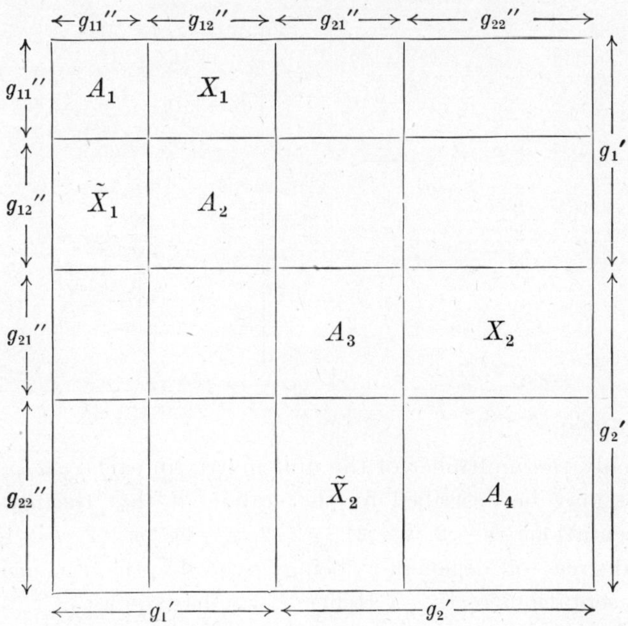

(10:86g)

Since, by hypothesis, all irreducible representations of Π_{n-1} are known, it actually remains only to find that of $\mathbf{P}_{n-1,\,n}$ for (n, k) of Π_n to bridge the gap, so to speak, the matrices of $\mathbf{P}_{in}$ $(i < n-1)$ obtaining from that of $\mathbf{P}_{n-1,\,n}$ by the relation $\mathbf{P}_{in} = \mathbf{P}_{n-1,\,n}\,\mathbf{P}_{i,\,n-1}\,\mathbf{P}_{n-1,\,n}$ $(i = 1, 2, \ldots n-2)$. The matrix of $\mathbf{P}_{n-1,\,n}$ is now easily obtained with the help of the semi-character $\zeta[2]$. From (10:86e) we know that $\sum_{i=1}^{n-1} \mathbf{P}_{in} = \mathbf{B}_n$ is diagonal with elements $(\mathbf{B}_n)_{ii} = 2 - k$ and $-n + k + 1$ for the parts of the representation (n, k) of Π_n coming from the representations for $(n-1, k-1)$ and $(n-1, k)$, respectively, of Π_{n-1}. Further,

$$\mathbf{P}_{n-1,\,n}\,\mathbf{B}_n\,\mathbf{P}_{n-1,\,n} = \mathbf{P}_{n-1,\,n} + \sum_{i=1}^{n-2} \mathbf{P}_{i,\,n-1} = \mathbf{P}_{n-1,\,n} + \mathbf{B}_{n-1}, \qquad (10:86h)$$

or

$$\mathbf{B}_n\,\mathbf{P}_{n-1,\,n} = 1 + \mathbf{P}_{n-1,\,n}\,\mathbf{B}_{n-1},$$

from which

$$(\mathbf{B}_n)_{ii}\,(\mathbf{P}_{n-1,\,n})_{ik} = \delta_{ik} + (\mathbf{P}_{n-1,\,n})_{ik}\,(\mathbf{B}_{n-1})_{kk}. \quad \ldots \quad (10:86i)$$

In other words, the diagonal elements of $\mathbf{P}_{n-1,\,n}$ are

$$(\mathbf{P}_{n-1,\,n})_{ii} = \frac{1}{(\mathbf{B}_n)_{ii} - (\mathbf{B}_{n-1})_{ii}}, \quad \ldots \quad (10:86j)$$

and non-diagonal elements occur, at most, for $(\mathbf{B}_n)_{ii} = (\mathbf{B}_{n-1})_{kk}$. From (10:86$e, f$) we see that the matrices of $\mathbf{B}_{n-1}$, $\mathbf{B}_n$ are given by

g_1'	g_{11}''	$2-k+1$			
	g_{12}''		$-n+k+1$		
g_2'	g_{21}''			$2-k$	
	g_{22}''				$-n+k+2$

d^{k-1}_{n-1}	d^{k-2}_{n-2}	$2-k$			
	d^{k-1}_{n-2}		$2-k$		
d^{k}_{n-1}	d^{k-1}_{n-2}			$-n+k+1$	
	d^{k}_{n-2}				$-n+k-1$

(10:86k)

where we give only the multiplier of the unit matrix in each case, and $g_{11}'' = d^{k-2}_{n-2}$, etc. This result may be described by the statement that the matrix parts come from the representations $(n-2,\ k-2)$, $(n-2,\ k-1)$, $(n-2,\ k-1)$ and $(n-2,\ k)$ of Π_{n-2}, their degrees of degeneracy being given by the dimensions of the corresponding representations of Π_{n-2}. Hence $\mathscr{P}_{n-1,\,n}$ has the form

d^{k-2}_{n-2}	$-I$				d^{k-1}_{n-1}	d^k_n
d^{k-1}_{n-2}		λI	X			
d^{k-1}_{n-2}		$\tilde{X}$	$-\lambda I$		d^{k}_{n-1}	
d^{k}_{n-2}				$-I$		

where $\lambda = \dfrac{1}{(n-2k+1)}$, which is the inverse of the multiplicity of the term for the representation under consideration. The appearance of the diagonal matrix $-I$ in the first and fourth parts may be understood, since the parts arising from the resultant spins $S+1$ and $S-1$ of $n-2$ electrons necessitate parallel spins for the last two electrons to produce the resultant S; or $\underline{\mathbf{s}}_{n-1} + \underline{\mathbf{s}}_n = \bar{1}$ and $P'_{n-1,\,n} = -1$. The off-diagonal matrix X is determined by noting that $\mathbf{P}_{n-1,\,n}$ commutes with every permutation belonging to Π_{n-2}, whose matrices are of the form (10:86g) *without* the off-diagonal parts, so that by Schur's lemma X must be a constant multiple of the unit matrix. The constant is determined from the unitary condition, or from $\mathbf{P}^2_{n-1,\,n} = 1$, and is given by $\nu = \pm\sqrt{(1-\lambda^2)}$, which is a real number. Here we may note that the choice of sign is arbitrary, since one is obtained from the other by similarity transformation with the diagonal matrix $\underbrace{1, 1, \ldots 1}_{g_1'},\ \underbrace{-1, -1 \ldots -1}_{g_2'}$, which does not affect the form of the representations of the elements contained in Π_{n-1}.

We list below typical results obtained for the first few groups which illustrate the simplicity and general working of the method. In each case we use the representations previously obtained for Π_{n-1} to write down directly the matrices of these elements of Π_n for the particular representation of Π_n under consideration, computing *only* $\mathscr{P}_{n-1,\,n}$.

Π_2:

We have the well-known result

$\underline{S = 1,\ k = 0.}$ $\mathscr{P}_{12} = -1$ (all $\mathscr{P}_{ij} = -1$ for state of highest multiplicity).

$\underline{S = 0,\ k = 1.}$ $\mathscr{P}_{12} = 1$.

Π_3:

$\underline{S = \tfrac{1}{2},\ k = 1.}$

The representation is 2-dimensional, and from the branching diagram only the second and third parts of the matrices (cf. above) appear. These originate from $n = 2$, $S = 1, 0$.

$$\mathscr{P}_{12} = \left\| \begin{array}{c|c} -1 & \\ \hline & 1 \end{array} \right\|,$$

$$\mathscr{P}_{23} = \left\| \begin{array}{c|c} \lambda & \nu \\ \hline \nu & -\lambda \end{array} \right\| = \left\| \begin{array}{c|c} \frac{1}{2} & \frac{\sqrt{3}}{2} \\ \hline \frac{\sqrt{3}}{2} & -\frac{1}{2} \end{array} \right\|,$$

$$\mathscr{P}_{13} = \mathscr{P}_{12}\mathscr{P}_{23}\mathscr{P}_{12} = \left\| \begin{array}{c|c} \frac{1}{2} & \frac{-\sqrt{3}}{2} \\ \hline \frac{-\sqrt{3}}{2} & -\frac{1}{2} \end{array} \right\|.$$

Π_4:

$\underline{S = 1,\ k = 1.}$

The representation is 3-dimensional, and the first part is absent.

$$\mathscr{P}_{12} = \left\| \begin{array}{c|c|c} -1 & & \\ \hline & -1 & \\ \hline & & 1 \end{array} \right\|, \quad \mathscr{P}_{13} = \left\| \begin{array}{c|c|c} -1 & & \\ \hline & \frac{1}{2} & \frac{-\sqrt{3}}{2} \\ \hline & \frac{-\sqrt{3}}{2} & -\frac{1}{2} \end{array} \right\|,$$

$$\mathscr{P}_{34} = \begin{Vmatrix} \lambda & \nu & \\ \nu & -\lambda & \\ & & -1 \end{Vmatrix} = \begin{Vmatrix} \frac{1}{3} & \frac{2\sqrt{2}}{3} & \\ \frac{2\sqrt{2}}{3} & -\frac{1}{3} & \\ & & -1 \end{Vmatrix},$$

$$\mathscr{P}_{14} = \mathscr{P}_{31}\mathscr{P}_{34}\mathscr{P}_{31} = \begin{Vmatrix} \frac{1}{3} & \frac{-\sqrt{2}}{3} & \frac{\sqrt{6}}{3} \\ \frac{-\sqrt{2}}{3} & \frac{-5}{6} & \frac{-\sqrt{3}}{6} \\ \frac{\sqrt{6}}{3} & \frac{-\sqrt{3}}{6} & -\frac{1}{2} \end{Vmatrix}.$$

$\underline{S = 0,\ k = 2.}$

$\mathscr{P}_{12}, \mathscr{P}_{13}, \mathscr{P}_{23}$ the same as for $S = \frac{1}{2}$, $k = 1$ of Π_3.

$$\mathscr{P}_{34} = \begin{Vmatrix} -1 & \\ & 1 \end{Vmatrix}, \quad \mathscr{P}_{14} = \begin{Vmatrix} \frac{1}{2} & \frac{\sqrt{3}}{2} \\ \frac{\sqrt{3}}{2} & -\frac{1}{2} \end{Vmatrix}.$$

Π_5:

$\underline{S = \frac{3}{2},\ k = 1.}$

$$\mathscr{P}_{12} = \begin{Vmatrix} -1 & & & \\ & -1 & & \\ & & -1 & \\ & & & 1 \end{Vmatrix}, \quad \mathscr{P}_{13} = \begin{Vmatrix} -1 & & & \\ & -1 & & \\ & & \frac{1}{2} & \frac{-\sqrt{3}}{2} \\ & & \frac{-\sqrt{3}}{2} & -\frac{1}{2} \end{Vmatrix},$$

$$\mathscr{P}_{14} = \begin{Vmatrix} -1 & & & \\ & \frac{1}{3} & \frac{-\sqrt{2}}{3} & \frac{\sqrt{6}}{3} \\ & \frac{-\sqrt{2}}{3} & \frac{-5}{6} & \frac{-\sqrt{3}}{6} \\ & \frac{\sqrt{6}}{3} & \frac{-\sqrt{3}}{6} & -\frac{1}{2} \end{Vmatrix},$$

$$\mathscr{P}_{45} = \begin{Vmatrix} \lambda & \nu & & \\ \nu & -\lambda & & \\ & & -1 & \\ & & & 1 \end{Vmatrix} = \begin{Vmatrix} \frac{1}{4} & \frac{\sqrt{15}}{4} & & \\ \frac{\sqrt{15}}{4} & -\frac{1}{4} & & \\ & & -1 & \\ & & & -1 \end{Vmatrix},$$

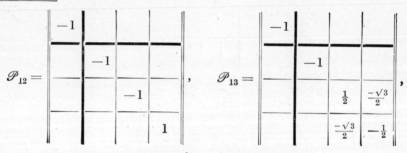

$$\mathscr{P}_{15} = \mathscr{P}_{45}\mathscr{P}_{14}\mathscr{P}_{45} = \left\|\begin{array}{c|c|c|c} \frac{1}{4} & \frac{-\sqrt{15}}{12} & \frac{\sqrt{30}}{12} & \frac{-\sqrt{10}}{4} \\ \hline \frac{-\sqrt{15}}{12} & \frac{-11}{12} & \frac{-\sqrt{2}}{12} & \frac{\sqrt{6}}{12} \\ \hline \frac{\sqrt{30}}{12} & \frac{-\sqrt{2}}{12} & \frac{-5}{6} & \frac{-\sqrt{3}}{6} \\ \hline \frac{-\sqrt{10}}{4} & \frac{\sqrt{6}}{12} & \frac{-\sqrt{3}}{6} & -\frac{1}{2} \end{array}\right\|.$$

$\underline{S = \frac{1}{2},\ k = 2.}$

$$\mathscr{P}_{12} = \left\|\begin{array}{ccc|cc} -1 & & & & \\ & -1 & & & \\ & & 1 & & \\ \hline & & & -1 & \\ & & & & 1 \end{array}\right\|, \quad \mathscr{P}_{14} = \left\|\begin{array}{ccc|cc} \frac{1}{3} & \frac{-\sqrt{2}}{3} & \frac{\sqrt{6}}{3} & & \\ \frac{-\sqrt{2}}{3} & \frac{-5}{6} & \frac{-\sqrt{3}}{6} & & \\ \frac{\sqrt{6}}{3} & \frac{-\sqrt{3}}{6} & -\frac{1}{2} & & \\ \hline & & & \frac{1}{2} & \frac{\sqrt{3}}{2} \\ & & & \frac{\sqrt{3}}{2} & -\frac{1}{2} \end{array}\right\|,$$

$$\mathscr{P}_{45} = \left\|\begin{array}{ccccc} -1 & & & & \\ & \lambda & & \nu & \\ & & \lambda & & \nu \\ & \nu & & -\lambda & \\ & & \nu & & -\lambda \end{array}\right\| = \left\|\begin{array}{ccccc} -1 & & & & \\ & \frac{1}{2} & & \frac{\sqrt{3}}{2} & \\ & & \frac{1}{2} & & \frac{\sqrt{3}}{2} \\ & \frac{\sqrt{3}}{2} & & -\frac{1}{2} & \\ & & \frac{\sqrt{3}}{2} & & -\frac{1}{2} \end{array}\right\|.$$

Π_6:

$\underline{S = 0,\ k = 3.}$

$\mathscr{P}_{12}, \ldots \mathscr{P}_{45}$ the same as for $S = \frac{1}{2}$, $k = 2$ of Π_5.

$$\mathscr{P}_{56} = \left\|\begin{array}{ccccc} -1 & & & & \\ & -1 & & & \\ & & -1 & & \\ & & & 1 & \\ & & & & 1 \end{array}\right\|.$$

The form of $\mathscr{P}_{56}$ may be understood, since the upper and lower parts arise from $S = 1$, $k = 1$ and $S = 0$, $k = 2$, respectively, of Π_4. To reach $S = 0$, $n = 6$ from these requires correspondingly $\underline{\mathbf{s}}_5 + \underline{\mathbf{s}}_6 = 1$, $P_{56}' = -1$ and $\underline{\mathbf{s}}_5 + \underline{\mathbf{s}}_6 = 0$, $P_{56}' = 1$.

The representations obtained by this method are necessarily equivalent to those obtained by the method of the preceding section, though they are clearly not identical, in general, since we now compound successive spins rather than successive pairs of spins to give the resultant spin S. In particular $\mathbf{P}_{12}$, $\mathbf{P}_{34}$, $\mathbf{P}_{56}$, . . . are now not in diagonal form except for certain singlets. For the calculation of atomic terms this is not of special import, since if we have a problem in which the first $2p$ of n

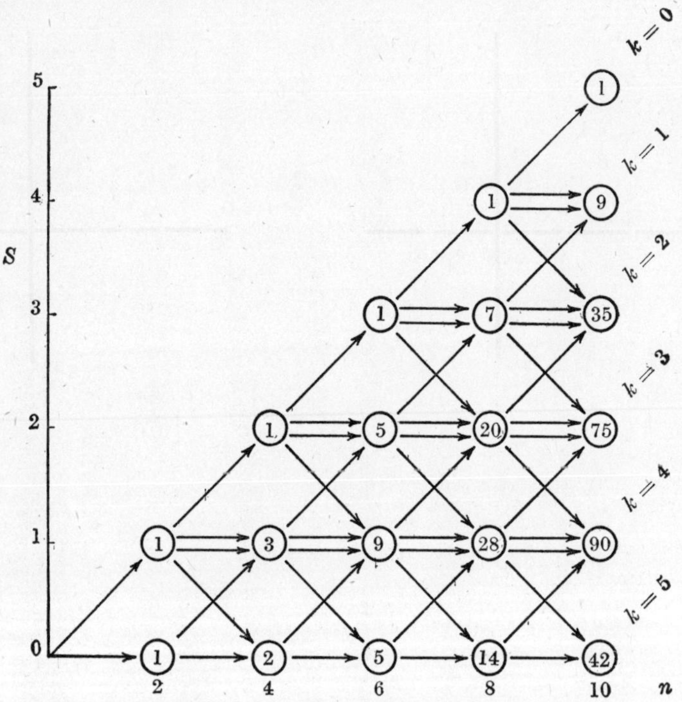

Fig. 10.1′.—Second branching diagram

orbits (1, 2) . . . $(2p - 1, 2p)$ are paired, this simply requires that, in the energy matrix, only those rows and columns are retained for which $P_{12}' = P_{34}' = \ldots = 1$, etc.[69] That is, in either method, we retain the parts of the representations coming from the alternate resultant spins

$$\underline{\mathbf{s}}_1 + \underline{\mathbf{s}}_2 = 0, \quad \underline{\mathbf{s}}_1 + \underline{\mathbf{s}}_2 + \underline{\mathbf{s}}_3 + \underline{\mathbf{s}}_4 = 0, \ldots, \quad \underline{\mathbf{s}}_1 + \underline{\mathbf{s}}_2 + \ldots \underline{\mathbf{s}}_{2p-1} + \underline{\mathbf{s}}_{2p} = 0,$$

which is to say that we follow the lowermost joining lines of the branching-rule diagram up to $2p$. If the number of states with resultant spin S arising from the composition of the remaining $n - 2p$ spins be g', then we use only the above-mentioned g'-dimensional parts of the representations for which $\mathscr{P}_{12}$, $\mathscr{P}_{34}$, . . . (and the elements of the subgroup generated from them) are the g'-dimensional unit matrix.

[69] See the next section for further details.

However, as we shall see in later sections, for molecular and other problems wherein elements of (space) symmetry appear, the requirement of diagonality for $\mathbf{P}_{12}$, $\mathbf{P}_{34}$, . . . becomes rather more than a matter of formal convenience in calculations.

To achieve the diagonality condition by the symbolical procedure we must compound successive spin pairs, obtaining thereby precisely the representations of the last section. We need not repeat the whole argument except to note that we now assume all irreducible representations of Π_{n-2} known, and the representations of Π_n chosen in reduced form for the elements contained in Π_{n-2}. The composition of spins by pairs now gives the modified branching diagram (Fig. 10.1′), in which each arrow represents as many components as the point from which it originates, e.g. the two arrows from $n = 6$, $S = 1$ to $n = 8$, $S = 1$ represent 18, while the arrow from $n = 6$, $S = 1$ to $n = 8$, $S = 2$ represents 9 states. We see that the representation $(n' = n - 2, k' = k - 1)$ of Π_{n-2} occurs *twice* in (n, k) of Π_n unless $k = 0$ or $\frac{1}{2}n$, and the diagram corresponding to (10:86*f*) is

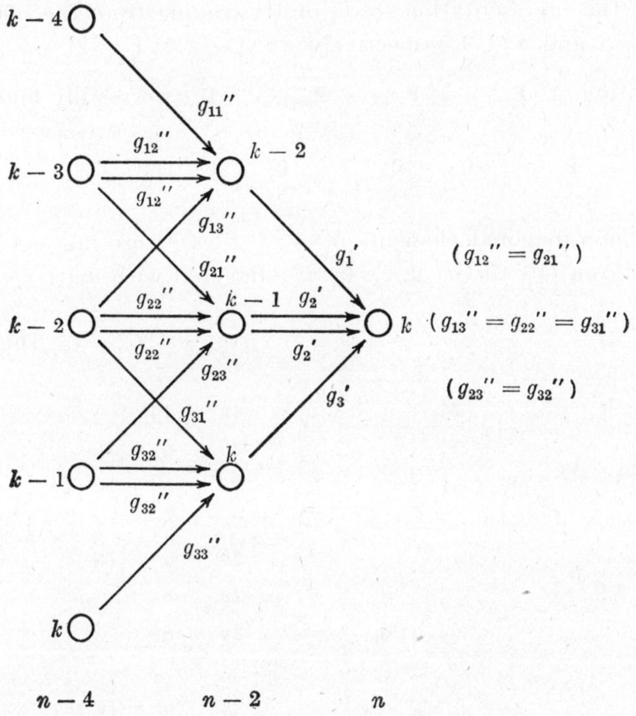

(10:87*a*)

For the present case the matrices of $\mathbf{P}_{i,\, n-2}$ $(i < n - 2)$ for the representation (n, k) of Π_n are known by hypothesis, and in addition $\mathbf{P}_{n-1,\, n}$ is diagonal with elements

$$\underbrace{-1, -1, \ldots -1}_{g_1'}, \quad \underbrace{-1, -1, \ldots -1}_{g_2'}, \quad \underbrace{1, 1, \ldots 1}_{g_2'}, \quad \underbrace{-1, -1, \ldots -1}_{g_3'},$$

according to the construction of the above diagram. It remains, therefore, to calculate the matrix $\mathscr{P}_{n-2,\, n-1}$ to bridge the remaining gap between elements of Π_{n-2} and Π_{n-1}, for a complete determination of the representation (n, k).

To this end we introduce semi-characters $\boldsymbol{\xi}_c$, now defined by

$$\boldsymbol{\xi}_c = \frac{1}{n_c - n_{c'}}\left(\sum_{c}^{(\Pi_n)} \mathbf{P}_c - \sum_{c}^{(\Pi_{n-2})} \mathbf{P}_c\right). \quad . \quad . \quad . \quad . \quad . \qquad (10:87b)$$

For the class of interchanges

$$\boldsymbol{\xi}\,[2] = \frac{1}{2n-3}\left\{\sum_{i=1}^{n-2}(\mathbf{P}_{i,\,n-1} + \mathbf{P}_{i,\,n}) + \mathbf{P}_{n-1,\,n}\right\}, \quad . \quad . \qquad (10:87c)$$

and its eigenvalues are readily found to be

$$\xi = \frac{1}{2n-3}\left\{\begin{matrix} 2S - n + 5 \\ -n + 3 \\ -2S - n + 3 \end{matrix}\right\} = \frac{1}{2n-3}\left\{\begin{matrix} -2k + 5 \\ -n + 3 \\ 2\,(k - n) + 3 \end{matrix}\right\} \qquad (10:87d)$$

for the parts of the representation (n, k) of Π_n coming from the representations of Π_{n-2} for $S + 1$, S and $S - 1$ respectively, i.e. $(n - 2, k - 2)$, $(n - 2, k - 1)$ and $(n - 2, k)$. Writing $\sum_{i=1}^{n-2}(\mathbf{P}_{i,\,n-1} + \mathbf{P}_{i,\,n}) + \mathbf{P}_{n-1,\,n} = \mathbf{C}_n$, we readily find that

$$\mathbf{P}_{n-2,\,n-1}(\mathbf{C}_n + \mathbf{C}_{n-2}) = (\mathbf{C}_n + \mathbf{C}_{n-2})\mathbf{P}_{n-2,\,n-1},$$

from which the non-diagonal elements of $\mathscr{P}_{n-2,\,n-1}$ are zero unless $(\mathbf{C}_n + \mathbf{C}_{n-2})_{kk} = (\mathbf{C}_n + \mathbf{C}_{n-2})_{ii}$. From (10:87*a*, *d*) $\mathbf{C}_{n-2}$, $\mathbf{C}_n$ are diagonal with matrix elements

C_{n-2}	C_n	$C_{n-2} + C_n$	Dimension
$-2k + 9$	$-2k + 5$	$-4k + 14$	g_{11}''
$-n + 5$	,,	$-2k - n + 10$	g_{12}''
$-n + 5$	,,	$-2k - n + 10$	g_{12}''
$2(k - n) + 3$	,,	$-2n + 8$	g_{13}''
$-2k + 7$	$-n + 3$	$-2k - n + 10$	g_{21}''
$-n + 5$	,,	$-2n + 8$	g_{22}''
$-n + 5$	,,	$-2n + 8$	g_{22}''
$2(k - n) + 5$	,,	$2k - 3n + 8$	g_{23}''
$-2k + 7$	,,	$-2k - n + 10$	g_{21}''
$-n + 5$	,,	$-2n + 8$	g_{22}''
$-n + 5$	,,	$-2n + 8$	g_{22}''
$2(k - n) + 5$	$2(k - n) + 3$	$2k - 3n + 8$	g_{23}''
$-2k + 5$	,,	$-2n + 8$	g_{31}''
$-n + 5$	,,	$2k - 3n + 8$	g_{32}''
$-n + 5$	,,	$2k - 3n + 8$	g_{32}''
$2(k - n) + 7$	,,	$4(k - n) + 10$	g_{33}''

(10:87*e*)

from which $\mathscr{P}_{n-2,\,n-1}$ is of the form (omitting transposed elements)

	g_{11}''	g_{12}''	g_{12}''	g_{13}''	g_{21}''	g_{22}''	g_{22}''	g_{23}''	g_{21}''	g_{22}''	g_{22}''	g_{23}''	g_{31}''	g_{32}''	g_{32}''	g_{33}''
g_{11}''	A_1															
g_{12}''		A_2	X_1		X_2				X_3							
g_{12}''			A_3		X_4				X_5							
g_{13}''				A_4		X_6	X_7			X_8	X_9					
g_{21}''					A_5											
g_{22}''						A_6	X_{10}			X_{11}	X_{12}		X_{13}			
g_{22}''							A_7			X_{14}	X_{15}		X_{16}			
g_{23}''								A_8				X_{17}		X_{18}	X_{19}	
{ g_{21}''									$-\frac{1}{2}$							
{ g_{22}''										$-\frac{1}{2}$	X_{20}		X_{21}			
{ g_{22}''											$-\frac{1}{2}$		X_{22}			
{ g_{23}''												$-\frac{1}{2}$		X_{23}	X_{24}	
g_{31}''													A_9			
g_{32}''														A_{10}	X_{25}	
g_{32}''															A_{11}	
g_{33}''																A_{12}

(10:87f)[70]

The bracketed elements correspond to $P'_{n-1,\,n} = 1$, for which, by a previous argument, the diagonal elements of $\mathscr{P}_{n-2,\,n-1}$ are $-\frac{1}{2}$. The remaining elements are obtained by use of the conditions $\mathbf{P}^*_{n-2,\,n-1} = \mathbf{P}^{-1}_{n-2,\,n-1}$, $\mathbf{P}^2_{n-2,\,n-1} = 1$, and the fact that $\mathbf{P}_{n-2,\,n-1}$ commutes with all elements of Π_{n-3}, whose matrices are known. In this way we find, for example,

Π_4:

$\underline{S = 0,\ k = 2.}$

$$\mathscr{P}_{12} = \left\| \begin{array}{c|c} -1 & \\ \hline & 1 \end{array} \right\|, \quad \mathscr{P}_{34} = \left\| \begin{array}{c|c} -1 & \\ \hline & 1 \end{array} \right\|,$$

[70] In the general case each entry denotes a matrix, but the full form above is not obtained until we come to $n = 12$, $S = 2$. For smaller n values most of the entries are just individual elements.

$$\mathscr{P}_{23} = \left\| \begin{array}{c|c} A_4 & X_9 \\ \hline X_9 & -\frac{1}{2} \end{array} \right\| = \left\| \begin{array}{c|c} \frac{1}{2} & -\sqrt{\frac{3}{4}} \\ \hline -\sqrt{\frac{3}{4}} & -\frac{1}{2} \end{array} \right\|.$$

Here, and in the following, the possible ambiguity in sign is of the type previously noted.

$\underline{S = 1, k = 1.}$

$$\mathscr{P}_{12} = \left\| \begin{array}{c|c|c} -1 & & \\ \hline & -1 & \\ \hline & & 1 \end{array} \right\|, \quad \mathscr{P}_{34} = \left\| \begin{array}{c|c|c} -1 & & \\ \hline & 1 & \\ \hline & & -1 \end{array} \right\|,$$

$$\mathscr{P}_{23} = \left\| \begin{array}{c|c|c} A_8 & X_{17} & X_{18} \\ \hline X_{17} & -\frac{1}{2} & X_{23} \\ \hline X_{18} & X_{23} & A_{10} \end{array} \right\| = \left\| \begin{array}{c|c|c} 0 & -\sqrt{\frac{1}{2}} & -\sqrt{\frac{1}{2}} \\ \hline -\sqrt{\frac{1}{2}} & -\frac{1}{2} & \frac{1}{2} \\ \hline -\sqrt{\frac{1}{2}} & \frac{1}{2} & -\frac{1}{2} \end{array} \right\|.$$

Π_6:

$\underline{S = 0, k = 3.}$

$$\mathscr{P}_{12} = \left\| \begin{array}{c|c|c|c|c} -1 & & & & \\ \hline & -1 & & & \\ \hline & & 1 & & \\ \hline & & & -1 & \\ \hline & & & & 1 \end{array} \right\|, \quad \mathscr{P}_{34} = \left\| \begin{array}{c|c|c|c|c} -1 & & & & \\ \hline & 1 & & & \\ \hline & & -1 & & \\ \hline & & & -1 & \\ \hline & & & & 1 \end{array} \right\|$$

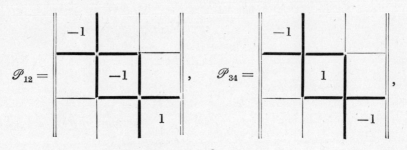

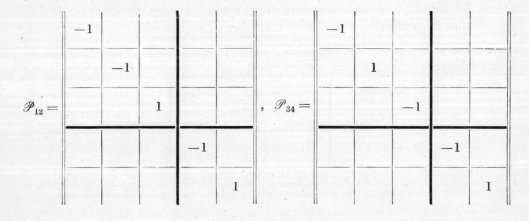

$$\mathscr{P}_{56} = \left\| \begin{array}{ccc|cc} -1 & & & & \\ & -1 & & & \\ & & -1 & & \\ \hline & & & 1 & \\ & & & & 1 \end{array} \right\|, \quad \mathscr{P}_{23} = \left\| \begin{array}{ccc|cc} 0 & -\sqrt{\frac{1}{2}} & -\sqrt{\frac{1}{2}} & & \\ -\sqrt{\frac{1}{2}} & -\frac{1}{2} & \frac{1}{2} & & \\ -\sqrt{\frac{1}{2}} & \frac{1}{2} & -\frac{1}{2} & & \\ \hline & & & \frac{1}{2} & -\sqrt{\frac{3}{4}} \\ & & & -\sqrt{\frac{3}{4}} & -\frac{1}{2} \end{array} \right\|,$$

$$\mathscr{P}_{45} = \left\| \begin{array}{ccccc} A_2 & X_1 & 0 & X_3 & 0 \\ X_1 & A_3 & 0 & X_5 & 0 \\ 0 & 0 & A_4 & 0 & X_8 \\ X_3 & X_5 & 0 & -\frac{1}{2} & 0 \\ 0 & 0 & X_8 & 0 & -\frac{1}{2} \end{array} \right\| = \left\| \begin{array}{ccccc} 0 & -\sqrt{\frac{1}{2}} & 0 & -\sqrt{\frac{1}{2}} & 0 \\ -\sqrt{\frac{1}{2}} & -\frac{1}{2} & 0 & \frac{1}{2} & 0 \\ 0 & 0 & \frac{1}{2} & 0 & -\sqrt{\frac{3}{4}} \\ -\sqrt{\frac{1}{2}} & \frac{1}{2} & 0 & -\frac{1}{2} & 0 \\ 0 & 0 & -\sqrt{\frac{3}{4}} & 0 & -\frac{1}{2} \end{array} \right\|.$$

$\underline{S = 1,\ k = 2.}$

$$\mathscr{P}_{12} = \left\| \begin{array}{c|ccc|ccc|cc} -1 & & & & & & & & \\ \hline & -1 & & & & & & & \\ & & -1 & & & & & & \\ & & & 1 & & & & & \\ \hline & & & & -1 & & & & \\ & & & & & -1 & & & \\ & & & & & & 1 & & \\ \hline & & & & & & & -1 & \\ & & & & & & & & 1 \end{array} \right\| \qquad \mathscr{P}_{34} = \left\| \begin{array}{c|ccc|ccc|cc} -1 & & & & & & & & \\ \hline & -1 & & & & & & & \\ & & 1 & & & & & & \\ & & & -1 & & & & & \\ \hline & & & & -1 & & & & \\ & & & & & 1 & & & \\ & & & & & & -1 & & \\ \hline & & & & & & & -1 & \\ & & & & & & & & 1 \end{array} \right\|$$

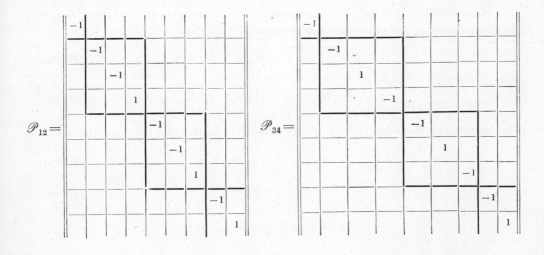

$$
\mathscr{P}_{56} = \left\| \begin{array}{c|ccc|ccc|cc}
-1 & & & & & & & & \\
\hline
 & -1 & & & & & & & \\
 & & -1 & & & & & & \\
 & & & -1 & & & & & \\
\hline
 & & & & 1 & & & & \\
 & & & & & 1 & & & \\
 & & & & & & 1 & & \\
\hline
 & & & & & & & -1 & \\
 & & & & & & & & -1
\end{array} \right\|
\qquad
\mathscr{P}_{13} = \left\| \begin{array}{c|ccc|ccc|cc}
-1 & & & & & & & & \\
\hline
 & 0 & -\sqrt{\frac{1}{2}} & \sqrt{\frac{1}{2}} & & & & & \\
 & -\sqrt{\frac{1}{2}} & -\frac{1}{2} & -\frac{1}{2} & & & & & \\
 & \sqrt{\frac{1}{2}} & -\frac{1}{2} & -\frac{1}{2} & & & & & \\
\hline
 & & & & 0 & -\sqrt{\frac{1}{2}} & \sqrt{\frac{1}{2}} & & \\
 & & & & -\sqrt{\frac{1}{2}} & -\frac{1}{2} & -\frac{1}{2} & & \\
 & & & & \sqrt{\frac{1}{2}} & -\frac{1}{2} & -\frac{1}{2} & & \\
\hline
 & & & & & & & \frac{1}{2} & \sqrt{\frac{3}{4}} \\
 & & & & & & & \sqrt{\frac{3}{4}} & -\frac{1}{2}
\end{array} \right\|
$$

$$
\mathscr{P}_{45} = \left\| \begin{array}{ccccccccc}
A_4 & X_6 & X_7 & 0 & X_8 & X_9 & 0 & 0 & 0 \\
 & A_6 & X_{10} & 0 & X_{11} & X_{12} & 0 & X_{13} & 0 \\
 & & A_7 & 0 & X_{14} & X_{15} & 0 & X_{16} & 0 \\
 & & & A_8 & 0 & 0 & X_{17} & 0 & X_{18} \\
 & & & & -\frac{1}{2} & X_{20} & 0 & X_{21} & 0 \\
 & & & & & -\frac{1}{2} & 0 & X_{22} & 0 \\
 & & & & & & -\frac{1}{2} & 0 & X_{23} \\
 & & & & & & & A_9 & 0 \\
 & & & & & & & & A_{10}
\end{array} \right\|
= \left\| \begin{array}{ccccccccc}
\frac{1}{4} & -\frac{1}{4}\sqrt{\frac{5}{3}} & -\frac{1}{2}\sqrt{\frac{5}{6}} & 0 & -\frac{1}{2}\sqrt{\frac{5}{6}} & -\frac{1}{2}\sqrt{\frac{5}{3}} & 0 & 0 & 0 \\
 & -\frac{1}{4} & -\frac{1}{2}\sqrt{\frac{1}{2}} & 0 & -\frac{1}{2}\sqrt{\frac{1}{2}} & \frac{1}{2} & 0 & -\sqrt{\frac{1}{3}} & 0 \\
 & & -\frac{1}{2} & 0 & \frac{1}{2} & 0 & 0 & \sqrt{\frac{1}{6}} & 0 \\
 & & & 0 & 0 & 0 & -\sqrt{\frac{1}{2}} & 0 & -\sqrt{\frac{1}{2}} \\
 & & & & -\frac{1}{2} & 0 & 0 & \sqrt{\frac{1}{6}} & 0 \\
 & & & & & -\frac{1}{2} & 0 & -\frac{1}{2}\sqrt{\frac{1}{3}} & 0 \\
 & & & & & & -\frac{1}{2} & 0 & \frac{1}{2} \\
 & & & & & & & -\frac{1}{2} & 0 \\
 & & & & & & & & -\frac{1}{2}
\end{array} \right\|
$$

§ 88. Generalization of the Dirac Vector Model*

(a) Configuration Interaction and Filled Orbits.

Let us consider now two configurations A, B of an n-electron system, denoting their respective prototype wave-functions as

$$\langle\, `x \mid A\,;\, `\alpha \,\rangle = \prod_j \langle\, x_j' \mid \alpha_j' \,\rangle, \quad . \quad . \quad . \quad . \quad . \qquad (10{:}88a)$$

and

$$\langle\, `x \mid B\,;\, ``\alpha \,\rangle = \prod_j \langle\, x_j' \mid \alpha_j'' \,\rangle. \quad . \quad . \quad . \quad . \quad . \qquad (10{:}88b)$$

The portions of the total energy matrix arising from the two configurations will be

$$\mathscr{V}^{AA} = \sum_{\mathscr{P}} \mathscr{V}^{AA}_{\mathscr{P}} \mathscr{P}, \quad . \quad . \quad . \quad . \quad . \quad . \quad . \qquad (10{:}89a)$$

$$\mathscr{V}^{BB} = \sum_{\mathscr{P}} \mathscr{V}^{BB}_{\mathscr{P}} \mathscr{P}, \quad . \quad . \quad . \quad . \quad . \quad . \quad . \qquad (10{:}89b)$$

* SERBER, R.: *Phys. Rev.*, **45**, 461 (1934).

where as before $\mathscr{V}^{AA}_{\mathscr{P}} = \langle P\,'\alpha \mid \mathbf{V} \mid {}'\alpha \rangle$, $\mathscr{V}^{BB}_{\mathscr{P}} = \langle P\,''\alpha \mid \mathbf{V} \mid {}''\alpha \rangle$; and each matrix $\mathscr{P}$ will be the same in both (10:89*a*, *b*) provided, as we shall assume to be the case, the states $\langle x \mid A\, ; P\,'\alpha \rangle$ and $\langle x \mid B\, ; P\,''\alpha \rangle$ are ordered in the same way. By the argument [cf. (10:28) *et seq.*] leading to (10:89*a*, *b*), we readily find

$$\langle P_a\,'\alpha \mid \mathbf{V} \mid P_b\,''\alpha \rangle = \langle P_a P_b^{-1}\,'\alpha \mid \mathbf{V} \mid {}''\alpha \rangle, \quad . \quad . \quad . \quad . \qquad (10:90)$$

so that the portion of the energy matrix in which the states $\langle\, 'x \mid B\, ; P\,''\alpha \rangle$ intersect the states $\langle\, 'x \mid A\, ; P\,'\alpha \rangle$ can be written as

$$\mathscr{V}^{BA} = \sum_{\mathscr{P}} \mathscr{V}^{BA}_{\mathscr{P}} \mathscr{P}. \quad . \quad . \quad . \quad . \quad . \quad . \quad . \quad . \qquad (10:91)$$

If a pair of orbits of B, say 1 and 2, are identical ($\alpha_1'' = \alpha_2''$), we know that with neglect of the perturbations due to other configurations, the energies of the states arising from B are the same as calculated for an $(n - 2)$-electron problem, except for an additive constant. However, if we wish to take account of configuration interaction we must formally distinguish between the identical orbits. The states $\langle\, 'x \mid B\, ; P\,''\alpha \rangle$ now will not form an orthogonal set since $\langle\, 'x \mid B\, ; P_a\,''\alpha \rangle = \langle\, 'x \mid B\, ; P_b\,''\alpha \rangle$ if $\mathbf{P}_a = \mathbf{P}_{12}\mathbf{P}_b$, and the modification required in the secular equation for non-orthogonal functions is that we calculate the matrix element of $\mathbf{V} - W\mathbf{I}$ (cf. § 32) instead of $\mathbf{V}$ for the configuration B, i.e. equation (10:89*b*) must be replaced by

$$(\mathscr{V} - W)^{BB} = \sum_{\mathscr{P}} (\mathscr{V} - W)^{BB}_{\mathscr{P}} \mathscr{P}. \quad . \quad . \quad . \quad . \quad . \qquad (10:92)$$ [71]

We assume for the present that all orbits of A are distinct (free). Then, if the degree of the matrices representing the $\mathbf{P}$'s is d, the complete energy matrix for both configurations A and B consists of four squares of degree d, viz.

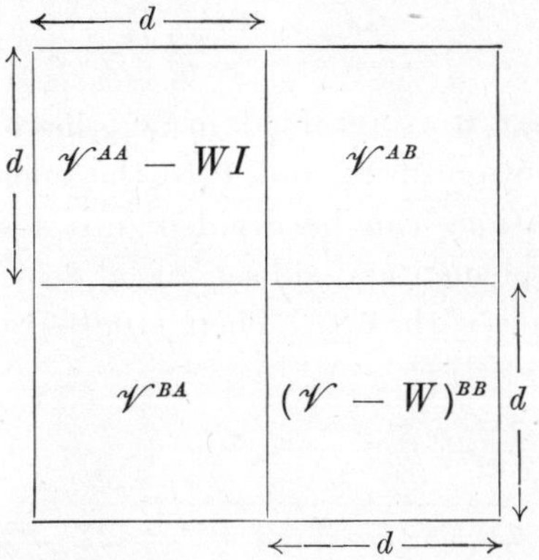

Fig. 10.3

We must now use a representation of the $\mathbf{P}$'s such that $\mathbf{P}_{12}$ is diagonal,[72] and there will be a number of rows, r, for which $\mathbf{P}_{12}$ has the eigenvalue 1, while for the remaining $(d - r)$ rows $\mathbf{P}_{12}$ has the eigenvalue -1. However, we know that in this case the

[71] (10:91) remains unchanged, since all states of configuration B will still be orthogonal to those of A.
[72] Cf. preceding sections.

only permissible states are those for which $P_{12}' = 1$, so that the $(d - r)$ rows and columns arising from B, for which $P_{12}' = -1$, must be deleted from the energy matrix, which then takes the form

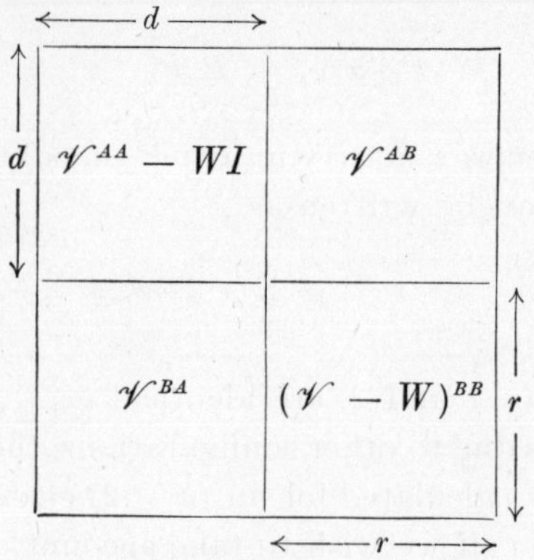

Fig. 10.4

We denote by $\mathscr{P}^{BA}$ the matrix obtained from $\mathscr{P}$ by deleting the improper $(d - r)$ rows, and by $\mathscr{P}^{BB}$ the matrix obtained by deleting the improper $(d - r)$ rows and columns; with which (10:91) and (10:92) become

$$\mathscr{V}^{BA} = \sum_{\mathscr{P}} \mathscr{V}_{\mathscr{P}}^{BA} \mathscr{P}^{BA}, \quad . \quad . \quad . \quad . \quad . \quad . \quad . \quad . \qquad (10{:}91')$$

$$(\mathscr{V} - W)^{BB} = \sum_{\mathscr{P}} (\mathscr{V} - W)_{\mathscr{P}}^{BB} \mathscr{P}^{BB}. \quad . \quad . \quad . \quad . \qquad (10{:}92')$$

Now, if $\mathbf{P}_a = \mathbf{P}_{12}\mathbf{P}$, then

$$(\mathscr{V} - W\delta_{B,X})_{\mathscr{P}_a}^{BX} = (\mathscr{V} - W\delta_{B,X})_{\mathscr{P}}^{BX} \qquad (X = A, B), \quad . \quad (10{:}93)$$

and $\mathscr{P}_a^{BX} = \mathscr{P}^{BX}$, since the r rows retained in $\mathscr{P}_{12}$ have only unity along the diagonal. Hence the contribution of $\mathbf{P}_a$ and $\mathbf{P}$ to the energy is $2(\mathscr{V} - W\delta_{B,X})_{\mathscr{P}}^{BX}\mathscr{P}^{BX}$, and the group of permutations can be divided into a subset of $n!/2$ independent permutations, and a complementary subset of $n!/2$ permutations obtained from the first by pre-multiplying with $\mathbf{P}_{12}$. Then (10:91′) and (10:92′) can be written in the form

$$\mathscr{V}^{BA} = 2\sum_{\mathscr{P}}{}' \mathscr{V}_{\mathscr{P}}^{BA} \mathscr{P}^{BA}, \quad . \quad . \quad . \quad . \quad . \quad . \quad . \quad . \quad . \quad . \qquad (10{:}94a)$$

$$(\mathscr{V} - W)^{BB} = 2\sum_{\mathscr{P}}{}' (\mathscr{V} - W)_{\mathscr{P}}^{BB} \mathscr{P}^{BB} = 2\sum_{\mathscr{P}}{}' \mathscr{V}_{\mathscr{P}}^{BB} \mathscr{P}^{BB} - 2WI, \quad (10{:}94b)$$

where the sum is now only over the $n!/2$ permutations of an independent subset; and the second form of (10:94b) follows since the exchange and higher-order permutation integrals of unity in (10:94b) are now zero.[73] The matrix $\mathscr{V}^{AB}$ can be obtained from $\mathscr{V}^{BA}$ by virtue of the Hermiticity of the energy matrix which now takes the form

[73] I.e. with the division into the above subsets, $\langle P''\alpha \,|\, \mathbf{I} \,|\, ''\alpha \rangle = 0$ unless $\mathbf{P} = \mathbf{I}$.

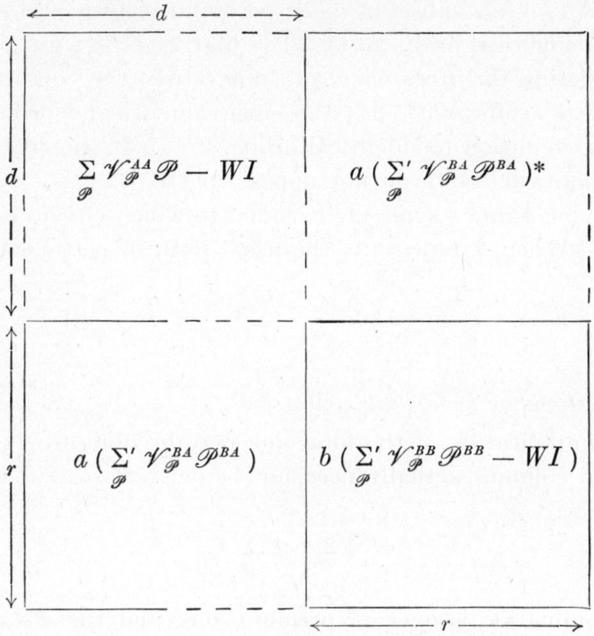

Fig. 10.5

with $a = b = 2$. The presence of the factor $-2W$ on the diagonal is particularly inconvenient, since we shall want to apply the diagonal sum theorem, and to this end we renormalize the energy matrix by dividing each row and column arising from the configuration B by $\sqrt{2}$, so that the final form is that of fig. 10.5 with $a = \sqrt{2}$, $b = 1$. The generalization of the preceding method to the case of more than one pair of identical orbits is now obvious. Thus, if orbits 1, 2 and 3, 4 of B are paired, we must use a representation in which both $\mathbf{P}_{12}$ and $\mathbf{P}_{34}$ are diagonal, retaining in the part of the energy matrix arising from B only those rows and columns for which both P_{12}' and P_{34}' are 1. The permutations $\mathbf{P}$, $\mathbf{P}_{12}\mathbf{P}$, $\mathbf{P}_{34}\mathbf{P}$ and $\mathbf{P}_{12}\mathbf{P}_{34}\mathbf{P}$ will contribute equal terms in the energy matrix, so that we have

$$\mathscr{V}^{BA} = 4 \sum_{\mathscr{P}}' \mathscr{V}^{BA}_{\mathscr{P}} \mathscr{P}^{BA}, \qquad (10{:}95a)$$

$$(\mathscr{V} - W)^{BB} = 4 \sum_{\mathscr{P}}' \mathscr{V}^{BB}_{\mathscr{P}} \mathscr{P}^{BB} - 4WI, \qquad (10{:}95b)$$

the summations now being over a subset of $n!/4$ permutations, and the normalized form of the energy matrix will be that of fig. 10.5 with $a = 2$, $b = 1$ (different numbers of rows and columns, of course).

In the general case there may be a set of configurations $C_1, C_2, \ldots C_i$, the configuration C_i containing p_i paired orbits.[74] Then we must use a representation in which $\mathbf{P}_{12}$, $\mathbf{P}_{34}$, etc., are diagonal, and if $p_i \geqslant p_j$ the normalized matrix $\mathscr{V}^{C_iC_j}$ is given by

$$\mathscr{V}^{C_iC_j} = \sqrt{2^{p_i - p_j}} \sum_{\mathscr{P}}' \mathscr{V}^{C_iC_j}_{\mathscr{P}} \mathscr{P}^{C_iC_j}, \qquad (10{:}96)$$

[74] The first, second, etc., pairs are always taken as orbits (1, 2), (3, 4), etc.

the summation being over a subset of $n!/2^{p_i}$ permutations which do not differ merely by interchanges of identical orbits in C_i. The matrices $\mathscr{P}^{C_iC_j}$ are obtained from the matrices $\mathscr{P}$ by deleting the rows which do not satisfy the condition that a transposition of identical orbits of C_i has the eigenvalue 1, and deleting the columns not satisfying this condition for identical orbits of C_j. It should be noted that the interchanges of identical orbits do not appear in (10:96); this corresponds to the procedure in applying Dirac's symbolic formula, to which (10:96) essentially reduces for $i = j$, $p_i = 0$. When $\mathbf{V}$ represents the usual form of perturbation, (10:96) with $i = j$ reduces to

$$\mathscr{V}^{C_iC_i} = \mathscr{V}_I^{C_iC_i} I + \sum_{k<l} \mathscr{V}_{\mathscr{P}_{kl}}^{C_iC_i} \mathscr{P}_{kl}^{C_iC_i}. \qquad (10:97)$$

(b) *Method of Iterations or Invariants—Matrical.*

An essential simplification of the foregoing may be obtained by noting that the *forbidden* rows and columns actually need not be deleted, so that instead of (10:96) we can write

$$\mathscr{V}^{C_iC_j} = \sqrt{2^{-p_i-p_j}} \sum_{\mathscr{P}} \mathscr{V}_{\mathscr{P}}^{C_iC_j} \mathscr{P}, \qquad (10:98)$$

where now the summation is over *all* permutations, and the $\mathscr{P}$'s are just the irreducible representations without any deletions. This follows from the observation [cf. (10:93)] that for permutations satisfying $\mathbf{P}_a = \mathbf{P}_{12}\mathbf{P}$, the matrix $\mathscr{P}_a$ equals $\mathscr{P}$ for the allowed part as previously noted, but is the negative of $\mathscr{P}$ for the rows and columns previously deleted, e.g. for $n = 3$ this condition obtains for the independent set $\mathbf{I}$, $\mathbf{P}_{13}$, $\mathbf{P}_{23}$ and $\mathbf{P}_{12}$, $\mathbf{P}_{123}$, $\mathbf{P}_{132}$. Hence, in using the full matrices $\mathscr{P}$, the undeleted rows and columns in (10:98) are all zero and the spurs are unaffected.

Correspondingly, the energy matrix has the form

$$
\begin{array}{c|c|c|c}
 & \longleftarrow d \longrightarrow & \multicolumn{1}{c}{} & \\
\cline{2-3}
d \updownarrow & \sum_{\mathscr{P}} \mathscr{V}_{\mathscr{P}}^{C_jC_j} \mathscr{P} - 2^{p_j} W I & \big(\sum_{\mathscr{P}} \mathscr{V}_{\mathscr{P}}^{C_iC_j} \mathscr{P}\big)^* & \\
\cline{2-3}
 & \sum_{\mathscr{P}} \mathscr{V}_{\mathscr{P}}^{C_iC_j} \mathscr{P} & \sum_{\mathscr{P}} \mathscr{V}_{\mathscr{P}}^{C_iC_i} \mathscr{P} - 2^{p_i} W I & \updownarrow d \\
\cline{2-3}
 & \multicolumn{1}{c}{} & \longleftarrow d \longrightarrow &
\end{array}
$$

Fig. 10.6

and renormalization now leads to the factor $\sqrt{2^{-p_i-p_j}}$.

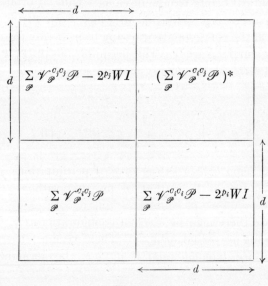

We can now set up the complete secular determinant for $M_L = 2$ required to separate the energies of the ${}^2D_{\pm}$ states of d^3 [cf. (10:55d)]. The four configurations are

$$C_1 : (\, d\pi \, d\pi_- \, d\delta \,), \quad C_2 : (\, d\sigma^2 \, d\delta \,), \quad C_3 : (\, d\pi^2 \, d\sigma \,), \quad C_4 : (\, d\delta^2 \, d\delta_- \,).$$

All the orbits of C_1 are different, so that if we use method I, the matrices $\mathscr{P}_{ij}^{C_1C_1}$ are just those given in (10:87); the orbits 1, 2 are paired in C_2, C_3, C_4 so that $\mathscr{P}_{ij}^{XC_1}$ ($X = C_2, C_3, C_4$) is the second row of $\mathscr{P}_{ij}$ and $\mathscr{P}_{ij}^{XY}$ ($X, Y = C_2, C_3, C_4$) is just the element in the second row and column of $\mathscr{P}_{ij}$. The energy matrix for the doublet states is then (using $\mathscr{V}_{12}^{C_1C_1}$ instead of $\mathscr{V}_{\mathscr{P}_{12}}^{C_1C_1}$, etc.) given by Table 10.3 (p. 226). The matrix elements are evaluated in the usual way and expressed in the S.C.S. F's and G's. The term values ${}^2H$, ${}^2G$, ${}^2F$, as well as the mean energy (ϵ) of the two ${}^2D$ levels, are known from the spur of $\mathscr{V}$. Similarly, the mean square energy (δ) is found by subtracting the squares of the three known term values from the spur of $\mathscr{V}^2$, which is simply the sum of the squares of the matrix elements. Then the energies of the two ${}^2D$ states are given by

$$ {}^2D_{\pm}\,(\, d^3 \,) = \epsilon \pm (\, \delta - \epsilon^2 \,)^{\frac{1}{2}}, \qquad . \; . \; . \; . \; . \quad (10{:}99)$$

which on evaluation in terms of the S.C.S. factors gives

$$ {}^2D_{\pm} = 3F_0 + 5F_2 + 3F_4 \pm (\, 193F_2{}^2 - 1650F_2F_4 + 8325F_4{}^2 \,)^{\frac{1}{2}}. \quad (10{:}100)$$ [75]

Alternatively with method (b) (10:98) we can avoid setting up the actual energy matrix, and compute $\mathscr{S}_p \mathscr{V}^2 = \sum_{ij} \mathscr{S}_p \mathscr{V}^{C_iC_j} \mathscr{V}^{C_jC_i}$ directly, using just the primitive characters, e.g. in the above illustration for d^3 we would have, for example,

$$\left.\begin{aligned} \mathscr{V}^{C_2C_1} &= \sqrt{\tfrac{1}{2}}\{\mathscr{V}_I^{C_2C_1}(I+\mathscr{P}_{12})+\mathscr{V}_{13}^{C_2C_1}(\mathscr{P}_{13}+\mathscr{P}_{132})+\mathscr{V}_{23}^{C_2C_1}(\mathscr{P}_{23}+\mathscr{P}_{123})\}. \\ \mathscr{V}^{C_1C_2} &= \sqrt{\tfrac{1}{2}}\{\mathscr{V}_I^{C_2C_1}(I+\mathscr{P}_{12})+\mathscr{V}_{13}^{C_2C_1}(\mathscr{P}_{13}+\mathscr{P}_{123})+\mathscr{V}_{23}^{C_2C_1}(\mathscr{P}_{23}+\mathscr{P}_{132})\}. \end{aligned}\right\} \quad (10{:}101)$$ [76]

The contribution of the interaction between C_1 and C_2 to $\mathscr{S}_p \mathscr{V}^2$ is then

$$\begin{aligned} \mathscr{S}_p \mathscr{V}^{C_2C_1}\mathscr{V}^{C_1C_2} + \mathscr{S}_p \mathscr{V}^{C_1C_2}\mathscr{V}^{C_2C_1} &= 2\,\mathscr{S}_p \mathscr{V}^{C_2C_1}\mathscr{V}^{C_1C_2} \\ &= (\,\mathscr{V}_I^{C_2C_1 2} + \mathscr{V}_{13}^{C_2C_1 2} + \mathscr{V}_{23}^{C_2C_1 2}\,)\,(\,2[\,\mathrm{I}\,] + 2[\,2\,])\\ &\quad + 2\,(\,\mathscr{V}_I^{C_2C_1}\mathscr{V}_{13}^{C_2C_1} + \mathscr{V}_I^{C_2C_1}\mathscr{V}_{23}^{C_2C_1} + \mathscr{V}_{13}^{C_2C_1}\mathscr{V}_{23}^{C_2C_1}\,)\,(\,2[\,2\,] + 2[\,3\,])\\ &= 2\,[\,(\,\mathscr{V}_I^{C_2C_1} - \mathscr{V}_{13}^{C_2C_1}\,)^2 + (\,\mathscr{V}_I^{C_2C_1} - \mathscr{V}_{23}^{C_2C_1}\,)^2 + (\,\mathscr{V}_{13}^{C_2C_1} - \mathscr{V}_{23}^{C_2C_1}\,)^2\,], \quad . \quad (10{:}102) \end{aligned}$$

since for $n = 3$, $S = \frac{1}{2}$ the primitive characters are $[I] = 2$, $[2] = 0$, $[3] = -1$. In the general case where there are more than two similar terms we should have to evaluate the invariants $\mathscr{S}_p \mathscr{V}$, $\mathscr{S}_p \mathscr{V}^2$, . . . $\mathscr{S}_p \mathscr{V}^r$, in order to separate the levels; e.g. for three similar terms we would have to obtain the mean (ϵ), mean square (δ),

[75] Cf. *T.A.S.*, § 8.

[76] We use the fact that $\mathscr{V}_{\mathscr{P}_a}^{C_2C_1} = \mathscr{V}_{\mathscr{P}}^{C_2C_1}$ for $\mathbf{P}_a = \mathbf{P}_{12}\mathbf{P}$, and obtain the matrix $\mathscr{V}^{C_1C_2}$ from its adjoint $\mathscr{V}^{C_2C_1}$; this process simply involves the replacement of each $\mathscr{P}$ in $\mathscr{V}^{C_2C_1}$ by its reciprocal, in virtue of the unitarity of the permutations.

† TABLE 10.3.—ENERGY MATRIX FOR DOUBLET STATES

$\mathcal{V}_{I}^{C_1C_1} - \mathcal{V}_{12}^{C_1C_1} + \frac{1}{2}\mathcal{V}_{13}^{C_1C_1} + \frac{1}{2}\mathcal{V}_{23}^{C_1C_1}$	$\sqrt{\frac{3}{4}}(\mathcal{V}_{13}^{C_1C_1} - \mathcal{V}_{23}^{C_1C_1})$	$\sqrt{\frac{3}{2}}(\mathcal{V}_{13}^{C_2C_1} - \mathcal{V}_{23}^{C_2C_1})$	$\sqrt{\frac{3}{2}}(\mathcal{V}_{13}^{C_3C_1} - \mathcal{V}_{23}^{C_3C_1})$	$\sqrt{\frac{3}{2}}(\mathcal{V}_{13}^{C_4C_1} - \mathcal{V}_{23}^{C_4C_1})$
	$\mathcal{V}_{I}^{C_1C_1} + \mathcal{V}_{12}^{C_1C_1} - \frac{1}{2}\mathcal{V}_{12}^{C_1C_1} - \frac{1}{2}\mathcal{V}_{23}^{C_1C_1}$	$\sqrt{2}(\mathcal{V}_{I}^{C_2C_1} - \frac{1}{2}\mathcal{V}_{13}^{C_2C_1} - \frac{1}{2}\mathcal{V}_{23}^{C_2C_1})$	$\sqrt{2}(\mathcal{V}_{I}^{C_3C_1} - \frac{1}{2}\mathcal{V}_{13}^{C_3C_1} - \frac{1}{2}\mathcal{V}_{23}^{C_3C_1})$	$\sqrt{2}(\mathcal{V}_{I}^{C_4C_1} - \frac{1}{2}\mathcal{V}_{13}^{C_4C_1} - \frac{1}{2}\mathcal{V}_{23}^{C_4C_1})$
		$\mathcal{V}_{I}^{C_2C_2} - \frac{1}{2}\mathcal{V}_{13}^{C_2C_2} - \frac{1}{2}\mathcal{V}_{23}^{C_2C_2}$	$\mathcal{V}_{I}^{C_3C_2} - \frac{1}{2}\mathcal{V}_{13}^{C_3C_2} - \frac{1}{2}\mathcal{V}_{23}^{C_3C_2}$	$\mathcal{V}_{I}^{C_4C_2} - \frac{1}{2}\mathcal{V}_{13}^{C_4C_2} - \frac{1}{2}\mathcal{V}_{23}^{C_4C_2}$
			$\mathcal{V}_{I}^{C_3C_3} - \frac{1}{2}\mathcal{V}_{13}^{C_3C_3} - \frac{1}{2}\mathcal{V}_{23}^{C_3C_3}$	$\mathcal{V}_{I}^{C_4C_3} - \frac{1}{2}\mathcal{V}_{13}^{C_4C_3} - \frac{1}{2}\mathcal{V}_{23}^{C_4C_3}$
				$\mathcal{V}_{I}^{C_4C_4} - \frac{1}{2}\mathcal{V}_{13}^{C_4C_4} - \frac{1}{2}\mathcal{V}_{23}^{C_4C_4}$

† The symmetrically located elements are not given in view of the Hermitian character of the energy matrix.

and mean cube (γ), from the spurs of $\mathscr{V}$, $\mathscr{V}^2$, and $\mathscr{V}^3$, whence the roots W would be obtained from

$$W^3 - 2\epsilon W^2 + (2\epsilon^2 - \delta) W - \tfrac{2}{3}(2\epsilon^3 - 3\epsilon\delta + \gamma) = 0.$$

For all but small values of r, the method (*b*) is likely to be more difficult than (*a*).

(*c*) *Method of Iterations or Invariants—Symbolical.*

The method (*b*) of iterations or invariants is of course implicit in the symbolic Dirac method, viz. in the case of a single configuration we know that the average energy of all states belonging to an exclusive set is given by

$$\langle V' \rangle = \epsilon = \sum_P V_P \chi'[P], \qquad (10:103)$$

and the same procedure can be used to calculate the average eigenvalue of any function of **V**. If we wish to include configuration interaction using the symbolic method (wherein each permutation is replaced by its appropriate character eigenvalue rather than primitive character), we must define the configuration operators and the total average as

$$\mathbf{V}^{c_i c_j} = \sqrt{2^{-p_i - p_j}} \sum_P V_P^{c_i c_j} \mathbf{P}, \qquad (10:104a)$$

$$\langle V' \rangle = \sum_i \langle V^{c_i c_i} \rangle = \sum_i 2^{-p_i} \sum_P V_P^{c_i c_i} \chi'[P], \qquad (10:104b)$$

and correspondingly *define* the total average square as

$$\langle V^{2\prime} \rangle = \sum_{ij} \langle V^{c_i c_j} V^{c_j c_i} \rangle = \delta. \qquad (10:104c)$$

This modification is of course somewhat artificial, but, as we shall see, the symbolic method can be used in its original form without modification to obtain the energies of similar terms in a large variety of molecular problems.

§ 89. Molecular Problems

(*a*) *Non-directional Valence.*

A large number of fundamental results in molecular problems can be easily obtained by the vector model, and we may illustrate with a few simple examples.

If we take the simplest case of a diatomic molecule AB, and assume that all the interatomic exchange integrals are equal, and neglect non-orthogonality corrections [77] [cf. § 89 (*c*)], then the interatomic exchange energy is given by (10:60*b*) with S_k, $S_{>k}$

[77] This is the usual assumption of the W. Heitler–G. Rumer theory of valence [*Z.f.P.*, **68**, 12 (1929)], which thus entirely neglects directional valence, e.g. in the chemistry of the light elements whose valence electrons are in orbits specified by the principal quantum number $n = 2$, this assumption means that the interatomic Coulomb and exchange integrals between electrons in the 2-quantum orbits $2s$, $2p\sigma_x$, $2p\sigma_y$, $2p\sigma_z$ of one atom (x, y, z denoting spatial quantization relative to the x axis, etc.) and an electron of another are equal, i.e. all valence electrons are effectively in s states. This is a particularly poor assumption for stereochemical purposes.

denoting the spins of the two atoms, and $K(1, n)$ the common exchange integral; or with $n - k = n = \nu$,

$$W_{ex} = -\{\tfrac{1}{2}\nu^2 + S(S+1) - S_A(S_A+1) - S_B(S_B+1)\}K(A, B), \quad (10{:}105)$$

which is Heitler's formula.[78] Moreover, since $K(A, B) < 0$ in the usual molecular case, it follows that the energy is minimized by making S_A, S_B as large as possible, and S as small as possible.

If instead of (10:56) we take the conditions

$$K(i, j) = \left.\begin{array}{ll} A & \text{for } i, j \leqslant k, \\ B & \text{for } i \leqslant k, j > k, \\ C & \text{for } i, j > k, \end{array}\right\} \quad . \ . \ . \ . \quad (10{:}106)$$

then corresponding to (10:57) the exchange energy term takes the form

$$-\tfrac{1}{2}A \sum_{\substack{i,j \\ i<j\leqslant k}} (1 + 4\underline{\mathbf{s}}_i \cdot \underline{\mathbf{s}}_j) - \tfrac{1}{2}B \sum_{\substack{i,j \\ i\leqslant k<j}} (1 + 4\underline{\mathbf{s}}_i \cdot \mathbf{s}_j) - \tfrac{1}{2}C \sum_{\substack{i,j \\ k<i<j}} (1 + 4\underline{\mathbf{s}}_i \cdot \underline{\mathbf{s}}_j), \quad (10{:}107a)$$

with the eigenvalues

$$\begin{aligned} -\tfrac{1}{2}A\{ \tfrac{1}{2}k(k-1) + 2[S_k(S_k+1) - \tfrac{3}{4}k]\} \\ -\tfrac{1}{2}B\{ k(n-k) + 2[S(S+1) - S_k(S_{k+1}) - S_{>k}(S_{>k}+1)]\} \\ -\tfrac{1}{2}C\{\tfrac{1}{2}(n-k)(n-k-1) + 2[S_{>k}(S_{>k}+1) - \tfrac{3}{4}(n-k)]\}. \quad (10{:}107b) \end{aligned}$$

Considering CH_4, for example, the non-directional theory of valence treats all electrons of C as alike, so that with $n - k = k = 4$, and K_{CC}, K_{CH}, K_{HH}, S_C, S_{4H} replacing A, B, C, S_k, $S_{>k}$ respectively, equation (10:107*b*) shows that if $K_{CH} < 0$, the CH exchange energy is minimized by taking S_C and S_{4H} as large as possible, and S as small as possible; or $S_C = S_{4H} = 2$, $S = 0$. Then (10:107*b*) becomes

$$W_{ex} = -6K_{CC} + 4K_{CH} - 6K_{HH}, \quad . \ . \ . \ . \quad (10{:}107c)$$

according to which the valence state[79] of the C atom should be $^5S(p^3s)$ [cf. (10:62*a*)]. The expression (10:107*c*) is to be compared with the result (10:110) based on directional valence and electron (bond) pairing. The non-directional theory assumes the repulsions between attached atoms to be the prime factor determining the space structure, or that one direction is as good as another, as far as the central atom is concerned, e.g. the repulsion of H atoms for $CH_4(K_{HH} < 0)$ from which we can infer the correct tetrahedral structure. But on the same basis we would be led to a plane model for NH_3 and linear model for H_2O, etc., which are not correct.

[78] HEITLER, W.: *Phys. Zeits.*, **31**, 197 (1930).

[79] In principle, the tetravalent state of carbon should be expected to be some linear combination of the atomic states ^5S, ^3S, ^3D, ^1D, ^3P, ^1P arising from the configuration sp^3; nor can one exclude the possibility that the carbon atom resonates between the excited configuration sp^3 and the normal s^2p^2. Cf. * VAN VLECK, J. H., SHERMAN, A.: *Rev. Mod. Phys.*, **7**, 167 (1935), and VAN VLECK, J. H.: *Jour. Chem. Phys.*, **2**, 20 (1934).

(*b*) *Pair Bonds.*

The interatomic exchange interaction $-\frac{1}{2}(1 + 4\underline{\mathbf{s}}_i \cdot \underline{\mathbf{s}}_j)K(i, j)$ for electrons i, j on different atoms takes its minimum value for the eigenvalue $+K(i, j)$, since the interatomic exchange integral is usually negative. An electron pair-bond may then be described as two electrons on *different* atoms whose spins are antiparallel, corresponding to a minimum exchange energy. Since it is obviously impossible to minimize all terms this way simultaneously, the next best thing is to minimize the large terms in the exchange energy

$$\mathbf{V}_{ex} = -\tfrac{1}{2}\sum_{i<j}(1 + 4\underline{\mathbf{s}}_i \cdot \underline{\mathbf{s}}_j)K(i, j), \quad \ldots \ldots \quad (10{:}108)$$

accepting as a necessary evil the unfavourable values for the small terms. This so-called electron pair-bonding approximation usually arises from directional valence,[80] where individual wave-functions project out from the central atom in particular directions, leading to a special affinity (large overlap of wave-functions) for atoms attached in these directions (cf. § 90). When this picture is applicable the exchange forces between electrons i and i' of different atoms may be large compared to all others acting on i, i', so that $\underline{\mathbf{s}}_i + \underline{\mathbf{s}}_{i'}$ is diagonal and equal to zero (for the state of deepest energy if $K(i, i') < 0$ as usual), and by a previous result $-\frac{1}{2}(1 + 4\underline{\mathbf{s}}_i \cdot \underline{\mathbf{s}}_j)K(i, j) = -\frac{1}{2}K(i, j)$ for a member of the bond pair and any other electron j. Hence, equation (10:108) gives

$$W_{ex} = \sum_{i<i'} K(i, i') - \tfrac{1}{2}\sum_{i<j\neq i'} K(i, j), \quad \ldots \ldots \quad (10{:}109)$$

showing that paired electrons, in effect, tend to repel other electrons. Considering again CH_4, we let K_{CH} denote the exchange integral connecting a tetrahedral wave-function of C (of which there are four)[81] and the nearest H atom; $K_{CH'}$ the exchange integral connecting it with any of the other H atoms, which are equidistant in virtue of the tetrahedral symmetry; K_{HH} the exchange integral connecting two H atoms; and K_{CC} that between tetrahedral orbitals of C. Then, according to (10:109), we find

$$W_{ex} = 4K_{CH} - \tfrac{1}{2}(12K_{CH'} + 6K_{HH} + 6K_{CC}). \quad \ldots \quad (10{:}110)$$

(*c*) *Non-orthogonality Corrections *—The Four-Electron Problem.*

The particular forte of the non-directional valence theory appears to be in the calculation of activation energies[82] of chemical reactions which cannot be computed on the electron-pair theory, since the chemical transformation is one of change of bond type, and the activation zone is just where the affinities are being changed,

[80] Cf. * Van Vleck and Sherman: *Rev. Mod. Phys.*, **7**, 167 (1935).

[81] Van Vleck and Sherman, *loc. cit.*, *also* § 90.

* Serber, R.: *Jour. Chem. Phys.*, **2**, 697 (1934). For related exchange problems in crystals, cf. Van Vleck, J. H.: *Phys. Rev.*, **49**, 232 (1936); Hulthén, L.: *Arkiv för Mat. Astr. Och Fys.*, **26**A, No. 11 (1938).

[82] The activation energy is the difference between the energy of the initial state and that of the intermediate (activated) state of highest energy, through which the system must pass from initial to final configuration.

so that there is no natural system of partnership. We consider this problem since it seems to illustrate the range of problems amenable to treatment by the vector problem, and also the power of the method in obtaining, so simply, a variety of fundamental results. In particular, we shall consider the determination of the energies of the singlet states of four electrons in non-identical orbits. The orbits need not be orthogonal,[83] and we consider here the necessary corrections, which are of two kinds. There will be a correction required owing to the non-vanishing of interchange and higher-order permutation integrals of unity, which is of minor importance and can easily be corrected for in the final results; however, it is important now to include third and higher-order permutations in the fundamental equation $\mathbf{V} = \sum_P V_P \mathbf{P}$, so that for four electrons, for example, we have

$$\begin{aligned}\mathbf{V} = V_{12}\mathbf{P}_{12} + \ldots + V_{34}\mathbf{P}_{34} + V_{123}(\mathbf{P}_{123} + \mathbf{P}_{132}) + V_{124}(\mathbf{P}_{124} + \mathbf{P}_{142}) \\ + V_{134}(\mathbf{P}_{134} + \mathbf{P}_{143}) + V_{234}(\mathbf{P}_{234} + \mathbf{P}_{243}) + V_{12,34}\mathbf{P}_{12}\mathbf{P}_{34} \\ + V_{13,24}\mathbf{P}_{13}\mathbf{P}_{24} + V_{14,23}\mathbf{P}_{14}\mathbf{P}_{23} + V_{1234}(\mathbf{P}_{1234} + \mathbf{P}_{1432}) \\ + V_{1243}(\mathbf{P}_{1243} + \mathbf{P}_{1342}) + V_{1324}(\mathbf{P}_{1324} + \mathbf{P}_{1423}). \quad . \quad . \quad (10{:}111)\end{aligned}$$

We omit the Coulomb energy V_I which contributes only an additive term to the energy, and assume that the permutation integrals are real so that $V_P = V_{P^{-1}}$. Then the mean energy of the two singlet states is given by replacing each $\mathbf{P}$ by $\chi'[P]$ corresponding [84] to $n = 4$, $S = 0$, which gives

$$\langle V' \rangle = \epsilon = -(V_{123} + V_{124} + V_{134} + V_{234}) + (V_{12,34} + V_{13,24} + V_{14,23}), \quad (10{:}112)$$

since here $\chi'[2] = 0$, $\chi'[3] = -\frac{1}{2}$, $\chi'[4] = 0$, and $\chi'[2^2] = 1$. Similarly, $\langle V^{2\prime} \rangle$ is readily found by noting that many similar terms will occur, so that we need only examine typical terms of each type, such as $V_{12}\mathbf{P}_{12}\mathbf{V}$, etc., rather than multiply term by term. The result may be conveniently given in the form

$$\begin{aligned}\langle V^{2\prime} \rangle - \langle V' \rangle^2 &= \delta - \epsilon^2 \\ &= [V_{12}{}^2 + V_{13}{}^2 + \ldots V_{34}{}^2] - [V_{12}V_{13} + V_{12}V_{14} + V_{12}V_{23} + \ldots] \\ &\quad + 2[V_{12}V_{34} + V_{13}V_{24} + V_{14}V_{23}] \\ &\quad - 2[(V_{12} + V_{14} + V_{23} + V_{34})V_{1234} + (V_{12} + V_{13} + V_{24} + V_{34})V_{1243} \\ &\qquad + (V_{13} + V_{14} + V_{23} + V_{24})V_{1324}] \\ &\quad + 4[V_{1234}^2 + V_{1243}^2 + V_{1324}^2] \\ &\quad - 4[V_{1234}V_{1243} + V_{1234}V_{1324} + V_{1243}V_{1324}], \quad . \quad . \quad (10{:}113)\end{aligned}$$

whence we have

$$\begin{aligned}W_{ex} = -(V_{123} + V_{124} + V_{134} + V_{234}) + (V_{12,34} + V_{13,24} + V_{14,23}) \\ \pm \{\tfrac{1}{2}[(\alpha - \beta)^2 + (\alpha - \gamma)^2 + (\beta - \gamma)^2]\}^{1/2}, \quad . \quad . \quad (10{:}114)\end{aligned}$$

[83] Generally, *are not* orthogonal in molecular problems.

[84] In the matrix analogue we take the spur, which then gives the sum directly instead of the average.

where

$$\alpha = V_{12} + V_{34} + 2V_{1324},$$

$$\beta = V_{13} + V_{24} + 2V_{1234},$$

$$\gamma = V_{14} + V_{23} + 2V_{1243}.$$

If we assume orthogonality (as is usually done), then (10:114) reduces to London's equation,

$$W_{ex} = \{ \tfrac{1}{2} [(K_{12} + K_{34} - K_{13} - K_{24})^2 + (K_{12} + K_{34} - K_{14} - K_{23})^2 + (K_{13} + K_{24} - K_{14} - K_{23})^2] \}^{1/2}, \quad . \; . \; . \; . \; . \; . \; . \quad (10:115)$$

which is required for computation of the energy of the activated state for reactions like $XY + WZ \rightarrow XW + YZ$ (each atom monovalent). Moreover, the exchange energy for three electrons in the doublet state follows immediately when we delete all terms referring to orbit 4.

§ 90. Note on Directional Valence

For the problem of the next section it is convenient to have available a few of the simple concepts of directed valence.[85] Without entering into detailed analysis we may note the following:

The simplest valence types are (1) the *s-valence*, in which an electron of a central atom is in an s state, hence exhibiting no directional properties; (2) the *p-valences* corresponding to the three possible p-electron functions $p\sigma$, $p\pi_+$, $p\pi_-$, whose angular parts are $\cos\theta$, $\sin\theta\, e^{i\varphi}/\sqrt{2}$, $\sin\theta\, e^{-i\varphi}/\sqrt{2}$ respectively, or rather the real linear combinations $p\sigma_x$, $p\sigma_y$, $p\sigma_z$ ($\sin\theta\cos\phi$, $\sin\theta\sin\phi$, $\cos\theta$) with dumb-bell-shaped charge distribution in the axial directions indicated. These functions lead directly to the simplest view of directional valence, since, for example, the exchange integral between a $p\sigma_{x,\,y,\,z}$ electron of a central atom (in a given molecule) and an s electron of an attached atom will be largest in absolute value (large overlap of wave-functions) for the attached atom on the x, y, z axis respectively.

The directed quadricovalence of the C atom is described as due to sp^3 hybridization, which neglects the energy difference between $2s$ and $2p$ carbon electrons, and forms four orthogonal linear combinations of the s, $p\sigma_x$, $p\sigma_y$, and $p\sigma_z$ functions. The hybridization ratio is the coefficient of the various functions in the linear combination; and for CH_4 the reasonable assumption of equal (in absolute magnitude) hybridization ratios leads directly to the tetrahedral structure. If the valence electron of an attached atom is in a p state, the foregoing principles again apply, with the difference that the paired p orbit is directed toward the central atom. Such single bonds are referred to as $\sigma\sigma$ bonds. Double and triple bonds are accounted

[85] Cf. * VAN VLECK and SHERMAN: *Rev. Mod. Phys.*, **3**, 167 (1935); and WALTER, EYRING, KIMBALL, *op. cit.* Chapters 12–14 of the latter give a general survey and, in particular, analysis of our illustrative molecular problems by the method of bond eigenfunctions and molecular orbitals, which may be profitably consulted for comparison with the vector model.

for by introducing the concept of $\pi\pi$ bonds wherein the axes of the dumb-bells of the two charge distributions are perpendicular to the interatomic axis.[86]

The planar hexagonal C_6H_6 structure is essentially accounted for by sp^2 hybridization, viz. three linear combinations which *in this case* lead to three coplanar equiangular bonds from each C atom. One of these, then, attaches the H atom, and the other two essentially form electron pairs with the adjacent C atoms. In

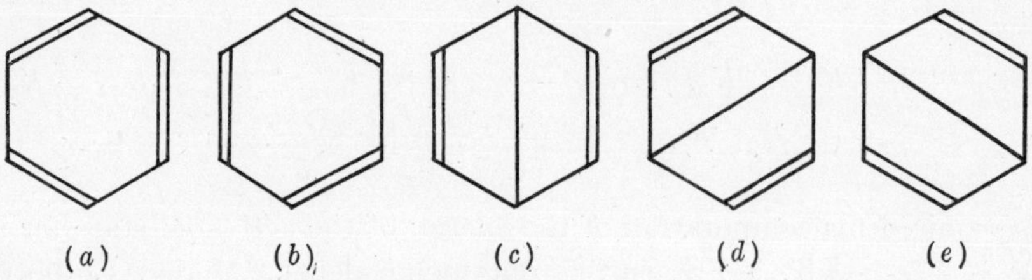

Fig. 10.7

addition to these σ bonds there are three $\pi\pi$ bonds (for the whole system) connecting the six available ($2p$) dumb-bell orbitals whose axes are perpendicular to the plane of the molecule. For these there is clearly no natural scheme of pairing, and they may be shown to lead to the five possible independent structures of fig. 10.7, in agreement with the fact that the six-electron problem of minimum spin gives rise to a fifth-degree secular problem.

§ 91. Factorization of the Secular Equation *

(a) The Six-Electron Problem.

As final examples of the application of the vector model we shall consider the six-electron problem for hexagonal structure (e.g. C_6H_6), and the eight-electron problem for simple cubic structure; which examples also serve to illustrate the factorization of the secular equation resulting from the presence of additional elements of symmetry.[87] The calculation for C_6H_6 corresponds to assuming the s, $p\sigma_x$ and $p\sigma_y$ C electrons and the H electrons to be localized in $\sigma\sigma$ bonds, so that we deal only with the part of the binding energy related to the interaction of the six $p\sigma_z$ C electrons.

In the general case, neglecting non-orthogonality and omitting the additive Coulomb term, one would have the Hamiltonian

$$\mathbf{V} = \sum_{i<j} K_{ij}\mathbf{P}_{ij}, \quad . \quad . \quad . \quad . \quad . \quad . \quad . \quad (10:116a)$$

or the equivalent form

$$\mathscr{V} = \sum_{i<j} K_{ij}\mathscr{P}_{ij}. \quad . \quad . \quad . \quad . \quad . \quad . \quad . \quad (10:116b)$$

[86] There will of course be less overlap of orbitals in $\pi\pi$ bonds, which must therefore be weaker than $\sigma\sigma$ bonds.

* Cf. SERBER, R.: *Jour. Chem. Phys.*, **2**, 697 (1934), also *Phys. Rev.*, **45**, 461 (1934).

[87] Viz. groups of rotations and reflections which send the space figure (structure) into itself.

The determination of the energy levels involves setting up the secular determinant for (10:116*b*) with the matrices $\mathscr{P}_{ij}$ appropriate to the multiplicities 1, 3, 5, 7 (calculated as in §§ 86, 87); or the application of the method of invariants using the symbolic form (10:116*a*) with the Dirac character eigenvalues; or the matrix form (10:116*b*) with the corresponding primitive characters. In either case the solution of the problem, even for the singlet states, is all but intractable.

In the case of C_6H_6 the distinct exchange integrals are of the type $K_{12} = \alpha$, $K_{13} = \beta$, $K_{14} = \gamma$ (owing to the hexagonal symmetry), and, neglecting all exchange integrals except between adjacent atoms, **V** becomes

$$\mathbf{V} = \alpha \{ \mathbf{P}_{12} + \mathbf{P}_{23} + \mathbf{P}_{34} + \mathbf{P}_{45} + \mathbf{P}_{56} + \mathbf{P}_{61} \}. \quad . \quad . \quad (10{:}117)$$ [88]

With this simplification we may determine the successive invariants for the singlet states, viz.

$$\langle V \rangle = \epsilon = \frac{-6}{5}\alpha, \quad . \quad . \quad . \quad . \quad . \quad . \quad (10{:}118a)$$

$$\langle V^2 \rangle = \delta = \frac{36}{5}\alpha, \quad . \quad . \quad . \quad . \quad . \quad . \quad (10{:}118b)$$

$$\langle V^3 \rangle = \lambda = \frac{-96}{5}\alpha^3, \quad . \quad . \quad . \quad . \quad . \quad (10{:}118c)$$

etc.,[89] from which we find the exchange energies

$$0, \quad -2\alpha, \quad -2\alpha, \quad -(1 \pm \sqrt{13})\,\alpha, \quad . \quad . \quad . \quad . \quad (10{:}119)$$

so that with $\alpha < 0$, the ground state (aside from Coulomb energy) is given by $-(1-\sqrt{13})\alpha \approx 2.61\alpha$. For *either* Kekulé structure (*a*, *b*, fig. 10.7, p. 232) we find the exchange energy 1.5α, which follows simply from (10:109) on noting that the exchange coefficient is $+1$ for 3 pairs (e.g. 1, 2 ; 3, 4 ; 5, 6) and $-\frac{1}{2}$ for 3 pairs (e.g. 2, 3 ; 4, 5 ; 6, 1). Clearly the structures *a*, *b* are the most stable of all, and the resonance energy, which is the difference between the actual energy and that of the most stable single structure,[90] is then 1.11α.

This application of the invariants technique is hardly to be recommended, and we shall now see that we can easily solve the problem without restriction, by consideration of the aforementioned symmetry elements. With the same labelling of the orbits we note that there exist twelve rotation symmetry operators which, in effect, simply permute the similar orbits among themselves. These operations according to classes are $C_1 = I$; $C_2 = R_2$; $C_3 = R_3^+, R_3^-$; $C_4 = R_6^+, R_6^-$; $C_5 = R_2(1-4), R_2(2-5), R_2(3-6)$; $C_6 = R_2(1 \perp 2), R_2(2 \perp 3), R_2(3 \perp 4)$; where,

[88] Numbering orbits consecutively clockwise.

[89] For the third and higher invariants we need to extend the results (10:15–21) to include Dirac characters for the class {23}, etc., or obtain them from the group formula (10:76).

[90] A simple calculation by the method of bond eigenfunctions (cf. *Quantum Chemistry*, Chaps. 12, 13) shows that the exchange energy for the *two* Kekulé structures is 2.40α, or that 0.90α of the energy arises from resonance between these two structures. This simplified calculation cannot be handled by the vector model.

for example, R_3^+ denotes a clockwise rotation of $2\pi/3$ about the (hexagonal) centre of symmetry, $R_2(1 - 4)$ a rotation of π about the symmetry axis through the atoms (1, 4), and $R_2(1 \perp 2)$ a rotation of π about the symmetry axis perpendicular to the bond between atoms 1 and 2. It is readily seen that each symmetry operation is equivalent to a certain permutation of the orbits, e.g. by classes as shown in Table 10.4.

TABLE 10.4

Class	Symmetry Element	Equivalent Permutation
C_1	I	I
C_2	R_2	$P_{14}P_{25}P_{36}$
C_3	R_3^+	$P_{135}P_{246}$
	R_3^-	$P_{153}P_{264}$
C_4	R_6^+	P_{123456}
	R_6^-	P_{165432}
C_5	$R_2(1 - 4)$	$P_{26}P_{35}$
	$R_2(2 - 5)$	$P_{13}P_{46}$
	$R_2(3 - 6)$	$P_{15}P_{24}$
C_6	$R_2(1 \perp 2)$	$P_{12}P_{36}P_{45}$
	$R_2(2 \perp 3)$	$P_{14}P_{23}P_{56}$
	$R_2(3 \perp 4)$	$P_{16}P_{25}P_{34}$

Hence, this group D_6 of symmetry operations[91] is abstractly identical with this subgroup of the symmetric group Π_6. The Hamiltonian (neglecting non-orthogonality) will now be

$$\mathbf{V} = \alpha\{\mathbf{P}_{12} + \mathbf{P}_{23} + \mathbf{P}_{34} + \mathbf{P}_{45} + \mathbf{P}_{56} + \mathbf{P}_{61}\} + \beta\{\mathbf{P}_{13} + \mathbf{P}_{15} + \mathbf{P}_{24} + \mathbf{P}_{26} + \mathbf{P}_{35} + \mathbf{P}_{46}\} + \gamma\{\mathbf{P}_{14} + \mathbf{P}_{25} + \mathbf{P}_{36}\}, \quad (10{:}120)$$

and it is readily verified that $\mathbf{V}$ commutes with the above subgroup of permutations. The group D_6 obviously has 6 non-equivalent irreducible representations of dimensions 1, 1, 1, 1, 2, 2; and from the orthogonality relations of the group character (cf. Chap. VI) we can readily construct Table 10.5 of group characters.[92]

[91] The extended group D_{6h} of order 24 (cf. MURNAGHAN, *op. cit.*, Chap. XI) includes the inversion which, however, is equivalent to R_2.

[92] In practice these tables are, of course, obtained from the standard group literature, cf. MURNAGHAN, p. 349.

TABLE 10.5

CHARACTER TABLE—DIHEDRAL GROUP D_6 CHARACTER TABLE—GROUP Π_6

		Representation						Representation			
		A_1	A_2	B_1	B_2	E_1	E_2	$S=0$	$S=1$	$S=2$	$S=3$
Class	Order	$\chi^{(1)}$	$\chi^{(2)}$	$\chi^{(3)}$	$\chi^{(4)}$	$\chi^{(5)}$	$\chi^{(6)}$				
$C_1\{1^6\}^+$	1	1	1	1	1	2	2	5	9	5	1
$C_2\{2^3\}^-$	1	1	1	−1	−1	−2	2	3	−3	1	−1
$C_3\{3^2\}^+$	2	1	1	1	1	−1	−1	2	0	−1	1
$C_4\{6\}^-$	2	1	1	−1	−1	1	−1	0	0	1	−1
$C_5\{1^2 2^2\}^+$	3	1	−1	1	−1	0	0	1	1	1	1
$C_6\{2^3\}^-$	3	1	−1	−1	1	0	0	3	−3	1	−1

The primitive characters of the symmetric group Π_6 are given in the right-hand table for the singlet, triplet, quintet, and septet states, and the irreducible representations of D_6 are given their customary (molecular) labelling A_1, A_2, etc. Obviously, the three irreducible representations of Π_6 for $S = 0, 1, 2$ are reducible representations of D_6, while the one-dimensional septet representation of Π_6 is identical with B_1 of D_6. The number of times each irreducible representation of D_6 occurs in the fifth ($S = 0$), ninth ($S = 1$), fifth ($S = 2$) degree representation of Π_6 is readily obtained from the orthogonality relation [equation (6:48) § 48], viz. indicating multiplicity $(2S + 1)$ by superscript, and omitting zero values:

$$\left.\begin{aligned}
c({}^1A_1) &= \tfrac{1}{12}[5+3+4+3+9] = 2.\\
c({}^1B_2) &= 1.\\
c({}^1E_2) &= 1.\\[4pt]
c({}^3A_2) &= 1.\\
c({}^3B_1) &= 2.\\
c({}^3E_1) &= 2.\\
c({}^3E_2) &= 1.\\[4pt]
c({}^5A_1) &= 1.\\
c({}^5E_1) &= 1.\\
c({}^5E_2) &= 1.\\[4pt]
c({}^7B_1) &= 1.
\end{aligned}\right\} \quad . \quad . \quad . \quad (10{:}121)$$

The Dirac character eigenvalues for the three irreducible representations (A_1, B_2, E_2 of D_6) to which the singlet states belong, the four irreducible representations A_2, B_1, E_1, E_2 to which the triplets belong, etc., are then as shown in Table 10.6.

† TABLE 10.6

DIRAC CHARACTER EIGENVALUES—GROUP D_6 (COMPONENTS IN Π_6)

	$S = 0$			$S = 1$				$S = 2$			$S = 3$
	A_1	B_2	E_2	A_2	B_1	E_1	E_2	A_1	E_1	E_2	B_1
Class	χ'	χ^{IV}	χ^{VI}	χ''	χ'''	χ^{V}	χ^{VI}	χ'	χ^{V}	χ^{VI}	χ'''
C_1	1	1	1	1	1	1	1	1	1	1	1
C_2	1	-1	1	1	-1	-1	1	1	-1	1	-1
C_3	1	1	$-\frac{1}{2}$	1	1	$-\frac{1}{2}$	$-\frac{1}{2}$	1	$-\frac{1}{2}$	$-\frac{1}{2}$	1
C_4	1	-1	$-\frac{1}{2}$	1	-1	$\frac{1}{2}$	$-\frac{1}{2}$	1	$\frac{1}{2}$	$-\frac{1}{2}$	-1
C_5	1	-1	0	-1	1	0	0	1	0	0	1
C_6	1	1	0	-1	-1	0	0	1	0	0	-1

Now in a representation (quantal) in which the energy matrix $\mathscr{V}$ is diagonal and in which the matrices representing the symmetry elements are completely reduced (cf. Chap. VI), the eigenvalues of $\mathscr{V}$ (or $\mathbf{V}$) for the singlet state can be written as ${}^1A_{1+}$, ${}^1A_{1-}$; ${}^1B_2$; ${}^1E_2$, ${}^1E_2$, since the (one-dimensional) irreducible representation A_1 occurs twice [cf. (10:121)], B_2 once, and E_2 (two-dimensional) once. From Table 10.6 ($S = 0$) the corresponding eigenvalues of χ_1, χ_2, for example, are 1, 1; 1; 1, 1 and 1, 1; -1; 1, 1 respectively, so that the eigenvalues of $\frac{1}{2}(\chi_1 - \chi_2)$ are 0, 0; 1; 0, 0. It follows that the eigenvalues of $\frac{1}{2}(\chi_1 - \chi_2)\mathbf{V}$ are 0, 0; ${}^1B_2$; 0, 0, so that this energy is simply $\mathscr{S}p\,\frac{1}{2}(\chi_1 - \chi_2)\mathbf{V}$. Similarly, the eigenvalues of $\chi_1 - \chi_6$ are 0, 0; 0; 1, 1, so that the sum of the energies of the ${}^1E_2$ levels is $2{}^1E_2 = \mathscr{S}p\,(\chi_1 - \chi_6)\mathbf{V}$. The sum of the energies ${}^1A_{1+}$, ${}^1A_{1-}$ can be obtained from ${}^1A_{1+} + {}^1A_{1-} + {}^1B_2 = \mathscr{S}p\,\chi_6\mathbf{V}$, and these are separated by finding the sum of their squares from $\mathscr{S}p\,\mathbf{V}^2$, and subtracting the squares of the other energy levels in the usual way. The pertinent primitive characters of Π_6 in these calculations are given in Table 10.7 [cf. (10:76) and Table 10.5].

† According to our notation the *group* character for, say, the third class and sixth representation E_2 (e.g. $\chi_3^{(6)}$) corresponds (except for factor) to the Dirac character eigenvalue χ_3^{VI}, e.g. $\chi_3^{(6)}$ from E_2 of Table 10.5 gives $\chi_3^{VI} = -\frac{1}{2}$ for E_2 in Table 10.6.

TABLE 10.7

S	[I]	[2]	[2^2]	[2^3]	[3]	[3^2]	[32]	[42]	[5]	[6]
0	5	−1	1	3	−1	2	−1	−1	0	0
1	9	−3	1	−3	0	0	0	1	−1	0
2	5	−3	1	1	2	−1	0	−1	0	1
3	1	−1	1	−1	1	1	−1	1	1	−1

From the symmetry of the problem we note that with **V** given by (10:120),

$$\mathscr{S}p\, \chi_j \mathbf{V} = \mathscr{S}p\, \chi_j \{ 6\alpha \mathbf{P}_{12} + 6\beta \mathbf{P}_{13} + 3\gamma \mathbf{P}_{14} \}. \quad . \quad . \quad (10{:}122)$$

We shall also require $\mathbf{V}^2$, which may be conveniently expressed as

$$\begin{aligned} \mathbf{V}^2 = {} & 6\alpha^2 \{ \mathbf{I} + 2\mathbf{P}_{123} + 2\mathbf{P}_{12}\mathbf{P}_{34} + \mathbf{P}_{12}\mathbf{P}_{45} \} + 6\beta^2 \{ \mathbf{I} + 2\mathbf{P}_{153} + 2\mathbf{P}_{13}\mathbf{P}_{24} + \mathbf{P}_{13}\mathbf{P}_{46} \} \\ & + 3\gamma^2 \{ \mathbf{I} + 2\mathbf{P}_{14}\mathbf{P}_{25} \} + 12\alpha\beta \{ 2\mathbf{P}_{123} + 2\mathbf{P}_{152} + 2\mathbf{P}_{12}\mathbf{P}_{35} \} \\ & + 12\alpha\gamma \{ 2\mathbf{P}_{152} + \mathbf{P}_{12}\mathbf{P}_{36} \} + 12\beta\gamma \{ 2\mathbf{P}_{152} + \mathbf{P}_{13}\mathbf{P}_{25} \}. \quad . \quad . \quad (10{:}123) \end{aligned}$$

Then we have

$$\mathscr{S}p\, \chi_1 \mathbf{V} = (6\alpha + 6\beta + 3\gamma) [2], \quad (10{:}124a)$$

$$\begin{aligned} \mathscr{S}p\, \chi_2 \mathbf{V} &= \mathscr{S}p \{ \mathbf{P}_{14}\mathbf{P}_{25}\mathbf{P}_{36} \} \{ 6\alpha \mathbf{P}_{12} + 6\beta \mathbf{P}_{13} + 3\gamma \mathbf{P}_{14} \} \\ &= (6\alpha + 6\beta) [42] + 3\gamma [2^2], \quad (10{:}124b) \end{aligned}$$

$$\begin{aligned} \mathscr{S}p\, \chi_3 \mathbf{V} &= \mathscr{S}p\, \tfrac{1}{2} \{ \mathbf{P}_{135}\mathbf{P}_{246} + \mathbf{P}_{153}\mathbf{P}_{264} \} \{ 6\alpha \mathbf{P}_{12} + 6\beta \mathbf{P}_{13} + 3\gamma \mathbf{P}_{14} \} \\ &= (6\alpha + 3\gamma) [6] + 6\beta [32], \quad (10{:}124c) \end{aligned}$$

$$\begin{aligned} \mathscr{S}p\, \chi_4 \mathbf{V} &= \mathscr{S}p\, \tfrac{1}{2} \{ \mathbf{P}_{123456} + \mathbf{P}_{165432} \} \mathbf{V} \\ &= 6\alpha [5] + 6\beta [42] + 3\gamma [3^2], \quad (10{:}124d) \end{aligned}$$

$$\begin{aligned} \mathscr{S}p\, \chi_6 \mathbf{V} &= \mathscr{S}p\, \tfrac{1}{3} \{ \mathbf{P}_{12}\mathbf{P}_{36}\mathbf{P}_{45} + \mathbf{P}_{14}\mathbf{P}_{23}\mathbf{P}_{56} + \mathbf{P}_{16}\mathbf{P}_{25}\mathbf{P}_{34} \} \mathbf{V} \\ &= 2\alpha \{ [2^2] + 2 [42] \} + 6\beta [42] + \gamma \{ 2 [42] + [2^2] \}. \quad (10{:}124e) \end{aligned}$$

Substituting the primitive characters corresponding to the singlet states (from Table 10.7), we find

$${}^1B_2 = \mathscr{S}p\, \tfrac{1}{2} (\chi_1 - \chi_2) \mathbf{V} = -3\gamma, \quad (10{:}125a)$$

$${}^1E_2 = \mathscr{S}p\, \tfrac{1}{2} (\chi_1 - \chi_6) \mathbf{V} = -2\alpha - \gamma, \quad (10{:}125b)$$

$$2\epsilon = {}^1A_{1^+} + {}^1A_{1^-} = \mathscr{S}p\, \chi_6 \mathbf{V} - {}^1B_2 = -2\alpha - 6\beta + 2\gamma, \quad (10{:}125c)$$

$$\begin{aligned} 2\delta &= ({}^1A_{1^+})^2 + ({}^1A_{1^-})^2 = \mathscr{S}p\, \mathbf{V}^2 - ({}^1B_2)^2 - 2 ({}^1E_2)^2 \\ &= 36\alpha^2 + 36\beta^2 + 21\gamma^2 - 24\alpha\beta - 12\alpha\gamma - 12\beta\gamma \\ &\qquad - 9\gamma^2 - 8\alpha^2 - 2\gamma^2 - 8\alpha\gamma; \quad (10{:}125d) \end{aligned}$$

and from (10:125*c*, *d*),

$$^1A_{1}{}^{\pm} = -\alpha - 3\beta + \gamma \pm [\,9\,(\,\alpha - \beta\,)^2 + 4\,(\,\alpha - \gamma\,)^2\,]^{\frac{1}{2}}. \qquad (10{:}125e)$$

For the triplet states the irreducible representations A_2 (one-dimensional) and E_2 (two-dimensional) appear once; and B_1 (one-dimensional), E_1 (two-dimensional) appear twice [cf. (10:121)], so that the eigenvalues of $\mathbf{V}$ may be written $^3A_2$; $^3B_1{}^+$, $^3B_1{}^-$; $^3E_1{}^{\pm}$, $^3E_1{}^{\pm}$; $^3E_2$, $^3E_2$. The corresponding eigenvalues of χ_2, for example, are (cf. Table 10.6, $S = 1$) 1; -1, -1; -1, -1, -1, -1; 1, 1, and the eigenvalues of $\frac{1}{2}(\chi_1 + \chi_2)\mathbf{V}$ are $^3A_2$; 0, 0; 0, 0, 0, 0; $^3E_2$, $^3E_2$, so that $^3A_2 + 2{}^3E_2 = \mathscr{S}\!p\,\frac{1}{2}(\chi_1 + \chi_2)\mathbf{V}$. Again, the eigenvalues of $(\chi_3 + \chi_4)\mathbf{V}$ are $2{}^3A_2$; 0, 0; 0, 0, 0, 0; $-{}^3E_2$, $-{}^3E_2$, whence $2({}^3A_2 - {}^3E_2) = \mathscr{S}\!p\,(\chi_3 + \chi_4)\mathbf{V}$. The eigenvalues of χ_6 are -1; -1, -1; 0, 0, 0, 0; 0, 0, from which it follows that $-{}^3A_2 - {}^3B_1{}^+ - {}^3B_1{}^- = \mathscr{S}\!p\,\chi_6\mathbf{V}$; and the levels $^1B_1{}^{\pm}$ are separated by computing the sum of their squares from $\mathscr{S}\!p\,\chi_5\mathbf{V}$. Similarly, we note that $\mathscr{S}\!p\,\mathbf{V} = {}^3A_2 + ({}^3B_1{}^+ + {}^3B_1{}^-) + 2({}^3E_1{}^+ + {}^3E_1{}^-) + 2{}^3E_2$, and the levels $^3E_1{}^{\pm}$ are again separated in the usual way by computing $\mathscr{S}\!p\,\mathbf{V}^2$. It is evident that the evaluation can be carried out in a variety of ways, and we obtain (using the values from Table 10.7 corresponding to $S = 1$)

$$^3A_2 = -4\alpha - \gamma, \qquad (10{:}126a)$$

$$^3E_2 = -\alpha - 3\beta - \gamma, \qquad (10{:}126b)$$

$$^3B_1{}^{\pm} = -(\,\alpha + 3\beta + \gamma\,) \pm [\,5\,(\,\alpha - \beta\,)^2 + 4\,(\,\beta - \gamma\,)^2\,]^{\frac{1}{2}}, \qquad (10{:}126c)$$

$$^3E_1{}^{\pm} = -\tfrac{1}{2}(5\alpha + 3\beta + 2\gamma) \pm [5(\alpha - \beta)^2 + 12(\alpha - \gamma)^2 + 4(\beta - \gamma)^2]^{\frac{1}{2}}. \qquad (10{:}126d)$$

In general we need only compute appropriate spurs once, and then use the appropriate primitive characters. Thus, we readily find

$$^5A_1 = \mathscr{S}\!p\,\chi_6\mathbf{V} = -2\alpha - 6\beta - \gamma, \qquad (10{:}127a)$$

$$^5A_1 + 2{}^5E_2 = \tfrac{1}{2}\mathscr{S}\!p\,(\,\chi_1 + \chi_2\,)\,\mathbf{V} = -12\alpha - 12\beta - 3\gamma,$$

$$^5E_2 = -5\alpha - 3\beta - \gamma, \qquad (10{:}127b)$$

$$2{}^5E_1 = \tfrac{1}{2}\mathscr{S}\!p\,(\,\chi_1 - \chi_2\,)\,\mathbf{V} = -6\alpha - 6\beta - 6\gamma, \qquad (10{:}127c)$$

$$^7B_1 = \mathscr{S}\!p\,\mathbf{V} = -6\alpha - 6\beta - 3\gamma. \qquad (10{:}128)$$

A convenient check on the calculations *at any stage* is provided by noting that when all exchange energies are made equal, $\alpha = \beta = \gamma$, the energies of all states of a given multiplicity are the same and given by (10:39*b*), viz.

$$^{2S+1}W_{ex} = -\tfrac{1}{4}\alpha\,[\,n\,(\,n - 4\,) + 4S\,(\,S + 1\,)\,]. \qquad (10{:}129)$$

In the present case ($n = 6$) the singlet, triplet, quintet, and septet energies must reduce to -3α, -5α, -9α and -15α respectively. For the singlets, $\mathscr{S}\!p\,\chi_6\mathbf{V}$, which is the sum of the energies of three states, must then reduce to -9α, $\mathscr{S}\!p\,\mathbf{V}^2$ to $45\alpha^2$, etc.

In the more matrical approach to the preceding problem the energy matrix is set up by direct computation of the matrices of the interchanges according to the procedure of Sections 86, 87, diagonalizing $\mathbf{P}_{12}$, $\mathbf{P}_{34}$, $\mathbf{P}_{56}$. For the singlet states one finds the matrices:

$$\mathscr{P}_{12} = \left\| \begin{array}{ccccc} -1 & 0 & 0 & 0 & 0 \\ 0 & -1 & 0 & 0 & 0 \\ 0 & 0 & 1 & 0 & 0 \\ 0 & 0 & 0 & -1 & 0 \\ 0 & 0 & 0 & 0 & 1 \end{array} \right\|, \quad \mathscr{P}_{34} = \left\| \begin{array}{ccccc} -1 & 0 & 0 & 0 & 0 \\ 0 & 1 & 0 & 0 & 0 \\ 0 & 0 & -1 & 0 & 0 \\ 0 & 0 & 0 & -1 & 0 \\ 0 & 0 & 0 & 0 & 1 \end{array} \right\|,$$

$$\mathscr{P}_{56} = \left\| \begin{array}{ccccc} -1 & 0 & 0 & 0 & 0 \\ 0 & -1 & 0 & 0 & 0 \\ 0 & 0 & -1 & 0 & 0 \\ 0 & 0 & 0 & 1 & 0 \\ 0 & 0 & 0 & 0 & 1 \end{array} \right\|, \quad \mathscr{P}_{13} = \left\| \begin{array}{ccccc} 0 & -\sqrt{\tfrac{1}{2}} & \sqrt{\tfrac{1}{2}} & 0 & 0 \\ -\sqrt{\tfrac{1}{2}} & -\tfrac{1}{2} & -\tfrac{1}{2} & 0 & 0 \\ \sqrt{\tfrac{1}{2}} & -\tfrac{1}{2} & -\tfrac{1}{2} & 0 & 0 \\ 0 & 0 & 0 & \tfrac{1}{2} & \sqrt{\tfrac{3}{4}} \\ 0 & 0 & 0 & \sqrt{\tfrac{3}{4}} & -\tfrac{1}{2} \end{array} \right\|,$$

$$\mathscr{P}_{35} = \left\| \begin{array}{ccccc} 0 & \sqrt{\tfrac{1}{2}} & 0 & -\sqrt{\tfrac{1}{2}} & 0 \\ \sqrt{\tfrac{1}{2}} & -\tfrac{1}{2} & 0 & -\tfrac{1}{2} & 0 \\ 0 & 0 & \tfrac{1}{2} & 0 & \sqrt{\tfrac{3}{4}} \\ -\sqrt{\tfrac{1}{2}} & -\tfrac{1}{2} & 0 & -\tfrac{1}{2} & 0 \\ 0 & 0 & \sqrt{\tfrac{3}{4}} & 0 & -\tfrac{1}{2} \end{array} \right\|, \quad \mathscr{P}_{15} = \left\| \begin{array}{ccccc} 0 & 0 & -\sqrt{\tfrac{1}{2}} & \sqrt{\tfrac{1}{2}} & 0 \\ 0 & \tfrac{1}{2} & 0 & 0 & \sqrt{\tfrac{3}{4}} \\ -\sqrt{\tfrac{1}{2}} & 0 & -\tfrac{1}{2} & -\tfrac{1}{2} & 0 \\ \sqrt{\tfrac{1}{2}} & 0 & -\tfrac{1}{2} & -\tfrac{1}{2} & 0 \\ 0 & \sqrt{\tfrac{3}{4}} & 0 & 0 & -\tfrac{1}{2} \end{array} \right\|, \qquad (10{:}130)$$

and all others are obtainable from the relation $\mathbf{P}_{bi} = \mathbf{P}_{ab}\mathbf{P}_{ai}\mathbf{P}_{ab}$, which with the diagonal form of $\mathbf{P}_{12}$, $\mathbf{P}_{34}$, $\mathbf{P}_{56}$ shows how they are obtained by changing the signs of certain rows and columns of the known matrices (e.g. $\mathbf{P}_{14} = \mathbf{P}_{34}\mathbf{P}_{13}\mathbf{P}_{34}$, etc.).

If now we label the orbits as 1, 6, 4, 2, 5, 3 in clockwise fashion, the subgroup of permutations becomes $C_1 = I$; $C_2 = P_{12}P_{34}P_{56}$; $C_3 = P_{145}P_{623}, P_{154}P_{632}$; $C_4 = P_{164253}, P_{135246}$; $C_5 = P_{36}P_{45}, P_{14}P_{36}, P_{15}P_{26}$; $C_6 = P_{16}P_{34}P_{25}, P_{12}P_{35}P_{46}, P_{13}P_{24}P_{56}$; so that this relabelling of orbits diagonalizes the symmetry element of the class C_2, viz.

$$\mathscr{P}_{12}\mathscr{P}_{34}\mathscr{P}_{56} = \left\| \begin{array}{ccccc} -1 & 0 & 0 & 0 & 0 \\ 0 & 1 & 0 & 0 & 0 \\ 0 & 0 & 1 & 0 & 0 \\ 0 & 0 & 0 & 1 & 0 \\ 0 & 0 & 0 & 0 & 1 \end{array} \right\| . \quad . \quad . \quad . \quad . \qquad (10{:}131)$$

From (10:121) and Table 10.5 it is evident that the state ${}^1B_2$ corresponds to the eigenvalue -1, while the states ${}^1A_1$, ${}^1E_2$ correspond to the eigenvalues 1. The energy matrix $\mathscr{V}$ clearly can have no elements between states corresponding to different eigenvalues of $\mathbf{P}_{12}\mathbf{P}_{34}\mathbf{P}_{56}$; so that we know *a priori* that the secular determinant factorizes into a linear factor referring to ${}^1B_2$, and a quartic for the other levels. Again, writing α, β, γ for exchange integrals of the type K_{16}, K_{14}, K_{12} respectively, the energy matrix takes the form

$$\begin{aligned} \mathscr{V} = \alpha\{ & \mathscr{P}_{13} + \mathscr{P}_{16} + \mathscr{P}_{24} + \mathscr{P}_{25} + \mathscr{P}_{35} + \mathscr{P}_{46} \} \\ & + \beta\{ \mathscr{P}_{14} + \mathscr{P}_{15} + \mathscr{P}_{23} + \mathscr{P}_{26} + \mathscr{P}_{36} + \mathscr{P}_{45} \} \\ & + \gamma\{ \mathscr{P}_{12} + \mathscr{P}_{34} + \mathscr{P}_{56} \}; \quad . \quad . \quad . \quad . \quad . \quad . \quad . \quad . \quad . \qquad (10{:}132) \end{aligned}$$

and the secular determinant is found to be

$-3\gamma-W$	0	0	0	0
0	$-\alpha-\beta-\gamma-W$	$-(\alpha-\beta)$	$-(\alpha-\beta)$	$-\sqrt{3}(\alpha-\beta)$
0	$-(\alpha-\beta)$	$-\alpha-\beta-\gamma-W$	$\alpha-\beta$	$\sqrt{3}(\alpha-\beta)$
0	$-(\alpha-\beta)$	$\alpha-\beta$	$-\alpha-\beta-\gamma-W$	$\sqrt{3}(\alpha-\beta)$
0	$-\sqrt{3}(\alpha-\beta)$	$\sqrt{3}(\alpha-\beta)$	$\sqrt{3}(\alpha-\beta)$	$-3\alpha-3\beta+3\gamma-W$

(10:133)

It immediately follows that one root is -3γ, and a double root of the quartic is given by $-\alpha-\beta-\gamma-W=\alpha-\beta$; whence, as before, ${}^1B_2=-3\gamma$, ${}^1E_2=-2\alpha-\gamma$. The levels ${}^1A_{1^+}$ are found from $\mathscr{S}_p\mathscr{V}$ and $\mathscr{S}_p\mathscr{V}^2$ in the usual way.

We note that by labelling the orbits in the order 1, 2, 4, 6, 5, 3, we diagonalize an element of C_6, and according to Table 10.5 factor out a ${}^1E_2$ level since $\chi_6^{(6)}=0$; which means that $\mathbf{P}_{12}\mathbf{P}_{34}\mathbf{P}_{56}$ (which now is an element of C_6) has the eigenvalue 1 for one ${}^1E_2$ level and -1 for the other. Similarly, labelling according to 1, 3, 5, 2, 6, 4, for example, diagonalizes an element of C_5 (e.g. $\mathbf{P}_{34}\mathbf{P}_{56}$) leading to a quadratic factor containing ${}^1B_2$, ${}^1E_2$, and a cubic in the remaining levels.

(b) The Eight-Electron Problem.

In order to treat the problem of the simple cubic configuration of 8 similar orbits we need to have available some additional simple concepts of crystallographic groups. Consider a cube (fig. 10.8) and, proceeding clockwise around the top face,

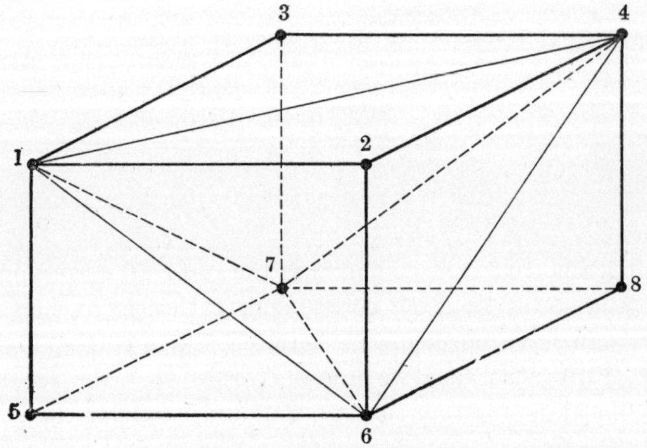

Fig. 10.8

label the orbits (corners) by the numbers 1, 3, 4, 2; those directly under being labelled as 5, 7, 8, 6 respectively. Then the diagonals connecting (1, 7, 4, 6) form a tetrahedron (Fig. 10.8), and this figure is sent into itself by the twelve operations of the tetrahedral group T (order 12): viz. (I) the identity; ($3R_2$) three rotations through π about the lines joining mid-points of opposite faces of the cube (or equivalently, the mid-points of opposite edges of the tetrahedron); $(8R_3)$ eight rotations through $\pm 2\pi/3$ about the diagonals of the cube.

The octahedral group O (order 24), which sends the regular octahedron whose corners are the mid-points of the cube faces into itself, contains in addition to the above rotations of the tetrahedral group: $(6R_4)$ six rotations through $\pm\pi/2$ about

TABLE 10.8.—CHARACTER TABLE

OCTAHEDRAL GROUP O

Class		Order	Representation A_1	A_2	E	T_1	T_2
C_1	I	1	1	1	2	3	3
C_2	$\{2^4\}^+$	3	1	1	2	−1	−1
C_3	$\{4^2\}^+$	6	1	−1	0	1	−1
C_4	$\{2^4\}^+$	6	1	−1	0	−1	1
C_5	$\{3^2\}^+$	8	1	1	−1	0	0

the lines joining mid-points of opposite cube faces; $(6R_2')$ six rotations through π about the six joins of opposite edges of the cube. The character table of this group [93] is Table 10.8, where the second column again indicates the partition of the permutations through which the symmetry operations are realized. Typical elements are

Symmetry Class—Group O	Permutation Realization	
C_1	I	
C_2	$P_{14}P_{23}P_{58}P_{67}$	
C_3	$P_{1342}P_{5786}$	. . . . (10:134)
C_4	$P_{15}P_{27}P_{36}P_{48}$	
C_5	$P_{176}P_{238}$	

The corresponding symmetry group of the cube is the extended group O_h (cubic holohedral) which differs from O in that it contains the inversion element which we denote by $\mathscr{I}$. The inversion corresponds to the group, consisting of the identity and central reflection, which is simply isomorphic with the two-group (cf. Chap. VI) or permutation group on two letters.[94] It follows that O_h is the *direct product* of these two groups and its character table (Table 10.9) is immediately obtained from that [95] of O.

[93] See EYRING, WALTER, KIMBALL, *op. cit.*, or any text on group theory.

[94] Cf. MURNAGHAN, *op. cit.*, pp. 346–349.

[95] Since the two-group table (6.3) is

1	1
1	−1

that of O_h is

A	A
A	−A

if [A] denotes that of O.

Table 10.9

Character Table
Cubic Holohedral Group O_h

Representation

Class		Order	A_1	A_2	E	T_1	T_2	$\mathscr{J}A_1$	$\mathscr{J}A_2$	$\mathscr{J}E$	$\mathscr{J}T_1$	$\mathscr{J}T_2$
C_1	I	1	1	1	2	3	3	1	1	2	3	3
C_2	$\{2^4\}^+$	3	1	1	2	–1	–1	1	1	2	–1	–1
C_3	$\{4^2\}^+$	6	1	–1	0	1	–1	1	–1	0	1	–1
C_4	$\{2^4\}^+$	6	1	–1	0	–1	1	1	–1	0	–1	1
C_5	$\{3^2\}^+$	8	1	1	–1	0	0	1	1	–1	0	0
$\mathscr{J}C_1$	$\{2^4\}^+$	1	1	1	2	3	3	–1	–1	–2	–3	–3
$\mathscr{J}C_2$	$\{2^4\}^+$	3	1	1	2	–1	–1	–1	–1	–2	1	1
$\mathscr{J}C_3$	$\{4^2\}^+$	6	1	–1	0	1	–1	–1	1	0	–1	1
$\mathscr{J}C_4$	$\{2^2\}^+$	6	1	–1	0	–1	1	–1	1	0	1	–1
$\mathscr{J}C_5$	$\{2, 6\}^+$	8	1	1	–1	0	0	–1	–1	1	0	0

$C_1 = I;\ C_2 = 3R_2;\ C_3 = 6R_4;\ C_4 = 6R_2';\ C_5 = 8R_3$

Character Table
Group Π_8

Representation

$S = 0$	$S = 1$	$S = 2$	$S = 3$	$S = 4$
14	28	20	7	1
6	–4	4	–1	1
2	0	0	–1	1
6	–4	4	–1	1
2	1	–1	1	1
6	–4	4	–1	1
6	–4	4	–1	1
2	0	0	–1	1
2	4	4	3	1
0	–1	1	–1	1

Corresponding to (10:134) we have

$$\begin{array}{cc} \text{Symmetry Class—Group } O_h & \text{Permutation (Typical) Realization} \\ C_1 & I \\ C_2 & P_{14}P_{23}P_{58}P_{67} \\ C_3 & P_{1342}P_{5786} \\ C_4 & P_{15}P_{27}P_{36}P_{48} \\ C_5 & P_{176}P_{238} \\ \mathscr{J}C_1 = \mathscr{J} & P_{18}P_{27}P_{36}P_{45} \\ \mathscr{J}C_2 & P_{15}P_{26}P_{37}P_{48} \\ \mathscr{J}C_3 & P_{1647}P_{2835} \\ \mathscr{J}C_4 & P_{14}P_{58} \\ \mathscr{J}C_5 & P_{126873}P_{45} \end{array} \quad . \quad . \quad . \quad (10{:}135)$$

Table 10.9 also gives the associated primitive characters of Π_8 from which the non-zero *group* multiplicites [corresponding to (10:121)] are

$$\left.\begin{array}{lllll} c(^1A_1) = 3 & c(^3T_1) = 2 & c(^5A_1) = 2 & c(^7T_2) = 1 & c(^9A_1) = 1 \\ c(^1E) = 2 & c(^3T_2) = 2 & c(^5E) = 2 & c(^7\mathscr{J}A_2) = 1 & \\ c(^1T_2) = 1 & c(^3\mathscr{J}A_2) = 2 & c(^5T_2) = 2 & c(^7\mathscr{J}T_1) = 1 & \\ c(^1\mathscr{J}A_1) = 1 & c(^3\mathscr{J}E) = 1 & c(^5\mathscr{J}E) = 1 & & \\ c(^1\mathscr{J}T_2) = 1 & c(^3\mathscr{J}T_1) = 3 & c(^5\mathscr{J}T_1) = 1 & & \\ & c(^3\mathscr{J}T_2) = 1 & c(^5\mathscr{J}T_2) = 1 & & \end{array}\right\} \quad (10{:}136)$$

and the required Dirac character eigenvalues are then given by Table 10.10.

The expression for the energy operator is now

$$\begin{aligned} \mathbf{V} = \alpha\{ & \mathbf{P}_{12} + \mathbf{P}_{13} + \mathbf{P}_{15} + \mathbf{P}_{24} + \mathbf{P}_{26} + \mathbf{P}_{34} + \mathbf{P}_{37} + \mathbf{P}_{48} + \mathbf{P}_{56} + \mathbf{P}_{57} + \mathbf{P}_{68} + \mathbf{P}_{78} \} \\ +\beta\{ & \mathbf{P}_{14} + \mathbf{P}_{16} + \mathbf{P}_{17} + \mathbf{P}_{23} + \mathbf{P}_{25} + \mathbf{P}_{28} + \mathbf{P}_{35} + \mathbf{P}_{38} + \mathbf{P}_{46} + \mathbf{P}_{47} + \mathbf{P}_{58} + \mathbf{P}_{67} \} \\ +\gamma\{ & \mathbf{P}_{18} + \mathbf{P}_{27} + \mathbf{P}_{36} + \mathbf{P}_{45} \}, \quad . \quad . \quad . \quad (10{:}137) \end{aligned}$$

and clearly

$$\mathscr{S}p\,\mathbf{V} = \mathscr{S}p\{ 12\alpha\mathbf{P}_{12} + 12\beta\mathbf{P}_{14} + 4\gamma\mathbf{P}_{18} \}. \quad . \quad . \quad . \quad (10{:}138)$$

All the energies may then be obtained from the spurs [96] of

$$\mathbf{V},\ \chi_2\mathbf{V},\ \chi_3\mathbf{V},\ {}_J\chi_1\mathbf{V},\ {}_J\chi_4\mathbf{V},\ \mathbf{V}^2,\ \chi_2\mathbf{V}^2,\ \chi_4\mathbf{V}^2,\ {}_J\chi_1\mathbf{V}^2,\ \text{and}\ \mathbf{V}^3.$$

Considering the 14 singlet states by way of illustration, we see from Table 10.9 and (10:136) that the eigenvalues of $\mathbf{V}$ will be

$$^1A_1{}',\, ^1A_1{}'',\, ^1A_1{}''';\ ^1E_\pm,\, ^1E_\pm;\ ^1T_2,\, ^1T_2,\, ^1T_2;\ ^1\mathscr{J}A_1;\ ^1\mathscr{J}T_2,\, ^1\mathscr{J}T_2,\, ^1\mathscr{J}T_2; \quad (10{:}139)$$

[96] The necessary primitive characters of Π_8 may be read from the Table, p. 149, MURNAGHAN, *op. cit.*, by comparison of the values given in Table 10.9 here. It may be mentioned that in Murnaghan's Table, the first, second, and third columns correspond to $S = 4, 3, 2$ respectively, and his fifth and eighth columns correspond to $S = 1, 0$.

Table 10.10

Dirac Character Table—Group O_h (Components in Π_8)

$S = 0$

Class	A_1	E	T_2	$\mathscr{J}A_1$	$\mathscr{J}T_2$
	χ'	χ'''	χ^{V}	${}_J\chi'$	${}_J\chi^{\mathrm{V}}$
C_1	1	1	1	1	1
C_2	1	1	$-\frac{1}{3}$	1	$-\frac{1}{3}$
C_3	1	0	$-\frac{1}{3}$	1	$-\frac{1}{3}$
C_4	1	0	$\frac{1}{3}$	1	$\frac{1}{3}$
C_5	1	$-\frac{1}{2}$	0	1	0
$\mathscr{J}$	1	1	1	−1	−1
$\mathscr{J}C_2$	1	1	$-\frac{1}{3}$	−1	$\frac{1}{3}$
$\mathscr{J}C_3$	1	0	$-\frac{1}{3}$	−1	$\frac{1}{3}$
$\mathscr{J}C_4$	1	0	$\frac{1}{3}$	−1	$-\frac{1}{3}$
$\mathscr{J}C_5$	1	$-\frac{1}{2}$	0	−1	0

$S = 1$

Class	T_1	T_2	$\mathscr{J}A_2$	$\mathscr{J}E$	$\mathscr{J}T_1$	$\mathscr{J}T_2$
	χ^{IV}	χ^{V}	${}_J\chi''$	${}_J\chi'''$	${}_J\chi^{\mathrm{IV}}$	${}_J\chi^{\mathrm{V}}$
C_1	1	1	1	1	1	1
C_2	$-\frac{1}{3}$	$-\frac{1}{3}$	1	1	$-\frac{1}{3}$	$-\frac{1}{3}$
C_3	$\frac{1}{3}$	$-\frac{1}{3}$	−1	0	$\frac{1}{3}$	$-\frac{1}{3}$
C_4	$-\frac{1}{3}$	$\frac{1}{3}$	−1	0	$-\frac{1}{3}$	$\frac{1}{3}$
C_5	0	0	1	$-\frac{1}{2}$	0	0
$\mathscr{J}$	1	1	−1	−1	−1	−1
$\mathscr{J}C_2$	$-\frac{1}{3}$	$-\frac{1}{3}$	−1	−1	$\frac{1}{3}$	$\frac{1}{3}$
$\mathscr{J}C_3$	$\frac{1}{3}$	$-\frac{1}{3}$	1	0	$-\frac{1}{3}$	$\frac{1}{3}$
$\mathscr{J}C_4$	$-\frac{1}{3}$	$\frac{1}{3}$	1	0	$\frac{1}{3}$	$-\frac{1}{3}$
$\mathscr{J}C_5$	0	0	−1	$\frac{1}{2}$	0	0

$S = 2$

Class	A_1	E	T_2	$\mathscr{J}E$	$\mathscr{J}T_1$	$\mathscr{J}T_2$
	χ'	χ'''	χ^{V}	${}_J\chi'''$	${}_J\chi^{\mathrm{IV}}$	${}_J\chi^{\mathrm{V}}$
C_1	1	1	1	1	1	1
C_2	1	1	$-\frac{1}{3}$	1	$-\frac{1}{3}$	$-\frac{1}{3}$
C_3	1	0	$-\frac{1}{3}$	0	$\frac{1}{3}$	$-\frac{1}{3}$
C_4	1	0	$\frac{1}{3}$	0	$-\frac{1}{3}$	$\frac{1}{3}$
C_5	1	$-\frac{1}{2}$	0	$-\frac{1}{2}$	0	0
$\mathscr{J}$	1	1	1	−1	−1	−1
$\mathscr{J}C_2$	1	1	$-\frac{1}{3}$	−1	$\frac{1}{3}$	$\frac{1}{3}$
$\mathscr{J}C_3$	1	0	$-\frac{1}{3}$	0	$-\frac{1}{3}$	$\frac{1}{3}$
$\mathscr{J}C_4$	1	0	$\frac{1}{3}$	0	$\frac{1}{3}$	$-\frac{1}{3}$
$\mathscr{J}C_5$	1	$-\frac{1}{2}$	0	$\frac{1}{2}$	0	0

$S = 3$

Class	T_2	$\mathscr{J}A_2$	$\mathscr{J}T_1$
	χ^{V}	${}_J\chi''$	${}_J\chi^{\mathrm{IV}}$
C_1	1	1	1
C_2	$-\frac{1}{3}$	1	$-\frac{1}{3}$
C_3	$-\frac{1}{3}$	−1	$\frac{1}{3}$
C_4	$\frac{1}{3}$	−1	$-\frac{1}{3}$
C_5	0	1	0
$\mathscr{J}$	1	−1	−1
$\mathscr{J}C_2$	$-\frac{1}{3}$	−1	$\frac{1}{3}$
$\mathscr{J}C_3$	$-\frac{1}{3}$	1	$-\frac{1}{3}$
$\mathscr{J}C_4$	$\frac{1}{3}$	1	$\frac{1}{3}$
$\mathscr{J}C_5$	0	−1	0

$S = 4$

Class	A_1
	χ'
C_1	1
C_2	1
C_3	1
C_4	1
C_5	1
$\mathscr{J}$	1
$\mathscr{J}C_2$	1
$\mathscr{J}C_3$	1
$\mathscr{J}C_4$	1
$\mathscr{J}C_5$	1

and the corresponding eigenvalues of χ_2, ${}_J\chi_2$, for example, are (from Table 10.10)

$$1, 1, 1; \quad 1, 1, 1, 1; \quad -\tfrac{1}{3}, -\tfrac{1}{3}, -\tfrac{1}{3}; \quad 1; \quad -\tfrac{1}{3}, -\tfrac{1}{3}, -\tfrac{1}{3}; \qquad (10:139a)$$

$$1, 1, 1; \quad 1, 1, 1, 1; \quad -\tfrac{1}{3}, -\tfrac{1}{3}, -\tfrac{1}{3}; \quad -1; \quad \tfrac{1}{3}, \tfrac{1}{3}, \tfrac{1}{3}. \quad . \quad . \qquad (10:139b)$$

Hence, the eigenvalues of $(\chi_2 - {}_J\chi_2)\mathbf{V}$ will be $2\,{}^1\mathscr{J}A_1$, $-\frac{2}{3}\,{}^1\mathscr{J}T_2$, $-\frac{2}{3}\,{}^1\mathscr{J}T_2$, $-\frac{2}{3}\,{}^1\mathscr{J}T_2$, from which $\mathscr{S}p\,(\chi_2 - {}_J\chi_2)\mathbf{V} = 2({}^1\mathscr{J}A_1 - {}^1\mathscr{J}T_2)$. Further, χ_2 and ${}_J\chi_2$ are given by

$$\chi_2 = \tfrac{1}{3}\{\,\mathbf{P}_{14}\mathbf{P}_{23}\mathbf{P}_{58}\mathbf{P}_{67} + \mathbf{P}_{17}\mathbf{P}_{28}\mathbf{P}_{35}\mathbf{P}_{46} + \mathbf{P}_{16}\mathbf{P}_{25}\mathbf{P}_{38}\mathbf{P}_{47}\,\}, \qquad (10:140a)$$

$${}_J\chi_2 = \tfrac{1}{3}\{\,\mathbf{P}_{15}\mathbf{P}_{26}\mathbf{P}_{37}\mathbf{P}_{48} + \mathbf{P}_{12}\mathbf{P}_{34}\mathbf{P}_{56}\mathbf{P}_{78} + \mathbf{P}_{13}\mathbf{P}_{24}\mathbf{P}_{57}\mathbf{P}_{68}\,\}. \qquad (10:140b)$$

Carrying out the algebra, and noting that $[2^24] = -2$, $[2^3] = 0$, for $S = 0$, we have

$$\tfrac{1}{2}\mathscr{S}p\,(\chi_2 - {}_J\chi_2)\,\mathbf{V} = -4\,(\alpha - \beta) = {}^1\mathscr{J}A_1 - {}^1\mathscr{J}T_2. \quad . \qquad (10:141)$$

Similarly, ${}^1\mathscr{J}T_2$ is given by $\frac{1}{2}\mathscr{S}p\,(\chi_5 - {}_J\chi_5)\mathbf{V}$, etc.

Thus the problem here involves no new principles and, carrying out the various algebraic steps, we find

$$
\begin{aligned}
{}^1A_1 &= W \\
&\quad \big[\, W^3 + 8\,(\alpha + 2\beta)\,W^2 - 16\,(\alpha^2 - 3\beta^2 + \gamma^2 - 9\alpha\beta - \alpha\gamma - \beta\gamma)\,W \\
&\qquad - 32\,(3\alpha^3 - 9\alpha\beta^2 - 6\alpha^2\beta + \alpha^2\gamma + 4\beta\gamma^2 - 3\beta^2\gamma - 6\alpha\beta\gamma) = 0\,\big], \\
{}^1E_{\pm} &= -2\,(2\alpha + \beta + \gamma) \pm 2\,[\,(\alpha - \beta)^2 + (\alpha - \gamma)^2\,]^{\frac{1}{2}}, \\
{}^1T_1 &= -4\,(\alpha + \beta), \\
{}^1\mathscr{J}A_1 &= -2\,(3\alpha + \gamma), \\
{}^1\mathscr{J}T_2 &= -2\,(\alpha + 2\beta + \gamma), \\
{}^3T_{1\pm} &= -\,(5\alpha + 3\beta + 2\gamma) \pm [\,(\alpha - \beta)^2 + 4\,(\alpha - \gamma)^2\,]^{\frac{1}{2}}, \\
{}^3T_{2\pm} &= -\,(3\alpha + 5\beta + 2\gamma) \pm [\,5\,(\alpha - \beta)^2 + 4\,(\beta - \gamma)^2\,]^{\frac{1}{2}}, \\
{}^3\mathscr{J}A_{2\pm} &= -2\,(\alpha + 4\beta) \pm 2^{\frac{1}{2}}\,[\,7\,(\alpha - \beta)^2 + (\alpha - \gamma)^2 + (\beta - \gamma)^2\,]^{\frac{1}{2}}, \\
{}^3\mathscr{J}E &= -2\,(2\alpha + 2\beta + \gamma), \\
{}^3\mathscr{J}T_1 &= U \\
&\quad \big[\, U^3 + 2\,(7\alpha + 7\beta + \gamma)\,U^2 \\
&\qquad + 4\,(13\alpha^2 + 14\beta^2 - \gamma^2 + 37\alpha\beta + 7\alpha\gamma + 5\beta\gamma)\,U \\
&\qquad + 8\,(5\alpha^3 + 8\beta^3 - \gamma^3 + 42\alpha^2\beta + 8\alpha^2\gamma + 41\alpha\beta^2 + 5\beta^2\gamma - 2\beta\gamma^2 + 19\alpha\beta\gamma) = 0\,\big], \\
{}^3\mathscr{J}T_2 &= -2\,(3\alpha + \beta + \gamma), \\
{}^5A_{1\pm} &= -2\,(2\alpha + 4\beta + \gamma) \pm 2^{\frac{1}{2}}\,[\,(\alpha + \gamma - 2\beta)^2 + 3\,(\alpha - \beta)^2 + (\beta - \gamma)^2\,]^{\frac{1}{2}}, \\
{}^5E_{\pm} &= -(7\alpha + 5\beta + 2\gamma) \pm [\,(\alpha - \beta)^2 + 4\,(\alpha - \gamma)^2\,]^{\frac{1}{2}}, \\
{}^5T_{2\pm} &= -2\,(3\alpha + 3\beta + \gamma) \pm 2^{\frac{1}{2}}\,[\,(\alpha - \beta)^2 + (\alpha - \gamma)^2 + (\beta - \gamma)^2\,]^{\frac{1}{2}}, \\
{}^5\mathscr{J}E &= -2\,(3\alpha + 3\beta + \gamma), \\
{}^5\mathscr{J}T_1 &= -2\,(2\alpha + 4\beta + \gamma), \\
{}^5\mathscr{J}T_2 &= -2\,(4\alpha + 2\beta + \gamma), \\
{}^7T_2 &= -4\,(2\alpha + 2\beta + \gamma), \\
{}^7\mathscr{J}A_2 &= -2\,(3\alpha + 6\beta + \gamma), \\
{}^7\mathscr{J}T_1 &= -2\,(5\alpha + 4\beta + \gamma), \\
{}^9A_1 &= -4\,(3\alpha + 3\beta + \gamma). \quad . \quad . \quad . \quad . \quad . \quad . \qquad (10:142)
\end{aligned}
$$

CHAPTER XI

Second Quantization *

§ 92. Introduction

In Chapter VII we considered the description of identical systems of the antisymmetric type, in terms of the density operator $\boldsymbol{\rho}$ whose eigenvalues essentially determine whether or not a given state is occupied. The logical extension of this type of description is to introduce operators, which may be termed *occupation variables*, describing the *number* of systems or particles for which a measurable quantity of interest has some definite value. It is seen that the description of an ensemble of identical systems by the eigenvalues of such occupation variables will give all possible physical information, *and*, by definition, the question of the (meaningless) individuality of single systems of the ensemble never arises.

This type of analysis, as we shall now see, can be carried out for systems of both symmetries, and is generally described as the process of *second* or *intensity* quantization.[1] For definiteness we consider the general properties of a system of n indistinguishable particles, and compare the description of the system by two different operator sets $\mathbf{x}_r$ and $\mathbf{E}_r$ associated with the rth particle ($r = 1, 2, \ldots n$). The operators $\mathbf{x}_r$ and $\mathbf{E}_r$ will, in general, stand for a complete commuting set of observables for each particle; thus, for electrons we may take $\mathbf{x}_r = (\mathbf{x}_r, \mathbf{y}_r, \mathbf{z}_r, \boldsymbol{\sigma}_r)$ and $\mathbf{E}_r = (\mathbf{H}_r, \underline{\mathbf{l}}_r^2, \mathbf{l}_{rz}, \boldsymbol{\sigma}_r)$; $\boldsymbol{\sigma}_r = \boldsymbol{\sigma}_{rz}$. However, for our general calculations we need only consider that the operators $\mathbf{E}$ have discrete spectra, without specifying their specific form beyond the condition that the operators (both $\mathbf{x}$ and $\mathbf{E}$) of any one particle commute with those of any other. All the $\mathbf{x}$'s together form a complete $\mathbf{x}$-representation and, likewise, the $\mathbf{E}$'s form an $\mathbf{E}$-representation.

Now any arbitrary physical state $|\, ; t \rangle$ can be expanded in terms of the eigen-$|\,\rangle$'s of either of these complete representations, and we have

$$
\begin{aligned}
|\, ; t \rangle &= \int \ldots \int |\, x_1' x_2' \ldots x_n' \rangle \, d^{\cdot}x \, \langle x_1' \ldots x_n' \,|\, ; t \rangle \\
&= \sum_{E_1' \ldots E_n'} |\, E_1' E_2' \ldots E_n' \rangle \langle E_1' \ldots E_n' \,|\, ; t \rangle . \qquad (11{:}1)
\end{aligned}
$$

* Dirac, P. A. M.: *Proc. Roy. Soc.* A, **114**, 243 (1927). Jordan, P.: *Zeits. f. Phys.*, **44**, 473 (1927). Klein, O., and Jordan, P.: *ibid.*, **45**, 751 (1927). Wigner, E., and Jordan, P.: *ibid.*, **47**, 631 (1928). Fock, V.: *ibid.*, **75**, 622 (1932).

[1] It should, however, be pointed out that in the non-relativistic case this term is somewhat of a misnomer from the modern methodological viewpoint, since the introduction of occupation variables of any type merely corresponds to working in a somewhat special representation (in the sense of the variables which are diagonal). The equations are superficially complex, but no *essentially* new principles are involved. Much of the mathematical formalism appears also in relativistic theory, but the actual quantization cannot be introduced there unless we know the wave-equations satisfied by the particular genus of particles under consideration; this is in sharp contrast to the non-relativistic case.

The two representatives $\langle x_1' \ldots x_n' \mid ; t \rangle$ and $\langle E_1' \ldots E_n' \mid ; t \rangle$ of a state $\mid ; t \rangle$ are connected by the equation

$$\langle x_1' \ldots x_n' \mid ; t \rangle = \sum_{E_1' \ldots E_n'} \langle x_1' \ldots x_n' \mid E_1' \ldots E_n' \rangle \langle E_1' \ldots E_n' \mid ; t \rangle$$

$$= \sum_{E_1' \ldots E_n'} \langle x_1' \mid E_1' \rangle \langle x_2' \mid E_2' \rangle \ldots \langle x_n' \mid E_n' \rangle \langle E_1' \ldots E_n' \mid ; t \rangle. \quad (11:2)$$

This last step is possible only because of the specified independence of the operators describing each particle.[2] In the Schroedinger picture (to which we have implicitly referred in the indicated time dependence of the state $\mid ; t \rangle$) the equation of motion of our state vector is

$$i\hbar \frac{d}{dt} \mid ; t \rangle = \mathbf{H} \mid ; t \rangle, \quad . \quad . \quad . \quad . \quad . \quad . \quad . \quad (11:3)$$ [3]

and in the $\mathbf{x}$- and $\mathbf{E}$-representations, we have the Schroedinger *wave-equations*

$$i\hbar \frac{d}{dt} \langle x_1' \ldots x_n' \mid ; t \rangle = \int \ldots \int \langle x_1' \ldots x_n' \mid \mathbf{H} \mid x_1'' \ldots x_n'' \rangle d''x \langle x_1'' \ldots x_n'' \mid ; t \rangle, \quad (11:4)$$

$$i\hbar \frac{d}{dt} \langle E_1' \ldots E_n' \mid ; t \rangle = \sum_{E_1'' \ldots E_n''} \langle E_1' \ldots E_n' \mid \mathbf{H} \mid E_1'' \ldots E_n'' \rangle \langle E_1'' \ldots E_n'' \mid ; t \rangle. \quad (11:5)$$

Suppose now that $\mathbf{H} = \mathbf{U} + \mathbf{V} = \sum_r \mathbf{u}(\mathbf{x}_r) + \sum_{r<s} \mathbf{v}(\mathbf{x}_r, \mathbf{x}_s)$. We shall require the representative of $\mathbf{H}$ in the $\mathbf{E}$-representation. Consider the part $\mathbf{U}$ of $\mathbf{H}$; then

$$\langle 'E \mid \sum_r \mathbf{u}_r \mid ''E \rangle = \int \ldots \int \langle 'E \mid 'x \rangle d'x \langle 'x \mid \sum_r \mathbf{u}_r \mid ''x \rangle d''x \langle ''x \mid ''E \rangle. \quad (11:6)$$

Now $\langle 'x \mid \sum_r \mathbf{u}_r \mid ''x \rangle = \sum_r \langle x_r' \mid \mathbf{u}_r \mid x_r'' \rangle \prod_{j \neq r} \delta(x_j' - x_j'')$, whence

$$\langle 'E \mid \mathbf{u}_r \mid ''E \rangle = \int \ldots \int \langle 'E \mid 'x \rangle d'x \langle x_r' \mid \mathbf{u}_r \mid x_r'' \rangle dx_r'' \langle x_1' \ldots x_{r-1}' x_r'' x_{r+1}' \ldots x_n' \mid ''E \rangle. \quad (11:7)$$

Furthermore

$$\langle 'E \mid 'x \rangle = \prod_j \langle E_j' \mid x_j' \rangle \quad \text{and} \quad \left\{ \begin{aligned} \int \langle E_l' \mid x_j' \rangle dx_j' \langle x_j' \mid E_m'' \rangle &= \delta(E_l', E_m''), \\ \sum_{E_j'} \langle x' \mid E_j' \rangle \langle E_j' \mid x'' \rangle &= \delta(x' - x''). \end{aligned} \right\}$$

[2] If the operators are those of electrons as specified above, the functions $\langle x_r' \mid E_r' \rangle$ may be considered as the ordinary Schroedinger eigenfunctions of a central field problem in zero approximation without interaction. However, the specific zero-order problem need not be restricted any further.

[3] $\mathbf{H}$ here need not be at all related to the $\mathbf{H}_r$ previously mentioned.

Therefore

$$\langle `E \mid \mathbf{u}_r \mid ''E \rangle = \prod_{j \neq r} \delta(E_j', E_j'') \iint \langle E_r' \mid x_r' \rangle \, dx_r' \langle x_r' \mid \mathbf{u}_r \mid x_r'' \rangle \, dx_r'' \langle x_r'' \mid E_r'' \rangle$$

$$= \prod_{j \neq r} \delta(E_j', E_j'') \langle E_r' \mid \mathbf{u}_r \mid E_r'' \rangle, \quad \ldots \quad (11:8)\,[4]$$

and

$$\sum_{E_1'' \ldots E_n''} \langle E_1' \ldots E_n' \mid \Sigma \mathbf{u}_r \mid E_1'' \ldots E_n'' \rangle \langle E_1'' \ldots E_n'' \mid ; t \rangle$$

$$= \sum_r \sum_{E_r''} \langle E_r' \mid \mathbf{u}_r \mid E_r'' \rangle \langle E_1' \ldots E_{r-1}' E_r'' E_{r+1}' \ldots E_n' \mid ; t \rangle. \quad (11:9)$$

Here the summation includes the case $E_r'' = E_r'$, and we could split the sum into a diagonal term, plus sum over non-diagonal, i.e. $E_r'' \neq E_r'$. Writing $\mathbf{v}(\mathbf{x}_r, \mathbf{x}_s) = \mathbf{v}_{rs}$, we have

$$\langle `x \mid \mathbf{v}_{rs} \mid ''x \rangle = \langle x_r' x_s' \mid \mathbf{v}_{rs} \mid x_r'' x_s'' \rangle \prod_{j \neq r, s} \delta(x_j' - x_j''), \quad . \quad (11:10)$$

$$\langle `E \mid \mathbf{v}_{rs} \mid ''E \rangle = \int \ldots \int \langle `E \mid `x \rangle \, d`x \langle `x \mid \mathbf{v}_{rs} \mid ''x \rangle \, d''x \langle ''x \mid ''E \rangle$$

$$= \int \ldots \int \langle `E \mid `x \rangle \, d`x \langle x_r' x_s' \mid \mathbf{v}_{rs} \mid x_r'' x_s'' \rangle \, dx_r'' \, dx_s'' \langle x_1' \ldots x_{r-1}' x_r'' x_{r+1}' \ldots x_{s-1}' x_s'' x_{s+1}' \ldots \mid ''E \rangle$$

$$= \prod_{j \neq r, s} \delta(E_j', E_j'') \int \ldots \int \langle E_r' \mid x_r' \rangle \langle E_s' \mid x_s' \rangle \, dx_r' \, dx_s' \langle x_r' x_s' \mid \mathbf{v}_{rs} \mid x_r'' x_s'' \rangle \, dx_r'' \, dx_s'' \langle x_r'' \mid E_r'' \rangle \langle x_s'' \mid E_s'' \rangle$$

$$= \prod_{j \neq r, s} \delta(E_j', E_j'') \langle E_r' E_s' \mid \mathbf{v}_{rs} \mid E_r'' E_s'' \rangle, \quad \ldots \quad (11:11)$$

and

$$\sum_{E_1'' \ldots E_n''} \langle E_1' \ldots E_n' \mid \mathbf{v}_{rs} \mid E_1'' \ldots E_n'' \rangle \langle E_1'' \ldots E_n'' \mid ; t \rangle \quad (11:12)$$

$$= \sum_{E_r'', E_s''} \langle E_r' E_s' \mid \mathbf{v}_{rs} \mid E_r'' E_s'' \rangle \langle E_1' \ldots E_{r-1}' E_r'' E_{r+1}' \ldots E_{s-1}' E_s'' E_{s+1}' \ldots E_n' \mid ; t \rangle.$$

Therefore (11:5) becomes

$$i\hbar \frac{d}{dt} \langle E_1' \ldots E_n' \mid ; t \rangle$$

$$= \sum_r \sum_{E_r''} \langle E_r' \mid \mathbf{u}_r \mid E_r'' \rangle \langle E_1' \ldots E_{r-1}' E_r'' E_{r+1}' \ldots E_n' \mid ; t \rangle$$

$$+ \sum_{r<s} \sum_{E_r'', E_s''} \langle E_r' E_s' \mid \mathbf{v}_{rs} \mid E_r'' E_s'' \rangle \langle E_1' \ldots E_{r-1}' E_r'' E_{r+1}' \ldots E_{s-1}' E_s'' E_{s+1}' \ldots E_n' \mid ; t \rangle. \quad (11:13)$$

[4] Here, as usually occurs for continuous representations, one integral is fictitious because of δ functions in the matrix element $\langle x_k' \mid \mathbf{u}_k \mid x_k'' \rangle$.

§ 93. Symmetry Properties

(*a*) *Symmetric Systems.*

For a symmetric wave-function $\langle 'E \mid \rangle = \langle E_1' \dots E_n' \mid \rangle$ we can specify each point in the domain of the function by giving the sequence $n_1', n_2', \dots n_k', \dots,$ which numbers specify the number of times the various eigenvalues $E^{(1)}, E^{(2)}, \dots E^{(k)}, \dots,$ respectively, occur in $\langle E_1' \dots E_n' \mid \rangle$. Here the sequence $E^{(1)}, E^{(2)}, \dots$ is the eigenvalue spectrum of an $\mathbf{E}$ (the same for all $\mathbf{E}$'s) ordered in any convenient manner. Thus the representatives of states may be expressed as functions of the variables $n_1', \dots n_k', \dots$ instead of $E_1' \dots E_n'$, the change being essentially a transformation to a new representation in which the rows and columns of matrices are labelled by the observables $\mathbf{n}_1, \mathbf{n}_2, \dots \mathbf{n}_k, \dots$ (infinite set), which are the numbers of particles or systems with $\mathbf{E}$'s having the values $E^{(1)}, E^{(2)}, \dots E^{(k)}, \dots$ respectively. As previously mentioned, we may also speak of them as *occupation* observables whose eigenvalues tell us how many particles are in the cell [5] $E^{(1)}, E^{(2)}, \dots$. The new observables are (non-analytic) functions of the observables $\mathbf{E}_1, \mathbf{E}_2, \dots \mathbf{E}_n$, so that the transformation consists essentially of a relabelling of rows and columns, and the only significant change to be made in the representative of a state will be that arising from the change in the weights of the different points of its domain (i.e. normalization). A given sequence [6] $n_1', n_2', \dots n_k', \dots$ defines a definite set of eigenvalues (or sets of values) $E_1'E_2' \dots E_n'$ without regard to the sequence of the latter.

For example, for $n = 3$, suppose $n_4' = 2$, $n_5' = 1$, while all other n_i''s $= 0$, then

$$\langle E_1^{(4)}, E_2^{(4)}, E_3^{(5)} \mid \rangle = \langle P\,; E_1^{(4)}, E_2^{(4)}, E_3^{(5)}, \mid \rangle \rightarrow \langle n_1', n_2', n_3', n_4', n_5', \dots \mid \rangle$$
$$= \langle 0, 0, 0, 2, 1, 0, 0, \dots \mid \rangle, \qquad (11:14)$$

where P is any permutation of the sub-indices of the E's. We normalize according to

$$\sum_{n_1' n_2'} \mid \langle n_1'n_2' \dots \mid \rangle \mid^2 = \sum_{E_1' \dots E_n'} \mid \langle E_1' \dots E_n' \mid \rangle \mid^2, \qquad (11:15)$$

from which we can infer that $\mid \langle n_1'n_2' \dots \mid \rangle \mid^2 = \Sigma \mid \langle E_1' \dots E_n' \mid \rangle \mid^2$, where the latter summation is over all values of the E''s such that n_1' of them are equal to $E^{(1)}$, n_2' equal to $E^{(2)}$, etc. The number of terms in the sum is then $n!/n_1'!\,n_2'! \dots,$ and they are all equal since $\langle E_1' \dots E_n' \mid \rangle$ is symmetrical; hence we must take

$$\langle n_1'n_2' \dots \mid \rangle = [\, n! / \prod_j n_j'! \,]^{\frac{1}{2}} \langle E_1'E_2' \dots E_n' \mid \rangle, \qquad (11:16)$$

neglecting a possible phase factor.

We must now obtain the transformation law for the representatives of dynamical variables from the $\mathbf{E}$-, to the $\mathbf{n}$-representations. Suppose $\mathbf{U} = \sum_r \mathbf{u}_r$, $\mathbf{u}_r$ being a function

[5] We speak of *cell* here rather than state, which is used in a somewhat different sense.

[6] Obviously, for a fixed number of systems or particles n, at most n of the numbers in the infinite set are non-zero.

of the variables describing the rth particle, and the form of $\mathbf{u}_r$ being the same for all r, as it must be if $\mathbf{U}$ is to be of physical significance. The representative of $\mathbf{U}$ has already been determined in the $\mathbf{E}$-representation (11:8), and a convenient way of transforming this representative to the $\mathbf{n}$-representation is to take the equation

$$|\,2\,\rangle = \mathbf{U}\,|\,1\,\rangle, \qquad (11{:}17)$$

and transform its representatives. In the $\mathbf{E}$-representation (11:17) becomes

$$\langle E_1'E_2'\ldots E_n'\,|\,2\,\rangle = \sum_{r}\sum_{E_r''}\langle E_r'\,|\,\mathbf{u}_r\,|\,E_r''\rangle\langle E_1'\ldots E_{r-1}'E_r''E_{r+1}'\ldots E_n'\,|\,1\,\rangle. \qquad (11{:}18)$$

Now in the symmetric case, the wave-function $\langle\, E_1'E_2' \ldots E_n' \,|\, \rangle$ may contain a number of equal arguments, e.g. $\langle\, E^{(p)}E^{(p)}E^{(p)}E^{(q)}E^{(q)}E^{(v)} \ldots E^{(z)} \,|\, \rangle$, the number of times $E^{(p)}$ occurs as argument being n_p' (variable) by definition. For this particular illustrative selection of E''s, we have

$$\begin{aligned}\langle\, E^{(p)}E^{(p)}E^{(p)}E^{(q)}E^{(q)}E^{(v)} \ldots \,|\, 2\,\rangle \\ = \sum_{E_1''}\langle\, E^{(p)} \,|\, \mathbf{u} \,|\, E_1''\,\rangle\langle\, E_1''E^{(p)}E^{(p)}E^{(q)}E^{(q)}E^{(v)} \ldots \,|\,1\,\rangle + \ldots \\ + \sum_{E_4''}\langle\, E^{(q)} \,|\, \mathbf{u} \,|\, E_4''\,\rangle\langle\, E^{(p)}E^{(p)}E^{(p)}E_4''E^{(q)}E^{(v)} \ldots \,|\,1\,\rangle + \ldots .\end{aligned} \qquad (11{:}19)$$

Thus we see that in general there are n_p' terms[7] on the right in which $E_r' = E^{(p)}$ ($r = 1, 2, 3$; $n_p' = 3$ in this special case) is replaced by $E_r'' = E^{(m)}$ say ($E_r'' = E^{(m)}$ being a prototype value for E_r''), and all these terms are equal since the wave-functions are symmetrical. Similarly, there are n_q' terms in which $E_r' = E^{(q)}$ ($r = 4, 5$; $n_q' = 2$ in this illustrative case) is replaced by $E_r'' = E^{(m)}$, and again we group these equal terms together. Thus, the right-hand side of (11:19) may be written as

$$\begin{aligned}\sum_m \langle\, E^{(p)} \,|\, \mathbf{u} \,|\, E^{(m)}\,\rangle\, n_p' \,[\, n_1'! \ldots (\, n_p' - 1\,)! \ldots (\, n_m' + 1\,)! \ldots /n!\,]^{\frac{1}{2}} \\ \times \langle\, n_1' \ldots n_p' - 1 \ldots n_m + 1 \ldots \,|\, 1\,\rangle + \ldots \\ + \sum_m \langle\, E^{(q)} \,|\, \mathbf{u} \,|\, E^{(m)}\,\rangle\, n_q' \,[\, n_1! \ldots (\, n_q' - 1\,)! \ldots (\, n_m' + 1\,)! \ldots /n!\,]^{\frac{1}{2}} \\ \times \langle\, n_1' \ldots n_q' - 1 \ldots n_m' + 1 \ldots \,|\, 1\,\rangle + \ldots ,\end{aligned} \qquad (11{:}20)$$

where the summation index m takes on all integer values. The wave-function $\langle\, n_1' \ldots n_p' - 1 \ldots n_m' + 1 \ldots \,|\, 1\,\rangle$, for example, appears because the corresponding wave-function in the $\mathbf{E}$-representation differs from $\langle\, E_1' \ldots E_n' \,|\, \rangle$ only in that E_r'' replaces E_r', so that the number of particles in the cell E_r' $(=E^{(p)})$ is reduced by one, while the number in the cell E_r'' $(=E^{(m)})$ is increased by one; and correspondingly it is necessary to give the wave-function its appropriate normalization factor $[n_1'! \ldots (n_p' - 1)! \ldots (n_m' + 1)! \ldots /n!]^{\frac{1}{2}}$. We can further simplify (11:20) and write

$$\begin{aligned}\sum_k\sum_m \langle\, k \,|\, \mathbf{u} \,|\, m\,\rangle\, n_k' \,[\, n_1'! \ldots (\, n_k' - 1\,)! \ldots (\, n_m' + 1\,)! \ldots /n!\,]^{\frac{1}{2}} \\ \times \langle\, n_1' \ldots n_k' - 1 \ldots n_m' + 1 \ldots \,|\, 1\,\rangle,\end{aligned} \qquad (11{:}21)$$

[7] The number of ways of choosing r and E_r'' such that $E_r' = E^{(p)}$ and $E_r'' = E^{(m)}$ is just n_p', the number of ways of choosing r such that $E_r' = E^{(p)}$, since there is always only one way of choosing $E_r'' = E^{(m)}$.

where $\langle E^{(k)} \mid \mathbf{u} \mid E^{(m)} \rangle$ is written as $\langle k \mid \mathbf{u} \mid m \rangle$ for convenience, and now k also takes on all values, since superfluous terms are eliminated by the presence of the factor n_k'. Combining (11:18) and (11:21), after cancelling like members in the respective normalization factors, we have

$$\langle n_1' n_2' \ldots \mid 2 \rangle = \sum_{k,m} \langle k \mid \mathbf{u} \mid m \rangle [n_k'(n_m'+1-\delta_{km})]^{\frac{1}{2}} \langle n_1' \ldots n_k'-1 \ldots n_m'+1 \ldots \mid 1 \rangle. \tag{11:22}$$ [8]

For an operator such as $\mathbf{V} = \sum_{r<s} \mathbf{v}_{rs}$, involving pairs of particles, we have from (11:13),

$$\mid 2 \rangle = \mathbf{V} \mid 1 \rangle, \tag{11:23}$$

$$\langle E_1' \ldots E_n' \mid 2 \rangle = \sum_{r<s} \sum_{E_r'', E_s''} \langle E_r' E_s' \mid \mathbf{v}_{rs} \mid E_r'' E_s'' \rangle \langle E_r' \ldots E_{r-1}' E_r'' E_{r+1}' \ldots E_{s-1}' E_s'' E_{s+1}' \ldots E_n' \mid 1 \rangle. \tag{11:24}$$

Considering again the illustrative wave-function $\langle E^{(p)} E^{(p)} E^{(p)} E^{(q)} E^{(q)} E^{(v)} \ldots \mid \rangle$, it is evident that the number of equal terms in (11:24) in which $E^{(p)}$ in this function is replaced by $E_s'' = E^{(n)}$, say, and $E_r'' = E^{(m)}$, is just $\frac{1}{2} n_p'(n_p'-1)$, i.e. the number of ways of choosing s such that $E_s' = E^{(p)}$, $E_s'' = E^{(n)}$, and r such that $E_r' = E^{(p)}$, $E_r'' = E^{(m)}$, with $r < s$. Further, there will be $n_p' n_q'$ equal terms in which $E_r' = E^{(p)}$ is replaced by $E_r'' = E^{(m)}$, and $E_s' = E^{(q)}$ by $E_s'' = E^{(n)}$, etc. Thus, collecting equal terms, the right-hand side of (11:24) may be written as

$$\begin{aligned}\sum_{m,n} \Big\{ & \langle pp \mid \mathbf{v} \mid mn \rangle \tfrac{1}{2} n_p'(n_p'-1) [n_1'! \ldots (n_p'-2)! \ldots (n_m'+1)! \ldots (n_n'+1)! \ldots / n!]^{\frac{1}{2}} \\ & \qquad \times \langle n_1' \ldots n_p'-2 \ldots n_m'+1 \ldots n_n'+1 \ldots \mid 1 \rangle + \ldots \\ & + \langle pq \mid \mathbf{v} \mid mn \rangle n_p' n_q' [n_1'! \ldots (n_p'-1)! \ldots (n_q'-1)! \ldots (n_m'+1)! \ldots (n_n'+1)! \ldots / n!]^{\frac{1}{2}} \\ & \qquad \times \langle \ldots n_p'-1 \ldots n_q'-1 \ldots n_m'+1 \ldots n_n'+1 \ldots \mid 1 \rangle + \ldots \\ & + \langle qq \mid \mathbf{v} \mid mn \rangle \tfrac{1}{2} n_q'(n_q'-1) [n_1'! \ldots (n_q'-2)! \ldots (n_m'+1)! \ldots (n_n'+1)! \ldots / n!]^{\frac{1}{2}} \\ & \qquad \times \langle n_1' \ldots n_q'-2 \ldots n_m'+1 \ldots n_n'+1 \ldots \mid 1 \rangle + \ldots \\ & + \ldots \Big\},\end{aligned} \tag{11:25}$$

or simply as

$$\begin{aligned}\tfrac{1}{2} \sum_{k,l,m,n} & \langle kl \mid \mathbf{v} \mid mn \rangle n_k'(n_l'-\delta_{kl}) [n_1'! \ldots (n_k'-1)! \ldots (n_l'-1)! \ldots (n_m'+1)! \ldots (n_n'+1)! \ldots / n!]^{\frac{1}{2}} \\ & \times \langle \ldots n_k'-1 \ldots n_l'-1 \ldots n_m'+1 \ldots n_n'+1 \ldots \mid 1 \rangle,\end{aligned} \tag{11:26}$$

with the previously mentioned convention that, for coincident summation indices, both the normalization factor and the wave-function above are to be taken accordingly, e.g. for $k = l$ there would be

$$[n_1'! \ldots (n_k'-2)! \ldots (n_m'+1)! \ldots (n_n'+1)! \ldots / n!]^{\frac{1}{2}} \langle n_1' \ldots n_k'-2 \ldots n_m'+1 \ldots n_n'+1 \ldots \mid 1 \rangle.$$

[8] $\langle n_1' \ldots n_k'-1 \ldots n_m'+1 \ldots \mid \rangle$ is understood as $\langle n_1' \ldots n_k' \ldots \mid \rangle$ for $k = m$.

Keeping this point in mind, (11:26) and (11:24) combine to give as a final result

$$\langle n_1'n_2' \dots | 2 \rangle$$
$$= \tfrac{1}{2} \sum_{k,\,l,\,m,\,n} \langle kl | \mathbf{v} | mn \rangle [n_k'(n_l' - \delta_{kl})(n_m' + 1 - \delta_{km} - \delta_{lm})(n_n' + 1 + \delta_{mn} - \delta_{kn} - \delta_{ln})]^{\frac{1}{2}}$$
$$\times \langle n_1' \dots n_k'-1 \dots n_l'-1 \dots n_m'+1 \dots n_n'+1 \dots | 1 \rangle, \quad (11:27)$$

where the factor under the root sign, which remains after clearing the normalization constants, is readily verified by considering (11:25) and (11:26), and the effect of various coincident summation indices on the normalization factor to be chosen in (11:26).

The eigenvalues of the new dynamical variables $\mathbf{n}_1, \mathbf{n}_2, \dots$ are the integers $0, 1, 2, \dots$, and are thus, apart from the factor $\hbar$, the same as those of the action variables $\mathbf{J}$ in the problem of the simple harmonic oscillator $\left[\mathbf{H} = \frac{1}{2m}(\mathbf{p}^2 + m^2\omega^2\mathbf{q}^2);\ \mathbf{J} = \mathbf{H}/\omega - \hbar/2\right]$. In the $\mathbf{H}$-diagonal representation for the oscillator, the matrix of $\mathbf{J}$ is (cf. DIRAC, *op. cit.*)

$$\| \langle H' | \mathbf{J} | H'' \rangle \| = \begin{Vmatrix} 0 & 0 & 0 & 0 & \dots \\ 0 & 1 & 0 & 0 & \dots \\ 0 & 0 & 2 & 0 & \dots \\ 0 & 0 & 0 & 3 & \dots \\ \cdot & \cdot & \cdot & \cdot & \dots \end{Vmatrix}, \quad (11:28)$$

and we can introduce the angle variable $\boldsymbol{\omega}$ defined by the matrices of $e^{i\boldsymbol{\omega}}$ and $e^{-i\boldsymbol{\omega}}$, i.e.

$$\begin{Vmatrix} 0 & 0 & 0 & 0 & \dots \\ 1 & 0 & 0 & 0 & \dots \\ 0 & 1 & 0 & 0 & \dots \\ 0 & 0 & 1 & 0 & \dots \\ \cdot & \cdot & \cdot & \cdot & \dots \end{Vmatrix} \quad \text{and} \quad \begin{Vmatrix} 0 & 1 & 0 & 0 & 0 & \dots \\ 0 & 0 & 1 & 0 & 0 & \dots \\ 0 & 0 & 0 & 1 & 0 & \dots \\ 0 & 0 & 0 & 0 & 1 & \dots \\ \cdot & \cdot & \cdot & \cdot & \cdot & \dots \end{Vmatrix}.$$

From the matrix representatives we see that $e^{i\boldsymbol{\omega}}$ and $e^{-i\boldsymbol{\omega}}$ are not truly reciprocal, since $e^{-i\boldsymbol{\omega}}e^{i\boldsymbol{\omega}} = \mathbf{I}$, but $e^{i\boldsymbol{\omega}}e^{-i\boldsymbol{\omega}} \neq \mathbf{I}$. Further, we observe that

$$\mathbf{J}e^{i\boldsymbol{\omega}} = e^{i\boldsymbol{\omega}}(\mathbf{J} + \hbar) \quad \text{and} \quad \mathbf{J}e^{-i\boldsymbol{\omega}} = e^{-i\boldsymbol{\omega}}(\mathbf{J} - \hbar). \quad (11:29)$$

Comparing the above with the relations for $\mathbf{q}$, $\mathbf{p}$ (Chap. III), i.e.

$$\mathbf{p}e^{ic\mathbf{q}} = e^{ic\mathbf{q}}(\mathbf{p} + c\hbar), \quad (11:30)$$

with $c = \pm 1$, we see that at least formally the equations (11:29) are consistent with the view that $\mathbf{J}$ and $\boldsymbol{\omega}$ are a pair of canonically conjugate dynamical variables satisfying the quantum condition $\boldsymbol{\omega}\mathbf{J} - \mathbf{J}\boldsymbol{\omega} = i\hbar$. This relation is entirely formal, since we can only define $e^{\pm i\boldsymbol{\omega}}$, not $\boldsymbol{\omega}$ itself, and furthermore, we know that to be canonically conjugate the dynamical variables must have continuous spectra, which

J has not. Nonetheless, the analogy is suggestive, and we shall make use of it with proper reservations. It is readily verified from the matrix forms that

$$\left.\begin{aligned} \mathbf{J}^{\frac{1}{2}}e^{i\omega} &= e^{i\omega}(\mathbf{J}+\hbar)^{\frac{1}{2}}, \\ e^{-i\omega}\mathbf{J} &= (\mathbf{J}+\hbar)^{\frac{1}{2}}e^{-i\omega}, \\ \mathbf{J}^{\frac{1}{2}}e^{i\omega}e^{-i\omega}\mathbf{J}^{\frac{1}{2}} &= \mathbf{J}, \\ e^{-i\omega}\mathbf{J}^{\frac{1}{2}}\mathbf{J}^{\frac{1}{2}}e^{i\omega} &= (\mathbf{J}+\hbar)^{\frac{1}{2}}e^{-i\omega}e^{i\omega}(\mathbf{J}+\hbar)^{\frac{1}{2}} = \mathbf{J}+\hbar. \end{aligned}\right\} \quad . \quad . \quad (11:31)$$

These results hold in spite of the inequality $e^{i\omega}e^{-i\omega} \neq \mathbf{I}$, and show that, when we deal with the quantities $\mathbf{J}^{\frac{1}{2}}e^{i\omega}$ and $e^{-i\omega}\mathbf{J}^{\frac{1}{2}}$, we can consider $e^{i\omega}$ and $e^{-i\omega}$ as truly reciprocal without getting into difficulty.

By analogy, we introduce $e^{\pm i\omega_k}$ for each of the variables $\mathbf{n}_k$, and corresponding to (11:29) we now have

$$e^{i\omega_k}\mathbf{n}_k = (\mathbf{n}_k - 1)e^{i\omega_k} \quad \text{and} \quad e^{-i\omega_k}\mathbf{n}_k = (\mathbf{n}_k + 1)e^{-i\omega_k}; \qquad (11:32)$$ [9]

and $e^{i\omega_k}$, $e^{-i\omega_k}$ and $\mathbf{n}_k$ commute with $e^{i\omega_l}$, $e^{-i\omega_l}$ and $\mathbf{n}_l$ for $k \neq l$. These results are in accord with the formal relation

$$\boldsymbol{\omega}_k\mathbf{n}_k - \mathbf{n}_k\boldsymbol{\omega}_k = i. \quad . \quad . \quad . \quad . \quad . \quad . \quad . \quad (11:33)$$

From the commutators (11:32) we have the selection rules

$$\left.\begin{aligned} (n_k'' - n_k' + 1)\langle n_k' | e^{i\omega_k} | n_k''\rangle &= 0, \\ (n_k'' - n_k' - 1)\langle n_k' | e^{-i\omega_k} | n_k''\rangle &= 0, \end{aligned}\right\} \quad . \quad . \quad . \quad (11:33')$$

and the explicit forms of these representatives are given by (11:28), namely,

$$\langle n_1'n_2' \ldots | e^{i\omega_k} | n_1''n_2'' \ldots\rangle = \delta(n_k', n_k''+1)\prod_{j\neq k}\delta(n_j', n_j''), \quad (11:34a)$$

$$\langle n_1'n_2' \ldots | e^{-i\omega_k} | n_1''n_2'' \ldots\rangle = \delta(n_k', n_k''-1)\prod_{j\neq k}\delta(n_j', n_j''). \quad (11:34b)$$

These relations mean that $e^{i\omega_k}$, operating on a $|\,\rangle$ whose representative is $\langle n_1'n_2' \ldots n_k' \ldots |\,\rangle$, gives a resultant whose representative is

$$\left\{\begin{matrix} \langle n_1'n_2' \ldots n_k' - 1 \ldots |\,\rangle \\ 0 \end{matrix}\right\} \begin{matrix} (n_k' \geqslant 1) \\ (n_k' = 0) \end{matrix}, \quad . \quad . \quad . \quad (11:35a)$$

and $e^{-i\omega_k}|\,\rangle$ for this same $|\,\rangle$ has the representative

$$\langle n_1' \ldots n_k' + 1 \ldots |\,\rangle, \quad . \quad . \quad . \quad . \quad . \quad . \quad (11:35b)$$

as may be readily verified by expressing $e^{\pm i\omega_k}|\,\rangle$ in the **n**-representation. Equation (11:33) suggests another equivalent definition of $e^{\pm i\omega_k}$:

[9] In general,

$$e^{i\omega_k}\mathbf{f}(\mathbf{n}_k) = \mathbf{f}(\mathbf{n}_k - 1)e^{i\omega_k},$$
$$e^{-i\omega_k}\mathbf{f}(\mathbf{n}_k) = \mathbf{f}(\mathbf{n}_k + 1)e^{-i\omega_k}.$$

If

$$| \rangle = \sum_{n_1' \dots} | n_1' \dots n_k' \dots \rangle \langle n_1' \dots n_k' \dots | \rangle, \quad . \quad . \quad . \quad (11{:}36)$$

then

$$e^{\pm i\omega_k} | \rangle = \sum_{n_1' \dots} | n_1' \dots n_k' \dots \rangle e^{\mp \partial/\partial n_k'} \langle n_1' \dots n_k' \dots | \rangle,$$

since by Taylor's Theorem

$$e^{\partial/\partial n_k'} f (n_k') = \sum_{r=0} \frac{1}{r!} \left(\frac{\partial}{\partial n_k'} \right)^r f = f (n_k' + 1), \text{ etc.}$$

It is here that the formal analogy of (11:33) to the commutator $[\mathbf{q}, \mathbf{p}]_- = i\hbar$ is useful.

We can now see that equation (11:22) is just the representative of

$$| 2 \rangle = \sum_{k, m} \langle k | \mathbf{u} | m \rangle \mathbf{n}_k^{\frac{1}{2}} (\mathbf{n}_m + 1 - \delta_{km})^{\frac{1}{2}} e^{i\omega_k} e^{-i\omega_m} | 1 \rangle. \quad . \quad (11{:}37)$$

Equation (11:37) must hold whenever $| 2 \rangle = \mathbf{U} | 1 \rangle$ holds, and hence

$$\begin{aligned} \mathbf{U} &= \sum_{k, m} \langle k | \mathbf{u} | m \rangle \mathbf{n}_k^{\frac{1}{2}} (\mathbf{n}_m + 1 - \delta_{km})^{\frac{1}{2}} e^{i\omega_k} e^{-i\omega_m} \\ &= \sum_{k, m} \langle k | \mathbf{u} | m \rangle \mathbf{n}_k^{\frac{1}{2}} e^{i\omega_k} (\mathbf{n}_m + 1)^{\frac{1}{2}} e^{-i\omega_m}, \quad . \quad . \quad . \quad . \quad (11{:}38) \end{aligned}$$

where we have used equations (11:32) in the last step. This result is the required expression of $\mathbf{U}$ in terms of the operators $\mathbf{n}$, and gives us immediately the $\mathbf{n}$-representative of $\mathbf{U}$. The $\langle k | \mathbf{u} | m \rangle$ here are of course just numerical coefficients. Equation (11:38) can be put into simpler form by introducing the dynamical variables

$$\left. \begin{aligned} \boldsymbol{\xi}_k &= (\mathbf{n}_k + 1)^{\frac{1}{2}} e^{-i\omega_k} = e^{-i\omega_k} \mathbf{n}_k^{\frac{1}{2}}, \\ \boldsymbol{\xi}_k^* &= e^{i\omega_k} (\mathbf{n}_k + 1)^{\frac{1}{2}} = \mathbf{n}_k^{\frac{1}{2}} e^{i\omega_k}, \end{aligned} \right\} \quad . \quad . \quad . \quad . \quad (11{:}39)$$

which satisfy the commutation conditions

$$\left. \begin{aligned} [\boldsymbol{\xi}_k, \boldsymbol{\xi}_l]_- &= 0, & \boldsymbol{\xi}_k \boldsymbol{\xi}_k^* &= \mathbf{n}_k + 1, \\ [\boldsymbol{\xi}_k^*, \boldsymbol{\xi}_l^*]_- &= 0, & \boldsymbol{\xi}_k^* \boldsymbol{\xi}_k &= \mathbf{n}_k, \\ [\boldsymbol{\xi}_k, \boldsymbol{\xi}_l^*]_- &= \delta_{kl}. & & \end{aligned} \right\} \quad . \quad . \quad . \quad (11{:}40)$$

In terms of these new variables, (11:38) takes the simple form

$$\mathbf{U} = \sum_{k,m} \langle k | \mathbf{u} | m \rangle \boldsymbol{\xi}_k^* \boldsymbol{\xi}_m, \quad . \quad . \quad . \quad . \quad . \quad . \quad (11{:}41)$$

and similarly (11:27) is the representative of

$$\begin{aligned} | 2 \rangle = \tfrac{1}{2} \sum_{klmn} \langle kl | \mathbf{v} | mn \rangle \Big[\mathbf{n}_k (\mathbf{n}_l - \delta_{kl})(\mathbf{n}_m + 1 - \delta_{km} - \delta_{lm})(\mathbf{n}_n + 1 + \delta_{mn} - \delta_{kn} - \delta_{ln}) \Big]^{\frac{1}{2}} \\ \times e^{i\omega_k} e^{i\omega_l} e^{-i\omega_m} e^{-i\omega_n} | 1 \rangle. \quad . \quad . \quad . \quad . \quad . \quad . \quad (11{:}42) \end{aligned}$$

Here we require the relations

$$e^{i\omega_k}(\mathbf{n}_l+1)^{\frac{1}{2}}=(\mathbf{n}_l+1-\delta_{kl})^{\frac{1}{2}}e^{i\omega_k}, \qquad (11{:}43a)$$

$$e^{i\omega_k}\mathbf{n}_l^{\frac{1}{2}}=(\mathbf{n}_l-\delta_{kl})^{\frac{1}{2}}e^{i\omega_k}, \qquad (11{:}43b)$$

$$e^{-i\omega_k}(\mathbf{n}_l+1)^{\frac{1}{2}}=(\mathbf{n}_l+1+\delta_{kl})^{\frac{1}{2}}e^{-i\omega_k}. \qquad (11{:}43c)$$

Applying (11:43a, b) to $e^{i\omega_k}$ in (11:42), for example, we obtain

$$[\,\xi_k{}^*\mathbf{n}_l^{\frac{1}{2}}(\mathbf{n}_m+1-\delta_{lm})^{\frac{1}{2}}(\mathbf{n}_n+1+\delta_{mn}-\delta_{ln})^{\frac{1}{2}}\,]\,e^{i\omega_l}e^{-i\omega_m}e^{-i\omega_n}, \qquad (11{:}44)$$

and repeating the operation for $e^{i\omega_l}$ and $e^{-i\omega_m}$, we obtain, as the final form of $\mathbf{V}$,

$$\mathbf{V}=\tfrac{1}{2}\sum_{klmn}\langle\, kl\mid \mathbf{v}\mid mn\,\rangle\,\xi_k{}^*\xi_l{}^*\xi_m\xi_n. \qquad (11{:}45)$$

(*b*) *Antisymmetric Systems.*

We introduce **n**-representations defined as before, $\mathbf{n}_k$ being the number of **E**'s having the value $E^{(k)}$, etc., except that in this case, since the wave-function $\langle\, E_1'E_2'\ldots E_n'\mid\,\rangle$ is antisymmetric, the **n**'s may take on only the eigenvalues 0, 1. (Otherwise the above wave-function would vanish identically, which property, of course, characterizes the antisymmetric case.) To each set of values of the **E**'s, there will be a definite set of values for the **n**'s, and conversely; but when a set of n''s is given we do not know which E''s have the values associated with the given n'-sequence, and of course the sign of the function is affected by the order of the E''s. Thus, when we pass to the representatives $\langle\, n_1'n_2'\ldots\mid\,\rangle$, we can only infer that

$$\langle\, E_1'E_2'\ldots E_n'\mid\,\rangle=\pm\langle\, n_1'n_2'\ldots\mid\,\rangle. \qquad (11{:}46)$$ [10]

The normalization factor is not required now, since the eigenvalues of the **n**'s are restricted to 0 and 1.

We must now set up a rule for specifying the sign in any particular case, and this can be done by ordering the eigenvalue spectrum of an **E** (the same for each $\mathbf{E}_r$) in some arbitrarily chosen way so as to establish first a *standard sequence.* This is most conveniently done by taking the standard sequence as

$$E^{(1)},\,E^{(2)},\,E^{(3)},\ldots, \qquad (11{:}47)$$

which is the same as the order in which the n''s are written in $\langle\, n_1'n_2'n_3'\ldots\mid\,\rangle$. We then require that the (+) sign in (11:46) shall be taken when the E''s in $\langle\, E_1'E_2'\ldots E_n'\mid\,\rangle$, which form a particular selection of n different members from the total set (11:47), can be brought into the order in which they appear in the standard sequence (gaps omitted) by an even number of interchanges; and the (−) sign for an odd number, i.e. according to whether the actual order of the E''s is an even or odd permutation of the standard order, with gaps omitted. Thus suppose we write the standard sequence as $E^{(1)}<E^{(2)}<E^{(3)}<\ldots<E^{(i)}<E^{(j)}<E^{(k)}<E^{(l)}\ldots$;

[10] We must emphasize that the indices of the arguments on the left refer to the eigenvalues of the first, second, . . . nth observable **E**, while those on the right are the numbers of E''s equal to $E^{(1)},\ldots$, i.e. n_1', etc., and there is obviously no correspondence of indices intended.

then, for $n = 5$, if $\langle E_1'E_2'E_3'E_4'E_5' \mid \rangle = \langle E^{(6)}E^{(k)}E^{(3)}E^{(l)}E^{(2)} \mid \rangle$, i.e. $E_1' = E^{(6)}$, $E_2' = E^{(k)}$, etc., the natural order for this selection of 5 members from (11:47) is $E^{(2)}$, $E^{(3)}$, $E^{(6)}$, $E^{(k)}$, $E^{(l)}$. The number of interchanges required to achieve this natural order is 6; consequently,

$$\langle E_1' \ldots E_5' \mid \rangle = \langle n_1'n_2'n_3' \ldots n_6' \ldots n_k'n_l' \ldots \mid \rangle = \langle 0, 1, 1, 0, 0, 1, \ldots 1, 1, 0, \ldots \mid \rangle.$$

For convenience in determining the correct sign in (11:46) let us introduce a comparison sequence (indicated by an underline)

$$\underline{E_1'E_2' \ldots E_n'}, \qquad (11:48)$$

defined by the condition that whatever the values of the E''s in (11:48), i.e. for *any* selection of n members from the set (11:47), the arguments in (11:48) are automatically arranged in the order of the standard sequence. It may happen that one or another member is not underlined, and these exceptions will be explained as they arise. By definition

$$\langle \underline{E_1'E_2' \ldots E_r' \ldots E_s' \ldots E_n'} \mid \rangle = + \langle n_1'n_2'n_3' \ldots n_{E_r}' \ldots n_{E_s}' \ldots \mid \rangle, \qquad (11:49)$$

so that the underline indicates the operation of ordering, and in particular makes possible a unique definition of position of the E_i''s for the given selection of n, counting from the left. Thus in (11:49), E_r' is at the normal [11] ordered position

$$r' = n_1' + n_2' + \ldots + n_{E_r'}', \qquad (11:50)$$

and E_s' at the position

$$s' = n_1' + n_2' + \ldots + n_{E_s'}'. \qquad (11:51)$$

We must now obtain the transformation law for dynamical variables from the **E**- to the **n**-representations. Following the procedure in the symmetric case, we write

$$\mid 2 \rangle = \mathbf{U} \mid 1 \rangle, \qquad (11:52)$$

or

$$\langle E_1'E_2' \ldots E_n' \mid 2 \rangle = \sum_r \sum_{E_r''} \langle E_r' \mid \mathbf{u}_r \mid E_r'' \rangle \langle E_1' \ldots E_{r-1}'E_r''E_{r+1}' \ldots E_n' \mid 1 \rangle. \qquad (11:53)$$

In the **n**-representation (11:53) becomes

$$\langle n_1'n_2' \ldots \mid 2 \rangle$$
$$= \sum_r \sum_{E_r''} \pm \langle E_r' \mid \mathbf{u}_r \mid E_r'' \rangle \langle n_1' \ldots n_{E_r'}' - 1 \ldots n_{E_r''}' + 1 \ldots \mid 1 \rangle. \qquad (11:54)$$ [12]

With regard to the ambiguity of sign in (11:54), it is clear that we must take the (—) sign in those cases where a (—) sign appears in one and only one of the equations

$$\langle E_1' \ldots E_r' \ldots E_n' \mid \rangle = \pm \langle n_1'n_2' \ldots n_{E_r'}' \ldots \mid \rangle, \qquad (11:55a)$$

$$\langle E_1' \ldots E_{r-1}'E_r''E_{r+1}' \ldots E_n' \mid \rangle = \pm \langle n_1' \ldots n_{E_r'}' - 1 \ldots n_{E_r''}' + 1 \ldots \mid \rangle. \qquad (11:55b)$$

[11] We say " normal " because there will, in general, be gaps.

[12] Here $\langle n_1' \ldots n_{E_r'}' - 1 \ldots n_{E_r''}' + 1 \ldots \mid 1 \rangle$ is understood simply as $\langle n_1' \ldots n_{E_r'}' \ldots \mid 1 \rangle$ for $E_r' = E_r''$.

We may standardize the procedure for determining the sign in (11:54) by the following procedure:

First, we observe that when E_r' in (11:55*a*) and E_r'' in (11:55*b*) are shifted to first place, the resultant sign in (11:54) is not affected, so that we may write consistently [13]

$$\langle E_r'E_1'\ldots E_{r-1}'E_{r+1}'\ldots E_n'\,|\,\rangle = \pm\langle n_1'\ldots n_{E_r}'\ldots\,|\,\rangle, \qquad (11:56a)$$

$$\langle E_r''E_1'\ldots E_{r-1}'E_{r+1}'\ldots E_n'\,|\,\rangle = \pm\langle n_1'\ldots n_{E_r}'-1\ldots n_{E_r''}'+1\ldots\,|\,\rangle. \qquad (11:56b)$$

Now, if we order the E''s in (11:56*a*, *b*) in standard sequence except for E_r', E_r'' respectively,[14] which remain at first place, we have

$$\langle E_r'\underline{E_1'\ldots E_{r-1}'E_{r+1}'\ldots E_n'}\,|\,\rangle = \pm\langle n_1'\ldots n_{E_r}'\ldots\,|\,\rangle, \qquad (11:57a)$$

$$\langle E_r''\underline{E_1'\ldots E_{r-1}'E_{r+1}'\ldots E_n'}\,|\,\rangle = \pm\langle n_1'\ldots n_{E_r}'-1\ldots n_{E_r''}'+1\ldots\,|\,\rangle, \qquad (11:57b)$$

and

$$\begin{aligned}\langle E_r'\underline{E_1'\ldots E_{r-1}'E_{r+1}'\ldots E_n'}\,|\,\rangle &= -(-)^{r'}\langle \underline{E_1'\ldots E_{r-1}'E_r'E_{r+1}'\ldots E_n'}\,|\,\rangle \\ &= -(-)^{r'}\langle n_1'\ldots n_{E_r}'\ldots\,|\,\rangle, \qquad (11:58a)\end{aligned}$$

$$\begin{aligned}\langle E_r''\underline{E_1'\ldots E_{r-1}'E_{r+1}'\ldots E_n'}\,|\,\rangle &= -(-)^{r''}\langle \underline{E_1'\ldots E_{r-1}'E_r''E_{r+1}'\ldots E_n'}\,|\,\rangle \\ &= -(-)^{r''}\langle n_1'\ldots n_{E_r}'-1\ldots n_{E_r''}'+1\ldots\,|\,\rangle. \qquad (11:58b)\end{aligned}$$

Equation (11:58*a*) results from the observation that shifting E_r' from its ordered position r' (in the middle term) to first place introduces a factor $-(-)^{r'}$, and from the definition (11:49). Similarly for (11:58*b*). Combining (11:55–58), we see that the sign in (11:54) is determined by the signature function $(-)^{r'+r''}$ or $(-)^{|r'-r''|}$, where r', r'' are defined for these sequences as in (11:50) and (11:51). From the nature of the signature as a power of (-1) it is clearly immaterial whether we take $(-)^{r'+r''}$ or $(-)^{|r'-r''|}$, the only difference being in the way we define and handle the signature operators to be introduced later. We shall use the latter definition in our calculation.[15]

Equation (11:54) may be written as

$$\begin{aligned}\langle n_1'n_2'\ldots\,|\,2\rangle &= \sum_r \langle E_r'\,|\,\mathbf{u}_r\,|\,E_r'\rangle\langle n_1'n_2'\ldots\,|\,1\rangle \\ &\quad + \sum_r \sum_{E_r''\neq E_r'} \pm\langle E_r'\,|\,\mathbf{u}_r\,|\,E_r''\rangle\langle n_1'\ldots n_{E_r}'-1\ldots n_{E_r''}'+1\ldots\,|\,1\rangle \qquad (11:59)\end{aligned}$$

[13] We note that the steps (11:56, 57) change the sign relations of both parts (*a*) and (*b*) consistently, if at all—thus not affecting the resultant sign in (11:54).

[14] This explains why E_r' and E_r'' are not underlined here.

[15] We could immediately obtain the signature in the present case by noting that the condition (11:55) for the ($\pm$) sign is the same as the condition that the numbers of E''s on the left in (11:55) that lie between E_r' and E_r'' (not inclusive) shall be even/odd, i.e. $\sum_\epsilon n_\epsilon'$, where the sum is over all ϵ for which $E^{(\epsilon)}$ lies between E_r' and E_r'', i.e. $|\,r'-r''\,|$. We develop the above procedure here since it is required later when considering more complicated operators than $\mathbf{U}$.

In the first sum a typical matrix element[16] is $\langle E^{(k)} \mid \mathbf{u} \mid E^{(k)} \rangle$ or simply $\langle k \mid \mathbf{u} \mid k \rangle$, and it appears a number of times equal to the number of ways of choosing r such that $E_r' = E^{(k)}$, which is $n_{E^{(k)}}' = n_k'$. In the second sum a typical matrix element $\langle E^{(k)} \mid \mathbf{u} \mid E^{(l)} \rangle = \langle k \mid \mathbf{u} \mid l \rangle$ appears a number of times equal to the number of ways of choosing r and E_r'' such that $E_r' = E^{(k)}$ and $E_r'' = E^{(l)}$, which is also n_k', and we have then

$$\langle n_1'n_2' \ldots \mid 2 \rangle = \sum_k \langle k \mid \mathbf{u} \mid k \rangle n_k' \langle n_1'n_2' \ldots \mid 1 \rangle + \sum_k \sum_{l \neq k} \pm \langle k \mid \mathbf{u} \mid l \rangle \langle n_1' \ldots n_k' - 1 \ldots n_l' + 1 \ldots \mid 1 \rangle. \quad (11:60)$$

The factor n_k' does not appear in the second term, since $\langle n_1' \ldots n_k' - 1 \ldots n_l' + 1 \ldots \mid \rangle$ is non-vanishing only for $n_k' = 1$, $n_l' = 0$.

The observable $1 - 2\mathbf{n}_k$ formed from $\mathbf{n}_k$ has the eigenvalues 1, -1, and from our previous acquaintance with the spin operators it is natural to write

$$1 - 2\mathbf{n}_k = \boldsymbol{\sigma}_{kz}. \quad (11:61)$$

In analogy with the symmetric case we introduce the *step operators* (cf. Chap. III) $\frac{1}{2}(\boldsymbol{\sigma}_{kx} - i\boldsymbol{\sigma}_{ky})$ and $\frac{1}{2}(\boldsymbol{\sigma}_{kx} + i\boldsymbol{\sigma}_{ky})$ associated with $\boldsymbol{\sigma}_{kz}$, which play the part of angle variables analogous to $e^{i\omega_k}$ and $e^{-i\omega_k}$ respectively, and are represented in a $\boldsymbol{\sigma}_{kz}$- or $\mathbf{n}_k$-diagonal representation by

$$\begin{pmatrix} 0 & 0 \\ 1 & 0 \end{pmatrix} \quad \text{and} \quad \begin{pmatrix} 0 & 1 \\ 0 & 0 \end{pmatrix} \quad \text{respectively.} \quad (11:62)$$

There will be a set $\boldsymbol{\sigma}_{kx}$, $\boldsymbol{\sigma}_{ky}$, $\boldsymbol{\sigma}_{kz}$ for each k, and the members of one set will commute with the members of any other. The form of the representatives (11:62) shows that when $\frac{1}{2}(\boldsymbol{\sigma}_{kx} - i\boldsymbol{\sigma}_{ky})$ or $\frac{1}{2}(\boldsymbol{\sigma}_{kx} + i\boldsymbol{\sigma}_{ky})$ is applied to a $\mid \rangle$ whose representative is $\langle n_1' \ldots n_k' \ldots \mid \rangle$, the representative of the product is $\langle n_1' \ldots n_k' - 1 \ldots \mid \rangle$ and $\langle n_1' \ldots n_k' + 1 \ldots \mid \rangle$ respectively, with obvious restrictions on n_k'. For convenience we introduce the suggestive notation

$$\left.\begin{aligned} \boldsymbol{\sigma}_k &= \boldsymbol{\sigma}_{kz}, \\ \partial_k^- &= \tfrac{1}{2}(\boldsymbol{\sigma}_{kx} - i\boldsymbol{\sigma}_{ky}), \\ \partial_k^+ &= \tfrac{1}{2}(\boldsymbol{\sigma}_{kx} + i\boldsymbol{\sigma}_{ky}), \end{aligned}\right\} \quad (11:63)$$

and we can readily verify that these satisfy the relations

$$\left.\begin{aligned} &\boldsymbol{\sigma}_k^2 = 1, & &\partial_k^{-2} = \partial_k^{+2} = 0, \\ &\boldsymbol{\sigma}_k\partial_k^- = -\partial_k^-, & &\boldsymbol{\sigma}_k\partial_k^+ = \partial_k^+, \\ &\partial_k^-\boldsymbol{\sigma}_k = \partial_k^-, & &\partial_k^+\boldsymbol{\sigma}_k = -\partial_k^+, \\ &\partial_k^+\partial_k^- = 1 - \mathbf{n}_k, & &\partial_k^+\partial_k^- + \partial_k^-\partial_k^+ = 1, \\ &\partial_k^-\partial_k^+ = \mathbf{n}_k. \end{aligned}\right\} \quad (11:64)$$

[16] We can write the matrix element this way, because $\mathbf{u}_r$ is of the same form for all r, and $\langle E_r' \mid \mathbf{u}_r \mid E_r'' \rangle$ is a matrix independent of r.

In this notation the step operator ∂_k^-, for example, has the representative

$$\langle n_1' \ldots | \partial_k^- | n_1'' \ldots \rangle = \langle n_k' | \partial_k^- | n_k'' \rangle \prod_{j \neq k} \delta (n_j', n_j''), \quad (11{:}65)$$

where $\langle n_k' | \partial_k^- | n_k'' \rangle = \delta (n_k', n_k'' + 1)$ with the obvious restriction $n_k' \not> 1$. Apropos of the above remarks on the properties of the step operators we have

$$\begin{aligned} \langle n_1' \ldots | \partial_k^- | 1 \rangle &= \langle n_1' \ldots | \partial_k^- \sum_{n_1'' \ldots} | n_1'' n_2'' \ldots \rangle \langle n_1'' n_2'' \ldots | 1 \rangle \\ &= \sum_{n_1'' \ldots} \langle n_1' \ldots | \partial_k^- | n_1'' \ldots \rangle \langle n_1'' \ldots | 1 \rangle \\ &= \left\{ \begin{matrix} \langle n_1' \ldots n_k' - 1 \ldots | 1 \rangle \\ 0 \end{matrix} \right\} \begin{matrix} (n_k' = 1) \\ (n_k' = 0) \end{matrix}. \end{aligned} \quad (11{:}66)$$

Hence, we see that (11:60) is the representative of

$$| 2 \rangle = \sum_k \langle k | \mathbf{u} | k \rangle \mathbf{n}_k | 1 \rangle + \sum_k \sum_{l \neq k} \pm \langle k | \mathbf{u} | l \rangle \partial_k^- \partial_l^+ | 1 \rangle. \quad (11{:}67)$$

Since this holds whenever (11:52) holds, we must have

$$\mathbf{U} = \sum_k \langle k | \mathbf{u} | k \rangle \mathbf{n}_k + \sum_k \sum_{l \neq k} \pm \langle k | \mathbf{u} | l \rangle \partial_k^- \partial_l^+ . \quad . \quad . \quad (11{:}68)$$

The $(\pm)$ sign in (11:69) is an awkward feature, and to remove it we need a *signature* operator which will automatically introduce the proper sign. To this end we introduce the variables

$$\boldsymbol{\xi}_l = \prod_{j=1}^{l-1} \boldsymbol{\sigma}_j \partial_l^+ = \boldsymbol{\nu}_l \partial_l^+, \qquad \boldsymbol{\xi}_k^* = \prod_{j=1}^{k-1} \partial_k^- \boldsymbol{\sigma}_j = \partial_k^- \boldsymbol{\nu}_k, \quad . \quad . \quad (11{:}69)$$

where the numbering is as in the standard sequence, and obviously all factors in the definition of a $\boldsymbol{\xi}$ or $\boldsymbol{\xi}^*$ commute. From the properties listed in (11:64) we see that

$$\boldsymbol{\xi}_k^* \boldsymbol{\xi}_l = \partial_k^- \left\{ \begin{matrix} \boldsymbol{\sigma}_k \boldsymbol{\sigma}_{k+1} \ldots \boldsymbol{\sigma}_{l-1} \\ \boldsymbol{\sigma}_l \boldsymbol{\sigma}_{l+1} \ldots \boldsymbol{\sigma}_{k-1} \end{matrix} \right\} \partial_l^+ \quad \begin{matrix} (k < l) \\ (k > l) \end{matrix}, \quad . \quad . \quad (11{:}70)$$

where, as indicated, we take the upper bracket for $k < l$ and the lower for $k > l$. Further, since $\boldsymbol{\sigma}_l \partial_l^+ = \partial_l^+$ and $\partial_k^- \boldsymbol{\sigma}_k = \partial_k^-$, we can omit the factor $\boldsymbol{\sigma}_k$ in the upper, and $\boldsymbol{\sigma}_l$ in the lower bracket, which may now be written as

$$\boldsymbol{\xi}_k^* \boldsymbol{\xi}_l = \partial_k^- \partial_l^+ \left\{ \begin{matrix} (1 - 2\mathbf{n}_{k+1}) (1 - 2\mathbf{n}_{k+2}) \ldots (1 - 2\mathbf{n}_{l-1}) \\ (1 - 2\mathbf{n}_{l+1}) (1 - 2\mathbf{n}_{l+2}) \ldots (1 - 2\mathbf{n}_{k-1}) \end{matrix} \right\} \begin{matrix} (k < l) \\ (k > l) \end{matrix}. \quad (11{:}71)$$

For the eigenvalue 0 each factor is 1, and for 1 it is -1. Hence, in each line the number of factors $(-)$ is equal to the number of non-zero n''s, which is the number of E''s actually found to lie between $E^{(k)}$ $(=E_r')$ and $E^{(l)}$ $(=E_r'')$ in any given sequence. This is just the required sign convention, agreeing with our previous result in giving

$(-)$ to the power $\sum_{\epsilon} n_{\epsilon}' = | r' - r'' |$ as signature when $\boldsymbol{\xi}_k^* \boldsymbol{\xi}_l$ operates on a $| \rangle$. Thus (11:68) becomes

$$\mathbf{U} = \sum_{k} \langle k \mid \mathbf{u} \mid k \rangle \mathbf{n}_k + \sum_{k} \sum_{l \neq k} \langle k \mid \mathbf{u} \mid l \rangle \boldsymbol{\xi}_k^* \boldsymbol{\xi}_l. \quad . \quad . \quad (11:72)$$

From the relations (11:64) we may readily obtain the commutation relations for the $\boldsymbol{\xi}$'s,

$$\left.\begin{array}{ll} [\boldsymbol{\xi}_k^*, \boldsymbol{\xi}_l^*]_+ = 0, & \boldsymbol{\xi}_k^* \boldsymbol{\xi}_k = \mathbf{n}_k, \\ [\boldsymbol{\xi}_k, \boldsymbol{\xi}_l^*]_+ = \delta_{kl}, & \boldsymbol{\xi}_k \boldsymbol{\xi}_k^* = 1 - \mathbf{n}_k, \end{array}\right\} \quad . \quad . \quad . \quad . \quad (11:73)$$

with which (11:72) simplifies to

$$\mathbf{U} = \sum_{k,l} \langle k \mid \mathbf{u} \mid l \rangle \boldsymbol{\xi}_k^* \boldsymbol{\xi}_l. \quad . \quad . \quad . \quad . \quad . \quad . \quad (11:74)$$

We must now consider the $\mathbf{E}$- and $\mathbf{n}$-representatives of a more general operator

$$\mathbf{V} = \sum_{r<s} \mathbf{v}_{rs}, \quad . \quad . \quad . \quad . \quad . \quad . \quad . \quad . \quad (11:75)$$

for which we may write $| 2 \rangle = \mathbf{V} \mid 1 \rangle$, i.e.

$$\langle E_1' \ldots E_n' \mid 2 \rangle = \tfrac{1}{2} \sum_{r \neq s} \sum_{E_r'', E_s''} \langle E_r' E_s' \mid \mathbf{v}_{rs} \mid E_r'' E_s'' \rangle$$
$$\times \langle E_1' \ldots E_{r-1}' E_r'' E_{r+1}' \ldots E_{s-1}' E_s'' E_{s+1}' \ldots E_n' \mid 1 \rangle, \quad (11:76)$$

and in the $\mathbf{n}$-representation

$$\langle n_1' n_1' \ldots \mid 2 \rangle = \tfrac{1}{2} \sum_{r \neq s} \sum_{E_r'', E_s''} \pm \langle E_r' E_s' \mid \mathbf{v}_{rs} \mid E_r'' E_s'' \rangle$$
$$\times \langle n_1' \ldots n_{E_r'}' - 1 \ldots n_{E_s'}' - 1 \ldots n_{E_r''}' + 1 \ldots n_{E_s''}' + 1 \ldots \mid 1 \rangle. \quad (11:77)$$

Here again the $(-)$ sign in (11:77) is to be taken when there is a $(-)$ in only one of the relations

$$\langle E_1' \ldots E_n' \mid \rangle = \pm \langle n_1' n_2' \ldots \mid \rangle, \quad . \quad . \quad . \quad . \quad (11:78a)$$

$$\langle E_1' \ldots E_{r-1}' E_r'' E_{r+1}' \ldots E_{s-1}' E_s'' E_{s+1}' \ldots E_n' \mid \rangle$$
$$= \pm \langle n_1' \ldots n_{E_r'}' - 1 \ldots n_{E_s'}' - 1 \ldots n_{E_r''}' + 1 \ldots n_{E_s''}' + 1 \ldots \mid \rangle. \quad (11:78b)$$

By the definition of the comparison sequence

$$\langle \underline{E_1' \ldots E_{r-1}' E_r' E_{r+1}' \ldots E_{s-1}' E_s' E_{s+1}' \ldots E_n'} \mid \rangle$$
$$= + \langle n_1' \ldots n_{E_r'}' \ldots n_{E_s'}' \ldots \mid \rangle, \quad (11:79a)$$

and

$$\langle \underline{E_1' \ldots E_{r-1}' E_r'' E_{r+1}' \ldots E_{s-1}' E_s'' E_{s+1}' \ldots E_n'} \mid \rangle$$
$$= + \langle n_1' \ldots n_{E_r'}' - 1 \ldots n_{E_s'}' - 1 \ldots n_{E_r''}' + 1 \ldots n_{E_s''}' + 1 \ldots \mid \rangle. \quad (11:79b)$$

Furthermore,

$$\langle E_r{}'E_s{}'\underline{E_1{}' \ldots E_{r-1}{}'E_{r+1}{}' \ldots E_{s-1}{}'E_{s+1}{}' \ldots E_n{}'} \mid \rangle$$

$$= \begin{matrix} -(-)^{r'+s'} \\ (-)^{r'+s'} \end{matrix} \left\{ \langle \underline{E_1{}' \ldots E_{r-1}{}'E_r{}'E_{r+1}{}' \ldots E_{s-1}{}'E_s{}'E_{s+1}{}' \ldots} \mid \rangle \right\} \begin{matrix} s' > r', & (11:80a) \\ s' < r', & (11:80b) \end{matrix}$$

since shifting $E_r{}'$ from its ordered position r' to first place multiplies the function by $-(-)^{r'}$, and in this process $E_s{}'$ remains at its ordered position s' if $E_s{}' > E_r{}'$, or moves one place to the right to $s'+1$, if $E_s{}' < E_r{}'$. Shifting $E_s{}'$ to second place now introduces another factor $(-)^{s'}$ or $-(-)^{s'}$ in these two cases. Similarly,

$$\langle E_r{}''E_s{}''\underline{E_1{}' \ldots E_{r-1}{}'E_{r+1}{}' \ldots E_{s-1}{}'E_{s+1}{}' \ldots E_n{}'} \mid \rangle$$

$$= \begin{matrix} -(-)^{r''+s''} \\ (-)^{r''+s''} \end{matrix} \left\{ \langle \underline{E_1{}' \ldots E_{r-1}{}'E_r{}''E_{r+1}{}' \ldots E_{s-1}{}'E_s{}''E_{s+1}{}' \ldots} \mid \rangle \right\} \begin{matrix} s'' > r'', & (11:81a) \\ s'' < r'', & (11:81b) \end{matrix}$$

By a previous argument, replacing (11:78a, b) by

$$\langle E_r{}'E_s{}'\underline{E_1{}' \ldots E_{r-1}{}'E_{r+1}{}' \ldots E_{s-1}{}'E_{s+1}{}' \ldots E_n{}'} \mid \rangle = \pm \langle n_1{}'n_2{}' \ldots \mid \rangle, \qquad (11:82a)$$

$$\langle E_r{}''E_s{}''\underline{E_1{}' \ldots E_{r-1}{}'E_{r+1}{}' \ldots E_{s-1}{}'E_{s+1}{}' \ldots E_n{}'} \mid \rangle$$

$$= \pm \langle n_1{}' \ldots n_{E_r{}'}{}'-1 \ldots n_{E_s{}'}{}'-1 \ldots n_{E_r{}''}{}'+1 \ldots n_{E_s{}''}{}'+1 \ldots \mid \rangle, \qquad (11:82b)$$

will not affect the resultant sign in (11:77), and we again combine equations (11:78–82) to determine the signature. With our definition (11:69) of the signature operators, we have four cases to consider, viz.

Case	Signature	Conditions	
I	$(-)^{s'-r'+s''-r''}$	$E_s{}' > E_r{}'$, $E_s{}'' > E_r{}''$	
II	$(-)^{r'-s'+r''-s''}$	$E_s{}' < E_r{}'$, $E_s{}'' < E_r{}''$	
III	$-(-)^{s'-r'+r''-s''}$	$E_s{}' > E_r{}'$, $E_s{}'' < E_r{}''$	(11:83)
IV	$-(-)^{r'-s'+s''-r''}$	$E_s{}' < E_r{}'$, $E_s{}'' > E_r{}''$	

If, as in (11:59), we change notation to $E^{(k)} = E_r{}'$, $E^{(l)} = E_s{}'$, $E^{(m)} = E_r{}''$, $E^{(n)} = E_s{}''$, we see that the transition from $\langle n_1{}' \ldots \mid \rangle$ to

$$\langle n_1{}' \ldots n_k{}'-1 \ldots n_l{}'-1 \ldots n_m{}'+1 \ldots n_n{}'+1 \ldots \mid \rangle$$

is achieved by operating on $\mid \rangle$ by

$$\partial_k{}^- \partial_l{}^- \partial_n{}^+ \partial_m{}^+. \qquad (11:84)$$

That the order of the factors ∂^- and ∂^+ is correct may be readily verified by considering (11:77) for the special cases $E_r{}'' = E_r{}'$, $E_s{}'' = E_s{}'$ ($m = k$, $n = l$), and

$E_r'' = E_s'$, $E_s'' = E_r'$ $(m = l, n = k)$, with the definitions (11:64). Combining (11:83) and (11:84) we have

$$\begin{matrix} \text{I.} & (-)^{s'-r'} \\ \text{II.} & (-)^{r'-s'} \\ \text{III.} & -(-)^{s'-r'} \\ \text{IV.} & -(-)^{r'-s'} \end{matrix} \left\{ \partial_{E_{r'}}{}^{-} \partial_{E_{s'}}{}^{-} \partial_{E_{s''}}{}^{+} \partial_{E_{r''}}{}^{+} \right\} \begin{matrix} (-)^{s''-r''} \\ (-)^{r''-s''} \\ (-)^{r''-s''} \\ (-)^{s''-r''} \end{matrix} = \begin{matrix} (-)^{l-k} \\ (-)^{k-l} \\ -(-)^{l-k} \\ -(-)^{k-l} \end{matrix} \left\{ \partial_k{}^{-} \partial_l{}^{-} \partial_n{}^{+} \partial_m{}^{+} \right\} \begin{matrix} (-)^{n-m} \\ (-)^{m-n} \\ (-)^{m-n} \\ (-)^{n-m} \end{matrix} \quad (11:85)$$

The use of k, l, m, n as exponents of $(-)$ in (11:85) should cause no difficulty on comparing with the equivalent expressions on the left.

Now we introduce

$$\boldsymbol{\xi}_l = \prod_{j=1}^{l-1} \boldsymbol{\sigma}_j \partial_l{}^{+} = \boldsymbol{\nu}_l \partial_l{}^{+}, \text{ etc.}, \quad \ldots \ldots \quad (11:86)$$

and for the various cases in (11:85) we find

$$\text{I, III,}\ \boldsymbol{\nu}_k\boldsymbol{\nu}_l = \boldsymbol{\sigma}_k\boldsymbol{\sigma}_{k+1} \cdots \boldsymbol{\sigma}_{l-1}. \qquad \text{I, IV,}\ \boldsymbol{\nu}_n\boldsymbol{\nu}_m = \boldsymbol{\sigma}_m\boldsymbol{\sigma}_{m+1} \cdots \boldsymbol{\sigma}_{n-1}.$$

$$\text{II, IV,}\ \boldsymbol{\nu}_k\boldsymbol{\nu}_l = \boldsymbol{\sigma}_l\boldsymbol{\sigma}_{l+1} \cdots \boldsymbol{\sigma}_{k-1}. \qquad \text{II, III,}\ \boldsymbol{\nu}_n\boldsymbol{\nu}_m = \boldsymbol{\sigma}_n\boldsymbol{\sigma}_{n+1} \cdots \boldsymbol{\sigma}_{m-1}.$$

From (11:86) the expression for $\boldsymbol{\xi}_k{}^*\boldsymbol{\xi}_l{}^*\boldsymbol{\xi}_n\boldsymbol{\xi}_m$ becomes

$$\boldsymbol{\xi}_k{}^*\boldsymbol{\xi}_l{}^*\boldsymbol{\xi}_n\boldsymbol{\xi}_m = \begin{matrix} k > l \\ \\ l > k \end{matrix} \left\{ \begin{matrix} -\boldsymbol{\sigma}_{l+1}\boldsymbol{\sigma}_{l+2} \cdots \boldsymbol{\sigma}_{k-1} \\ \\ \boldsymbol{\sigma}_{k+1}\boldsymbol{\sigma}_{k+2} \cdots \boldsymbol{\sigma}_{l-1} \end{matrix} \right\} \partial_k{}^{-}\partial_l{}^{-}\partial_n{}^{+}\partial_m{}^{+} \left\{ \begin{matrix} \boldsymbol{\sigma}_{m+1}\boldsymbol{\sigma}_{m+2} \cdots \boldsymbol{\sigma}_{n-1} \\ \\ -\boldsymbol{\sigma}_{n+1}\boldsymbol{\sigma}_{n+2} \cdots \boldsymbol{\sigma}_{m-1} \end{matrix} \right\} \begin{matrix} n > m, \\ \\ m > n, \end{matrix} \quad (11:87)$$

where the conditions in (11:83) or (11:85) are obtained by taking combinations of upper and lower brackets (one at each end) as indicated. If we rewrite (11:69) in terms of the operators $(1 - 2\mathbf{n})$, we find that these equations provide just the required signature in all cases, and our final result is

$$\mathbf{V} = \tfrac{1}{2} \sum_{klmn} \langle kl \mid \mathbf{v} \mid mn \rangle \boldsymbol{\xi}_k{}^*\boldsymbol{\xi}_l{}^*\boldsymbol{\xi}_n\boldsymbol{\xi}_m, \quad \ldots \quad (11:88)$$

and

$$\mathbf{H} = \sum_r \mathbf{u}_r + \sum_{r<s} \mathbf{v}_{rs} = \sum_{kl} \langle k \mid \mathbf{u} \mid l \rangle \boldsymbol{\xi}_k{}^*\boldsymbol{\xi}_l + \tfrac{1}{2} \sum_{klmn} \langle kl \mid \mathbf{v} \mid mn \rangle \boldsymbol{\xi}_k{}^*\boldsymbol{\xi}_l{}^*\boldsymbol{\xi}_n\boldsymbol{\xi}_m. \quad (11:89)$$

§ 94. Note on Higher-Order Interaction Operators

Normally in calculations involving electronic motions in atomic systems only pair, or two-particle, interactions of the form of **V** above are considered—the higher approximations involving many- or p-particle interactions being entirely negligible in this case.[17] However, it is of some interest to obtain the quantized form of the

[17] See PRIMAKOFF–HOLSTEIN: *Phys. Rev.*, **55**, 1218 (1939). These authors also find that this approximation *is not* very satisfactory in the phenomenological description of the heavy particles (nucleons) in nuclei.

more general operators, since the derivation proceeds by a simpler method than the preceding, with the use of only the single-particle form

$$\mathbf{U} = \sum_{kl} \langle k \mid \mathbf{u} \mid l \rangle \, \xi_k^* \xi_l \qquad \text{[cf. (11:41, 74)].}$$

We consider two operators of the type $\mathbf{U}$, viz. $\mathbf{A} = \sum_r \mathbf{a}_r$, $\mathbf{B} = \sum_r \mathbf{b}_r$, for which

$$\left.\begin{aligned} \mathbf{A} &= \sum_{kl} \langle k \mid \mathbf{a} \mid l \rangle \, \xi_k^* \xi_l, \\ \mathbf{B} &= \sum_{mn} \langle m \mid \mathbf{b} \mid n \rangle \, \xi_m^* \xi_n, \end{aligned}\right\} \qquad (11{:}90a)$$

and we wish to obtain first the quantized form for $\mathbf{V} = \frac{1}{2} \sum_{r \neq s} \mathbf{v}_{rs}$, as above. We have

$$\mathbf{AB} = \sum_{rs} \mathbf{a}_r \mathbf{b}_s = \sum_r \mathbf{a}_r \mathbf{b}_r + \sum_{r \neq s} \mathbf{a}_r \mathbf{b}_s \qquad (11{:}90b)$$

$$= \sum_{klmn} \langle k \mid \mathbf{a} \mid l \rangle \langle m \mid \mathbf{b} \mid n \rangle \, \xi_k^* \xi_l \xi_m^* \xi_n, \qquad (11{:}90c)$$

and the previously obtained commutators

$$\begin{aligned} \xi_l \xi_m^* &= \delta_{lm} - \epsilon \xi_m^* \xi_l, && (\epsilon = 1, \quad \text{Fermi-Dirac Statistic}) \\ \xi_l \xi_n &= -\epsilon \xi_n \xi_l, && (\epsilon = -1, \quad \text{Bose-Einstein Statistic}) \\ \xi_k^* \xi_k &= \mathbf{n}_k, \\ \xi_k \xi_k^* &= 1 - \epsilon \mathbf{n}_k; \end{aligned}$$

and applying the first two C.R.'s to (11:90c) in succession, we find

$$\mathbf{AB} = \sum_{kln} \langle k \mid \mathbf{a} \mid l \rangle \langle l \mid \mathbf{b} \mid n \rangle \, \xi_k^* \xi_n + \sum_{klmn} \langle k \mid \mathbf{a} \mid l \rangle \langle m \mid \mathbf{b} \mid n \rangle \, \xi_k^* \xi_m^* \xi_n \xi_l. \qquad (11{:}90d)$$

The first term is seen to be $\sum_r \mathbf{a}_r \mathbf{b}_r$, and by comparison with (11:90b) it follows that

$$\sum_{r \neq s} \mathbf{a}_r \mathbf{b}_s = \sum_{klmn} \langle k \mid \mathbf{a} \mid l \rangle \langle m \mid \mathbf{b} \mid n \rangle \, \xi_k^* \xi_m^* \xi_n \xi_l. \qquad (11{:}90e)$$

Hence, if $\mathbf{v}_{rs}$ in $\mathbf{V} = \sum_{r \neq s} \mathbf{v}_{rs}$ is of the form $\mathbf{a}_r \mathbf{b}_s$, then

$$\mathbf{V} = \sum_{klmn} \langle km \mid \mathbf{v} \mid ln \rangle \, \xi_k^* \xi_m^* \xi_n \xi_l = \sum_{klmn} \langle kl \mid \mathbf{v} \mid mn \rangle \, \xi_k^* \xi_l^* \xi_n \xi_m, \qquad (11{:}90f)$$

since $\langle kl \mid \mathbf{ab} \mid mn \rangle = \langle k \mid \mathbf{a} \mid m \rangle \langle l \mid \mathbf{b} \mid n \rangle$. However, any $\mathbf{v}_{rs}$ can be written as a linear combination of terms of the form $\mathbf{a}_r \mathbf{b}_s$, so that *every* $\mathbf{V}$ can be written as above.

The same sort of argument readily shows that an operator $\mathbf{L} = \sum_{r \neq s \neq t ..} \mathbf{l}_{rst \ldots}$, involving p particles, can be expressed as

$$\mathbf{L} = \sum_{\substack{j_1 j_2 \ldots j_p \\ k_1 k_2 \ldots k_p}} \langle j_1 j_2 \ldots j_p \mid \mathbf{l} \mid k_1 k_2 \ldots k_p \rangle \, \xi_{j_1}^* \xi_{j_2}^* \ldots \xi_{j_p}^* \xi_{k_p} \xi_{k_{p-1}} \ldots \xi_{k_1}. \qquad (11{:}90g)$$

§ 95. Equations of Motion

If we consider the systems or particles of the assembly (in either statistic) to be moving under the action of some external field of force without interaction between individual systems, the total Hamiltonian will be of the form **U** [equation (11:7)]. Then the equations of motion for the ξ's will be

$$i\hbar \frac{d}{dt}\xi_j = \xi_j\mathbf{H} - \mathbf{H}\xi_j = \sum_{k,l} \langle k \mid \mathbf{u} \mid l \rangle [\, \xi_j, \xi_k{}^*\xi_l{}^* \,]_- = \sum_{k,l} \langle k \mid \mathbf{u} \mid l \rangle (\, \xi_j\xi_k{}^* + \epsilon\xi_k{}^*\xi_j \,)\, \xi_l$$

$$= \sum_l \langle j \mid \mathbf{u} \mid l \rangle \, \xi_l. \quad . \quad . \quad (11:91)$$

The Schroedinger wave-equation for one system alone with Hamiltonian **u**, say, is

$$i\hbar \frac{d}{dt}\langle j \mid \rangle = \sum_l \langle j \mid \mathbf{u} \mid l \rangle \langle l \mid \rangle. \quad . \quad . \quad . \quad . \quad . \quad (11:92)$$

Furthermore, it is readily shown [18] that the operator ξ_j and the wave-function $\langle j \mid \rangle$ obey the same transformation law in passing from one representation to another. The analogy is further enhanced since the interpretation of $\xi_j{}^*\xi_j$ is very similar to that of $| \langle E^{(j)} \mid \rangle |^2$, so that we may say that the transition from the wave-function procedure to that of the operators (in either statistic) corresponds to assuming that the wave-function $\langle E^{(j)} \mid \rangle$ describing a single system is not a numerical function of the parameter $E^{(j)}$, but an operator for each $E^{(j)}$, satisfying the quantum conditions (11:90). It is essentially this transcription which suggests the descriptive term *second quantization*. We may further note that the initial transcription from the **x**- to the **E**-representation, which has been used here for illustrative purposes, is not essential, and we may pass directly from either to the **n**-representation with appropriate changes of sums to integrals in the former case.

§ 96. Equivalence Theorem and Complex Representations

Probably the most fundamental consequence of the quantization procedure for symmetric systems is that it establishes the mathematical equivalence of the assembly of bosons, and a system of harmonic oscillators, since the variables describing the assembly are essentially the action and angle variables describing oscillators, and the correlation is such that to each independent state of a system of the assembly (e.g. single system or particle cell) there corresponds an oscillator whose action variable describes the number of systems in the associated state. On the other hand, it is well known that a radiation field may be described in terms of an infinite set of canonical variables, each set corresponding to a Fourier component and describing an independent harmonic oscillator.[19] It follows that a boson

[18] See DIRAC, *Q.M.*, § 62.

[19] Cf. HEITLER: *Quantum Theory of Radiation* (Oxford), § 6; also, DIRAC, *op. cit.*

assembly is dynamically equivalent to a system of waves, and this leads to the equivalence of the wave-particle interpretations of radiation.

Since the electromagnetic field may be interpreted in terms of a set of harmonic oscillators, it is desirable to obtain the simplest possible description of the latter. We have already considered the description in terms of action and angle variables, but it is worth while to examine another formulation in terms of complex operators.[20] This will serve *primarily* to illustrate the principles and application of the more general *complex* representation theory, and incidentally show the above-mentioned boson-oscillator equivalence in a more direct way.

Neglecting unessential constants, we write the oscillator Hamiltonian in the form

$$\mathbf{H} = \tfrac{1}{2}\,(\,\mathbf{p}^2 + \mathbf{q}^2\,) - \hbar/2, \qquad (11{:}93)$$

where $-\hbar/2$ is included to avoid difficulties with the zero-point energy. The essence of Fock's method is to introduce complex operators defined by

$$\left.\begin{aligned} \boldsymbol{\xi} &= \mathbf{p} + i\mathbf{q}/\sqrt{(2\hbar)}, \\ \boldsymbol{\xi}^* &= \mathbf{p} - i\mathbf{q}/\sqrt{(2\hbar)}, \end{aligned}\right\} \qquad (11{:}94)$$

which then satisfy the quantum condition

$$\boldsymbol{\xi}^*\boldsymbol{\xi} - \boldsymbol{\xi}\boldsymbol{\xi}^* = 1, \qquad (11{:}95)$$

and in terms of which $\mathbf{H}$ takes the form

$$\mathbf{H} = \hbar\boldsymbol{\xi}\boldsymbol{\xi}^* = \hbar\,(\,\boldsymbol{\xi}^*\boldsymbol{\xi} - 1\,). \qquad (11{:}96)$$

Here again, we see that if $|\,H'\,\rangle$ is an eigen-$|\,\rangle$ of $\mathbf{H}$ belonging to H', then $\boldsymbol{\xi}^*\,|\,H'\,\rangle$ is an eigen-$|\,\rangle$ belonging to $H' - \hbar$ unless it vanishes, i.e.

$$\mathbf{H}\,|\,H'\,\rangle = \hbar\boldsymbol{\xi}\boldsymbol{\xi}^*\,|\,H'\,\rangle = H'\,|\,H'\,\rangle, \qquad (11{:}97a)$$

and by pre-multiplication with $\boldsymbol{\xi}^*$ we have [cf. (11:96)]

$$\left.\begin{aligned} \hbar\,(\,\boldsymbol{\xi}^*\boldsymbol{\xi}\,)\,\boldsymbol{\xi}^*\,|\,H'\,\rangle &= (\,\mathbf{H} + \hbar\,)\,\boldsymbol{\xi}^*\,|\,H'\,\rangle = H'\boldsymbol{\xi}^*\,|\,H'\,\rangle, \\ \mathbf{H}\boldsymbol{\xi}^*\,|\,H'\,\rangle &= (\,H' - \hbar\,)\,\boldsymbol{\xi}^*\,|\,H'\,\rangle. \end{aligned}\right\} \qquad (11{:}97b)$$

Similarly, expressing (11:97*a*) in the alternate form permitted by (11:96), and pre-multiplying by $\boldsymbol{\xi}$, it follows that $\boldsymbol{\xi}\,|\,H'\,\rangle$ is an eigen-$|\,\rangle$ of $\mathbf{H}$ belonging to $H' + \hbar$, unless it vanishes; and the eigenvalues are given by $\ldots H' - \hbar, H', H' + \hbar, \ldots$, unless one of the conditions is violated. We note that if $\boldsymbol{\xi}^*\,|\,H'\,\rangle = 0$, then $\boldsymbol{\xi}\boldsymbol{\xi}^*\,|\,H'\,\rangle = 0$ or $H' = 0$; whereas if $\boldsymbol{\xi}\,|\,H'\,\rangle = 0$, it follows that $H' = -\hbar$, which cannot be, since the eigenvalues of $\mathbf{H}$ are essentially positive, thus

$$H'\,\langle\,H'\,|\,H'\,\rangle = \hbar\,\langle\,H'\,|\,\boldsymbol{\xi}\boldsymbol{\xi}^*\,|\,H'\,\rangle = \hbar\,\langle\,H'\,|\,\boldsymbol{\xi}\,(\,\langle\,H'\,|\,\boldsymbol{\xi}\,)^* \geqslant 0. \qquad (11{:}98)$$

The eigenvalues are the usual $0, \hbar, 2\hbar, \ldots$, and for convenience we shall denote the nth eigenvector as $|\,n\,\rangle$.

[20] Fock: *Zeits. f. Phys.*, **49**, 339 (1928), and *Phys. Z. Sow. U.*, **6**, 428 (1934). * Dirac: *Comm. Dub. Inst. for Adv. Studies*, Ser. **A. 1**, (1934).

The preceding symbolical calculation is of course the same as Dirac's method except for notation, but the important difference appears when we actually go over to the corresponding work in terms of a representation which is diagonal in either $\boldsymbol{\xi}$ or $\boldsymbol{\xi}^*$, rather than in the usual *real* dynamical variable $\mathbf{q}$. Now the quantum condition (11:95) suggests that, at least formally, we might take

$$\boldsymbol{\xi}^* = \frac{d}{d\boldsymbol{\xi}}, \quad \text{(11:99}a\text{)}$$

or

$$\boldsymbol{\xi} = -\frac{d}{d\boldsymbol{\xi}^*}, \quad \text{(11:99}b\text{)}$$

depending on whether we wish to work in terms of the variable[21] $\boldsymbol{\xi}$ or $\boldsymbol{\xi}^*$. If this association is to have significance we must assume that the $\boldsymbol{\xi}$-representation, for example, supports the relations

$$\left.\begin{aligned} \boldsymbol{\xi} \mid \xi' \rangle &= \xi' \mid \xi' \rangle, \\ \langle \xi' \mid \boldsymbol{\xi} &= \xi' \langle \xi' \mid, \end{aligned}\right\} \quad \text{(11:100)}$$

$$\langle \xi' \mid \frac{d}{d\boldsymbol{\xi}} = \frac{d}{d\xi'} \langle \xi' \mid, \quad \text{(11:101)}$$

$$\frac{d}{d\boldsymbol{\xi}} \mid \xi'' \rangle = -\frac{d}{d\xi''} \mid \xi'' \rangle, \quad \text{(11:102)}$$

i.e. relations of the same form as hold for the $\mathbf{q}$-diagonal representation (cf. Chap. IV, § 19). The above relations then corroborate the quantum condition (11:95), but it is important to note that the consistency of (11:100–102) requires further proof. In particular, we are *not* justified in assuming that $\langle \xi' \mid \xi'' \rangle$, and hence $\langle \xi' \mid \boldsymbol{\xi} \mid \xi'' \rangle$ and $\langle \xi' \mid \frac{d}{d\boldsymbol{\xi}} \mid \xi'' \rangle$, are obtained simply by relabelling the corresponding expressions in the real $\mathbf{q}$-representation (4:1–3), since the conjugate of $\mid \xi' \rangle$ is now $\langle \xi'^* \mid$ instead of $\langle \xi' \mid$—as follows by taking the conjugate of $\boldsymbol{\xi} \mid \xi' \rangle = \xi' \mid \xi' \rangle$. Relative to the $\boldsymbol{\xi}$-representation the eigenfunctions of $\mathbf{H}$, or simply $\boldsymbol{\xi}\boldsymbol{\xi}^*$, are given by

$$\langle \xi' \mid \boldsymbol{\xi} \frac{d}{d\boldsymbol{\xi}} \mid n \rangle = \xi' \frac{d}{d\xi'} \langle \xi' \mid n \rangle = n \langle \xi' \mid n \rangle \quad \text{(11:103)}$$

or

$$\langle \xi' \mid n \rangle = c_n \xi'^n,$$

and

$$\langle n \mid \boldsymbol{\xi} \frac{d}{d\boldsymbol{\xi}} \mid \xi' \rangle = -\frac{d}{d\xi'} \{ \xi' \langle n \mid \xi' \rangle \} = n \langle n \mid \xi' \rangle \quad \text{(11:104)}$$

or

$$\langle n \mid \xi' \rangle = d_n \xi'^{-n-1};$$

which equations show that $\langle \xi' \mid n \rangle \neq \langle n \mid \xi' \rangle^*$, as previously remarked. However, by taking (11:99*b*), and making the necessary changes in (11:100–102), we

[21] It must obviously make no difference which choice we make.

may readily show that $\langle n \mid \xi^{*\prime} \rangle$, $\langle \xi^{*\prime} \mid n \rangle$ are of the form $\xi^{*\prime n}$, $\xi^{*\prime -n-1}$ respectively, and are the corresponding conjugates of $\langle \xi' \mid n \rangle$, $\langle n \mid \xi' \rangle$ in accord with (11:103) and (11:104). One of the conveniences of the $\boldsymbol{\xi}$-representation is that the eigenfunctions (11:103) are powers of ξ', and correspondingly, the general state is a power series in ξ' instead of the associated Hermite polynomials of the usual treatment. From (11:103–104) it follows that the representative of any $| \rangle$ is an ascending series in ξ' while that of a $\langle |$ is a descending series, e.g.

$$\left.\begin{aligned} | a \rangle &= \sum_n | n \rangle \langle n | a \rangle, \\ \langle \xi' | a \rangle &= \sum_n c_n \xi'^n \langle n | a \rangle = \sum_n a_n \xi'^n; \end{aligned}\right\} \quad . \quad . \quad . \quad (11{:}105a)$$

$$\left.\begin{aligned} \langle b | &= \sum_n \langle b | n \rangle \langle n |, \\ \langle b | \xi' \rangle &= \sum_n \langle b | n \rangle \langle n | \xi' \rangle = \sum_n b_n \xi'^{-n-1}. \end{aligned}\right\} \quad . \quad . \quad (11{:}105b)$$

Correspondingly,

$$\langle b | a \rangle = \sum_n \langle b | n \rangle \langle n | a \rangle = \sum_n a_n b_n, \quad . \quad . \quad . \quad (11{:}106)$$

provided $c_n d_n = 1$, which we shall presently see to be necessary.

We now note that in terms of the $\boldsymbol{\xi}$-representation, the result (11:106) may be interpreted as

$$\langle b | a \rangle = \frac{1}{2\pi i} \oint \langle b | \xi' \rangle d\xi' \langle \xi' | a \rangle, \quad . \quad . \quad . \quad (11{:}107a)$$

according to the usual calculus of residues, or symbolically,[22]

$$\frac{1}{2\pi i} \oint | \xi' \rangle d\xi' \langle \xi' | = \mathbf{I}. \quad . \quad . \quad . \quad . \quad . \quad . \quad . \quad (11{:}107b)$$

Assuming that (11:107) is the complex analogue of the expansion theorem, we must now determine the representatives of $\mathbf{I}$, $\boldsymbol{\xi}$, $\boldsymbol{\xi}^*$, etc., and show them to be consistent with (11:100–102) and the proviso in (11:106). It is readily seen that $\mathbf{I}$ must be represented by

$$\langle \xi' | \mathbf{I} | \xi'' \rangle = \langle \xi' | \xi'' \rangle = \frac{1}{\xi'' - \xi'}, \quad . \quad . \quad . \quad (11{:}108a)$$

since with this;

$$\left.\begin{aligned} \langle \xi' | \mathbf{I} | \rangle &= \frac{1}{2\pi i} \oint \langle \xi' | \mathbf{I} | \xi'' \rangle d\xi'' \langle \xi'' | \rangle = \langle \xi' | \rangle, \\ \langle | \mathbf{I} | \xi'' \rangle &= \frac{1}{2\pi i} \oint \langle | \xi' \rangle d\xi' \langle \xi' | \mathbf{I} | \xi'' \rangle = \langle | \xi'' \rangle. \end{aligned}\right\} \quad . \quad (11{:}108b)$$

Now, according to (11:101) the representative of $\boldsymbol{\xi}^*$ should be

$$\langle \xi' | \frac{d}{d\boldsymbol{\xi}} | \xi'' \rangle = \frac{d}{d\xi'} \langle \xi' | \xi'' \rangle = \frac{1}{(\xi'' - \xi')^2}, \quad . \quad . \quad (11{:}109a)$$

[22] The corresponding operator for real representations is

$$\int | x' \rangle dx' \langle x' | = \mathbf{I}.$$

which is correct since it leads to

$$\left.\begin{aligned}\langle\, \xi' \mid \frac{d}{d\boldsymbol{\xi}} \mid \rangle &= \frac{1}{2\pi i}\oint \langle\, \xi' \mid \frac{d}{d\boldsymbol{\xi}} \mid \xi'' \,\rangle\, d\xi''\, \langle\, \xi'' \mid \rangle = \frac{d}{d\xi'} \langle\, \xi' \mid \rangle, \\ \langle \mid \frac{d}{d\boldsymbol{\xi}} \mid \xi'' \,\rangle &= \frac{1}{2\pi i}\oint \langle \mid \xi' \,\rangle\, d\xi'\, \langle\, \xi' \mid \frac{d}{d\boldsymbol{\xi}} \mid \xi'' \,\rangle = -\frac{d}{d\xi''} \langle \mid \xi'' \,\rangle.\end{aligned}\right\} \qquad (11{:}109b)$$

Considering the normalization, we verify the proviso $c_n d_n = 1$, since for normalized $|\, n \,\rangle$,

$$\langle\, n \mid n \,\rangle = \frac{1}{2\pi i}\oint \langle\, n \mid \xi' \,\rangle\, d\xi'\, \langle\, \xi' \mid n \,\rangle = c_n d_n = 1, \qquad (11{:}110a)$$

$$\langle\, \xi' \mid \xi'' \,\rangle = \sum_n \langle\, \xi' \mid n \,\rangle \langle\, n \mid \xi'' \,\rangle = \sum_n \frac{c_n d_n}{\xi''}\left(\frac{\xi'}{\xi''}\right)^n = \frac{1}{\xi'' - \xi'}. \qquad (11{:}110b)$$

All of the relations are thus consistent and a particular feature is that the usual δ function is replaced by (11:108*a*), avoiding improper functions; but a minor difficulty arises as regards the representative of $\boldsymbol{\xi}$ which is *either*

$$\frac{\xi'}{\xi'' - \xi'} \quad \text{or} \quad \frac{\xi''}{\xi'' - \xi'}. \qquad (11{:}111)$$

Either representative gives the correct result, but their difference (=1) contributes a constant when multiplied into $\langle \mid \xi' \,\rangle$, and integrated with respect to ξ'; it contributes nothing to the integral of $\langle\, \xi'' \mid \rangle$ over ξ'' [cf. (11:105*a*, *b*)]. The two representatives must be counted as equal, and to remove the difficulty we must assume that an arbitrary constant may be added to the representative $\langle \mid \xi' \,\rangle$, and it still represents the same $\langle \mid$. More generally, it is necessary to assume that an arbitrary ascending series may be added to $\langle \mid \xi' \,\rangle$, and it still represents the same $\langle \mid$; this generalization is needed because such series in ξ'' may be added to both (11:108*a*) and (11:109*a*) without affecting their behaviour in integration. It is also seen that this lack of uniqueness does not affect the scalar product (11:107) which is the important quantity.

From our first calculations it follows that the nth oscillator $\mid \rangle$ is given by $\boldsymbol{\xi}^n \mid 0 \,\rangle$, and we now need to find the normalization factor, provided $\langle\, 0 \mid 0 \,\rangle = 1$. From (11:95) we find

$$\boldsymbol{\xi}^*\boldsymbol{\xi}^n - \boldsymbol{\xi}^n\boldsymbol{\xi}^* = n\boldsymbol{\xi}^{n-1}, \qquad (11{:}112)$$

whence

$$\begin{aligned}\langle\, 0 \mid \boldsymbol{\xi}^{*n}\boldsymbol{\xi}^n \mid 0 \,\rangle &= \langle\, 0 \mid \boldsymbol{\xi}^{*n-1}\boldsymbol{\xi}^n\boldsymbol{\xi}^* + n\boldsymbol{\xi}^{*n-1}\boldsymbol{\xi}^{n-1} \mid 0 \,\rangle = n \langle\, 0 \mid \boldsymbol{\xi}^{*n-1}\boldsymbol{\xi}^{n-1} \mid 0 \,\rangle \\ &= \ldots = n!\, \langle\, 0 \mid 0 \,\rangle, \end{aligned} \qquad (11{:}113a)$$

or

$$|\, n \,\rangle = \frac{\boldsymbol{\xi}^n}{\sqrt{n!}} \mid 0 \,\rangle. \qquad (11{:}113b)\ [23]$$

[23] We may note that much of the foregoing may be obtained symbolically if we introduce $\boldsymbol{\xi}^{-1}$ defined by $\boldsymbol{\xi}^{-1}\boldsymbol{\xi}^n \mid 0 \,\rangle = \boldsymbol{\xi}^{n-1} \mid 0 \,\rangle$, $n \geqslant 1$, $\boldsymbol{\xi}^{-1} \mid 0 \,\rangle = 0$; this is not quite a true reciprocal since $\boldsymbol{\xi}^{-1}\boldsymbol{\xi} = \mathbf{I}$ and $\boldsymbol{\xi}\,\boldsymbol{\xi}^{-1} \neq \mathbf{I}$ in view of the definition. It is then possible to show that $\langle\, n \mid = \sqrt{n!}\, \langle\, 0 \mid \boldsymbol{\xi}^{-n}$, and hence any $\langle\, b \mid$ may be expressed as $\langle\, b \mid = \langle\, 0 \mid \sum_n b_n \boldsymbol{\xi}^{-n}$. This leads to the same results, but also shows that since $\langle\, 0 \mid \boldsymbol{\xi} = 0$ (i.e. $\boldsymbol{\xi}^* \mid 0 \,\rangle = 0$), $\langle\, b \mid$ is not affected by adding any power series in $\boldsymbol{\xi}$ to the above, although it does result in arbitrary representatives $\langle\, b \mid \xi' \,\rangle$.

Then

$$\langle \xi' \mid \boldsymbol{\xi} \mid n \rangle = \xi' \langle \xi' \mid n \rangle = \langle \xi' \mid \frac{\boldsymbol{\xi}^{n+1}}{\sqrt{n!}} \mid 0 \rangle = \sqrt{n+1} \langle \xi' \mid n+1 \rangle, \quad (11:114)$$

or $c_n = \sqrt{n+1}\, c_n + 1$, so that we may take

$$c_n = \frac{1}{\sqrt{n!}}, \quad d_n = \sqrt{n!}. \quad . \quad . \quad . \quad . \quad . \quad . \quad . \quad (11:115)$$

This result, combined with the definitions (11:105a, b) of a_n, b_n, leads to

$$b_n = n!\, a_n^*, \quad . \quad . \quad . \quad . \quad . \quad . \quad . \quad . \quad . \quad (11:116)$$

if $| a \rangle$, $\langle b |$ are conjugate vectors; and (11:106) becomes

$$\langle a \mid a \rangle = \sum_n n! \mid a_n \mid^2 = \sum_n \frac{1}{n!} \mid b_n \mid^2, \quad . \quad . \quad . \quad . \quad (11:117)$$ [24]

which must be convergent for vectors representing quantum states. A consequence of this is that $\langle \xi' \mid a \rangle$ must be convergent for all ξ', but $\langle b \mid \xi' \rangle$ need not converge for any ξ', and for this reason $\langle \xi' \mid \rangle$ is generally more convenient. If $| a \rangle$ is normalized, then (11:117) shows that it represents a state for which the probability of the energy having the value $n\hbar$ is

$$P_n = n! \mid a_n \mid^2$$
$$= \frac{1}{n!} \mid b_n \mid^2. \quad . \quad . \quad . \quad . \quad . \quad . \quad . \quad . \quad (11:118)$$

The addition of an arbitrary ascending series to $\langle b \mid \xi' \rangle$ corresponds to letting the index n in (11:105b) take on negative integral values and, as remarked, this has no effect, since P_n in the second form above is zero for negative integers.

The equation of motion for $\boldsymbol{\xi}$ is seen to be

$$\frac{d}{dt} \boldsymbol{\xi} = i\boldsymbol{\xi}. \quad . \quad . \quad . \quad . \quad . \quad . \quad . \quad . \quad . \quad (11:119)$$

The generalization of these results to an assembly of independent oscillators is straightforward. We introduce $\boldsymbol{\xi}_i$, $\boldsymbol{\xi}_i^*$ for the ith oscillator, which satisfy the commutators

$$\left.\begin{aligned} \boldsymbol{\xi}_i\boldsymbol{\xi}_j - \boldsymbol{\xi}_j\boldsymbol{\xi}_i &= 0, \\ \boldsymbol{\xi}_i^*\boldsymbol{\xi}_j - \boldsymbol{\xi}_j\boldsymbol{\xi}_i^* &= \delta_{ij}, \end{aligned}\right\} \quad . \quad . \quad . \quad . \quad . \quad . \quad . \quad (11:120)$$

and all previous results are simply adjusted to take account of the number of oscillators involved. In particular, the normalized basic $| \rangle$-vector denoting the eigenstate wherein the first oscillator has the energy $n_1'\hbar$, the second $n_2'\hbar$, etc., is [cf. (11:113b)]

$$| n_1' n_2' \ldots \rangle = \frac{\boldsymbol{\xi}_1^{n_1'} \boldsymbol{\xi}_2^{n_2'} \ldots | 0 \rangle}{\sqrt{n_1'!\, n_2'! \ldots}}, \quad . \quad . \quad . \quad . \quad (11:121)$$

[24] It is necessary to retain some distinction in labelling, such as a_n, b_n, even for this case, since the $\boldsymbol{\xi}$-representatives of $| a \rangle$ and $\langle a |$ are not simple conjugates.

where $|\,0\,\rangle$ denotes the lowest eigenstate for which all oscillators have zero energy. Correspondingly, a general $|\,a\,\rangle$ is now expressible as

$$|\,a\,\rangle = \{ \sum_{n_1'n_2'\ldots} a_{n_1'n_2'\ldots}\, \xi_1^{n_1'}\xi_2^{n_2'}\ldots \}\,|\,0\,\rangle, \quad \ldots \quad (11{:}122)$$

and, if correctly normalized, represents a state for which the probability of the various oscillators being in the energy states n_1', n_2', . . . , respectively, is given by

$$P_{n_1'n_2'\ldots} = n_1'!\, n_2'! \ldots |\, a_{n_1'n_2'} \ldots |^2. \quad \ldots \quad (11{:}123)$$

Considering again an assembly of bosons, we note that if the basic states of a single boson are $|\,E^{(1)}\,\rangle$, $|\,E^{(2)}\,\rangle$, . . . and $\langle\, E^{(i)}\,|\,E^{(j)}\,\rangle = \delta_{ij}$, then the states of an assembly of n bosons are obtained by taking direct products of n of these, e.g.

$$|\,{}'E\,\rangle = |\,E_1'E_2' \ldots E_n'\,\rangle = |\,E_1'\,\rangle\,|\,E_2'\,\rangle \ldots |\,E_n'\,\rangle, \quad . \quad (11{:}124)$$

which, however, is not symmetric as required until we apply the symmetrizer $\mathbf{S}$ (cf. § 57), i.e.

$$\mathbf{S}\,|\,E_1' \ldots E_n'\,\rangle = \frac{1}{\sqrt{n!}} \sum_P \mathbf{P}\,|\,E_1' \ldots E_n'\,\rangle. \quad \ldots \quad (11{:}125)$$

As previously noted, the modulus of this $|\,{}'E\,\rangle$ will be

$$n_1'!\, n_2'! \ldots = \Pi n_i'! \quad \ldots \quad (11{:}126)$$

in the general case when n_1' of the E''s equal $E^{(1)}$, n_2' equal $E^{(2)}$, etc. Rather than introduce a new symbol, we shall now let $|\,E_1'E_2' \ldots E_n'\,\rangle$ [as in § 93 (a)] denote the symmetric eigen-$|\,\rangle$ above, and it is now evident that with one ξ associated with each independent state (cell) of a boson, the set of symmetric eigenvectors for the boson assembly and the eigen-$|\,\rangle$'s (11:121) for the oscillator set, stand in one-to-one correspondence—there being the same number of each and their moduli being essentially the same. The identity is complete if we set

$$\xi_1^{n_1'}\xi_2^{n_2'} \ldots |\,0\,\rangle = |\,E_1'E_2' \ldots E_n'\,\rangle, \quad \ldots \quad (11{:}127a)$$

or

$$|\,n_1'n_2' \ldots\,\rangle = \left[\frac{n!}{n_1'!\,n_2'! \ldots}\right]^{\frac{1}{2}} |\,E_1'E_2' \ldots E_n'\,\rangle, \quad . \quad (11{:}127b)$$

which is just the relation (11:16). Again, since n_1' is the number of E''s on the right equal to $E^{(1)}$, n_2' the same for $E^{(2)}$, etc., we establish the complete mathematical equivalence of the boson assembly with the set of oscillators. As before, we have dealt with a system of a fixed number of particles, and the appropriate generalization to an indeterminate number has already been noted, namely, that we then consider a series of sets of eigen-$|\,{}'E\,\rangle$'s expressed in terms of 0, 1, 2, . . . $\mathbf{E}$-variables corresponding to the eigenvalues of the total number of particles. A general state $|\,\rangle$ may be represented by

$$|\,\rangle = \sum_{E_1' \ldots E_n'} |\,E_1' \ldots E_n'\,\rangle\,\langle\, E_1' \ldots E_n'\,|\,\rangle, \quad \ldots \quad (11{:}128a)$$

and from (11:127a) its representative in the complete $\boldsymbol{\xi}$-diagonal representation is

$$\langle\, `\xi \mid \rangle = \sum_{E_1' \ldots E_n'} \xi_1^{n_1'} \xi_2^{n_2'} \ldots \langle\, E_1' \ldots E_n' \mid \rangle, \quad . \quad . \quad (11{:}128b)$$ [25]

which is a polynomial in the ξ's. The terms of the form $\xi_1^{n_1'}\xi_2^{n_2'}\ldots$ correspond to the distribution with n_1' bosons in cell $E^{(1)}$, n_2' in $E^{(2)}$, etc., and clearly the operator $\boldsymbol{\xi}_i\boldsymbol{\xi}_i^*$ may be written as $\mathbf{n}_i$ since its eigenvalues n_i' are the numbers of bosons in the cell $E^{(i)}$. Similarly, the oscillator variables $\boldsymbol{\xi}_i$, $\boldsymbol{\xi}_i^*$ operating to the right correspond to the increase or decrease by one of the number of bosons in the cell, i.e. absorption or emission.[26] The coefficient of $\xi_1^{n_1'}\xi_2^{n_2'}\ldots$ for a given set of n''s (i.e. distribution of bosons) is the corresponding prototype wave-function $\langle\, E_1'E_2' \ldots E_n' \mid \rangle$ multiplied by $\left(\frac{n!}{\Pi n_i'!}\right)$, so that the usual total probability of there being n_1' bosons in (1), n_2' in (2), etc., for that state, namely [cf. (11:16), (11:127b)]

$$\frac{n!}{\Pi n_i'!} \,|\, \langle\, E_1'E_2' \ldots E_n' \mid \rangle \,|^2, \quad . \quad . \quad . \quad . \quad . \quad (11{:}129)$$ [27]

is given by $\Pi n_i'!/n!$ times the squared modulus of the coefficient of $\xi_1^{n_1'}\xi_2^{n_2'}\ldots$ in the representative $\langle\, `\xi \mid \rangle$, which is also the probability (11:123) of the oscillators being in the various quantum states [cf. (11:127*a*, *b*)].

§ 97. Quantized Wave-Functions

We obtain a convenient expression for the Hamiltonian (11:89) for both symmetric and antisymmetric particles, by introducing the quantized wave-functions $\boldsymbol{\Psi}$, $\boldsymbol{\Psi}^*$, defined by the equations

$$\boldsymbol{\Psi}(x) = \sum_r \langle\, x \mid E^r \,\rangle\, \boldsymbol{\xi}_r \quad . \quad . \quad . \quad . \quad . \quad . \quad (11{:}130a)$$

$$\boldsymbol{\Psi}^*(x') = \sum_r \langle\, E^r \mid x' \,\rangle\, \boldsymbol{\xi}_r^*, \quad . \quad . \quad . \quad . \quad . \quad (11{:}130b)$$

$$\mathbf{n} = \sum_r \boldsymbol{\xi}_r^*\boldsymbol{\xi}_r = \int \boldsymbol{\Psi}^*(x)\, dx\, \boldsymbol{\Psi}(x). \quad . \quad . \quad . \quad (11{:}130c)$$

[25] In the general case of indeterminate boson numbers this expression includes a summation over n as the prototype eigenvalue of the "total particle" dynamical variable $\mathbf{n}$, and the terms of degree n correspond to an assembly in which there are n bosons.

[26] E.g.

$$\boldsymbol{\xi} \mid n \,\rangle = \sqrt{n+1} \mid n+1 \,\rangle,$$
$$\boldsymbol{\xi}^* \mid n \,\rangle = \sqrt{n} \mid n-1 \,\rangle.$$

[27] The interested reader is referred to the original papers mentioned (especially Dirac's) for the applications of this method, since this involves details of quantum electrodynamics and relativity outside the plan of this volume. Also, see DIRAC: *Comm. Dublin Inst. for Adv. Studies.*, Ser. **A**, **3** (1946). Professor Dirac's revised volume on *Quantum Mechanics* will contain the detailed electrodynamic applications (personal communication).

Using (11:90), it is readily seen that these operators satisfy the commutation relations

$$\Psi(x')\Psi^*(x'') + \epsilon\Psi^*(x'')\Psi(x') = \mathbf{I}\,\delta(x' - x''), \qquad (11{:}131a)$$

$$\Psi(x')\Psi(x'') + \epsilon\Psi(x'')\Psi(x') = 0, \quad . \quad . \quad . \quad . \qquad (11{:}131b)$$

$$\mathbf{n}\Psi - \Psi\mathbf{n} = -\Psi \qquad [(n' - n'' + 1)\langle n' | \Psi | n'' \rangle = 0], \qquad (11{:}131c)$$

$$\mathbf{n}\Psi^* - \Psi^*\mathbf{n} = \Psi^* \qquad [(n' - n'' - 1)\langle n' | \Psi^* | n'' \rangle = 0], \qquad (11{:}131d)$$

$$\mathbf{n}_j\Psi - \Psi\mathbf{n}_j = -\langle x' | E^j \rangle \xi_j, \quad . \quad . \quad . \quad . \qquad (11{:}131e)$$

$$\mathbf{n}_j\Psi^* - \Psi^*\mathbf{n}_j = \langle E^j | x' \rangle \xi_j^*. \quad . \quad . \quad . \quad . \qquad (11{:}131f)$$

From the definitions (11:130) and the commutator properties, **H** takes the form

$$\mathbf{H} = \iint \Psi^*(x')\,dx'\,\langle x' | \mathbf{u} | x'' \rangle\,dx''\,\Psi(x'')$$
$$+ \tfrac{1}{2}\int \ldots \int \Psi^*(x')\Psi^*(x'')dx'dx''\langle x'x'' | \mathbf{v} | x'''x^{\mathrm{IV}} \rangle dx'''dx^{\mathrm{IV}}\,\Psi(x^{\mathrm{IV}})\Psi(x'''), \qquad (11{:}132)$$

where we have used $\langle E^rE^s | x'x'' \rangle = \langle E^r | x' \rangle \langle E^s | x'' \rangle$, and since the **x**'s are homologous, $\langle x_r' | \mathbf{u} | x_r'' \rangle$ and $\langle x_r'x_s' | \mathbf{v} | x_r''x_s'' \rangle$ are written as $\langle x' | \mathbf{u} | x'' \rangle$, $\langle x'x'' | \mathbf{v} | x'''x^{\mathrm{IV}} \rangle$, respectively. Here, we may again note that $\langle x' | \mathbf{u} | x'' \rangle = u(x')\,\delta(x' - x'')$ and $\langle x'x'' | \mathbf{v} | x'''x^{\mathrm{IV}} \rangle = v(x', x'')\,\delta(x' - x''')\,\delta(x'' - x^{\mathrm{IV}})$. The selection rules (11:131*c*, *d*, *e*, *f*) hold for both symmetry cases, but for definiteness we shall now consider Ψ and Ψ^* for the symmetric case, so that

$$\Psi = \sum_k \langle x' | E^k \rangle (\mathbf{n}_k + 1)^{\frac{1}{2}} e^{-i\omega_k}, \quad . \quad . \quad . \quad . \qquad (11{:}133a)$$

$$\Psi^* = \sum_k \langle E^k | x' \rangle \mathbf{n}_k^{\frac{1}{2}} e^{i\omega_k}, \quad . \quad . \quad . \quad . \quad . \quad . \quad . \qquad (11{:}133b)$$

and in the complete **n**-representation, the representatives are

$$\langle n_1' \ldots | \Psi | n_1'' \ldots \rangle = \sum_k \langle x' | E^k \rangle (n_k' + 1)^{\frac{1}{2}} \delta(n_k', n_k'' - 1) \prod_{i \neq k} \delta(n_i', n_i''), \qquad (11{:}134a)$$

$$\langle n_1' \ldots | \Psi^* | n_1'' \ldots \rangle = \sum_k \langle E^k | x' \rangle n_k'^{\frac{1}{2}} \delta(n_k', n_k'' + 1) \prod_{i \neq k} \delta(n_i', n_i''). \qquad (11{:}134b)$$

From these, the representatives of the equations $| 2 \rangle = \Psi | 1 \rangle$ and $| 2 \rangle = \Psi^* | 1 \rangle$ are, respectively,

$$\langle n_1' \ldots | 2 \rangle = \sum_k \langle x' | E^k \rangle (n_k' + 1)^{\frac{1}{2}} \langle n_1' \ldots n_k' + 1 \ldots | 1 \rangle, \qquad (11{:}135a)$$

$$\langle n_1' \ldots | 2 \rangle = \sum_k \langle E^k | x' \rangle n_k'^{\frac{1}{2}} \langle n_1' \ldots n_k' - 1 \ldots | 1 \rangle. \quad . \quad . \qquad (11{:}135b)$$

Both these equations differ from our previous equations of this type [e.g. (11:22, 27, 60)], in that the total number of particles (as given by the sum of the function arguments on the right) is not conserved. Thus, Ψ applied to a $| \,\rangle$ whose representative is $\langle n_1' \ldots | \,\rangle$ in n-particle space gives a resultant with representative

$\sim \langle n_1' \ldots n_k' + 1 \ldots | \rangle$, i.e. in $(n+1)$-particle space, and the representative of $\Psi^* | \rangle \sim \langle n_1' \ldots n_k' - 1 \ldots | \rangle$, i.e. in $(n-1)$-particle space.

Hence we see, as is already implicit in the selection rules (11:131*c*, *d*), that operators which do not commute with **n** are of a type for which we cannot obtain a representative in a representation with a fixed number of observables diagonal or, as we may say, in a configuration space of a fixed number of dimensions. Nevertheless, the general representation theory permits us to transcribe equations (11:135*a*, *b*) to other representations, by a procedure that is essentially the inverse of the method used in developing the equations of the second quantization, and this is sufficient for all practical purposes.

Equation (11:135*a*) is the **n**-transcription of

$$\langle E_1' \ldots E_n' | 2 \rangle = (n+1)^{\frac{1}{2}} \sum_{E'} \langle \mathsf{x}' | E' \rangle \langle E'E_1' \ldots E_n' | 1 \rangle$$

$$= (n+1)^{\frac{1}{2}} \sum_{k} \langle \mathsf{x}' | E^k \rangle \langle E^k E_1' E_2' \ldots E_n' | 1 \rangle, \qquad (11{:}136a)$$ [28]

and in the **x**-representation this becomes

$$\langle \mathsf{x}_1' \ldots \mathsf{x}_n' | 2 \rangle$$

$$= (n+1)^{\frac{1}{2}} \sum_{E_1' \ldots E_n'} \sum_{E'} \langle \mathsf{x}' | E' \rangle \langle \mathsf{x}_1' | E_1' \rangle \ldots \langle \mathsf{x}_n' | E_n' \rangle \langle E'E_1' \ldots E_n' | 1 \rangle$$

$$= (n+1)^{\frac{1}{2}} \langle \mathsf{x}'\mathsf{x}_1' \ldots \mathsf{x}_n' | 1 \rangle. \qquad (11{:}137a)$$

Equation (11:135*b*), however, arises from the equation

$$\langle E_1' \ldots E_n' | 2 \rangle = \frac{1}{n^{\frac{1}{2}}} \Big\{ \langle E_1' | \mathsf{x}' \rangle \langle E_2' E_3' \ldots E_n' | 1 \rangle + \langle E_2' | \mathsf{x}' \rangle \langle E_1' E_3' \ldots E_n' \rangle + \ldots + \langle E_n' | \mathsf{x}' \rangle \langle E_1' E_2' \ldots E_{n-1}' | 1 \rangle \Big\}$$

$$= \frac{1}{n^{\frac{1}{2}}} \sum_{j=1}^{n} \langle E_j' | \mathsf{x}' \rangle \langle E_1' \ldots E_{j-1}' E_{j+1}' \ldots E_n' | 1 \rangle, \qquad (11{:}136b)$$

since a typical wave-function on the right above, say $\langle E^k | \mathsf{x}' \rangle$, appears n_k' times, and the factor $1/n^{\frac{1}{2}}$ is required because in the transition to (11:135*b*) the normalization factor appears as

$$[n_1'! \ldots (n_k' - 1)! \ldots / (n-1)!]^{\frac{1}{2}} \langle n_1' \ldots n_k' - 1 \ldots | 1 \rangle.$$

In the **x**-representation this becomes [see (11:2) and the orthogonality conditions (11:7)]

$$\langle \mathsf{x}_1' \ldots \mathsf{x}_n' | 2 \rangle = \frac{1}{n^{\frac{1}{2}}} \sum_{j=1}^{n} \delta(\mathsf{x}_j' - \mathsf{x}') \langle \mathsf{x}_1' \ldots \mathsf{x}_{j-1}' \mathsf{x}_{j+1}' \ldots \mathsf{x}_n' | 1 \rangle. \qquad (11{:}137b)$$

[28] The factor $(n+1)^{\frac{1}{2}}$ here is necessary because in the transition to (11:135*a*) the appropriate normalization factor appears as

$$[n_1'! \ldots (n_k' + 1)! \ldots / (n+1)!]^{\frac{1}{2}} \langle n_1' \ldots n_k' + 1 \ldots | 1 \rangle.$$

Let us now consider $|2\rangle = \Psi^*(x)\Psi(x')|1\rangle$ and $|2\rangle = \Psi(x')\Psi^*(x)|1\rangle$, which we refer to as cases A, B, respectively. For A we have

$$\langle n_1' \ldots | 2 \rangle = \sum_{n_1'' \ldots} \sum_{n_1''' \ldots} \sum_k n_k'^{\frac{1}{2}} \langle E^k | x \rangle \delta(n_k', n_k''' + 1) \prod_{i \neq k} \delta(n_i', n_i''')$$

$$\times \sum (n_j''' + 1)^{\frac{1}{2}} \langle x' | E^j \rangle \delta(n_j''', n_j'' - 1) \prod_{l \neq j} \delta(n_l''', n_l'') \langle n_1'' \ldots | 1 \rangle$$

$$= \sum_{k,j} n_k'^{\frac{1}{2}} (n_j' + 1 - \delta_{jk})^{\frac{1}{2}} \langle E^k | x \rangle \langle x' | E^j \rangle$$

$$\times \langle n_1' \ldots n_k' - 1 \ldots n_j + 1 \ldots | 1 \rangle, \quad (11{:}138a)$$

which is the **n**-transcription of

$$\langle E_1' \ldots E_n' | 2 \rangle = \sum_{r=1} \sum_{E_r''} \langle E_r' | x \rangle \langle x' | E_r'' \rangle \langle E_1' \ldots E_{r-1}' E_r'' E_{r+1}' \ldots E_n' | 1 \rangle, \quad (11{:}138b)$$

or

$$\langle x_1' x_2' \ldots x_n' | 2 \rangle = \delta(x_1' - x) \langle x' x_2' x_3' \ldots x_n' | 1 \rangle + \delta(x_2' - x) \langle x_1' x' x_3' \ldots x_n' | 1 \rangle + \ldots$$

$$= \sum_{r=1}^{n} \delta(x_r' - x) \langle x_1' \ldots x_{r-1}' x' x_{r+1}' \ldots x_n' | 1 \rangle; \quad (11{:}138c)$$

whence

$$\langle x_1' \ldots x_n' | \Psi^*(x) \Psi(x') | x_1'' \ldots x_n'' \rangle = \sum_{r=1}^{n} \delta(x_r' - x) \delta(x_r'' - x') \prod_{i \neq r} \delta(x_i'' - x_i'). \quad (11{:}138d)$$

For B we have

$$\langle n_1' \ldots | 2 \rangle = \sum_{n_1'' \ldots} \sum_{n_1''' \ldots} \sum_j (n_j' + 1)^{\frac{1}{2}} \langle x' | E^j \rangle \delta(n_j', n_j''' - 1) \prod_{i \neq j} \delta(n_i', n_i''')$$

$$\times \sum_k n_k'''^{\frac{1}{2}} \langle E^k | x \rangle \delta(n_k''', n_k'' + 1) \prod_{l \neq k} \delta(n_l''', n_l'') \langle n_1'' n_2'' \ldots | 1 \rangle$$

$$= \sum_{j,k} \langle x' | E^j \rangle \langle E^k | x \rangle (n_j' + 1)^{\frac{1}{2}} (n_k' + \delta_{jk})^{\frac{1}{2}}$$

$$\times \langle n_1' \ldots n_j' + 1 \ldots n_k' - 1 \ldots | 1 \rangle. \quad (11{:}139a)$$

which is the **n**-transcription of

$$\langle E_1' \ldots E_n' | 2 \rangle = \sum_{E'} \langle x' | E' \rangle \langle E' | x \rangle \langle E_1' \ldots E_n' | 1 \rangle + \sum_{r=1}^{n} \sum_{E_r''} \langle x' | E_r'' \rangle \langle E_r' | x \rangle \langle E_1' \ldots E_{r-1}' E_r'' E_{r+1}' \ldots E_n' | 1 \rangle, \quad (11{:}139b)$$

or

$$\langle x_1' \ldots x_n' | 2 \rangle = \delta(x' - x) \langle x_1' \ldots x_n' | 1 \rangle + \sum_{r=1}^{n} \delta(x_r' - x) \langle x_1' \ldots x_{r-1}' x' x_{r+1}' \ldots x_n' | 1 \rangle. \quad (11{:}139c)$$

From these results we find that the representative of

$$|\,2\,\rangle = \{\,\Psi(x)\,\Psi^*(x') - \Psi^*(x')\,\Psi(x)\,\}\,|\,1\,\rangle$$

is

$$\langle\, x_1' \ldots x_n' \,|\, 2\,\rangle = \delta(x' - x)\,\langle\, x_1' \ldots x_n' \,|\, 1\,\rangle, \quad \text{(11:140)}$$

which merely verifies the relation (11:131*a*). Similarly, the representative of $|\,2\,\rangle = \{\,\Psi(x')\,\Psi(x) - \Psi(x)\,\Psi(x')\,\}\,|\,1\,\rangle$ is

$$\langle x_1' x_2' \ldots x_n' \,|\, 2\rangle = [(n+2)(n+1)]^{\frac{1}{2}}\{\langle x' x x_1' \ldots x_n' \,|\, 1\rangle - \langle x x' x_1' \ldots x_n' \,|\, 1\,\rangle\}$$
$$= 0, \quad \text{(11:141)}$$

which verifies the relation (11:131*b*).

The same results may be readily obtained for the antisymmetric case, the only difference being in the change of sign in the appropriate places, and we may note that the operators Ψ, Ψ^* do not affect the symmetry properties of the wave-functions.

From (11:138*c*), with $x = x'$, the representative of $|\,2\,\rangle = \Psi^*(x)\,\Psi(x)\,|\,1\,\rangle$ is

$$\langle\, x_1' \ldots x_n' \,|\, 2\,\rangle = \sum_{r=1}^{n} \delta(x_r - x)\,\langle\, x_1' \ldots x_{r-1}' x x_{r+1}' \ldots x_n' \,|\, 1\,\rangle$$
$$= \sum_{r=1}^{n} \delta(x_r' - x)\,\langle\, x_1' \ldots x_{r-1}' x_r' x_{r+1}' \ldots x_n' \,|\, 1\,\rangle, \quad \text{(11:142)}[29]$$

whence

$$\langle\, x_1' \ldots x_n' \,|\, \Psi^*\Psi \,|\, x_1'' \ldots x_n''\,\rangle = \prod_{i=1}^{n} \delta(x_i'' - x_i') \sum_{r=1}^{n} \delta(x_r' - x). \quad \text{(11:143)}$$

We shall also require the **x**-representative of $\Psi^*(x')\Psi^*(x'')\Psi(x'')\Psi(x')$, and this can be calculated directly in the **x**-representation by first applying the commutation rules (11:131*a*, *b*) to obtain its equivalent

$$\Psi^*(x')\,\Psi(x')\,\Psi^*(x'')\,\Psi(x'') - \Psi^*(x')\,\Psi(x'')\,\mathbf{I}\,\delta(x' - x''),$$

and then using (11:138*c*, *d*) with x' and x'' for **x**. We thus obtain the equation

$$\langle\, x_1' \ldots x_n' \,|\, 2\,\rangle$$
$$= \delta(x' - x'')\sum_{r=1}^{n} \delta(x_r' - x')\,\langle\, x_1' \ldots x_{r-1}' x'' x_{r+1}' \ldots x_n' \,|\, 1\,\rangle$$
$$+ \sum_{s \neq r} \delta(x_s' - x')\,\delta(x_r' - x'')\,\langle\, x_1' \ldots x_{s-1}' x' x_{s+1}' \ldots x_{r-1}' x'' x_{r+1}' \ldots x_n' \,|\, 1\,\rangle$$
$$- \delta(x' - x'')\sum_{r=1}^{n} \delta(x_r' - x')\,\langle\, x_1' \ldots x_{r-1}' x'' x_{r+1}' \ldots x_n' \,|\, 1\,\rangle$$
$$= \sum_{s \neq r} \delta(x_s' - x')\,\delta(x_r' - x'')\,\langle x_1' \ldots x_{s-1}' x' x_{s+1}' \ldots x_{r-1}' x'' x_{r+1}' \ldots x_n' \,|\, 1\rangle, \quad \text{(11:144)}$$

[29] $\delta(x_r' - x)\,f(x) = \delta(x_r' - x)\,f(x_r')$.

and finally

$$\langle x_1' \ldots x_n' \mid \mathbf{\Psi}^*(x')\mathbf{\Psi}^*(x'')\mathbf{\Psi}(x'')\mathbf{\Psi}(x') \mid x_1'' \ldots x_n'' \rangle$$

$$= \sum_{r \neq s} \delta(x_s' - x')\delta(x_r' - x'')\delta(x_s'' - x')\delta(x_r'' - x'') \prod_{i \neq r, s} \delta(x_i'' - x_i'). \quad (11:145)$$

The use of these results allows us rather more flexibility in passing from the **x**- to the **n**-representation, and conversely. In fact, we are now in a position to make this transition at any desired point in our calculations. To illustrate the preceding work we shall consider a few examples.

The Coulomb potential operator which arises in the first part of (11:132) reduces to

$$\mathbf{U}(x_0) = \int \frac{\mathbf{\Psi}^*(x')\mathbf{\Psi}(x')}{|\underline{x}_0 - \underline{x}'|} dx', \quad . \quad . \quad . \quad . \quad (11:146)$$

and from (11:142, 143)

$$\langle x_1' \ldots x_n' \mid \mathbf{U} \mid x_1'' \ldots x_n'' \rangle = \int \frac{\langle x_1' \ldots x_n' \mid \mathbf{\Psi}^*(x')\mathbf{\Psi}(x') \mid x_1'' \ldots x_n'' \rangle}{|\underline{x}_0 - \underline{x}'|} dx'$$

$$= \int \sum_k \frac{\delta(x_k' - x')}{|\underline{x}_0 - \underline{x}'|} dx' \prod_{i=1}^{n} \delta(x_i'' - x_i')$$

$$= \sum_k \frac{1}{|\underline{x}_0 - \underline{x}_k'|} \prod_i \delta(x_i'' - x_i'). \quad . \quad . \quad . \quad (11:147)$$

Finally, $|2\rangle = \mathbf{U}|1\rangle$ becomes

$$\langle x_1' \ldots x_n' \mid 2 \rangle = \sum_k \frac{1}{|\underline{x}_0 - \underline{x}_k'|} \langle x_1' \ldots x_n' \mid 1 \rangle, \quad . \quad (11:148)$$

which brings us back essentially to our starting-point, § 93 (*b*).

§ 98. The Self-consistent Field—Wave Field Method

The development of the second quantization thus far has laid emphasis on the operational aspect of the method and its place in the general representation theory. It should be clear, however, that from a purely mathematical point of view the central theme is the expansion of a symmetric or antisymmetric function of n variables (in particular eigenfunctions of the Hamiltonian) in terms of a complete set of orthonormal functions, i.e. in terms of symmetrized or antisymmetrized product functions whose individual members are the $\langle x' \mid E^r \rangle$ of (11:2), (11:130), etc. Except for the orthonormality conditions these functions have been essentially arbitrary, and thus appeared in a subsidiary role. In order to apply our results to the determination of the eigenfunctions and energy values, it is necessary to compute the diagonal matrix components of the latter, and apply the variation principle. In particular, we shall see that we are led to the equations of the self-consistent field which will, of course, include *exchange*.

The diagonal matrix elements can now be obtained in a variety of ways, using either of the equivalent quantized forms (11:89) or (11:132), and it suffices to consider the occupation variable set $n_1' = n_2' = \ldots = n_n' = 1$, all others being zero.[30] We take the latter form

$$\mathbf{H} = \iint \boldsymbol{\Psi}^*(x')\,dx'\,\langle x' \mid \mathbf{u} \mid x'' \rangle\,dx''\,\boldsymbol{\Psi}(x'')$$
$$+ \tfrac{1}{2}\int \ldots \int \boldsymbol{\Psi}^*(x')\boldsymbol{\Psi}^*(x'')\,dx'dx''\,\langle x'x'' \mid \mathbf{v} \mid x'''x^{\mathrm{IV}} \rangle\,dx'''dx^{\mathrm{IV}}\,\boldsymbol{\Psi}(x^{\mathrm{IV}})\boldsymbol{\Psi}(x''') \quad (11{:}149)$$

and, recalling the definitions of the $\boldsymbol{\Psi}$'s, $\boldsymbol{\xi}$'s, etc., readily find

$$\langle n_1' \ldots \mid \boldsymbol{\Psi}^*(x')\boldsymbol{\Psi}(x'') \mid n_1' \ldots \rangle = \sum_{r,s} \langle r \mid x' \rangle \langle x'' \mid s \rangle \langle n_1' \ldots \mid \boldsymbol{\xi}_r^* \boldsymbol{\xi}_s \mid n_1' \ldots \rangle$$
$$= \sum_{r=1}^{n} \langle r \mid x' \rangle \langle x'' \mid r \rangle$$
$$= \langle x'' \mid \boldsymbol{\rho} \mid x' \rangle, \quad (11{:}150)$$

and

$$\langle n_1' \ldots \mid \boldsymbol{\Psi}^*(x')\boldsymbol{\Psi}^*(x'')\boldsymbol{\Psi}(x^{\mathrm{IV}})\boldsymbol{\Psi}(x''') \mid n_1' \ldots \rangle$$
$$= \sum_{r,s,t,u} \langle r \mid x' \rangle \langle s \mid x'' \rangle \langle x^{\mathrm{IV}} \mid t \rangle \langle x''' \mid u \rangle \langle n_1' \ldots \mid \boldsymbol{\xi}_r^* \boldsymbol{\xi}_s^* \boldsymbol{\xi}_t \boldsymbol{\xi}_u \mid n_1' \ldots \rangle$$
$$= \sum_{r,s}^{n} \Big\{ \langle r \mid x' \rangle \langle s \mid x'' \rangle \langle x^{\mathrm{IV}} \mid s \rangle \langle x''' \mid r \rangle - \langle r \mid x' \rangle \langle s \mid x'' \rangle \langle x^{\mathrm{IV}} \mid r \rangle \langle x''' \mid s \rangle \Big\}$$
$$= \langle x^{\mathrm{IV}} \mid \boldsymbol{\rho} \mid x'' \rangle \langle x''' \mid \boldsymbol{\rho} \mid x' \rangle - \langle x^{\mathrm{IV}} \mid \boldsymbol{\rho} \mid x' \rangle \langle x''' \mid \boldsymbol{\rho} \mid x'' \rangle. \quad (11{:}151)$$

Thus,

$$\langle n_1' \ldots \mid \mathbf{H} \mid n_1' \ldots \rangle$$
$$= \iint \langle x' \mid \mathbf{u} \mid x'' \rangle\,dx''\,\langle x'' \mid \boldsymbol{\rho} \mid x' \rangle\,dx'$$
$$+ \tfrac{1}{2}\int \ldots \int \Big\{ \langle x^{\mathrm{IV}} \mid \boldsymbol{\rho} \mid x'' \rangle \langle x''' \mid \boldsymbol{\rho} \mid x' \rangle - \langle x^{\mathrm{IV}} \mid \boldsymbol{\rho} \mid x' \rangle \langle x''' \mid \boldsymbol{\rho} \mid x'' \rangle \Big\}$$
$$\times \langle x'x'' \mid \mathbf{v} \mid x'''x^{\mathrm{IV}} \rangle\,dx' \ldots dx^{\mathrm{IV}}, \quad (11{:}152)$$

and if $\mathbf{u}$, $\mathbf{v}$ are of the usual form

$$\left.\begin{aligned} \langle x' \mid \mathbf{u} \mid x'' \rangle &= u(x')\,\delta(x' - x''), \\ \langle x'x'' \mid \mathbf{v} \mid x'''x^{\mathrm{IV}} \rangle &= \frac{e^2}{|\underline{x}' - \underline{x}''|}\,\delta(x' - x''')\,\delta(x'' - x^{\mathrm{IV}}), \end{aligned}\right\} \quad (11{:}153)$$

this becomes

$$W = \int u(x')\langle x' \mid \boldsymbol{\rho} \mid x' \rangle\,dx' + \frac{e^2}{2}\iint \frac{\langle x' \mid \boldsymbol{\rho} \mid x' \rangle \langle x'' \mid \boldsymbol{\rho} \mid x'' \rangle - |\langle x' \mid \boldsymbol{\rho} \mid x'' \rangle|^2}{|\underline{x}' - \underline{x}''|}, \quad (11{:}154)$$

which is the familiar integral form of the Fock equation.[31]

[30] This selection corresponds to the first-order perturbation theory, neglecting configuration interaction [cf. (11:195) *et seq.*].

[31] * Fock, V.: *Zeits. f. Phys.*, **61**, 126 (1930); **75**, 622 (1932); **81**, 195 (1933).

It is easily verified that with the alternate form (11:89) we obtain

$$\langle n_1' \ldots | \mathbf{H} | n_1' \ldots \rangle = \sum_{k=1}^{n} \langle k | \mathbf{u} | k \rangle + \sum_{k,l=1}^{n} \Big\{ \langle kl | \mathbf{v} | kl \rangle - \langle kl | \mathbf{v} | lk \rangle \Big\}, \quad (11:155)$$

which is, of course, merely another form of (11:154).

Finally, it is of interest to note that the operators $\mathbf{\Psi}(x)$, $\mathbf{\Psi}(x)\mathbf{\Psi}(x')$, $\mathbf{\Psi}(x)\mathbf{\Psi}(x')\mathbf{\Psi}(x'')$, etc., may be described by the statement that applied to a $|\,\rangle$ whose representative is $\langle x_1' x_2' \ldots x_n' |\,\rangle$, the representative of the resultant is a function of $n+1$, $n+2$, $n+3$, etc., variables, respectively, those numbering beyond n being unsigned. Considered in terms of various dimensions n, we may set up the following matrix correspondences (e.g. in the symmetric case),

Initial representative ⟶ resultant representative

$$\mathbf{\Psi}(x): \quad \begin{Bmatrix} \text{constant} \\ \langle x_1' |\,\rangle \\ \langle x_1' x_2' |\,\rangle \\ \cdot \\ \cdot \\ \cdot \end{Bmatrix} \qquad \begin{Bmatrix} \langle x |\,\rangle \\ \sqrt{2}\,\langle x x_1' |\,\rangle \\ \sqrt{3}\,\langle x x_1' x_2' |\,\rangle \\ \cdot \\ \cdot \\ \cdot \end{Bmatrix} \quad . \quad . \quad (11:156)$$

$$\mathbf{\Psi}(x)\mathbf{\Psi}(x'): \quad \begin{Bmatrix} \text{constant} \\ \langle x_1' |\,\rangle \\ \langle x_1' x_2' |\,\rangle \\ \cdot \\ \cdot \\ \cdot \end{Bmatrix} \qquad \begin{Bmatrix} \sqrt{2\cdot 1}\,\langle x x' |\,\rangle \\ \sqrt{3\cdot 2}\,\langle x x' x_1' |\,\rangle \\ \sqrt{4\cdot 3}\,\langle x x' x_1' x_2' |\,\rangle \\ \cdot \\ \cdot \\ \cdot \end{Bmatrix} \quad . \quad . \quad (11:157)$$

etc.

§ 99. The Dirac Vector Model—Wave Field Method

The Dirac vector model, which was considered in Chapter X, led to the approximate operator relation

$$\mathbf{V} = \sum_{k<l} \langle kl | \mathbf{v} | kl \rangle - \sum_{k<l} \langle kl | \mathbf{v} | lk \rangle\, \mathbf{P}_{kl}^{\sigma}$$
$$= \sum_{k<l} \langle kl | \mathbf{v} | kl \rangle - \tfrac{1}{2} \sum_{k<l} \langle kl | \mathbf{v} | lk \rangle \,(1 + \underline{\boldsymbol{\sigma}}_k \cdot \underline{\boldsymbol{\sigma}}_l), \quad . \quad (11:158)$$

the eigenvalues of which determine the first-order correction in energy levels. However, the derivation of this result required a not inconsiderable mathematical machinery even as a rather intuitive application of group concepts. It is therefore somewhat striking that the formalism of the second quantization affords a very simple, even primitive, derivation of this important result.[32] It is clear from the previous considerations of Chapter X that we must first of all explicitly bring the spin variables into play and adjust the notation of our quantization formalism

[32] JORDAN, P.: *Zeits. f. Phys.*, **91**, 284 (1934).

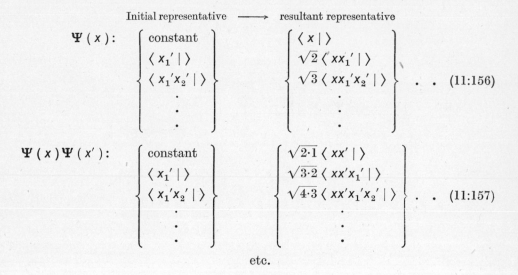

accordingly. To this end we now let the Roman indices [cf. §§ 93 (*a*), (*b*)] k, l, m, n, etc. (ranging from 1 to ∞), label all but spin variables in the energy representation of the one-electron state (cell);[33] the corresponding spin variables are associated with the Greek indices $\kappa, \lambda, \mu, \nu$, etc. (ranging from 1 to 2), so that, for example, the diagonal matrix exhibiting the spin-independent energy of the one-electron problem takes the form

$$\langle k\kappa \mid \mathbf{u} \mid l\lambda \rangle = \epsilon_k \, \delta(k, l)\, \delta(\kappa, \lambda), \quad \ldots \quad (11{:}159)$$

and the commutators (11:73) become

$$\left.\begin{array}{ll} [\, \xi_{k\kappa}, \xi_{l\lambda} \,]_+ = 0, & \xi_{k\kappa}{}^* \xi_{k\kappa} = \mathbf{n}_{k\kappa}, \\ [\, \xi_{k\kappa}, \xi_{l\lambda}{}^* \,]_+ = \delta(k, l)\, \delta(\kappa, \lambda), & \xi_{k\kappa} \xi_{k\kappa}{}^* = 1 - \mathbf{n}_{k\kappa}. \end{array}\right\} \quad (11{:}160)$$

Finally, the spin-independent pair interaction $\mathbf{v}$ has the typical representative

$$\langle k\kappa l\lambda \mid \mathbf{v} \mid m\mu n\nu \rangle = \langle kl \mid \mathbf{v} \mid mn \rangle\, \delta(\kappa, \mu)\, \delta(\lambda, \nu), \quad . \quad (11{:}161)$$

and the quantized Hamiltonian (11:89) takes the form

$$\begin{aligned} \mathbf{H} &= \sum_{\substack{k,l \\ \kappa,\lambda}} \langle k\kappa \mid \mathbf{u} \mid l\lambda \rangle\, \xi_{k\kappa}{}^* \xi_{l\lambda} + \tfrac{1}{2} \sum_{\substack{k,l,m,n \\ \kappa,\lambda,\mu,\nu}} \langle k\kappa l\lambda \mid \mathbf{v} \mid m\mu n\nu \rangle\, \xi_{k\kappa}{}^* \xi_{l\lambda}{}^* \xi_{n\nu} \xi_{m\mu} \\ &= \sum_k \epsilon_k (\mathbf{n}_{k1} + \mathbf{n}_{k2}) + \tfrac{1}{2} \sum_{\substack{k,l,m,n \\ \kappa,\lambda}} \langle kl \mid \mathbf{v} \mid mn \rangle\, \xi_{k\kappa}{}^* \xi_{l\lambda}{}^* \xi_{n\lambda} \xi_{m\kappa}. \quad . \quad (11{:}162) \end{aligned}$$

The first term here corresponds to the fact that each eigenvalue ϵ_k is associated with a one-electron state (spinless) of statistical weight two, and as indicated by (11:159) we are assuming that only spin degeneracy exists—which is precisely the assumption of the rudimentary Dirac model. This degeneracy appears in the quantized Hamiltonian $\mathbf{U}$ of the unperturbed problem because each term $\epsilon_k(\mathbf{n}_{k1} + \mathbf{n}_{k2})$ has the two-fold degenerate eigenvalue ϵ_k as well as the simple values 0 and $2\epsilon_k$. The usual first-order solution of the degenerate problem consists in properly selecting those representatives of the perturbation $\mathbf{V}$ whose rows and columns refer to one degenerate level (of the whole system), and determining the eigenvalues of the resulting finite matrix.[34] As previously discussed, this procedure is equivalent to splitting off, either in operator or representative form, that part of the perturbation which is a constant of the unperturbed motion. The prescription for this part is that it commute with the unperturbed Hamiltonian, and our problem now is to apply this criterion to the present case. Let us then denote by $\mathbf{O}_r\mathbf{V}$ that part of $\mathbf{V}$ which commutes with a typical term

$$\epsilon_r (\mathbf{n}_{r1} + \mathbf{n}_{r2}) \quad \ldots\ldots\ldots \quad (11{:}163)$$

of $\mathbf{U}$, and as will be seen the operator $\mathbf{O}_r$ is linear, so that the required part of $\mathbf{V}$ which commutes with $\mathbf{U}$ will be given by

$$\mathbf{V}_c = \mathbf{O}\mathbf{V} = \prod_r \mathbf{O}_r\mathbf{V}. \quad \ldots\ldots \quad (11{:}164)$$

[33] Hence $\langle kl \mid \mathbf{v} \mid mn \rangle$, for example, no longer involves a summation over spin variables.

[34] I.e. the solution of the secular equation.

In order to define $\mathbf{O}_r$ we consider, instead of (11:163), the related operator

$$\boldsymbol{\Omega}_r = \mathbf{n}_{r1} + \mathbf{n}_{r2} - 1, \qquad (11:165)$$

which has the eigenvalues -1, 0, 1, and from which we can form the associated orthogonal idempotent forms

$$\left.\begin{aligned} \boldsymbol{\omega}_{r^1} &= \frac{\boldsymbol{\Omega}_r(\boldsymbol{\Omega}_r - 1)}{2}, \\ \boldsymbol{\omega}_{r^2} &= 1 - \boldsymbol{\Omega}_r^{\,2}, \\ \boldsymbol{\omega}_{r^3} &= \frac{\boldsymbol{\Omega}_r(\boldsymbol{\Omega}_r + 1)}{2}. \end{aligned}\right\} \qquad (11:166)$$

These are readily seen to satisfy the orthogonality conditions

$$\boldsymbol{\omega}_{r^i}\boldsymbol{\omega}_{r^j} = \boldsymbol{\omega}_{r^i}\,\delta(i, j), \qquad (11:167)$$

which, with (11:163) and the relation

$$\boldsymbol{\Omega}_r = -\boldsymbol{\omega}_{r^1} + \boldsymbol{\omega}_{r^3}, \qquad (11:168)$$

shows that for any operator $\mathbf{Q}$, the part

$$\mathbf{O}_r\mathbf{Q} = \boldsymbol{\omega}_{r^1}\mathbf{Q}\boldsymbol{\omega}_{r^1} + \boldsymbol{\omega}_{r^2}\mathbf{Q}\boldsymbol{\omega}_{r^2} + \boldsymbol{\omega}_{r^3}\mathbf{Q}\boldsymbol{\omega}_{r^3} \qquad (11:169)$$

commutes with (11:163) and, more generally, with any function of $\boldsymbol{\Omega}_r$. $\mathbf{O}_r$ is obviously linear, idempotent, and also satisfies the equation $\mathbf{O}_r\mathbf{Q} = \mathbf{Q}$ when $\mathbf{Q}$ is an operator in the space of the $\mathbf{n}$'s (or any operator) not involving the index[35] r. Hence $\mathbf{O}_r$ does not affect the operator $\xi_{k\kappa}{}^*\xi_{l\lambda}{}^*\xi_{n\lambda}\xi_{m\kappa}$ when r is not in the set (k, l, m, n), which with the idempotency of $\mathbf{O}_r$ leads to the result

$$\mathbf{V}_c = \prod_r \mathbf{O}_r\mathbf{V} = \tfrac{1}{2} \sum_{\substack{k,l,m,n\\ \kappa,\lambda}} \langle kl \mid \mathbf{v} \mid mn \rangle\, \mathbf{O}_k\mathbf{O}_l\mathbf{O}_m\mathbf{O}_n\xi_{k\kappa}{}^*\xi_{l\lambda}{}^*\xi_{n\lambda}\xi_{m\kappa}. \qquad (11:170)$$

The form of $\mathbf{V}_c$ is further simplified by noting that

$$\xi_{r1}\boldsymbol{\Omega}_r = (\mathbf{n}_{r2} - \mathbf{n}_{r1})\,\xi_{r1}, \qquad (11:171a)$$

and

$$\left.\begin{aligned} \boldsymbol{\Omega}_r(\mathbf{n}_{r2} - \mathbf{n}_{r1}) &= 0, \\ (1 - \boldsymbol{\Omega}_r^{\,2})(1 - [\mathbf{n}_{r2} - \mathbf{n}_{r1}]^2) &= 0, \end{aligned}\right\} \qquad (11:171b)$$

which follow simply from (11:160) and (11:163). Hence,

$$\begin{aligned} 4\mathbf{O}_r\xi_{r1} = \{ &\boldsymbol{\Omega}_r(\boldsymbol{\Omega}_r - 1)(\mathbf{n}_{r2} - \mathbf{n}_{r1})(\mathbf{n}_{r2} - \mathbf{n}_{r1} - 1) + 4(1 - \boldsymbol{\Omega}_r^{\,2})(1 - [\mathbf{n}_{r2} - \mathbf{n}_{r1}]^2) \\ &+ \boldsymbol{\Omega}_r(\boldsymbol{\Omega}_r + 1)(\mathbf{n}_{r2} - \mathbf{n}_{r1})(\mathbf{n}_{r2} - \mathbf{n}_{r1} + 1)\} = 0, \end{aligned} \qquad (11:172)$$

which tells us that the only non-vanishing terms in (11:170) are, at most, those in

$$\langle kk \mid \mathbf{v} \mid kk \rangle,\ \langle kl \mid \mathbf{v} \mid kl \rangle,\ \langle kl \mid \mathbf{v} \mid lk \rangle,\ \langle kk \mid \mathbf{v} \mid ll \rangle \quad (k \neq l), \qquad (11:173)$$

since any term for which at least one of the indices k, l, m, n differs from all the

[35] As will be seen, there are other operators depending on r which also satisfy this relation.

others will vanish. The remaining terms may be reduced through the easily derived relations

$$\left.\begin{array}{ll}
(a)\ \mathbf{\Omega}_k\xi_{k\kappa}{}^*\xi_{k\kappa} = \xi_{k\kappa}{}^*\xi_{k\kappa}\mathbf{\Omega}_k. & (a')\ \mathbf{O}_k\xi_{k\kappa}{}^*\xi_{k\kappa} = \xi_{k\kappa}{}^*\xi_{k\kappa}. \\
(b)\ \mathbf{\Omega}_k\xi_{k\kappa}{}^*\xi_{k\lambda} = -\xi_{k\kappa}{}^*\xi_{k\lambda}\mathbf{\Omega}_k = 0 \quad (\lambda \neq \kappa). & (b')\ \mathbf{O}_k\xi_{k\kappa}{}^*\xi_{k\lambda} = \xi_{k\kappa}{}^*\xi_{k\lambda}. \\
(c)\ \mathbf{\Omega}_k\xi_{k\kappa}{}^2 \equiv 0, \text{ since } \xi_{k\kappa}{}^2 \equiv 0. & (c')\ \mathbf{O}_k\xi_{k\kappa}{}^2 \equiv 0. \\
(d)\ \mathbf{\Omega}_k\xi_{k\kappa}\xi_{k\lambda} = -\xi_{k\kappa}\xi_{k\lambda}\mathbf{\Omega}_k = \xi_{k\kappa}\xi_{k\lambda} \quad (\lambda \neq \kappa). & (d')\ \mathbf{O}_k\xi_{k\kappa}\xi_{k\lambda} = 0. \\
(e)\ \mathbf{\Omega}_k\xi_{k\kappa}{}^{*2} \equiv 0 \quad (\text{cf. } c). & (e')\ \mathbf{O}_k\xi_{k\kappa}{}^{*2} \equiv 0. \\
(f)\ \mathbf{\Omega}_k\xi_{k\kappa}{}^*\xi_{k\lambda}{}^* = -\xi_{k\kappa}{}^*\xi_{k\lambda}{}^*\mathbf{\Omega}_k & (f')\ \mathbf{O}_k\xi_{k\kappa}{}^*\xi_{k\lambda}{}^* = 0. \\
\qquad = \xi_{k\kappa}{}^*\xi_{k\lambda}{}^* \quad (\lambda \neq \kappa). &
\end{array}\right\} \quad (11{:}174)$$

from which it immediately follows that

$$\left.\begin{array}{l}
(a)\quad \mathbf{O}_k\,(\,\xi_{k\kappa}{}^*\xi_{k\lambda}{}^*\xi_{k\lambda}\xi_{k\kappa}\,) = \xi_{k\kappa}{}^*\xi_{k\lambda}{}^*\xi_{k\lambda}\xi_{k\kappa}. \\
(b)\quad \mathbf{O}_k\mathbf{O}_l\,(\,\xi_{k\kappa}{}^*\xi_{l\lambda}{}^*\xi_{l\lambda}\xi_{k\kappa}\,) = \xi_{k\kappa}{}^*\xi_{l\lambda}{}^*\xi_{l\lambda}\xi_{k\kappa}. \\
(c)\quad \mathbf{O}_k\mathbf{O}_l\,(\,\xi_{k\kappa}{}^*\xi_{l\lambda}{}^*\xi_{k\lambda}\xi_{l\kappa}\,) = \xi_{k\kappa}{}^*\xi_{l\lambda}{}^*\xi_{k\lambda}\xi_{l\kappa}. \\
(d)\quad \mathbf{O}_k\mathbf{O}_l\,(\,\xi_{k\kappa}{}^*\xi_{k\lambda}{}^*\xi_{l\lambda}\xi_{l\kappa}\,) = 0.
\end{array}\right\} \quad . \ . \ (11{:}175)$$

Thus, finally $\mathbf{V}_c$ reduces to

$$\mathbf{V}_c = \tfrac{1}{2}\sum_{\substack{k,l\\ \kappa,\lambda}} \langle\, kl \mid \mathbf{v} \mid kl \,\rangle\, \xi_{k\kappa}{}^*\xi_{l\lambda}{}^*\xi_{l\lambda}\xi_{k\kappa} + \tfrac{1}{2}\sum_{\substack{k\neq l\\ \kappa,\lambda}} \langle\, kl \mid \mathbf{v} \mid lk \,\rangle\, \xi_{k\kappa}{}^*\xi_{l\lambda}{}^*\xi_{k\lambda}\xi_{l\kappa}, \quad (11{:}176)$$

which is just the Dirac equation (11:158) and, as seen from the second term, already contains the restriction ($k \neq l$) that exchange terms are omitted for identical spinless orbits. The complete equivalence of these two forms is most readily seen by expanding (11:176) in the form

$$\mathbf{V}_c = \sum_{\substack{k\\ \kappa<\lambda}} \langle\, kk \mid \mathbf{v} \mid kk \,\rangle\, \mathbf{n}_{k\kappa}\mathbf{n}_{k\lambda} + \sum_{\substack{k<l\\ \kappa,\lambda}} \langle\, kl \mid \mathbf{v} \mid kl \,\rangle\, \mathbf{n}_{k\kappa}\mathbf{n}_{l\lambda} - \sum_{\substack{k<l\\ \kappa}} \langle\, kl \mid \mathbf{v} \mid lk \,\rangle\, \mathbf{n}_{k\kappa}\mathbf{n}_{l\kappa}$$
$$- \sum_{\substack{k<l\\ \kappa\neq\lambda}} \langle\, kl \mid \mathbf{v} \mid lk \,\rangle\, \xi_{k\kappa}{}^*\xi_{k\lambda}\xi_{l\lambda}{}^*\xi_{l\kappa}, \quad (11{:}177)$$

and considering the effect of $\mathbf{V}_c$ on an eigenvector of $\mathbf{U} = \sum_{k,\kappa} \epsilon_k \mathbf{n}_{k\kappa}$ corresponding to a definite assignment of electrons among cells. Moreover, the above form gives directly the expanded form of the Dirac equation (10:41) which takes account of the existence of paired orbits.

§ 100. The Hole Formalism

As we have seen, the explicit development of the second quantization in terms of the Dirac-Jordan representation theory places the occupation number representation on the same footing with all others, and further shows that it is mathematically entirely equivalent to the usual methods of configuration space. However, it is clear that unless we deal with problems involving creation and annihilation (non-conservation of particle numbers), or systems intrinsically composed of extremely many particles—as is the case in radiation theory—this formalism does not possess any special advantages because of the enormous number of variables which must, in principle, be considered. Hence, it has not been extensively applied in the antisymmetric case.[36] It is nonetheless probably the most *anschaulich* expression of the exclusion principle, which is incorporated from the outset, and by its nature does permit various interesting theoretical investigations which are inherently more difficult in other modes of approach. Two rather striking examples are the preceding simple derivation of the Dirac model, and the *hole* formalism [37] or description of missing electrons which we shall now consider. For our further work it is convenient to take $\mathbf{u}(\mathbf{x}_r)$ in the general form

$$\mathbf{u}_r = \mathbf{H}_r + \boldsymbol{\varphi}_r, \qquad (11:178)$$

where $\boldsymbol{\varphi}_r$ indicates an arbitrary (single-particle) perturbation, and $\mathbf{H}_r$ defines the unperturbed problem as before. Denoting the eigenvalues of $\mathbf{H}_r$ by ϵ, our previous equation (11:89) becomes

$$\mathbf{H} = \sum_{k,l}\Big(\epsilon_k\,\delta(k,l) + \langle k\,|\,\boldsymbol{\varphi}\,|\,l\rangle\Big)\boldsymbol{\xi}_k{}^*\boldsymbol{\xi}_l + \tfrac{1}{2}\sum_{k,l,m,n}\langle kl\,|\,\mathbf{v}\,|\,mn\rangle\,\boldsymbol{\xi}_k{}^*\boldsymbol{\xi}_l{}^*\boldsymbol{\xi}_n\boldsymbol{\xi}_m. \qquad (11:179)$$

From the fact that the *electron* occupation variables $\mathbf{n}_i$ take on only the eigenvalues 0, 1, it is evident that the distribution of electrons among cells is equally well determined by the complementary eigenvalues 1, 0 of the *hole* occupation variables $\underline{\underline{\mathbf{n}}}_i = 1 - \mathbf{n}_i$ which indicate the presence or absence of a hole in the ith cell. It follows from (11:73) that the hole creation and annihilation operators are given by $\underline{\underline{\boldsymbol{\xi}}}_i = \boldsymbol{\xi}_i{}^*$, $\underline{\underline{\boldsymbol{\xi}}}_i{}^* = \boldsymbol{\xi}_i$, since these satisfy the same commutation rules, interpreted for holes, namely,

$$\left.\begin{aligned} [\,\underline{\underline{\boldsymbol{\xi}}}_k, \underline{\underline{\boldsymbol{\xi}}}_l\,]_+ &= 0, & \underline{\underline{\boldsymbol{\xi}}}_k\underline{\underline{\boldsymbol{\xi}}}_k{}^* &= 1 - \underline{\underline{\mathbf{n}}}_k, \\ [\,\underline{\underline{\boldsymbol{\xi}}}_k{}^*, \underline{\underline{\boldsymbol{\xi}}}_l\,]_+ &= \delta_{kl}, & \underline{\underline{\boldsymbol{\xi}}}_k{}^*\underline{\underline{\boldsymbol{\xi}}}_k &= \underline{\underline{\mathbf{n}}}_k, \end{aligned}\right\} \qquad (11:180)$$

with which (11:179) takes the form

$$\underline{\underline{\mathbf{H}}} = \sum_{k,l}\Big(\epsilon_k\,\delta(k,l) + \langle k\,|\,\boldsymbol{\varphi}\,|\,l\rangle\Big)\underline{\underline{\boldsymbol{\xi}}}_k\underline{\underline{\boldsymbol{\xi}}}_l{}^* + \tfrac{1}{2}\sum_{k,l,m,n}\langle kl\,|\,\mathbf{v}\,|\,mn\rangle\,\underline{\underline{\boldsymbol{\xi}}}_k\underline{\underline{\boldsymbol{\xi}}}_l\underline{\underline{\boldsymbol{\xi}}}_n{}^*\underline{\underline{\boldsymbol{\xi}}}_m{}^*, \qquad (11:181)\ [38]$$

and, like (11:179), is still an exact equation. In order to examine the problem in terms of the hole formalism, $\underline{\underline{\mathbf{H}}}$ must be brought into the standard form (11:179) as regards the order of the operators $\underline{\underline{\boldsymbol{\xi}}}$, $\underline{\underline{\boldsymbol{\xi}}}^*$. This step corresponds to establishing a connection between the quantized Hamiltonian (11:181) and an *effective* Hamiltonian in the ordinary space variables of the holes, i.e. a reversal of the previous

[36] However, cf. * JOHNSON, M. H.: *Phys. Rev.*, **43**, 627 (1933), and BROWN, F. W.: *Phys. Rev.*, **44**, 214 (1933).

[37] * HEISENBERG, W.: *Ann. der. Phys.*, **10**, 888 (1931), and DIRAC, P. A. M.: *Ann. d. L'Inst. H. Poincaré*, **1**, Part 4, 391 (1929).

[38] $\underline{\underline{\mathbf{H}}}$, $\underline{\underline{\boldsymbol{\xi}}}$, etc., doubly underlined, simply indicate the interpretation in terms of hole variables.

procedure in obtaining the quantized Hamiltonian for the electrons. With the help of the commutators (11:180) we find

$$\underline{\underline{\xi}}_k \underline{\underline{\xi}}_l^* = \delta(k, l) - \underline{\underline{\xi}}_l^* \underline{\underline{\xi}}_k, \quad \ldots \quad (11:182a)$$

$$\begin{aligned} \underline{\underline{\xi}}_k \underline{\underline{\xi}}_l \underline{\underline{\xi}}_n^* \underline{\underline{\xi}}_m^* = {} & \delta(l, n)\,\delta(k, m) - \delta(k, n)\,\delta(l, m) - \delta(l, n)\,\underline{\underline{\xi}}_m^* \underline{\underline{\xi}}_k + \delta(k, n)\,\underline{\underline{\xi}}_m^* \underline{\underline{\xi}}_l \\ & + \delta(l, m)\,\underline{\underline{\xi}}_n^* \underline{\underline{\xi}}_k - \delta(k, m)\,\underline{\underline{\xi}}_n^* \underline{\underline{\xi}}_l + \underline{\underline{\xi}}_n^* \underline{\underline{\xi}}_m^* \underline{\underline{\xi}}_k \underline{\underline{\xi}}_l; \quad \ldots \quad (11:182b) \end{aligned}$$

and (11:181) takes the form

$$\begin{aligned} \underline{\underline{\mathbf{H}}} = {} & \sum_k \{ \epsilon_k + \langle k \mid \boldsymbol{\varphi} \mid k \rangle \} + \tfrac{1}{2} \sum_{k, l} \{ \langle kl \mid \mathbf{v} \mid kl \rangle - \langle kl \mid \mathbf{v} \mid lk \rangle \} \\ & - \sum_{k, l} \Big\{ \epsilon_k\, \delta(k, l) + \langle l \mid \boldsymbol{\varphi} \mid k \rangle \\ & + \tfrac{1}{2} \sum_m \Big(\langle lm \mid \mathbf{v} \mid km \rangle - \langle ml \mid \mathbf{v} \mid km \rangle + \langle ml \mid \mathbf{v} \mid mk \rangle - \langle lm \mid \mathbf{v} \mid mk \rangle \Big) \Big\} \underline{\underline{\xi}}_k^* \underline{\underline{\xi}}_l \\ & + \tfrac{1}{2} \sum_{k, l, m, n} \langle nm \mid \mathbf{v} \mid lk \rangle\, \underline{\underline{\xi}}_k^* \underline{\underline{\xi}}_l^* \underline{\underline{\xi}}_n \underline{\underline{\xi}}_m. \quad \ldots \quad (11:183) \end{aligned}$$

Aside from the appearance of new terms which will be discussed in detail later, the notable difference in (11:183) as compared with (11:179) is that here $\boldsymbol{\varphi}$ appears with a negative sign, and the indices in the representatives of $\boldsymbol{\varphi}$ and $\mathbf{v}$ are transposed. As regards the latter, the normal order [cf. (11:179)] is obtained if we define the wave-function of a hole to be the conjugate of the electron wave-function, so that

$$\left. \begin{aligned} \langle r \mid x \rangle &= \underline{\underline{\langle x \mid r \rangle}}, \\ \langle l \mid \boldsymbol{\varphi} \mid k \rangle &= \underline{\underline{\langle k \mid \boldsymbol{\varphi} \mid l \rangle}}, \\ \langle mn \mid \mathbf{v} \mid kl \rangle &= \underline{\underline{\langle kl \mid \mathbf{v} \mid mn \rangle}}, \end{aligned} \right\} \quad \ldots \quad (11:184)$$

provided, of course, that the operators $\boldsymbol{\varphi}$, etc., involved are Hermitian as here assumed. With this reservation we can readily verify the correctness of this assignment of hole wave-functions by considering the quantized wave formalism (cf. § 97).

The consistent transcription and interpretation of the equations (11:130) in terms of hole variables requires

$$\underline{\underline{\Psi}}^*(x) = \underline{\underline{\Psi}}(x) = \sum_r \langle x \mid r \rangle\, \xi_r = \sum_r \underline{\underline{\langle r \mid x \rangle}}\, \underline{\underline{\xi}}_r^*, \quad . \quad (11:185a)$$

$$\underline{\underline{\Psi}}(x') = \underline{\underline{\Psi}}^*(x') = \sum_r \langle r \mid x' \rangle\, \xi_r^* = \sum_r \underline{\underline{\langle x' \mid r \rangle}}\, \underline{\underline{\xi}}_r, \quad . \quad (11:185b)$$

$$\underline{\underline{\mathbf{n}}} = \sum_r \underline{\underline{\xi}}_r^* \underline{\underline{\xi}}_r = \int \underline{\underline{\Psi}}^*(x)\, dx\, \underline{\underline{\Psi}}(x), \quad \ldots \quad (11:185c)$$

and it is readily seen that these satisfy the commutation rules (11:131). The Hamiltonian (11:132) may now be expressed in terms of the $\underline{\underline{\Psi}}$'s and $\underline{\underline{\Psi}}^*$'s, as

$$\underline{\underline{\mathbf{H}}} = \iint \underline{\underline{\Psi}}(x')\, dx' \langle x' \mid \mathbf{u} \mid x'' \rangle\, dx'' \underline{\underline{\Psi}}^*(x'')$$
$$+ \tfrac{1}{2}\int \cdots \int \underline{\underline{\Psi}}(x')\underline{\underline{\Psi}}(x'')\, dx'\, dx'' \langle x'x'' \mid \mathbf{v} \mid x'''x^{\mathrm{IV}} \rangle\, dx'''\, dx^{\mathrm{IV}}\, \underline{\underline{\Psi}}^*(x^{\mathrm{IV}})\underline{\underline{\Psi}}^*(x'''), \tag{11:186}$$

which again needs to be rewritten in standard form. Applying the commutation rules, we find

$$\underline{\underline{\mathbf{H}}} = \int \underline{\underline{\langle x' \mid \mathbf{u} \mid x' \rangle}}\, dx' + \tfrac{1}{2}\iint \Big(\underline{\underline{\langle x'x'' \mid \mathbf{v} \mid x'x'' \rangle}} - \underline{\underline{\langle x'x'' \mid \mathbf{v} \mid x''x' \rangle}} \Big)\, dx'\, dx''$$
$$- \iint \underline{\underline{\Psi}}^*(x'')\, dx'' \underline{\underline{\langle x'' \mid \mathbf{u} \mid x' \rangle}}\, dx' \underline{\underline{\Psi}}(x')$$
$$- \tfrac{1}{2}\int \cdots \int \Big\{ \Big(\underline{\underline{\Psi}}^*(x''')\underline{\underline{\Psi}}(x') \underline{\underline{\langle x'''x'' \mid \mathbf{v} \mid x'x'' \rangle}} - \underline{\underline{\Psi}}^*(x''')\underline{\underline{\Psi}}(x'') \underline{\underline{\langle x'''x' \mid \mathbf{v} \mid x'x'' \rangle}} \Big)\, dx'\, dx''\, dx'''$$
$$+ \Big(\underline{\underline{\Psi}}^*(x^{\mathrm{IV}})\underline{\underline{\Psi}}(x'') \underline{\underline{\langle x'x^{\mathrm{IV}} \mid \mathbf{v} \mid x'x'' \rangle}} - \underline{\underline{\Psi}}^*(x^{\mathrm{IV}})\underline{\underline{\Psi}}(x') \underline{\underline{\langle x''x^{\mathrm{IV}} \mid \mathbf{v} \mid x'x'' \rangle}} \Big)\, dx'\, dx''\, dx^{\mathrm{IV}} \Big\}$$
$$+ \tfrac{1}{2}\int \cdots \int \underline{\underline{\Psi}}^*(x''')\underline{\underline{\Psi}}^*(x^{\mathrm{IV}})\, dx'''\, dx^{\mathrm{IV}} \underline{\underline{\langle x'''x^{\mathrm{IV}} \mid \mathbf{v} \mid x'x'' \rangle}}\, dx'\, dx'' \underline{\underline{\Psi}}(x'')\underline{\underline{\Psi}}(x'), \tag{11:187}$$

which (as can be seen by inspection) is *term for term* just equation (11:183) expressed in hole variables and wave-functions, viz.

$$\underline{\underline{\mathbf{H}}} = \sum_k \{ \epsilon_k + \underline{\underline{\langle k \mid \boldsymbol{\varphi} \mid k \rangle}} \} + \tfrac{1}{2}\sum_{k,l} \{ \underline{\underline{\langle kl \mid \mathbf{v} \mid kl \rangle}} - \underline{\underline{\langle lk \mid \mathbf{v} \mid kl \rangle}} \}$$
$$- \sum_{k,l} \Big\{ \epsilon_k \delta(k,l) + \underline{\underline{\langle k \mid \boldsymbol{\varphi} \mid l \rangle}} + \sum_m \Big(\underline{\underline{\langle km \mid \mathbf{v} \mid lm \rangle}} - \underline{\underline{\langle km \mid \mathbf{v} \mid ml \rangle}} \Big) \Big\} \underline{\underline{\xi}}_k^* \underline{\underline{\xi}}_l$$
$$+ \tfrac{1}{2} \sum_{k,l,m,n} \underline{\underline{\langle kl \mid \mathbf{v} \mid mn \rangle}}\, \underline{\underline{\xi}}_k^* \underline{\underline{\xi}}_l^* \underline{\underline{\xi}}_n \underline{\underline{\xi}}_m. \tag{11:188}$$

We can now reverse our quantization process and determine the Hamiltonian in the Schroedinger variables of the holes which leads to the above quantized form. To this end, we must first determine the proper operator in the space variables of the holes leading to the coefficients $\sum_m \Big(\underline{\underline{\langle km \mid \mathbf{v} \mid ml \rangle}} - \underline{\underline{\langle km \mid \mathbf{v} \mid lm \rangle}} \Big)$ of $\underline{\underline{\xi}}_k^* \underline{\underline{\xi}}_l$ which constitute a major difference in behaviour of holes as compared with electrons, since they represent a single-particle perturbation in addition to $-\boldsymbol{\varphi}$, i.e. in the absence of hole-pair interaction. This additional potential is seen to be the exchange and Coulomb interaction arising from all the (electron) filled cells, and this interpretation readily leads to the required operator in the configuration space of the holes. The required hole operator $\underline{\underline{\boldsymbol{\chi}}}$ must be such that

$$\underline{\boldsymbol{\chi}} = \sum_k^{\text{holes}} \underline{\boldsymbol{\mu}}_k = \sum_{kl} \underline{\underline{\langle k \mid \boldsymbol{\mu} \mid l \rangle}}\, \underline{\underline{\xi}}_k^* \underline{\underline{\xi}}_l = \sum_{k,l,m} \Big(\underline{\underline{\langle km \mid \mathbf{v} \mid ml \rangle}} - \underline{\underline{\langle km \mid \mathbf{v} \mid lm \rangle}} \Big) \underline{\underline{\xi}}_k^* \underline{\underline{\xi}}_l, \tag{11:189}$$

and the form of $\underline{\underline{\mu}}$ is obtained by noting that the matrix element $\langle \underline{\underline{k \mid \mu \mid l}} \rangle$ satisfies the equation

$$\langle \underline{\underline{k \mid \mu \mid l}} \rangle = \iint \langle \underline{\underline{k \mid x'}} \rangle \, dx' \, \langle \underline{\underline{x' \mid \mu \mid x''}} \rangle \, dx'' \, \langle \underline{\underline{x'' \mid l}} \rangle$$

$$= \sum_m \left(\langle \underline{\underline{km \mid \mathbf{v} \mid ml}} \rangle - \langle \underline{\underline{km \mid \mathbf{v} \mid lm}} \rangle \right), \quad . \quad . \quad (11{:}190)$$

if $\langle \underline{\underline{x' \mid \mu \mid x''}} \rangle$ is given by

$$\langle \underline{\underline{x' \mid \mu \mid x''}} \rangle = \sum_m \iint \langle \underline{\underline{m \mid x'''}} \rangle \, dx''' \left(\langle \underline{\underline{x'x''' \mid \mathbf{v} \mid x^{\mathrm{IV}}x''}} \rangle - \langle \underline{\underline{x'x''' \mid \mathbf{v} \mid x''x^{\mathrm{IV}}}} \rangle \right) dx^{\mathrm{IV}} \langle \underline{\underline{x^{\mathrm{IV}} \mid m}} \rangle$$

$$= \iint \langle \underline{\underline{x^{\mathrm{IV}} \mid \rho \mid x'''}} \rangle \, dx''' \left(\langle \underline{\underline{x'x''' \mid \mathbf{v} \mid x^{\mathrm{IV}}x''}} \rangle - \langle \underline{\underline{x'x''' \mid \mathbf{v} \mid x''x^{\mathrm{IV}}}} \rangle \right) dx^{\mathrm{IV}}.$$

(11:191) [39]

Now, if the summation over m extends over the infinite range, it follows that $\langle \underline{\underline{x^{\mathrm{IV}} \mid \rho \mid x'''}} \rangle = \delta \, (x^{\mathrm{IV}} - x''')$, but for our further work we shall retain the above form in ρ. Then from the definitions [cf. (8:75*a*, *b*)] of the Dirac exchange and pair interaction operators **A**, **B**, we see that the above result gives simply

$$\underline{\underline{\mu}} = - \, (\underline{\underline{\mathbf{B}}} - \underline{\underline{\mathbf{A}}}), \quad . \quad . \quad . \quad . \quad . \quad . \quad . \quad (11{:}192)$$ [40]

whence it follows that the quantized Hamiltonian of the holes (calculated for hole wave-functions) results from the Schroedinger form

$$\underline{\underline{\mathbf{H}}} = - \underline{\underline{\mathbf{U}}} + \underline{\underline{\chi}} + \underline{\underline{\mathbf{V}}} + C$$

$$= - \sum_r (\underline{\underline{\mathbf{H}_r}} + \underline{\underline{\varphi_r}}) + \sum_r \underline{\underline{\mu_r}} + \sum_{r<s} \underline{\underline{\mathbf{v}_{rs}}} + C \qquad \text{(summed over holes).} \quad (11{:}193)$$ [41]

Thus we may, in principle, approach a given problem either through the Hamiltonian of the *electrons*

$$\mathbf{H} = \mathbf{U} + \mathbf{V} = \sum_r (\mathbf{H}_r + \varphi_r) + \sum_{r<s} \mathbf{v}_{rs} \qquad \text{(summed over electrons),} \quad (11{:}194)$$

or the equivalent operator for the *holes* (11:193). In general, however, we would be dealing with an infinite number of holes, so that (as the reader has probably noted) the factor C which represents the total energy, including Coulomb and exchange interaction, for all cells filled, would be an infinite quantity, as would be *all* terms in the *hole* Hamiltonian (11:193). The utility of this formalism appears, however, when we go to approximate solutions in the sense of first-order perturbation theory. Before turning to this question we may make the general observation that the above hole Hamiltonian is consistent with the view that the holes behave as positive electrons for most purposes.[42]

[39] Cf. Chap. VIII, § 66.

[40] Note the difference in sign of the combination **B** − **A** as compared with the case for electrons.

[41] C represents the first (constant) term in (11:188), and the underlines again indicate that this is an equation in the (Schroedinger) variables of the holes.

[42] Compare (11:210) *et seq.* for a more precise statement of this correlation.

Let us now examine the modifications in the quantized Hamiltonians for electrons and holes (11:179, 188) which result when we consider only a limited number of distributions of electrons among cells or electronic states, e.g. the summations in (11:179) and (11:188) are now to be restricted to a definite number N of cells, and correspondingly (11:193) becomes a Schroedinger Hamiltonian in $(N - n)$ holes if n is the number of electrons in the original problem. The significance of this restriction is readily seen. Thus, if the unperturbed one-electron problem is characterized by the usual quantum numbers n_i, l_i, etc., the totality of electronic states naturally divides into subgroups (i) each consisting of $2(2l_i + 1)$ electronic states (= subshell) corresponding to the axial projections of spin and orbital momentum; and the number of electrons in the subgroup i is given by the eigenvalues of

$$\mathbf{N}_i = \sum_k (\, i \,)\, \mathbf{n}_k = \sum_k \mathbf{n}_k\, \delta\binom{k}{i}, \quad \ldots \ldots \quad (11{:}195)$$

where $\sum_k (i)$ indicates a summation restricted to the cells of the subgroup i, and $\delta\binom{k}{i}$ is unity if k is in the subgroup i, zero otherwise. If now we consider a limited number of distributions of electrons among cells such that $\mathbf{N}_i$, $\mathbf{N}_j$, etc., have *fixed* values, then these distributions correspond to the *states* of an atomic configuration in which there are N_i' equivalent electrons with principle and azimuthal quantum numbers n_i, l_i; N_j' equivalent $n_j l_j$ electrons, etc. However, if these *subgroup* occupation variables $\mathbf{N}_i$, etc., are to have definite *constant* values there must obviously be a strong restriction on the form of the quantized Hamiltonian (11:179), since a necessary condition is that

$$[\, \mathbf{H}, \mathbf{N}_i \,]_- = 0, \quad \ldots \ldots \ldots \quad (11{:}196)$$

which is not generally the case. From the commutation rules (11:90) it follows that

$$\left. \begin{aligned} [\, \boldsymbol{\xi}_k, \mathbf{n}_m \,]_- &= \boldsymbol{\xi}_m\, \delta\,(\, k, m\,), \\ [\, \boldsymbol{\xi}_k{}^*, \mathbf{n}_m \,]_- &= -\boldsymbol{\xi}_m{}^*\, \delta\,(\, k, m\,), \end{aligned} \right\} \quad \ldots \quad (11{:}197)$$

so that for any single-particle operator $\mathbf{U}$ contained in $\mathbf{H}$, the condition (11:196) becomes

$$\begin{aligned} [\, \mathbf{U}, \mathbf{N}_i \,]_- &= \sum_{k,l,m} [\, \boldsymbol{\xi}_k{}^*\boldsymbol{\xi}_l, \mathbf{n}_m \,]_-\, \delta\binom{m}{i} \langle\, k \mid \mathbf{u} \mid l \,\rangle \\ &= \sum_{k,l} \boldsymbol{\xi}_k{}^*\boldsymbol{\xi}_l \langle\, k \mid \mathbf{u} \mid l \,\rangle \left\{ \delta\binom{l}{i} - \delta\binom{k}{i} \right\} = 0, \quad . \quad (11{:}198) \end{aligned}$$

or

$$\langle\, k \mid \mathbf{u} \mid l \,\rangle \left\{ \delta\binom{l}{i} - \delta\binom{k}{i} \right\} = 0, \quad \ldots \quad (11{:}199)$$

which requires that we omit from $\sum_{k,l} \langle\, k \mid \mathbf{u} \mid l \,\rangle\, \boldsymbol{\xi}_k{}^*\boldsymbol{\xi}_l$ all terms except those for which k and l both lie in the *same subgroup*; or

$$\mathbf{U} = \sum_i \mathbf{U}_i = \sum_i \sum_{k,l} (\, i \,)\, \boldsymbol{\xi}_k{}^*\boldsymbol{\xi}_l \langle\, k \mid \mathbf{u} \mid l \,\rangle. \quad \ldots \quad (11{:}200)$$ [43]

[43] Here and in our further work the approximate nature of $\mathbf{U}_i$ and other operators will be evident from the context, so that we shall not need to indicate this fact explicitly.

The omitted terms obviously involve matrix elements connecting different electron configurations, since in the general case $\xi_k{}^*\xi_l$ operating on a vector $| n_1' \ldots \rangle$ removes an electron from the subgroup to which l refers, and places it in the subgroup to which k refers. It is also clear that the omission of these inter-group terms is simply the statement of the usual first-order perturbation theory, which considers together only those states (of the whole system) that originate from a single atomic configuration. Similarly, for any pair-operator $\mathbf{V}$, the condition (11:196) leads to

$$\begin{aligned}[\,\mathbf{V}, \mathbf{N}_i\,]_- &= \tfrac{1}{2}\sum_{klmnp} [\,\xi_k{}^*\xi_l{}^*\xi_n\xi_m, \mathbf{n}_p\,]_-\,\delta\binom{p}{i}\langle\, kl \mid \mathbf{v} \mid mn\,\rangle \\ &= -\tfrac{1}{2}\sum_{klmn}\langle\, kl \mid \mathbf{v} \mid mn\,\rangle\left\{\delta\binom{k}{i}+\delta\binom{l}{i}-\delta\binom{m}{i}-\delta\binom{n}{i}\right\}\xi_k{}^*\xi_l{}^*\xi_n\xi_m \\ &= 0, \qquad (11{:}201)\end{aligned}$$

and if this is to be zero we must retain in $\mathbf{V}$ only those terms for which m or n is in the subgroup (i) if k or l is in (i), or for which all four indices are in (i). Thus,

$$\mathbf{V} = \sum_i \mathbf{V}_{ii} + \sum_{i>j}\mathbf{V}_{ij}, \qquad (11{:}202a)$$

$$\left.\begin{aligned}\mathbf{V}_{ii} &= \tfrac{1}{2}\sum_{klmn}(\,i\,)\langle\, kl \mid \mathbf{v} \mid mn\,\rangle\,\xi_k{}^*\xi_l{}^*\xi_n\xi_m, \\ \mathbf{V}_{ij} &= \sum_{km}(\,i\,)\sum_{ln}(\,j\,)[\,\langle\, kl \mid \mathbf{v} \mid mn\,\rangle - \langle\, kl \mid \mathbf{v} \mid nm\,\rangle\,]\,\xi_k{}^*\xi_l{}^*\xi_n\xi_m.\end{aligned}\right\} \qquad (11{:}202b)$$

These considerations have an important corollary when we apply them to the total orbital momentum and spin vectors $\underline{\mathbf{L}}$, $\underline{\mathbf{S}}$; e.g. in the sense of (11:200) we write

$$\underline{\mathbf{L}} = \sum_i \underline{\mathbf{l}}_i = \sum_i\sum_{km}(\,i\,)\langle\, k \mid \underline{\mathbf{l}} \mid m\,\rangle\,\xi_k{}^*\xi_m, \qquad (11{:}203a)$$

$$\underline{\mathbf{S}} = \sum_i \underline{\mathbf{s}}_i = \sum_i\sum_{km}(\,i\,)\langle\, k \mid \underline{\mathbf{s}} \mid m\,\rangle\,\xi_k{}^*\xi_m, \qquad (11{:}203b)$$ [44]

and from the commutation rules (11:90) it follows that every component of $\underline{\mathbf{l}}_i$ commutes with every component of $\underline{\mathbf{l}}_j$ for $i \neq j$, and similarly for $\underline{\mathbf{s}}$. Moreover, every component of $\underline{\mathbf{s}}_i$ commutes with all components of $\underline{\mathbf{l}}_j$ for all j, and further

$$\underline{\mathbf{l}}_i \times \underline{\mathbf{l}}_i = \sum_{km}(\,i\,)\langle\, k \mid \underline{\mathbf{l}} \times \underline{\mathbf{l}} \mid m\,\rangle\,\xi_k{}^*\xi_m = i\hbar\underline{\mathbf{l}}_i, \qquad (11{:}204a)$$

$$\underline{\mathbf{s}}_i \times \underline{\mathbf{s}}_i = \sum_{km}(\,i\,)\langle\, k \mid \underline{\mathbf{s}} \times \mathbf{s} \mid m\,\rangle\,\xi_k{}^*\xi_m = i\hbar\underline{\mathbf{s}}_i, \qquad (11{:}204b)$$

which follow readily from the fact that for $\mathbf{A}$, $\mathbf{B}$ given by

$$\left.\begin{aligned}\mathbf{A} &= \sum_r \mathbf{a}(\,\mathbf{x}_r\,) = \sum_{kl}\langle\, k \mid \mathbf{a} \mid l\,\rangle\,\xi_k{}^*\xi_l, \\ \mathbf{B} &= \sum \mathbf{b}(\,\mathbf{x}_r\,) = \sum_{mn}\langle\, m \mid \mathbf{b} \mid n\,\rangle\,\xi_m{}^*\xi_n,\end{aligned}\right\} \qquad (11{:}205)$$

$$\begin{aligned}[\,\mathbf{A}, \mathbf{B}\,]_- &= \sum_{klmn}\langle\, k \mid \mathbf{a} \mid l\,\rangle\langle\, m \mid \mathbf{b} \mid n\,\rangle[\,\xi_k\xi_l, \xi_m{}^*\xi_n\,]_- \\ &= \sum_{klm}\{\,\langle\, k \mid \mathbf{a} \mid m\,\rangle\langle\, m \mid \mathbf{b} \mid l\,\rangle - \langle\, k \mid \mathbf{b} \mid m\,\rangle\langle\, m \mid \mathbf{a} \mid l\,\rangle\,\}\,\xi_k{}^*\xi_l \\ &= \sum_{kl}\langle\, k \mid [\,\mathbf{a}, \mathbf{b}\,]_- \mid l\,\rangle\,\xi_k{}^*\xi_l. \qquad (11{:}206)\end{aligned}$$

[44] Do not confuse the vector operators here, with the hole variable notation.

Thus we find that in this approximation the total $\underline{\mathbf{L}}$ and $\underline{\mathbf{S}}$ are decomposed into a set of independent vectors $\underline{\mathbf{l}}_1\underline{\mathbf{s}}_1$, $\underline{\mathbf{l}}_2\underline{\mathbf{s}}_2$, . . . , etc.; a pair $\underline{\mathbf{l}}_i\underline{\mathbf{s}}_i$ is associated with each subgroup (i), and obeys the usual commutation rules. In other words, in the usual vector picture we are justified in speaking of the orbital and spin momentum of the ith shell or subgroup, but we have not obtained anything corresponding to the individual momenta of the electrons within the subgroup. This results again because within the framework of the antisymmetry principle there is no possibility of distinguishing individual electrons.

Returning to the hole formalism we observe that the relations

$$\mathbf{L}_z = \sum_i \mathbf{l}_{zi} = \sum_i \sum_{km} (\, i\,) \langle\, k \mid \mathbf{l}_z \mid m \,\rangle\, \xi_k{}^*\xi_m = \sum_i \sum_k (\, i\,)\, \mathbf{n}_k m_{l_k}, \qquad (11{:}207a)$$

$$\mathbf{S}_z = \sum_i \mathbf{s}_{zi} = \sum_i \sum_{km} (\, i\,) \langle\, k \mid \mathbf{s}_z \mid m \,\rangle\, \xi_k{}^*\xi_m = \sum_i \sum_k (\, i\,)\, \mathbf{n}_k m_{s_k}, \qquad (11{:}207b)$$

transcribed to the hole variables, become

$$\underline{\underline{\mathbf{L}}}_z = \sum_i \underline{\underline{\mathbf{l}}}_{zi} = \sum_i \sum_k (\, i\,)\,(\, 1 - \underline{\underline{\mathbf{n}}}_k\,)\, m_{l_k} = -\sum_i \sum_k (\, i\,)\, \underline{\underline{\mathbf{n}}}_k m_{l_k}, \qquad (11{:}208a)$$

$$\underline{\underline{\mathbf{S}}}_z = \sum_i \underline{\underline{\mathbf{s}}}_{zi} = \sum_i \sum_k (\, i\,)\,(\, 1 - \underline{\underline{\mathbf{n}}}_k\,)\, m_{s_k} = -\sum_i \sum_k (\, i\,)\, \underline{\underline{\mathbf{n}}}_k m_{s_k}, \qquad (11{:}208b)$$

and on comparing (11:207–208), it follows that the correct M_L, M_S values of the atomic states are obtained if the m_l, m_s values associated with the holes are taken with a negative sign.[45] Moreover, it is clear that this result implicitly contains the well-known rule that the number and type of terms are the same for the atomic configurations $l_a{}^x l_b{}^y$ and $l_a{}^x l_b{}^{\tau - y}$, where l_a, $l_b = s, p, d, f \ldots$; $\tau = 2\,(\,2l_b + 1\,)$; and $y \leqslant \tau/2$.

From the result (11:208) and our previous inference that the holes behave as though positively charged, we can already see what changes must be made in the calculation of term values for $l_a{}^x l_b{}^y$ by Slater's method in order to obtain those of $l_a{}^x l_b{}^{\tau-y}$. However, it is perhaps worthwhile to make the procedure precise by considering explicitly the hole formulation of the problem of one or more almost filled shells plus other electrons. In particular, we may consider the case where the subgroups (arbitrarily) labelled 1 and 2 are almost filled, and for simplicity we consider only the terms of the quantized Hamiltonian referring to electrostatic interaction, namely (11:202).[46] It is only advantageous to transform the hole variables in the almost filled subgroups 1 and 2, but it will simplify our notation if we introduce the $\underline{\underline{\xi}}$'s throughout with the understanding that

$$\left.\begin{array}{l} \underline{\underline{\xi}}_k{}^* = \xi_k \text{ if } k \text{ is in subgroups 1 or 2,} \\ \underline{\underline{\xi}}_k{}^* = \xi_k{}^* \text{ if } k \textit{ is not} \text{ in subgroups 1 or 2.} \end{array}\right\} \quad . \quad . \quad . \qquad (11{:}209)$$

[45] E.g. if the hole in $np^5n'p$ corresponds to $m_l = -1$, $m_s = -\frac{1}{2}$, and $m_l = 1$, $m_s = \frac{1}{2}$ for $n'p$, then $M_L = 2$, $M_S = 1$ as required. This is in accord with the interpretation of hole wave-function as (electron) conjugate, since this means $e^{im\varphi} \to e^{-im\varphi}$.

[46] The spin-orbit terms are easily introduced if required, namely (11:200) with $\boldsymbol{\varphi}$ replacing $\mathbf{u}$.

Then all terms in $\mathbf{V} = \sum_i \mathbf{V}_{ii} + \sum_{i>j} \mathbf{V}_{ij}$ for which $i, j > 2$ are unaffected by the transformation, except for the trivial change in notation, and

$$\underline{\underline{\mathbf{V}}} = \sum_i \underline{\underline{\mathbf{V}}}_{ii} + \sum_{i>j} \underline{\underline{\mathbf{V}}}_{ij} \quad \text{(11:210)}$$

is defined by [cf. (11:183)]

$$\underline{\underline{\mathbf{V}}}_{ii} = \tfrac{1}{2} \sum_{klmn} (\,i\,) \underline{\underline{\langle\, kl \mid \mathbf{v} \mid mn \,\rangle}}\, \underline{\underline{\boldsymbol{\xi}}}_k^* \underline{\underline{\boldsymbol{\xi}}}_l^* \underline{\underline{\boldsymbol{\xi}}}_n \underline{\underline{\boldsymbol{\xi}}}_m \quad (\,i = 1,\,2\,), \quad \text{(11:211}a\text{)}$$ [47]

$$\underline{\underline{\mathbf{V}}}_{ii} = \tfrac{1}{2} \sum_{klmn} (\,i\,) \langle\, kl \mid \mathbf{v} \mid mn \,\rangle\, \underline{\underline{\boldsymbol{\xi}}}_k^* \underline{\underline{\boldsymbol{\xi}}}_l^* \underline{\underline{\boldsymbol{\xi}}}_n \underline{\underline{\boldsymbol{\xi}}}_m \quad (\,i > 2\,), \quad \text{(11:211}b\text{)}$$

$$\underline{\underline{\mathbf{V}}}_{ij} = \sum_{km} (i) \sum_{ln} (j)\, [\,\underline{\underline{\langle kl|\mathbf{v}|mn\rangle}} - \underline{\underline{\langle kl\,|\,\mathbf{v}\,|nm\rangle}}\,]\, \underline{\underline{\boldsymbol{\xi}}}_k^* \underline{\underline{\boldsymbol{\xi}}}_l^* \underline{\underline{\boldsymbol{\xi}}}_n \underline{\underline{\boldsymbol{\xi}}}_m \quad (i=2, j=1), \quad \text{(11:211}c\text{)}$$ [47]

$$\underline{\underline{\mathbf{V}}}_{ij} = -\sum_{km} (\,i\,) \sum_{ln} (\,j\,)\, [\,\langle\, kn \mid \mathbf{v} \mid ml \,\rangle - \langle\, kn \mid \mathbf{v} \mid lm \,\rangle\,]\, \underline{\underline{\boldsymbol{\xi}}}_k^* \underline{\underline{\boldsymbol{\xi}}}_l^* \underline{\underline{\boldsymbol{\xi}}}_n \underline{\underline{\boldsymbol{\xi}}}_m \quad (\,i > 2,\, j = 1, 2\,), \quad \text{(11:211}d\text{)}$$ [47]

$$\underline{\underline{\mathbf{V}}}_{ij} = \sum_{km} (\,i\,) \sum_{ln} (\,j\,)\, [\,\langle\, kl \mid \mathbf{v} \mid mn \,\rangle - \langle\, kl \mid \mathbf{v} \mid nm \,\rangle\,]\, \underline{\underline{\boldsymbol{\xi}}}_k^* \underline{\underline{\boldsymbol{\xi}}}_l^* \underline{\underline{\boldsymbol{\xi}}}_n \underline{\underline{\boldsymbol{\xi}}}_m \quad (i, j > 2). \quad \text{(11:211}e\text{)}$$

The complete equivalence of the second quantization to the usual coordinate space calculations with antisymmetric wave-functions guarantees that the matrix of any quantized operator $\mathbf{V}$ computed for the set of $\mathbf{n}$-space eigenvectors corresponding to a given configuration will be the same as calculated with the corresponding Slater determinants. Correspondingly, the matrix of $\underline{\underline{\mathbf{V}}}$ in the hole variables may be constructed with the same set of eigenvectors referred to the $\underline{\underline{\mathbf{n}}}$'s. From the fact that the $\underline{\underline{\boldsymbol{\xi}}}$'s bear the same relation to the $\underline{\underline{\mathbf{n}}}$'s as the $\boldsymbol{\xi}$'s to the $\mathbf{n}$'s, it follows that if $\underline{\underline{\mathbf{V}}}$ has the same form in the $\underline{\underline{\boldsymbol{\xi}}}$'s as $\mathbf{V}$ has in the $\boldsymbol{\xi}$'s, its matrix for a given electronic configuration (equivalently complementary configuration of holes) may be obtained by simple comparison with the matrix of $\mathbf{V}$ for the associated[48] configuration obtained by replacing the holes by electrons. Comparing (11:211) with (11:202), we see that the matrix components of electrostatic energy (11:211) correspond to the interpretation that the holes interact with each other and with other electrons as though they were positively charged. Hence, the calculation of electrostatic energies for a configuration described in terms of holes and other electrons (almost filled shells plus electrons in other shells) proceeds in the usual way except that the Coulomb and exchange integrals involving a hole and an electron are taken with

[47] In these expressions we have omitted terms corresponding to the electrostatic energies of closed shells, interactions of electrons with closed shells and closed shells with one another, since these only contribute constant factors in the final result. Thus, in (d) there is another term

$$\sum_{km} (\,i\,) \sum_{l} (\,j\,)\, [\,\langle\, kl \mid \mathbf{v} \mid ml \,\rangle - \langle\, kl \mid \mathbf{v} \mid lm \,\rangle\,]\, \underline{\underline{\boldsymbol{\xi}}}_k^* \underline{\underline{\boldsymbol{\xi}}}_m$$

representing the interaction of the electrons in subgroup i with the closed shell j and, similarly, the omitted terms in (a) and (c) may be obtained by inspection from our previous result (11:183), e.g. for (a) they are

$$\tfrac{1}{2} \sum_{k,l} (\,i\,)\, [\,\underline{\underline{\langle\, kl \mid \mathbf{v} \mid kl \,\rangle}} - \underline{\underline{\langle\, kl \mid \mathbf{v} \mid lk \,\rangle}}\,] + \sum_{klm} (\,i\,)\, [\,\underline{\underline{\langle\, km \mid \mathbf{v} \mid ml \,\rangle}} - \underline{\underline{\langle\, km \mid \mathbf{v} \mid lm \,\rangle}}\,]\, \underline{\underline{\boldsymbol{\xi}}}_k^* \underline{\underline{\boldsymbol{\xi}}}_l.$$

[48] E.g. the matrix of $\underline{\underline{\mathbf{V}}}$ for the configuration p^5p, i.e. $(p)p$ [where (p) denotes a p hole] is obtained by comparison with the matrix of $\mathbf{V}$ for the associated configuration pp.

a negative sign.[49] We must also keep in mind that in applying the diagonal sum procedure the M_L, M_S values are given by the negatives of the values of the holes, *plus* those of the electrons [cf. (11:208)].

To illustrate we may consider the configuration p^5p [$=(p)p$] and its associate pp; and listing first the m_l, m_s values of the hole, the values of M_L, M_S are given by (cf. Table 10.2, p. 192) Table 11.1. From the tables of S.C.S. coefficients

TABLE 11.1

	p^5p	M_S = 1	M_S = 0
M_L	2	(-1^-1^+)	$(-1^-1^-)\ (-1^+1^+)$
	1	$(-1^-0^+)\ (0^-1^+)$	$(-1^-0^-)\ (0^-1^-)\ (-1^+0^+)\ (0^+1^+)$
	0	$(-1^- -1^+)\ (0^-0^+)$ (1^-1^+)	$(-1^- -1^-)\ (0^-0^-)\ (1^-1^-)$ $(-1^+ -1^+)\ (0^+0^+)\ (1^+1^+)$

(Appendix II) we find

$$\left.\begin{aligned} ({}^3D) &= -J\,(p\pi_-, p\pi) = -F_0 - F_2, \\ ({}^1D) + ({}^3D) &= -2J\,(p\pi_-, p\pi) + 2K\,(p\pi_-, p\pi) \\ &= -2F_0 - 2F_2 + 12G_2, \\ ({}^3D) + ({}^3P) &= -J\,(p\pi_-, p\sigma) - J\,(p\pi, p\sigma) = -2F_0 + 4F_2, \\ ({}^3S) + ({}^3P) + ({}^3D) &= -[\,J\,(p\pi_-, p\pi) + J\,(p\sigma, p\sigma) + J\,(p\pi, p\pi)\,] \\ &= -3F_0 - 6F_2; \end{aligned}\right\} \quad (11{:}212a)$$ [50]

and similarly,

$$\left.\begin{aligned} &({}^3P) + ({}^3D) + ({}^1D) + ({}^1P) = -4F_0 + 8F_2 + 12G_2, \\ &({}^3S) + (3P) + ({}^1S) + ({}^1P) + ({}^1D) = -6F_0 - 12F_2 + 6G_0 + 12G_2. \\ &({}^3D) = -F_0 - F_2. \qquad ({}^1D) = -F_0 - F_2 + 12G_2. \\ &({}^3P) = -F_0 + 5F_2. \qquad ({}^1P) = -F_0 + 5F_2. \\ &({}^3S) = -F_0 - 10F_2. \qquad ({}^1S) = -F_0 - 10F_2 + 6G_0. \end{aligned}\right\} \quad (11{:}212b)$$

It is a simple corollary to these considerations that, apart from a constant, the terms of the configuration $l_b^{\tau-y}$ are the same as those of l_b^y, i.e. the electrostatic energies

[49] A further difference occurs for non-diagonal terms since according to (11:211*d*) the interaction $\langle kl \mid \mathrm{v} \mid mn \rangle - \langle kl \mid \mathrm{v} \mid nm \rangle$ which would occur for two electrons or two holes is to be replaced by $\langle kn \mid \mathrm{v} \mid ml \rangle - \langle kn \mid \mathrm{v} \mid lm \rangle$.

[50] It should be noted that the Coulomb contributions (i.e. F_k's) to the terms of p^5p are obtained from those of pp by mere sign reversal, but the exchange contributions (G_k's) must be computed for the singlets of p^5p for which, at most, they are non-zero. Further examples may be found in the article by JOHNSON, *loc. cit.*, or *T A.S.*, Chap. XIII.

are the same. The procedure of term calculations for configurations involving almost filled shells may be somewhat simplified if we write (11:208a, b) as

$$\underline{\underline{\mathbf{L}}}_z = -\sum_i \sum_k (\,i\,)\, \underline{\underline{\mathbf{n}}}_k m_{l_k} = \sum_i \sum_k (\,i\,)\, \underline{\underline{\mathbf{n}}}_k \underline{\underline{m}}_{l_k}, \qquad (11{:}213a)$$

$$\underline{\underline{\mathbf{S}}}_z = -\sum_i \sum_k (\,i\,)\, \underline{\underline{\mathbf{n}}}_k m_{s_k} = \sum_i \sum_k (\,i\,)\, \underline{\underline{\mathbf{n}}}_k \underline{\underline{m}}_{s_k}, \qquad (11{:}213b)$$

so that we formally consider that the m_l, m_s values of a hole are the negatives of the values labelling the cell which the hole may be said to occupy. With this convention the M_L, M_S values for $l_a^x l_b^{\tau-y}$ $[= l_a^x(l_b^y)]$, where (l_b^y) indicates holes, are obtained in the ordinary way and the M_L, M_S table is in fact just that for $l_a^x l_b^y$. Then Slater's rule that in the diagonal sum the exchange integrals $K(i, j)$ have the coefficient -1 if the spins are parallel, and zero if antiparallel, remains unchanged for hole pairs and electron pairs, but for a hole-electron pair the coefficient must be taken as 0 for spins parallel, and $+1$ for spins antiparallel. Furthermore, the exchange integral in this case is $K^+(i, j) = K(n_i l_i m_{l_i};\, n_j l_j - m_{l_j})$, and of course the corresponding Coulomb integral $J(i, j)$ must be taken with a negative sign.

The Dirac vector model affords a particularly simple and concise formulation of these results; namely, that apart from a common additive constant, the terms belonging to $l_a^x l_b^{\tau-y}$ are given by the same calculation as for $l_a^x l_b^y$ if in the latter we replace $J(i, j) - \frac{1}{2}(1 + 4\underline{\mathbf{s}}_i \cdot \underline{\mathbf{s}}_j)K(i, j)$ by $-J(i, j) + \frac{1}{2}(1 - 4\underline{\mathbf{s}}_i \cdot \underline{\mathbf{s}}_j)K^+(i, j)$ whenever i refers to an electron in the subgroup a and j to one in b, or vice versa. No changes are made if both i and j refer to the same subgroup.[51] If now we apply this rule twice to the configuration $l_a^{\rho-x} l_b^{\tau-y}$ $(\rho = 4l_a + 2)$, we may infer that its energy levels are the same as those of $l_a^x l_b^y$ apart from a constant, since the reduction of $l_a^{\rho-x} l_b^{\tau-y}$ to $l_a^x l_b^{\tau-y}$ introduces a sign change which is cancelled by the subsequent reduction of $l_a^x l_b^{\tau-y}$ to $l_a^x l_b^y$.

[51] Cf. * Van Vleck, *loc. cit.*

CHAPTER XII

The S-Matrix Theory

§ 101. Ultimate Observables

It has become almost conventional to speak of quantum mechanics as a theory of only *directly observable* quantities, and, indeed, that physical description should be so delimited was essentially the argument advanced by Heisenberg in support of the logical jump from the classical to the matrical representation of atomic systems—rejecting thereby such concepts as orbits, etc., as unobservable and hence operationally meaningless. There is no need to belabour the fact that a literal adherence to this viewpoint cannot now be supported, since even so fundamental a quantity as the Schroedinger wave-function is only part of the mathematical scaffolding and does not *per se* correspond to anything observable. Apart from this point, to which we shall return, the difficulties in field theories of elementary particles and nuclear forces—the much-discussed divergencies—have led various investigators to re-examine critically the whole meaning of our basic kinematical, causal, and space-time concepts; *inter alia*, in relation to the possibility of the existence of a fundamental length limiting the applicability of present quantal concepts in much the same way that the existence of the action-quantum limits the applicability of classical concepts. It is outside the scope of our treatment to discuss the field-theoretical aspects, nor is this necessary to a qualitative consideration of logical difficulties in quantum mechanics.

As noted in the preface, quantum mechanics is essentially a correspondence principle hybridization of classical mechanics. The quantization consists of setting up a classical description of a dynamical system and then transcribing to new equations within the framework of quantum theory, such that the classical equations are recovered in the limit of large quantum numbers. It is clear that the prescription is not unique, since there may be several quantum-theoretical equations corresponding to a given classical picture, and conversely, several classical pictures corresponding to the macroscopic limit of the quantal description—although in non-relativistic extra-nuclear processes the prescription has been generally successful.

It seems doubtful that such concepts as position of a particle, wave-function at a given space-time point, etc., can appear in a proper future theory—if there exists a fundamental length of the order of magnitude $l \sim 10^{-13}$ cm. (the so-called electron radius), as is suggested, for example, by the observation that a mass cannot be expressed in terms of just the two universal constants $\hbar$ and c. The probability of finding a particle at a certain point, if at all meaningful, can then scarcely be independent of the *means* by which the position is measured—as in quantum mechanics. The measuring particles (e.g. electrons, γ-rays, etc.) themselves will have an *effective* size of the same order, so that the results of such an experiment cannot be translated into an objective probability distribution for the measured particle.

From a different point of view, a difficulty of current theory appears in the concept of state, or, in the language of Dirac, maximal specification. According to quantum theory, the experimental procedure to determine the state of a system consists of making the maximum number of compatible measurements. From this information, the future development of the state also follows by the time-dependent Schroedinger equation. However, if the system has a very large (eventually infinite) number of degrees of freedom, this requires an infinite number of observations —which does not seem reasonable.

Both arguments, the first due largely to Heisenberg,[1] and the second to von Neumann,[2] imply (though for different reasons) that no *total* energy operator will appear in a future theory. The immediate questions are then how the Schroedinger equation is to be modified or replaced, and which dynamical variables may be expected to appear, in such a theory. The S-matrix theory of Heisenberg, which, as previously emphasized, has not yet found a basis independent of the Hamiltonian formalism, is one attempt to answer these questions.

With regard to modification of the Schroedinger equation, one important theorem can be immediately stated: If *all* bounded operators are assumed to correspond to observables, the Schroedinger equation must obtain. The proof is essentially as given by von Neumann (*ibid.*) in another connection.

In the usual quantum theory, we have

$$\frac{d}{dt}\,|\,;t\,\rangle = -i\mathbf{A}\,|\,;t\,\rangle \qquad (\,\mathbf{A} = \mathbf{H}/\hbar\,), \qquad . \; . \; . \; . \; . \quad (12{:}1)$$

or

$$|\,;t\,\rangle = e^{-i\mathbf{A}t}\,|\,;o\,\rangle,$$

if $\mathbf{H}$ is independent of the time, and for an observable ξ,

$$\xi_t = e^{i\mathbf{A}t}\xi_0 e^{-i\mathbf{A}t}. \qquad . \; . \; . \; . \; . \; . \; . \; . \; . \quad (12{:}2)$$

These give an *isomorphism* of the system on itself of the type called *inner* ($\xi \rightarrow \xi_\tau = \mathbf{U}\xi\mathbf{U}^{-1}$, where $\mathbf{U}$ is a fixed unitary operator).

A system left undisturbed must undergo an automorphism, the observable $\xi = \xi_0$ becoming, in the course of time, the observable ξ_t—with the meaning that we do not make the observation ξ now, but wait a time t and then make it. Denote this isomorphism by

$$\xi_t = \mathbf{O}_t\xi_0, \qquad . \; . \; . \; . \; . \; . \; . \; . \; . \quad (12{:}3a)$$

and, since there is no difference between the time o and the time s, we have

$$\xi_{t+s} = \mathbf{O}_t\xi_s. \qquad . \; . \; . \; . \; . \; . \; . \; . \; . \quad (12{:}3b)$$

Hence, $\mathbf{O}_{t+s} = \mathbf{O}_t\mathbf{O}_s$, which is to say the $\mathbf{O}_t$ form a one-parameter group.

[1] HEISENBERG, W.: *Zeits. f. Phys.*, **120**, 513, 673 (1943); Cambridge Lectures (1947).
[2] VON NEUMANN, J.: Princeton Lectures, 1936.

If the $\mathbf{O}_t$ are inner isomorphisms,

$$\xi_t = \mathbf{O}_t\xi_0 = \mathbf{U}_t\xi_0\mathbf{U}_t^{-1} \qquad (\mathbf{U}_t \text{ unitary}), \qquad (12{:}4)$$

and it follows that

$$\mathbf{U}_{t+s} = c_{ts}\mathbf{U}_t\mathbf{U}_s \qquad (c_{ts} \text{ constant}), \qquad (12{:}5a)$$

whence (apart from a possible constant factor)

$$\mathbf{U}_t = e^{i\mathbf{A}t} \qquad (\mathbf{A} \text{ a fixed operator}). \qquad (12{:}5b)$$

Thus, for observables

$$\xi_t = e^{i\mathbf{A}t}\xi_0 e^{-i\mathbf{A}t}, \qquad (12{:}6)$$

$$\frac{d}{dt}\xi_t = i(\mathbf{A}\xi_t - \xi_t\mathbf{A}), \qquad (12{:}7)$$

and, from correspondence arguments, it is difficult to identify **A** with anything but the total energy operator. *The usual equations of motion, including the Schroedinger form, depend essentially on all isomorphisms* $\mathbf{O}_t$ *being inner isomorphisms.* It can be shown mathematically that the system of *all* bounded operators possesses only inner isomorphisms.[3]

In agreement with the previous physical arguments, it follows that the class of observables in the hypothesized *future* theory would have to be much more limited than in present theory—if the Schroedinger equation is not to appear. There is much to be said for a programme of reduction, or elimination, of redundant concepts, that is, quantities which themselves do not correspond to anything observable or which convey operationally meaningless information—but it is not obvious that this will not result in a scaffolding too bare to stand by itself. This appears to be the present status of the S-matrix theory.

If we assume that the Hamiltonian will lose its present dominant position (and with it, the simple connection with classical systems),[4] the problem becomes the specification of the new function(s) which will define atomic systems, or, more generally, the quantities which will be *observable* in the new theory. There is, of course, no clear-cut answer to this problem, although one may reasonably assume that any quantity not intimately related to the problem of small distances (more specifically, a minimum length) may be considered as one of the *ultimate observables.* Such quantities are: the energy and momentum of a free particle, the cross-section of any collision process, the discrete energy levels of atomic systems in closed stationary states, the decay constants of radioactive systems.

When the Hamiltonian of the system is known, these quantities can be calcu-

[3] The development here is seen to be a more formal statement of the results of §§ 25, 26.

[4] The theory must go over into the usual formalism for dimensions large compared to $l \sim 10^{-13}$ cm. The whole question of correspondence derives from the existence of the long-range forces, and would not appear if only short-range forces, of the nuclear type, occurred in Nature. As emphasized by Bohr, the numerical value of $e^2/\hbar c$ (coupling with electromagnetic field) plays a decisive role in this correspondence, since, if $e^2/\hbar c$ were of the order of unity, the atomic scale would be much smaller, the atomic spectra would be replaced by something different (radiation forces of the same order as all others), and there would be no classical picture requiring any correspondence arguments.

lated by the usual methods of quantum mechanics. However, collision cross-sections are exhibited more directly in terms of the matrix elements of a certain unitary matrix $\mathscr{S}$, which depends on the Hamiltonian in a rather complicated way. It is Heisenberg's basic assumption that the role of the Hamiltonian, in the description of atomic systems, will be taken over by this *characteristic* or *scattering* matrix $\mathscr{S}$, or by a Hermitian matrix η, the *phase* matrix, defined [5] by $\mathscr{S} = e^{i\eta}$.

§ 102.* Scattering Formalism—Definition and Properties of S.

For the purpose of defining the elementary properties of the S-matrix, it suffices to consider the stationary description of the collision process between two particles, which for simplicity are taken as spinless and distinguishable. Let $\underline{\mathbf{k}}_i$ denote the momentum of the ith particle, $W_i = \sqrt{(\kappa^2 + \underline{\mathbf{k}}_i^2)}$ the corresponding *relativistic* kinetic energy, κ the rest mass, and $\underline{\mathbf{K}}$, $\mathbf{W}$, the total momentum and kinetic energy of the particles—all in natural units, i.e. $\hbar$ and $c = 1$.

The wave-function belonging to a definite state in the continuous spectrum can be characterized by the momenta $\underline{k}_i'$ of the incoming plane wave, and, since the wave-function itself depends on the momenta $\underline{k}_i''$ of the particles, it may be denoted by the symbol $\langle\, ''\underline{k} \mid \Psi \mid {'\underline{k}}\,\rangle$. Considered for all possible collisions with varying initial momenta $'\underline{k}$ $(= \underline{k}_1', \underline{k}_2')$, these functions define a wave-matrix or momentum representation of a wave-operator $\mathbf{\Psi}$. In the absence of interaction, $\mathbf{\Psi} = \mathbf{I}$, since the initial set of plane waves in configuration space corresponds to

$$\langle\, ''\underline{k} \mid \Psi \mid {'\underline{k}}\,\rangle = \delta\,(\,\underline{k}_1'' - \underline{k}_1'\,)\,\delta\,(\,\underline{k}_2'' - \underline{k}_2'\,). \quad . \quad . \quad . \quad (12:8)$$

However, to obtain a solution of the corresponding Schroedinger equation, with interaction, an outgoing wave (or wave-operator $\mathbf{T}$) must be added, which, as shown by Dirac (*loc. cit.*), must have a special singularity at the point $\underline{K}'' = \underline{K}'$, $W'' = W'$, since momentum and energy must be conserved for the outgoing particles. Thus, with the Hamiltonian $\mathbf{H} = \mathbf{W} + \mathbf{V}$, the Schroedinger equation reads:

$$\mathbf{\Psi W} - \mathbf{W\Psi} = \mathbf{V\Psi}, \quad . \quad . \quad . \quad . \quad . \quad . \quad . \quad (12:9a)$$

or, in the momentum representation,

$$(\,W' - W''\,)\,\langle\, ''\underline{k} \mid \Psi \mid {'\underline{k}}\,\rangle = \langle\, ''\underline{k} \mid \mathbf{V\Psi} \mid {'\underline{k}}\,\rangle. \quad . \quad . \quad (12:9b)$$

If now we introduce

$$\mathbf{\Psi} = \mathbf{I} + \mathbf{T}, \quad . \quad . \quad . \quad . \quad . \quad . \quad . \quad . \quad . \quad . \quad (12:10)$$

$$\mathbf{U} = -2\pi i \mathbf{V\Psi}, \quad . \quad . \quad . \quad . \quad . \quad . \quad . \quad . \quad . \quad (12:11)$$

[5] In other words, it is implied that *all* observable quantities are obtainable from the asymptotic behaviour of (current) wave-functions at large relative separation of the particles involved. It is not clear that this can always be fulfilled, even in principle. Cf. Pauli, W.: *Meson Theory* (Interscience, New York, 1946).

* Møller, C.: *K. danske vidensk. Sels.*, **23**, No. 1 (1945); **24**, No. 19 (1946). Heisenberg, W.: *Zeits. f. Phys.*, **120**, 513, 673 (1943); *Zeits. f. Naturforschung*, **1**, 608 (1946). Ma, S. T.: *Phys. Rev.*, **69**, 668 (1946); **71**, 195 (1947). Jost, R.: *Helv. Phys. Acta*, **20**, 256 (1947). Ter Haar, D.: *Physica*, **12**, 509 (1946).

we obtain from (12.9)

$$(W' - W'') \langle {}''\underline{k} \,|\, \mathbf{T} \,|\, {}'\underline{k} \rangle = -\frac{1}{2\pi i} \langle {}''\underline{k} \,|\, \mathbf{U} \,|\, {}'\underline{k} \rangle, \qquad (12{:}12a)$$

and solving for **T**,

$$\langle {}''\underline{k} \,|\, \mathbf{T} \,|\, {}'\underline{k} \rangle = \frac{1}{2\pi i} \langle {}''\underline{k} \,|\, \mathbf{U} \,|\, {}'\underline{k} \rangle \left\{ \frac{1}{W'' - W'} + i\pi\delta (W'' - W') \right\}. \qquad (12{:}12b)^{6}$$

With the notation

$$\delta_{\pm} (W'' - W') = \tfrac{1}{2}\delta (W'' - W') \pm \frac{1}{2\pi i\, (W'' - W')}, \qquad (12{:}13)$$

this becomes

$$\langle {}''\underline{k} \,|\, \mathbf{T} \,|\, {}'\underline{k} \rangle = \delta_{+} (W'' - W') \langle {}''\underline{k} \,|\, \mathbf{U} \,|\, {}'\underline{k} \rangle. \qquad (12{:}14)$$

From (12:11) and its adjoint we obtain

$$\mathbf{\Psi}^{*}\mathbf{U} + \mathbf{U}^{*}\mathbf{\Psi} = 0, \qquad (12{:}15a)$$

or

$$\mathbf{U} + \mathbf{U}^{*} + \mathbf{T}^{*}\mathbf{U} + \mathbf{U}^{*}\mathbf{T} = 0, \qquad (12{:}15b)$$

which represents a general condition on the wave-matrices; and noting (12.14), this has the representative form

$$\langle {}''\underline{k} \,|\, \mathbf{U} + \mathbf{U}^{*} \,|\, {}'\underline{k} \rangle + \int \langle {}''\underline{k} \,|\, \mathbf{U}^{*} \,|\, {}'''\underline{k} \rangle\, d'''\underline{k} \,|\, \langle {}'''\underline{k} \,|\, \mathbf{U} \,|\, {}'\underline{k} \rangle$$
$$\left\{ \delta_{+} (W'' - W''') + \delta_{+} (W''' - W') \right\} = 0. \qquad (12{:}16)$$

Now define a matrix **R** by

$$\langle {}''\underline{k} \,|\, \mathbf{R} \,|\, {}'\underline{k} \rangle = \delta (W'' - W') \langle {}''\underline{k} \,|\, \mathbf{U} \,|\, {}'\underline{k} \rangle \qquad (12{:}17)$$
$$= \delta (\underline{K}'' - \underline{K}')\, \delta (W'' - W') \langle {}''\underline{k} \,|\, \mathbf{U}_{\underline{K}'W'} \,|\, {}'\underline{k} \rangle,$$

where $\langle {}''k \,|\, \mathbf{U}_{K'W'} \,|\, {}'k \rangle$ denotes a so-called submatrix on the energy shell, corresponding to fixed values $\underline{K}'$ and W' for the total energy and momentum.[7] From the definition of the δ_{+} function, it follows that when (12:16) is multiplied by $\delta(W'' - W')$ the integral will contain a factor $\delta(W'' - W''')\delta(W''' - W')$, so that with (12:17) we get the symbolic equation

$$\mathbf{R} + \mathbf{R}^{*} + \mathbf{R}^{*}\mathbf{R} = 0, \qquad (12{:}18)$$

or

$$\mathbf{S}^{*}\mathbf{S} = \mathbf{I}, \qquad (12{:}19)$$

where $\mathbf{S} = \mathbf{I} + \mathbf{R}$. The operator (matrix) **S** may be considered as a transformation

[6] The coefficient $i\pi$, as shown by Dirac, arises from the physical requirement that **T** represent *only* outgoing waves, and it is understood that an integral over W'' containing the singular part $1/W'' - W'$ is to be taken as the Cauchy principal value.

[7] Elements of the wave-operators **Ψ**, **T**, **U** must have the form

$$\langle {}''\underline{k} \,|\, \mathbf{U} \,|\, {}'\underline{k} \rangle = \delta (\underline{K}'' - \underline{K}') \langle {}''\underline{k} \,|\, \mathbf{U}_{\underline{K}'} \,|\, {}'\underline{k} \rangle,$$

corresponding to a submatrix for a fixed value $\underline{K}' = \underline{K}''$ of the total momentum, which is conserved.

$I + IR^{*} + RI + R^{*}R = I$

function which transforms from the momentum variables before the collision to the same variables after collision.[8] In accord with this interpretation, (12:19) *implies* that $\mathbf{S}$ is unitary, but $\mathbf{SS}^* = \mathbf{I}$ does not follow, since we do not know that $\mathbf{S}^{-1}$ exists. To prove that $\mathbf{S}$ is unitary, we need only show that $\mathbf{R}$ and $\mathbf{R}^*$ commute, as follows on repeating the above considerations for that solution of the Schroedinger equation (12:9) in which the outgoing waves $\mathbf{T}$ are replaced by incoming waves (cf. Møller, *loc. cit.*). Møller also obtains the result:

$$\mathbf{\Psi}^*\mathbf{\Psi} = \mathbf{I}. \qquad \qquad (12:20)$$

This result simply shows that the representatives $\langle\, ''\underline{k} \mid \mathbf{\Psi} \mid '\underline{k}\,\rangle$, considered as functions of $''\underline{k}$ for fixed $'\underline{k}$, are normalized eigenfunctions of the Hamiltonian $\mathbf{H} = \mathbf{W} + \mathbf{V}$ belonging to the continuous eigenvalues W'. The reverse product will generally not equal unity, because these wave-functions do not include the discrete stationary states and therefore do not form a complete-orthonormal set.[9]

Ordinarily, a unitary operator or matrix in quantum mechanics does not lead to an eigenvalue problem and cannot be diagonalized, since its rows and columns refer to different types and numbers of states. However, in the case of the S-matrix, the states are homologous, referring, as they do, to the momenta of the incoming and outgoing particles, so that $\mathbf{S}$ can be diagonalized. *In principle* the procedure consists of combining wave-functions of the type (12:10), corresponding to a given energy, in such a way that, for the resulting wave, the outgoing wave has the same form as the incoming wave, apart from a phase[10] factor $S' = e^{i\eta'}$, which is the eigenvalue of $\mathbf{S}$. As remarked by Heisenberg, this is essentially the usual procedure in central-field scattering problems where one has simply to transform from plane to spherical waves, the phase differences between outgoing and incoming waves, for the various spherical harmonics, determining the effective scattering cross-sections.

The procedure for diagonalizing $\mathbf{S}$ may be placed on a systematic basis by introducing the concept of *constants of collision*, which are dynamical variables that commute with $\mathbf{S}$ and $\mathbf{W}$, and have the same values (or mean values) in the initial and final states. Thus, the collision constants play a role analogous to that of the constants of the motion in the ordinary theory, but, since $\mathbf{S}$ is invariant under a larger group of transformations than the Hamiltonian, there is *a priori* a larger number of such quantities.[11] For example, as seen from the factor $\delta(\underline{K}'' - \underline{K}')\,\delta(W'' - W')$ in (12:17), the total momentum and kinetic energy $\underline{\mathbf{K}}$, W, commute with $\mathbf{R}$ and, therefore, with $\mathbf{S}$. Further details and applications may be found in the papers cited.

The connection between the scattering cross-sections and the matrix elements of $\mathbf{S}$ is also studied in these papers, so that we shall here consider only the connection with the probability distribution. The wave-function $\langle\, ''\underline{k} \mid \mathbf{\Psi} \mid '\underline{k}\,\rangle\, e^{-iW't}$ is a solution

[8] More precisely, transforms from the asymptotic form of the incoming part to the asymptotic form of the outgoing part of the stationary state.

[9] When $\mathbf{\Psi}$ is unitary, $\mathbf{\Psi}^{-1}$ exists, and from (12:9a) it follows that $\mathbf{H} = \mathbf{\Psi W \Psi}^{-1}$, showing that $\mathbf{H}$ and $\mathbf{W}$ have the same eigenvalues. Thus, $\mathbf{\Psi\Psi}^* = \mathbf{I}$ only for systems which have no closed states.

[10] Because the phase of a wave is relativistically invariant, it may be inferred that the same holds for the eigenvalues of $\boldsymbol{\eta}$ (and $\mathbf{S}$).

[11] The S-matrix (that is, with respect to its eigenvalues) is invariant under space-time translations and rotations. This is directly related to its connection with the scattering cross-sections which must, of course, be independent of the particular Lorentz frame.

of the time-dependent Schroedinger equation, so that the wave-function

$$\langle\, ''\underline{k} \mid \mathbf{\Psi} \mid '\underline{k}\,\rangle^{\dagger} = \langle\, ''\underline{k} \mid \mathbf{\Psi} \mid '\underline{k}\,\rangle\, e^{i(W''-W')t},$$

arising from a simple change of the arbitrary phases in the $\underline{\mathbf{k}}$-representation (cf. § 26), satisfies the wave-equation

$$i\frac{d}{dt}\langle\, ''\underline{k} \mid \mathbf{\Psi} \mid '\underline{k}\,\rangle^{\dagger} = \int \langle\, ''\underline{k} \mid \mathbf{V} \mid '''\underline{k}\,\rangle\, d'''\underline{k}\, e^{i(W''-W''')t} \langle\, '''\underline{k} \mid \mathbf{\Psi} \mid '\underline{k}\,\rangle^{\dagger}, \tag{12:21}$$

$$i\frac{d}{dt}\langle\, ''\underline{k} \mid \mathbf{\Psi} \mid '\underline{k}\,\rangle^{\dagger} = \int \langle\, ''\underline{k} \mid \mathbf{V} \mid '''\underline{k}\,\rangle^{\dagger}\, d'''\underline{k}\, \langle\, '''\underline{k} \mid \mathbf{\Psi} \mid '\underline{k}\,\rangle^{\dagger}, \tag{12:22}$$

with $\langle\, ''\underline{k} \mid \mathbf{V} \mid '''\underline{k}\,\rangle^{\dagger} = \langle\, ''\underline{k} \mid \mathbf{V} \mid '''\underline{k}\,\rangle e^{i(W''-W''')t}$. All the matrix equations established in the original $\underline{\mathbf{k}}$-representation must also hold with the new choice of phases, so that, noting (12:11), the above reads:

$$\frac{d}{dt}\langle\, ''\underline{k} \mid \mathbf{\Psi} \mid '\underline{k}\,\rangle^{\dagger} = \frac{1}{i}\langle\, ''\underline{k} \mid \mathbf{V\Psi} \mid '\underline{k}\,\rangle^{\dagger} = \frac{1}{2\pi}\langle\, ''\underline{k} \mid \mathbf{U} \mid '\underline{k}\,\rangle^{\dagger}. \tag{12:23}$$

The relative probability, per unit range, that the particles of the system have their momenta in the neighbourhood $''\underline{k} - ''\underline{k} + d''k$ for the stated initial conditions, is

$$P(\,''\underline{k}\,) = |\langle\, ''\underline{k} \mid \mathbf{\Psi} \mid '\underline{k}\,\rangle|^2 = \langle\, '\underline{k} \mid \mathbf{\Psi}^* \mid ''\underline{k}\,\rangle^{\dagger} \langle\, ''\underline{k} \mid \mathbf{\Psi} \mid '\underline{k}\,\rangle^{\dagger}, \tag{12:24}$$

and from (12:23) we find

$$\frac{dP}{dt}(\,''k\,) = \frac{1}{2\pi}\left\{\langle\, '\underline{k} \mid \mathbf{\Psi}^* \mid ''\underline{k}\,\rangle^{\dagger} \langle\, ''\underline{k} \mid \mathbf{U} \mid '\underline{k}\,\rangle^{\dagger} + \langle\, '\underline{k} \mid \mathbf{U}^* \mid ''\underline{k}\,\rangle^{\dagger} \langle\, ''\underline{k} \mid \mathbf{\Psi} \mid '\underline{k}\,\rangle^{\dagger}\right\}. \tag{12:25}$$

Substituting from the equation [cf. (12:10), (12:14)]

$$\langle\, ''\underline{k} \mid \mathbf{\Psi} \mid '\underline{k}\,\rangle^{\dagger} = \langle\, ''\underline{k} \mid \mathbf{I} \mid '\underline{k}\,\rangle^{\dagger} + \delta_{+}(\,W'' - W'\,)\,\langle\, ''\underline{k} \mid \mathbf{U} \mid '\underline{k}\,\rangle^{\dagger} \tag{12:26}$$

and adjoint, equation (12:25) reduces to

$$\frac{dP}{dt}(\,''\underline{k}\,) = \frac{1}{2\pi}\Big\{\langle\, ''\underline{k} \mid \mathbf{I} \mid '\underline{k}\,\rangle \left[\langle\, ''\underline{k} \mid \mathbf{U} \mid '\underline{k}\,\rangle + \langle\, '\underline{k} \mid \mathbf{U}^* \mid ''\underline{k}\,\rangle\right] + \delta(\,W'' - W'\,)\,\langle\, '\underline{k} \mid \mathbf{U}^* \mid ''\underline{k}\,\rangle \langle\, ''\underline{k} \mid \mathbf{U} \mid '\underline{k}\,\rangle\Big\}. \tag{12:27}$$

We now introduce a new representation in which the total momentum $\underline{\mathbf{K}}$, the total energy **W**, and two other variables **x** (*which may be angular coordinates*) replace the $\underline{\mathbf{k}}$'s. Then, as noted in Section 12, the representatives of any operator in the two representations are related by

$$\langle\, ''\underline{k} \mid \mathbf{R} \mid '\underline{k}\,\rangle = J''^{\frac{1}{2}} \langle\, \underline{K}''W''x'' \mid \mathbf{R} \mid \underline{K}'W'x'\,\rangle\, J'^{\frac{1}{2}},$$

with $J' = \partial(\underline{K}', W', x')/\partial(\underline{k}_1', \underline{k}_2')$; and (12:27) takes the form

$$\frac{dP}{dt}(\,''\underline{k}\,) = \frac{J''J'}{2\pi}\,\delta(\,\underline{K}'' - \underline{K}'\,)\,\delta(\,\underline{K}'' - '\underline{K}\,)\,\delta(\,W'' - W'\,) \times \left\{\delta(\,x'' - x'\,)\langle\, x' \mid \mathbf{R} + \mathbf{R}^* \mid x'\,\rangle + \langle\, x' \mid {}^*\mathbf{R} \mid x''\,\rangle\langle\, x'' \mid \mathbf{R} \mid x'\,\rangle\right\}. \tag{12:28}$$

With the equation [cf. (12:18)]

$$\mathbf{R} + \mathbf{R}^* + \mathbf{R}^*\mathbf{R} = 0,$$

or

$$\langle x' \mid \mathbf{R} + \mathbf{R}^* \mid x' \rangle = -\int |\langle x'' \mid \mathbf{R} \mid x' \rangle|^2 \, dx'', \qquad . \; . \quad (12:29)$$

this reduces to

$$\frac{dP}{dt}(\,''k\,) = \frac{J''J'}{2\pi}\,\delta(\,\underline{K}'' - \underline{K}'\,)\,\delta(\,\underline{K}'' - \underline{K}'\,)\,\delta(\,W'' - W'\,)$$
$$\times \left\{ |\langle x'' \mid \mathbf{R} \mid x' \rangle|^2 - \delta(\,x'' - x'\,)\int |\langle x'' \mid \mathbf{R} \mid x' \rangle|^2 \, dx'' \right\}. \quad (12:30)$$

Thus, the only matrix elements of **R** (and hence **S**) which occur are those corresponding to *real* transitions, for which energy and momentum are conserved. From the usual expression for the δ-function, the first $\delta(\underline{K}'' - \underline{K}')$ can be replaced by $\Omega/(2\pi)^3$, where Ω denotes the infinite volume of physical space, and

$$\frac{dP}{dt} = \frac{\Omega}{(\,2\pi\,)^4} J''J'\,\delta(\,\underline{K}'' - \underline{K}'\,)\,\delta(\,W'' - W'\,)$$
$$\times \left\{ |\langle x'' \mid \mathbf{R} \mid x' \rangle|^2 - \delta(\,x'' - x'\,)\int |\langle x'' \mid \mathbf{R} \mid x' \rangle|^2 \, dx'' \right\}. \quad (12:31)$$

Noting that $J''\,d''\underline{k} = d\underline{K}''\,dW''\,dx''$, we find

$$\frac{d}{dt}\int P(\,''\underline{k}\,)\,d''\underline{k} = 0, \qquad . \; . \; . \; . \; . \; . \quad (12:32)$$

which simply expresses the conservation of the number of systems in the ensemble. The number of transitions into a state in the range $''\underline{k} - ''\underline{k} + d''\underline{k}$, per unit four-dimensional volume, is given by

$$dN = \frac{1}{(\,2\pi\,)^4}\,\delta(\,\underline{K}'' - \underline{K}'\,)\,\delta(\,W'' - W'\,)\,J''\,|\langle x'' \mid \mathbf{R} \mid x' \rangle|^2 J'\,d'\underline{k}, \quad (12:33a)$$

or

$$dN = \frac{1}{(\,2\pi\,)^4}\,\delta(\,\underline{K}'' - \underline{K}'\,)\,\delta(\,W'' - W'\,)\,|\langle\,''\underline{k} \mid \mathbf{U}_{K',W'} \mid '\underline{k}\,\rangle|^2\,d''\underline{k}. \quad (12:33b)$$ [12]

Most of the foregoing results are, of course, still only a reformulation of standard procedures in the treatment of scattering problems. The first point at which any real difference in principle appears is in the determination of the energies of stationary states from the properties of the *S*-matrix. How this can come about may be easily seen by considering the simple problem of the scattering of a single particle in a central field. At large distances, the incoming wave has the form $\sim \frac{1}{r}\,e^{-i\underline{k}\cdot\underline{r}}$, the outgoing wave the form $\sim \frac{1}{r}\,e^{i\underline{k}\cdot\underline{r}}$ with factors which are essentially the eigenvalues S_l' of **S**—if the incoming wave is chosen without any phase factor.

[12] If we take account of the fact that the functions $\delta(\underline{k}_i'' - \underline{k}_i')$ correspond to planes waves $(2\pi)^{-3/2}e^{i(\underline{k}_i'\cdot\underline{x}_i')}$ in which the particle density is $(2\pi)^{-3}$, and allow for incident particle densities ρ_1, ρ_2, the numerical coefficient is replaced by $(2\pi)^2\rho_1\rho_2$.

The eigenvalue S_l' is a function of the momentum or energy of the system, and it can be shown (cf. Møller, *loc. cit.*), as first noted by Kramers, that, in all simple cases, it is an analytic function of k. If this is true, S' will still have meaning if one goes to complex values of k, i.e. negative values of the energy. If then, in this region, $k = -i\kappa$ ($\kappa > 0$), say, the incoming wave takes the form $\sim \frac{1}{r} e^{-\kappa r}$, the outgoing wave $\sim \frac{1}{r} e^{\kappa r}$. Now, for a stationary state, the solution of the wave equation only contains the exponentially decreasing part, so that S' must become zero for the energies of the discrete stationary states. Thus, the discrete stationary states would appear to be given by the zeroes of S' on the imaginary axis in the momentum space. In other cases, S' has no zero points, but is singular for certain complex values of W in the lower half of the W-plane, and these are interpreted as specifying the radioactive decay states—for which $e^{-iWt} \sim e^{-iEt-\lambda t}$.

However, it is found that there are serious difficulties in applications of the S-matrix method even within the framework of the Hamiltonian formalism. For example, there exist *redundant* zeroes of $S'(k)$ in some instances, i.e. zeroes which do not correspond to bound states, and there apparently exist *phase equivalent* potentials, i.e. which give the same phase shifts $\eta'(k)$, but which lead to *different* bound states. These difficulties have to be resolved, and the properties of S-matrices for many-body problems with bound states determined, before further progress along these lines can be expected.

APPENDIX I

In the following we consider always a finite group $G = \{ S_1, S_2, \ldots S_g \}$ of order g. The methods used are essentially after Wigner.

Theorem I.—*Every representation of a finite group is equivalent to a unitary representation,* i.e. *the matrices* $\Gamma = \{ D(S_j) \}$ *are simultaneously transformable to unitary form.*

We construct the Hermitian matrix $\mathscr{T} = \sum_{j=1}^{g} \mathscr{D}(S_j)\mathscr{D}^*(S_j)$ which we know can be transformed to real diagonal form t by a unitary matrix $\mathscr{U}$, viz.

$$\begin{aligned} t &= \mathscr{U}\mathscr{T}\mathscr{U}^{-1} \\ &= \sum_j \mathscr{U}\mathscr{D}(S_j)\mathscr{U}^{-1}\left(\mathscr{U}\mathscr{D}(S_j)\mathscr{U}^{-1}\right)^* = \sum_j \mathscr{F}(S_j)\mathscr{F}^*(S_j). \qquad (1) \end{aligned}$$

Then multiplying by t^{-1}, we have

$$t^{-1}\sum_j \mathscr{F}(S_j)\mathscr{F}^*(S_j) = t^{-\frac{1}{2}}\sum_j \mathscr{F}(S_j)\mathscr{F}^*(S_j)t^{-\frac{1}{2}} = \mathscr{I}, \qquad (2)$$

whence, on introducing

$$\mathscr{H}(S_j) = t^{-\frac{1}{2}}\mathscr{F}(S_j)t^{\frac{1}{2}} = (t^{-\frac{1}{2}}\mathscr{U})\mathscr{D}(S_j)(t^{-\frac{1}{2}}\mathscr{U})^{-1},$$

it follows that

$$\begin{aligned} \mathscr{H}(S_j)\mathscr{H}^*(S_j) &= t^{-\frac{1}{2}}\mathscr{F}(S_j)t^{\frac{1}{2}}\left(t^{-\frac{1}{2}}\sum_k \mathscr{F}(S_k)\mathscr{F}^*(S_k)t^{-\frac{1}{2}}\right)t^{\frac{1}{2}}\mathscr{F}^*(S_j)t^{-\frac{1}{2}} \\ &= t^{-\frac{1}{2}}\sum_k \mathscr{F}(S_j)\mathscr{F}(S_k)\left(\mathscr{F}(S_j)\mathscr{F}(S_k)\right)^* t^{-\frac{1}{2}} \\ &= t^{-\frac{1}{2}}\sum_l \mathscr{F}(S_l)\mathscr{F}^*(S_l)t^{-\frac{1}{2}} = \mathscr{I}. \qquad (3) \end{aligned}$$

Theorem II.—*A matrix which commutes with an irreducible representation is necessarily scalar.*

By hypothesis

$$\mathscr{D}(S_j)\mathscr{C} = \mathscr{C}\mathscr{D}(S_j) \quad \text{(for all } j\text{)}, \qquad (1)$$

and, since we may assume the representation to be unitary, it follows from the adjoint of (1) that

$$\mathscr{D}(S_j)\mathscr{C}^* = \mathscr{C}^*\mathscr{D}(S_j). \qquad (2)$$

Therefore the Hermitian matrices $\mathscr{C} + \mathscr{C}^*$ and $i(\mathscr{C} - \mathscr{C}^*)$ also commute with Γ, and, since $\mathscr{C}$ is expressible in terms of these two forms, it suffices to show that every Hermitian matrix which commutes with Γ is scalar. We may therefore simply take $\mathscr{C}$ to be Hermitian.

Let $\mathscr{C}$ be brought to diagonal form $c = \mathscr{U}\mathscr{C}\mathscr{U}^{-1}$ by the unitary matrix $\mathscr{U}$, and correspondingly set $\mathscr{F}(S_j) = \mathscr{U}\mathscr{D}(S_j)\mathscr{U}^{-1}$. Equation (1) takes the form

$$\mathscr{F}(S_j)\,c = c\mathscr{F}(S_j). \qquad (3)$$

If the diagonal matrix c is not scalar it has at least two unequal elements, say c_{rr} and c_{ss}, and the (r, s) element of (3) reads

$$\mathscr{F}(S_j)_{rs} = 0, \qquad (4)$$

which implies that the representation Γ is reducible, contrary to the original hypothesis. Hence c, and correspondingly $\mathscr{C} = \mathscr{U}^{-1}c\mathscr{U}$, must be scalar.

Theorem III.—*Schur's Lemma. If* $\Gamma_1 = \{\mathscr{D}_1(S_j)\}$, $\Gamma_2 = \{\mathscr{D}_2(S_j)\}$ *are two irreducible representations of dimensions* m, n *respectively, and if there exists an* $m \times n$ *matrix* $\mathscr{X}$ *such that*

$$\mathscr{X}\mathscr{D}_2(S_j) = \mathscr{D}_1(S_j)\mathscr{X} \qquad (\text{for all } j), \qquad (1)\dagger$$

then either

(a) $\mathscr{X}$ *is the zero* $m \times n$ *matrix; or*

(b) $\mathscr{X}$ *is square* ($m = n$) *and non-singular and* Γ_2 *is equivalent to* Γ_1.

For definiteness we take $m \geqslant n$ (the proof is similar in the case $m < n$); then from the unitarity of the representations the adjoint of (1) can be expressed in the form

$$\mathscr{D}_2(S_j^{-1})\mathscr{X}^* = \mathscr{X}^*\mathscr{D}_1(S_j^{-1}). \qquad (2)$$

Pre-multiplying (2) by $\mathscr{X}$ and post-multiplying (1)—for the element S_j^{-1}—by $\mathscr{X}^*$, we obtain

$$\mathscr{X}\mathscr{X}^*\mathscr{D}_1(S_j^{-1}) = D_1(S_j^{-1})\mathscr{X}\mathscr{X}^*, \qquad (3)$$

so that the Hermitian matrix $\mathscr{X}\mathscr{X}^*$ commutes with $\Gamma_1 = \{\mathscr{D}_1(S_j)\}$, and is therefore scalar, say $\mathscr{X}\mathscr{X}^* = \kappa\mathscr{I}$.

If Γ_1 and Γ_2 are equivalent, $n = m$, and either $\kappa \neq 0$ and $\det \mathscr{X}\mathscr{X}^* = \kappa^m$, whence $\det \mathscr{X} \neq 0$ and $\mathscr{X}^{-1}$ exists; or $\kappa = 0$, in which case $\mathscr{X}$ must be the zero matrix, since from $\mathscr{X}\mathscr{X}^* = 0$ it follows that every $\mathscr{X}_{rs} = 0$.

If $m \neq n$, say $m > n$, then $\mathscr{X}$ is not square, but may be augmented to the form $\mathscr{Z} = [\mathscr{X}O]$, where O is the $m \times m - n$ zero matrix. Then, since $\mathscr{Z}\mathscr{Z}^* = \mathscr{X}\mathscr{X}^*$ and $\det \mathscr{Z} = 0$, it follows that κ above must vanish, and the preceding argument again shows that $\mathscr{X}$ is the zero $m \times n$ matrix.

† We again assume the representations to be unitary since in the contrary case we can transform Γ_1, Γ_2 to unitary form $\mathscr{U}\Gamma_1\mathscr{U}^{-1}$, $\mathscr{V}\Gamma_2\mathscr{V}^{-1}$ by unitary matices $\mathscr{U}, \mathscr{V}$ of dimensions m, n respectively, and take $\mathscr{U}\mathscr{X}\mathscr{V}^{-1}$ as the new $\mathscr{X}$.

APPENDIX II

The Coulomb and exchange integrals are reducible to the forms

$$J\,(lm_l\,;\,l'm_l') = \sum_{k=0}^{\infty} a^k\,(lm_l\,;\,l'm_l')\,F^k\,(nl\,;\,n'l'),$$

$$K\,(lm_l\,;\,l'm_l') = \delta\,(m_s, m_s')\sum_{k=0}^{\infty} b^k\,(lm_l\,;\,l'm_l')\,G^k\,(nl\,;\,n'l'),$$

the coefficients a^k and b^k arising from the angular integrals, the F's and G's denoting the (undetermined) Slater-Condon-Shortley radial integrals. We list here the values of the non-zero a's and b's required for the electron configurations in the text, and refer the reader to *T.A.S.*, § 8[6], for the detailed derivation and discussion of the above forms.

Following Condon and Shortley, we have in the text used the forms $F_k = F^k/D_k$ and $G_k = G^k/D_k$, where the D_k are the denominators of the corresponding a's and b's in the tables below—thus avoiding fractional coefficients. We note particularly that for equivalent electrons $F^k(nl\,;\,nl) = G^k(nl\,;\,nl)$.

† TABLE I.—$a^k\,(lm_l\,;\,l'm_l')$

$l\ l'$	$\lvert m_l \rvert$	$\lvert m_l' \rvert$	a^0	a^2	a^4
$s\ s$	0	0	1		
$s\ p$	0	1	1		
	0	0	1		
$p\ p$	1	1	1	1/25	
	1	0	1	−2/25	
	0	0	1	4/25	
$p\ d$	1	2	1	2/35	
	1	1	1	−1/35	
	1	0	1	−2/35	
	0	2	1	−4/35	
	0	1	1	2/35	
	0	0	1	4/35	
$d\ d$	2	2	1	4/49	1/441
	2	1	1	−2/49	−4/441
	2	0	1	−4/49	6/441
	1	1	1	1/49	16/441
	1	0	1	2/49	−24/441
	0	0	1	4/49	36/441

† $a^k\,(l'm_l'\,;\,lm_l) = a^k\,(lm_l\,;\,l'm_l')$

Table II.—$b^k\,(lm_l\,;\,l'm_l')$

$l\ l'$	m_l	m_l'	b^0	b^1	b^2	b^3	b^4
$s\ s$	0	0	1				
$s\ p$	0	± 1		1/3			
	0	0		1/3			
$p\ p$	± 1	± 1	1		1/25		
	± 1	0			3/25		
	± 1	∓ 1			6/25		
	0	0	1		4/25		
$p\ d$	± 1	± 2		6/15		3/245	
	± 1	± 1		3/15		9/245	
	± 1	0		1/15		18/245	
	0	± 2				15/245	
	0	± 1		3/15		24/245	
	0	0		4/15		27/245	
	± 1	∓ 2				45/245	
	± 1	∓ 1				30/245	
$d\ d$	± 2	± 2	1		4/49		1/441
	± 2	± 1			6/49		5/441
	± 2	0			4/49		15/441
	± 1	± 1	1		1/49		16/441
	± 2	∓ 2					70/441
	± 2	∓ 1					35/441
	± 1	∓ 1			6/49		40/441
	± 1	0			1/49		30/441
	0	0	1		4/49		36/441

NAME INDEX

SUBJECT INDEX